EAS107P

Introduction to Engineering

Project-Based

Tagliatela College of Engineering

University of New Haven

A Pearson Custom Publication

Pearson Prentice Hall
Vice President and Editorial Director, ECS: *Marcia J. Horton*
Executive Editor: *Eric Svendsen*
Associate Editor: *Dee Bernhard*
Vice President and Director of Production and Manufacturing, ESM: *David W. Riccardi*
Executive Managing Editor: *Vince O'Brien*
Managing Editor: *David A. George*
Production Editor: *Barbara A. Till*
Director of Creative Services: *Paul Belfanti*
Creative Director: *Carole Anson*
Art Director: *Jayne Conte*
Art Editor: *Greg Dulles*
Manufacturing Manager: *Trudy Pisciotti*
Manufacturing Buyer: *Lisa McDowell*
Marketing Manager: *Holly Stark*

Pearson Custom Publishing
Director of Database Publishing: *Michael Payne*
Executive Marketing Manager: *Nathan L. Wilbur*
Operations Manager: *Eric M. Kenney*
Editorial Assistant: *Victoria L. Ravin*
Project Specialist: *Zach LaRosa*
Cover Designer: *Renee Sartell*

2004, 1999 by Pearson Education, Inc.
Pearson Prentice Hall
Pearson Education, Inc.
Upper Saddle River, NJ 074588

2007 by Pearson Custom Publishing

ISBN-13: 9780536420961
ISBN-10: 0536420963

Package ISBN-13: N/A
Package ISBN-10: N/A

Excerpts taken from:

Design Concepts for Engineers, 2/e by Mark N. Horenstein
0-13-093430-5 © 2002 by Prentice-Hall, Inc., a Pearson Education Company

Engineering Design and Problem Solving, 2/e by Steven K. Howell
0-13-093399-6 © 2002 by Prentice-Hall, Inc., a Pearson Education Company

Engineering Ethics by Charles B. Fleddermann
0-13-784224-4 © 1999 by Prentice-Hall, Inc., a Pearson Education Company

Engineering with Excel by Ronald W. Larsen
0-13-017696-6 © 2002 by Prentice-Hall, Inc., a Pearson Education Company

Engineering Success, 2/e by Peter Schiavone
0-13-041827-7 © 2002 by Prentice-Hall, Inc., a Pearson Education Company

Exploring Engineering, 2/e by Joe King
0-13-093442-9 © 2002 by Prentice-Hall, Inc., a Pearson Education Company

Graphics Concepts by Richard M. Lueptow
0-13-030687-8 © 2000 by Prentice-Hall, Inc., a Pearson Education Company

Introduction to AutoCAD® 2000 by Mark Dix and Paul Riley
0-13-016732-0 © 2000 by Prentice-Hall, Inc., a Pearson Education Company

Introduction to Engineering Analysis by Kirk D. Hagen
0-13-016733-9 © 2000 by Prentice-Hall, Inc., a Pearson Education Company

Introduction to Excel 2002 by David C. Kuncicky
0-13-008175-2 © 2003 by Pearson Education, Inc.

Introduction to MathCad® 2000 by Ronald W. Larsen
0-13-020007-7 © 2001 by Prentice-Hall, Inc., a Pearson Education Company

Introduction to MatLab® 6 by Delores M. Etter and David C. Kuncicky with Doug Hull
0-13-032845-6 © 2002 by Prentice-Hall, Inc., a Pearson Education Company

Introduction to PowerPoint 2002 by Jack Leifer
0-13-008179-5 © 2003 by Pearson Education, Inc.

Introduction to Unix® by David I. Schwartz
0-13-095135-8 © 1999 by Prentice-Hall, Inc., a Pearson Education Company

Introduction to Word 2002 by David C. Kuncicky
0-13-008170-1 © 2003 by Pearson Education, Inc.

Power Programming with VBA/Excel by Steven C. Chapra
0-13-047377-4 © 2003 by Pearson Education, Inc.

About ESource

ESource—The Prentice Hall Engineering Source—
www.prenhall.com/esource

ESource—The Prentice Hall Engineering Source gives professors the power to harness the full potential of their text and their first-year engineering course. More than just a collection of books, ESource is a unique publishing system revolving around the ESource website—www.prenhall.com/esource. ESource enables you to put your stamp on your book just as you do your course. It lets you:

Control You choose exactly what chapters are in your book and in what order they appear. Of course, you can choose the entire book if you'd like and stay with the authors' original order.

Optimize Get the most from your book and your course. ESource lets you produce the optimal text for your students needs.

Customize You can add your own material anywhere in your text's presentation, and your final product will arrive at your bookstore as a professionally formatted text. Of course, all titles in this series are available as stand-alone texts, or as bundles of two or more books sold at a discount. Contact your PH sales rep for discount information.

ESource ACCESS

Professors who choose to bundle two or more texts from the ESource series for their class, or use an ESource custom book will be providing their students with an on-line library of intro engineering content—ESource Access. We've designed ESource ACCESS to provide students a flexible, searchable, on-line resource. Free access codes come in bundles and custom books are valid for one year after initial log-on. Contact your PH sales rep for more information.

ESource Content

All the content in ESource was written by educators specifically for freshman/first-year students. Authors tried to strike a balanced level of presentation, an approach that was neither formulaic nor trivial, and one that did not focus too heavily on advanced topics that most introductory students do not encounter until later classes. Because many professors do not have extensive time to cover these topics in the classroom, authors prepared each text with the idea that many students would use it for self-instruction and independent study. Students should be able to use this content to learn the software tool or subject on their own.

While authors had the freedom to write texts in a style appropriate to their particular subject, all followed certain guidelines created to promote a consistency that makes students comfortable. Namely, every chapter opens with a clear set of **Objectives**, includes **Practice Boxes** throughout the chapter, and ends with a number of **Problems**, and a list of **Key Terms**. **Applications Boxes** are spread throughout the book with the intent of giving students a real-world perspective of engineering. **Success Boxes** provide the student with advice about college study skills, and help students avoid the common pitfalls of first-year students. In addition, this series contains an entire book titled ***Engineering Success*** by Peter Schiavone of the University of Alberta intended to expose students quickly to what it takes to be an engineering student.

Creating Your Book

Using ESource is simple. You preview the content either on-line or through examination copies of the books you can request on-line, from your PH sales rep, or by calling 1-800-526-0485. Create an on-line outline of the content you want, in the order you want, using ESource's simple interface. Insert your own material into the text flow. If you are not ready to order, ESource will save your work. You can come back at any time and change, re-arrange, or add more material to your creation. Once you're finished you'll automatically receive an ISBN. Give it to your bookstore and your book will arrive on their shelves four to six weeks after they order. Your custom desk copies with their instructor supplements will arrive at your address at the same time.

To learn more about this new system for creating the perfect textbook, go to www.prenhall.com/esource. You can either go through the on-line walkthrough of how to create a book, or experiment yourself.

Supplements

Adopters of ESource receive an instructor's CD that contains professor and student code from the books in the series, as well as other instruction aides provided by authors. The website also holds approximately **350 PowerPoint transparencies** created by Jack Leifer of University of Kentucky–Paducah. Professors can either follow these transparencies as pre-prepared lectures or use them as the basis for their own custom presentations.

http://www.prenhall.com/esource

Titles in the ESource Series

Design Concepts for Engineers, 2/e
0-13-093430-5
Mark Horenstein

Engineering Success, 2/e
0-13-041827-7
Peter Schiavone

Engineering Design and Problem Solving, 2E
ISBN 0-13-093399-6
Steven K. Howell

Exploring Engineering
ISBN 0-13-093442-9
Joe King

Engineering Ethics
0-13-784224-4
Charles B. Fleddermann

Introduction to Engineering Analysis
0-13-016733-9
Kirk D. Hagen

Introduction to Engineering Experimentation
0-13-032835-9
Ronald W. Larsen, John T. Sears, and Royce Wilkinson

Introduction to Mechanical Engineering
0-13-019640-1
Robert Rizza

Introduction to Electrical and Computer Engineering
0-13-033363-8
Charles B. Fleddermann and Martin Bradshaw

Introduction to MATLAB 6—Update
0-13-140918-2
Delores Etter and David C. Kuncicky, with Douglas W. Hull

MATLAB Programming
0-13-035127-X
David C. Kuncicky

Introduction to MATLAB
0-13-013149-0
Delores Etter with David C. Kuncicky

Introduction to Mathcad 2000
0-13-020007-7
Ronald W. Larsen

Introduction to Mathcad 11
0-13-008177-9
David W. Larsen

Introduction to Maple 8
0-13-032844-8
David I. Schwartz

Mathematics Review
0-13-011501-0
Peter Schiavone

Power Programming with VBA/Excel
0-13-047377-4
Steven C. Chapra

Introduction to Excel 2002
0-13-008175-2
David C. Kuncicky

About the Authors

No project could ever come to pass without a group of authors who have the vision and the courage to turn a stack of blank paper into a book. The authors in this series, who worked diligently to produce their books, provide the building blocks of the series.

Martin D. Bradshaw was born in Pittsburg, KS in 1936, grew up in Kansas and the surrounding states of Arkansas and Missouri, graduating from Newton High School, Newton, KS in 1954. He received the B.S.E.E. and M.S.E.E. degrees from the University of Wichita in 1958 and 1961, respectively. A Ford Foundation fellowship at Carnegie Institute of Technology followed from 1961 to 1963 and he received the Ph.D. degree in electrical engineering in 1964. He spent his entire academic career with the Department of Electrical and Computer Engineering at the University of New Mexico (1961-1963 and 1991-1996). He served as the Assistant Dean for Special Programs with the UNM College of Engineering from 1974 to 1976 and as the Associate Chairman for the EECE Department from 1993 to 1996. During the period 1987-1991 he was a consultant with his own company, EE Problem Solvers. During 1978 he spent a sabbatical year with the State Electricity Commission of Victoria, Melbourne, Australia. From 1979 to 1981 he served an IPA assignment as a Project Officer at the U.S. Air Force Weapons Laboratory, Kirkland AFB, Albuquerque, NM. He has won numerous local, regional, and national teaching awards, including the George Westinghouse Award from the ASEE in 1973. He was awarded the IEEE Centennial Medal in 2000.

Acknowledgments: Dr. Bradshaw would like to acknowledge his late mother, who gave him a great love of reading and learning, and his father, who taught him to persist until the job is finished. The encouragement of his wife, Jo, and his six children is a never-ending inspiration.

Stephen J. Chapman received a B.S. degree in Electrical Engineering from Louisiana State University (1975), the M.S.E. degree in Electrical Engineering from the University of Central Florida (1979), and pursued further graduate studies at Rice University.

Mr. Chapman is currently Manager of Technical Systems for British Aerospace Australia, in Melbourne, Australia. In this position, he provides technical direction and design authority for the work of younger engineers within the company. He also continues to teach at local universities on a part-time basis.

Mr. Chapman is a Senior Member of the Institute of Electrical and Electronics Engineers (and several of its component societies). He is also a member of the Association for Computing Machinery and the Institution of Engineers (Australia).

Steven C. Chapra presently holds the Louis Berger Chair for Computing and Engineering in the Civil and Environmental Engineering Department at Tufts University. Dr. Chapra received engineering degrees from Manhattan College and the University of Michigan. Before joining the faculty at Tufts, he taught at Texas A&M University, the University of Colorado, and Imperial College, London. His research interests focus on surface water-quality modeling and advanced computer applications in environmental engineering. He has published over 50 refereed journal articles, 20 software packages and 6 books. He has received a number of awards including the 1987 ASEE Merriam/Wiley Distinguished Author Award, the 1993 Rudolph Hering Medal, and teaching awards from Texas A&M, the University of Colorado, and the Association of Environmental Engineering and Science Professors.

Acknowledgments: To the Berger Family for their many contributions to engineering education. I would also like to thank David Clough for his friendship and insights, John Walkenbach for his wonderful books, and my colleague Lee Minardi and my students Kenny William, Robert Viesca and Jennifer Edelmann for their suggestions.

Mark Dix began working with AutoCAD in 1985 as a programmer for CAD Support Associates, Inc. He helped design a system for creating estimates and bills of material directly from AutoCAD drawing databases for use in the automated conveyor industry. This system became the basis for systems still widely in use today. In 1986 he began collaborating with Paul Riley to create AutoCAD training materials, combining Riley's background in industrial design and training with Dix's background in writing, curriculum development, and programming. Mr. Dix received the M.S. degree in education from the University of Massachusetts. He is currently the Director of Dearborn Academy High School in Arlington, Massachusetts.

Delores M. Etter is a Professor of Electrical and Computer Engineering at the University of Colorado. Dr. Etter was a faculty member at the University of New Mexico and also a Visiting Professor at Stanford University. Dr. Etter was responsible for the Freshman Engineering Program at the University of New Mexico and is active in the Integrated Teaching Laboratory at the University of Colorado. She was elected a Fellow of the Institute of Electrical and Electronics Engineers for her contributions to education and for her technical leadership in digital signal processing.

Charles B. Fleddermann is a professor in the Department of Electrical and Computer Engineering at the University of New Mexico in Albuquerque, New Mexico. All of his degrees are in electrical engineering: his Bachelor's degree from the University of Notre Dame, and the Master's and Ph.D. from the University of Illinois at Urbana-Champaign. Prof. Fleddermann developed an engineering ethics course for his department in response to the ABET requirement to incorporate ethics topics into the undergraduate engineering curriculum. *Engineering Ethics* was written as a vehicle for presenting ethical

theory, analysis, and problem solving to engineering undergraduates in a concise and readily accessible way.

Acknowledgments: I would like to thank Profs. Charles Harris and Michael Rabins of Texas A & M University whose NSF sponsored workshops on engineering ethics got me started thinking in this field. Special thanks to my wife Liz, who proofread the manuscript for this book, provided many useful suggestions, and who helped me learn how to teach "soft" topics to engineers.

Kirk D. Hagen is a professor at Weber State University in Ogden, Utah. He has taught introductory-level engineering courses and upper-division thermal science courses at WSU since 1993. He received his B.S. degree in physics from Weber State College and his M.S. degree in mechanical engineering from Utah State University, after which he worked as a thermal designer/analyst in the aerospace and electronics industries. After several years of engineering practice, he resumed his formal education, earning his Ph.D. in mechanical engineering at the University of Utah. Hagen is the author of an undergraduate heat transfer text.

Mark N. Horenstein is a Professor in the Department of Electrical and Computer Engineering at Boston University. He has degrees in Electrical Engineering from M.I.T. and U.C. Berkeley and has been involved in teaching engineering design for the greater part of his academic career. He devised and developed the senior design project class taken by all electrical and computer engineering students at Boston University. In this class, the students work for a virtual engineering company developing products and systems for real-world engineering and social-service clients.

Acknowledgments: I would like to thank Prof. James Bethune, the architect of the Peak Performance event at Boston University, for his permission to highlight the competition in my text. Several of the ideas relating to brainstorming and teamwork were derived from a workshop on engineering design offered by Prof. Charles Lovas of Southern Methodist University. The principles of estimation were derived in part from a freshman engineering problem posed by Prof. Thomas Kincaid of Boston University.

Steven Howell is the Chairman and a  Professor of Mechanical Engineering at Lawrence Technological University. Prior to joining LTU in 2001, Dr. Howell led a knowledge-based engineering project for Visteon Automotive Systems and taught computer-aided design classes for Ford Motor Company engineers. Dr. Howell also has a total of 15 years experience as an engineering faculty member at Northern Arizona University, the University of the Pacific, and the University of Zimbabwe. While at Northern Arizona University, he helped develop and implement an award-winning interdisciplinary series of design courses simulating a corporate engineering-design environment.

Douglas W. Hull is a graduate student in the Department of Mechanical Engineering at Carnegie Mellon University in Pittsburgh, Pennsylvania. He is the author of *Mastering Mechanics I Using Matlab 5*, and contributed to *Mechanics of Materials* by Bedford and Liechti. His research in the Sensor Based Planning lab involves motion planning for hyper-redundant manipulators, also known as serpentine robots.

Scott D. James is a staff lecturer at  Kettering University (formerly GMI Engineering & Management Institute) in Flint, Michigan. He is currently pursuing a Ph.D. in Systems Engineering with an emphasis on software engineering and computer-integrated manufacturing. He chose teaching as a profession after several years in the computer industry. "I thought that it was really important to know what it was like outside of academia. I wanted to provide students with classes that

were up to date and provide the information that is really used and needed."

Acknowledgments: Scott would like to acknowledge his family for the time to work on the text and his students and peers at Kettering who offered helpful critiques of the materials that eventually became the book.

Joe King received the B.S. and M.S. degrees from the University of California  at Davis. He is a Professor of Computer Engineering at the University of the Pacific, Stockton, CA, where he teaches courses in digital design, computer design, artificial intelligence, and computer networking. Since joining the UOP faculty, Professor King has spent yearlong sabbaticals teaching in Zimbabwe, Singapore, and Finland. A licensed engineer in the state of California, King's industrial experience includes major design projects with Lawrence Livermore National Laboratory, as well as independent consulting projects. Prof. King has had a number of books published with titles including MATLAB, MathCAD, Exploring Engineering, and Engineering and Society.

David C. Kuncicky is a native Floridian. He earned his Baccalaureate in psy-  chology, Master's in computer science, and Ph.D. in computer science from Florida State University. He has served as a faculty member in the Department of Electrical Engineering at the FAMU–FSU College of Engineering and the Department of Computer Science at Florida State University. He has taught computer science and computer engineering courses for over 15 years. He has published research in the areas of intelligent hybrid systems and neural networks. He is currently the Director of Engineering at Bioreason, Inc. in Sante Fe, New Mexico.

Acknowledgments: Thanks to Steffie and Helen for putting up with my late nights and long weekends at the computer. Finally, thanks to Susan Bassett for having faith in my abilities, and for providing continued tutelage and support.

Ron Larsen is a Professor of Chemical Engineering at Montana State University, and received his Ph.D. from the Pennsylvania State University. He was initially attracted to engineering by the challenges the profession offers, but also appreciates that engineering is a serving profession. Some of the greatest challenges he has faced while teaching have involved non-traditional teaching methods, including evening courses for practicing engineers and teaching through an interpreter at the Mongolian National University. These experiences have provided tremendous opportunities to learn new ways to communicate technical material. Dr. Larsen views modern software as one of the new tools that will radically alter the way engineers work, and his book *Introduction to Math-CAD* was written to help young engineers prepare to meet the challenges of an ever-changing workplace.

Acknowledgments: To my students at Montana State University who have endured the rough drafts and typos, and who still allow me to experiment with their classes—my sincere thanks.

Sanford Leestma is a Professor of Mathematics and Computer Science at Calvin College, and received his Ph.D. from New Mexico State University. He has been the long-time co-author of successful textbooks on Fortran, Pascal, and data structures in Pascal. His current research interest are in the areas of algorithms and numerical computation.

Jack Leifer is an Assistant Professor in the Department of Mechanical Engineering at the University of Kentucky Extended Campus Program in Paducah, and was previously with the Department of Mathematical Sciences and Engineering at the University of South Carolina–Aiken. He received his Ph.D. in Mechanical Engineering from the University of Texas at Austin in December 1995. His current research interests include the analysis of ultra-light and inflatable (Gossamer) space structures.

Acknowledgments: I'd like to thank my colleagues at USC–Aiken, especially Professors Mike May and Laurene Fausett, for their encouragement and feedback; and my parents, Felice and Morton Leifer, for being there and providing support (as always) as I completed this book.

Richard M. Lueptow is the Charles Deering McCormick Professor of Teaching Excellence and Associate Professor of Mechanical Engineering at Northwestern University. He is a native of Wisconsin and received his doctorate from the Massachusetts Institute of Technology in 1986. He teaches design, fluid mechanics, an spectral analysis techniques. Rich has an active research program on rotating filtration, Taylor Couette flow, granular flow, fire suppression, and acoustics. He has five patents and over 40 refereed journal and proceedings papers along with many other articles, abstracts, and presentations.

Acknowledgments: Thanks to my talented and hardworking co-authors as well as the many colleagues and students who took the tutorial for a "test drive." Special thanks to Mike Minbiole for his major contributions to Graphics Concepts with SolidWorks. Thanks also to Northwestern University for the time to work on a book. Most of all, thanks to my loving wife, Maiya, and my children, Hannah and Kyle, for supporting me in this endeavor. (Photo courtesy of Evanston Photographic Studios, Inc.)

Larry Nyhoff is a Professor of Mathematics and Computer Science at Calvin College. After doing bachelor's work at Calvin, and Master's work at Michigan, he received a Ph.D. from Michigan State and also did graduate work in computer science at Western Michigan. Dr. Nyhoff has taught at Calvin for the past 34 years—mathematics at first and computer science for the past several years.

Acknowledgments: We thank our families—Shar, Jeff, Dawn, Rebecca, Megan, Sara, Greg, Julie, Joshua, Derek, Tom, Joan; Marge, Michelle, Sandy, Lory, Michael—for being patient and understanding. We thank God for allowing us to write this text.

http://www.prenhall.com/esource

Paul Riley is an author, instructor, and designer specializing in graphics and design for multimedia. He is a founding partner of CAD Support Associates, a contract service and professional training organization for computer-aided design. His 15 years of business experience and 20 years of teaching experience are supported by degrees in education and computer science. Paul has taught AutoCAD at the University of Massachusetts at Lowell and is presently teaching AutoCAD at Mt. Ida College in Newton, Massachusetts. He has developed a program, Computer-aided Design for Professionals that is highly regarded by corporate clients and has been an ongoing success since 1982.

Robert Rizza is an Assistant Professor of Mechanical Engineering at North Dakota State University, where he teaches courses in mechanics and computer-aided design. A native of Chicago, he received the Ph.D. degree from the Illinois Institute of Technology. He is also the author of *Getting Started with Pro/ENGINEER*. Dr. Rizza has worked on a diverse range of engineering projects including projects from the railroad, bioengineering, and aerospace industries. His current research interests include the fracture of composite materials, repair of cracked aircraft components, and loosening of prostheses.

Peter Schiavone is a professor and student advisor in the Department of Mechanical Engineering at the University of Alberta, Canada. He received his Ph.D. from the University of Strathclyde, U.K. in 1988. He has authored several books in the area of student academic success as well as numerous papers in international scientific research journals. Dr. Schiavone has worked in private industry in several different areas of engineering including aerospace and systems engineering. He founded the first Mathematics Resource Center at the University of Alberta, a unit designed specifically to teach new students the necessary survival skills in mathematics and the physical sciences required for success in first-year engineering. This led to the Students' Union Gold Key Award for outstanding contributions to the university. Dr. Schiavone lectures regularly to freshman engineering students and to new engineering professors on engineering success, in particular about maximizing students' academic performance.

Acknowledgements: Thanks to Richard Felder for being such an inspiration; to my wife Linda for sharing my dreams and believing in me; and to Francesca and Antonio for putting up with Dad when working on the text.

David I. Schneider holds an A.B. degree from Oberlin College and a Ph.D. degree in Mathematics from MIT. He has taught for 34 years, primarily at the University of Maryland. Dr. Schneider has authored 28 books, with one-half of them computer programming books. He has developed three customized software packages that are supplied as supplements to over 55 mathematics textbooks. His involvement with computers dates back to 1962, when he programmed a special purpose computer at MIT's Lincoln Laboratory to correct errors in a communications system.

David I. Schwartz is an Assistant Professor in the Computer Science Department at Cornell University and earned his B.S., M.S., and Ph.D. degrees in Civil Engineering from State University of New York at Buffalo. Throughout his graduate studies, Schwartz combined principles of computer science to applications of civil engineering. He became interested in helping students learn how to apply software tools for solving a variety of engineering problems. He teaches his students to learn incrementally and practice frequently to gain the maturity to tackle other subjects. In his spare time, Schwartz plays drums in a variety of bands.

Acknowledgments: I dedicate my books to my family, friends, and students who all helped in so many ways.

Many thanks go to the schools of Civil Engineering and Engineering & Applied Science at State University of New York at Buffalo where I originally developed and tested my UNIX and Maple books. I greatly appreciate the opportunity to explore my goals and all the help from everyone at the Computer Science Department at Cornell.

John T. Sears received the Ph.D. degree from Princeton University. Currently, he is a Professor and the head of the Department of Chemical Engineering at Montana State University. After leaving Princeton he worked in research at Brookhaven National Laboratory and Esso Research and Engineering, until he took a position at West Virginia University. He came to MSU in 1982, where he has served as the Director of the College of Engineering Minority Program and Interim Director for BioFilm Engineering. Prof. Sears has written a book on air pollution and economic development, and over 45 articles in engineering and engineering education.

Michael T. Snyder is President of Internet startup Appointments123.com. He is a native of Chicago, and he received his Bachelor of Science degree in Mechanical Engineering from the University of Notre Dame. Mike also graduated with honors from Northwestern University's Kellogg Graduate School of Management in 1999 with his Masters of Management degree. Before Appointments123.com, Mike was a mechanical engineer in new product development for Motorola Cellular and Acco Office Products. He has received four patents for his mechanical design work. "Pro/ENGINEER was an invaluable design tool for me,

and I am glad to help students learn the basics of Pro/ENGINEER."

Acknowledgments: Thanks to Rich Lueptow and Jim Steger for inviting me to be a part of this great project. Of course, thanks to my wife Gretchen for her support in my various projects.

Jim Steger is currently Chief Technical Officer and cofounder of an Internet applications company. He graduated with a Bachelor of Science degree in Mechanical Engineering from Northwestern University. His prior work included mechanical engineering assignments at Motorola and Acco Brands. At Motorola, Jim worked on part design for two-way radios and was one of the lead mechanical engineers on a cellular phone product line. At Acco Brands, Jim was the sole engineer on numerous office product designs. His Worx stapler has won design awards in the United States and in Europe. Jim has been a Pro/ENGINEER user for over six years.

Acknowledgments: Many thanks to my co-authors, especially Rich Lueptow for his leadership on this project. I would also like to thank my family for their continuous support.

Royce Wilkinson received his undergraduate degree in chemistry from Rose-Hulman Institute of Technology in 1991 and the Ph.D. degree in chemistry from Montana State University in 1998 with research in natural product isolation from fungi. He currently resides in Bozeman, MT and is involved in HIV drug research. His research interests center on biological molecules and their interactions in the search for pharmaceutical advances.

http://www.prenhall.com/esource

Reviewers

We would like to thank everyone who has reviewed texts in this series.

ESource Reviewers

Christopher Rowe, *Vanderbilt University*
Steve Yurgartis, *Clarkson University*
Heidi A. Diefes-Dux, *Purdue University*
Howard Silver, *Fairleigh Dickenson University*
Jean C. Malzahn Kampe, *Virginia Polytechnic Institute and State University*
Malcolm Heimer, *Florida International University*
Stanley Reeves, *Auburn University*
John Demel, *Ohio State University*
Shahnam Navee, *Georgia Southern University*
Heshem Shaalem, *Georgia Southern University*
Terry L. Kohutek, *Texas A & M University*
Liz Rozell, *Bakersfield College*
Mary C. Lynch, *University of Florida*
Ted Pawlicki, *University of Rochester*
James N. Jensen, *SUNY at Buffalo*
Tom Horton, *University of Virginia*
Eileen Young, *Bristol Community College*
James D. Nelson, *Louisiana Tech University*
Jerry Dunn, *Texas Tech University*
Howard M. Fulmer, *Villanova University Berkeley*
Naeem Abdurrahman *University of Texas, Austin*
Stephen Allan *Utah State University*
Anil Bajaj *Purdue University*
Grant Baker *University of Alaska–Anchorage*
William Beckwith *Clemson University*
Haym Benaroya *Rutgers University*
John Biddle *California State Polytechnic University*
Tom Bledsaw *ITT Technical Institute*
Fred Boadu *Duke University*
Tom Bryson *University of Missouri, Rolla*
Ramzi Bualuan *University of Notre Dame*
Dan Budny *Purdue University*
Betty Burr *University of Houston*
Dale Calkins *University of Washington*
Harish Cherukuri *University of North Carolina –Charlotte*
Arthur Clausing *University of Illinois*

Barry Crittendon *Virginia Polytechnic and State University*
James Devine *University of South Florida*
Ron Eaglin *University of Central Florida*
Dale Elifrits *University of Missouri, Rolla*
Patrick Fitzhorn *Colorado State University*
Susan Freeman *Northeastern University*
Frank Gerlitz *Washtenaw College*
Frank Gerlitz *Washtenaw Community College*
John Glover *University of Houston*
John Graham *University of North Carolina–Charlotte*
Ashish Gupta *SUNY at Buffalo*
Otto Gygax *Oregon State University*
Malcom Heimer *Florida International University*
Donald Herling *Oregon State University*
Thomas Hill *SUNY at Buffalo*
A.S. Hodel *Auburn University*
James N. Jensen *SUNY at Buffalo*
Vern Johnson *University of Arizona*
Autar Kaw *University of South Florida*
Kathleen Kitto *Western Washington University*
Kenneth Klika *University of Akron*
Terry L. Kohutek *Texas A&M University*
Melvin J. Maron *University of Louisville*
Robert Montgomery *Purdue University*
Mark Nagurka *Marquette University*
Romarathnam Narasimhan *University of Miami*
Soronadi Nnaji *Florida A&M University*
Sheila O'Connor *Wichita State University*
Michael Peshkin *Northwestern University*
Dr. John Ray *University of Memphis*
Larry Richards *University of Virginia*
Marc H. Richman *Brown University*
Randy Shih *Oregon Institute of Technology*
Avi Singhal *Arizona State University*
Tim Sykes *Houston Community College*
Neil R. Thompson *University of Waterloo*
Dr. Raman Menon Unnikrishnan *Rochester Institute of Technology*
Michael S. Wells *Tennessee Tech University*
Joseph Wujek *University of California, Berkeley*
Edward Young *University of South Carolina*
Garry Young *Oklahoma State University*
Mandochehr Zoghi *University of Dayton*

Contents

Technical Communication

Engineering Profession

1

Introduction to Discovering Engineering

1 INTRODUCTION

You are beginning an exploration of engineering that will continue throughout your life. This chapter will explore the ways that this journey may begin. In Section 2, you will be asked to examine your own motivation for becoming an engineer. In Section 3, some surprising advice on how to discover engineering is shared. In Section 4, the clock is turned back 175 years to show how history affects your engineering education.

2 WELCOME TO ENGINEERING

In some ways, it is amazing that you found engineering in the first place. Most people select careers and academic programs based on their high school experiences. You probably took math and science classes in high school, perhaps even some technology classes. However, you probably did not take *engineering* classes in high school.

Some of your high school friends may be comfortable with their exposure to chemistry or French or English literature in secondary school. They may be looking forward to majoring in one of those fields in college. Although their college experiences will challenge and extend them, your friends probably have a pretty good idea what to expect in college based on their high school experiences.

You may be a little envious. After all, you took a chance on a field that is a little less familiar to you. Your motivation for doing so is unique to you.

OBJECTIVES

After reading this chapter, you will be able to:

- identify why people choose engineering as a career;
- find engineers to speak with about engineering;
- list what you should expect in your engineering education.

PONDER THIS

What is *your* motivation for becoming an engineer?

Key idea: Engineering is the right place for people who have curiosity, a strong work ethic, a desire to help other people, and a deep respect for math and science.

Many students pursue a degree in engineering because they performed well in math and science classes in high school. Some engineering students have relatives who are engineers. Some pursue engineering because the job opportunities and salaries for recent engineering graduates are pretty good. Whatever your motivation, you are taking a small leap of faith in entering a profession that may seem a mystery to you right now. Have no fear: if you have curiosity, a strong work ethic, a desire to help other people, and a deep respect for math and science, then you have found a home in engineering. For a few stories about why working engineers chose engineering, see *Focus on Choosing Engineering: So Why Did You Become an Engineer?*

FOCUS ON CHOOSING ENGINEERING: SO WHY DID YOU BECOME AN ENGINEER?

Every engineer has a unique answer to the question: Why did you choose engineering? Compare your motivation for becoming an engineer with the following stories from practicing engineers.

Helping People

My long-term goal has been to work for and with people, that's why I became an engineer. I like helping people, and that's why I want to use my talents to better other people's lives. This project is exactly the kind of thing I want to do with the rest of my life.

—From a Northwestern University senior, commenting on her involvement in a project to build a toy car for disabled children (http://www.asme.org/mechanicaladvantage/fall98/CHILD'SPLAYCARPAGE.HTM)

Problem Solving

When the tragic Challenger disaster occurred in 1986, I found myself not only touched by the loss, but also driven to understand why, and motivated to ensure such a tragedy did not happen again.

—From a Lockheed Martin mechanical engineer (http://www.lmaeronautics.com.about/eweek/why)

Math and Science

I always liked science and math anyway, so the idea of working in a profession where one can apply the laws of nature for the benefit of mankind was very inspiring.

—From a civil engineer working at the Philadelphia District of the U.S. Army Corps of Engineers (*District Observer ONLINE*, Jan–Feb 2000)

Curiosity

Growing up on a 200-acre cotton farm in middle Georgia, I became fascinated and elated with the mechanical equipment that was becoming available to do work on the farm.

—From another Lockheed Martin mechanical engineer (http://www.lmaeronautics.com/about/eweek/why)

Impact

One of the reasons why I became an engineer is because I believe engineering is a profession that allows you to predict the future. As I tell my students, "… (Y)ou can use (the laws of physics) to predict how something … should work. Then, you can … build that something and test it. If it works the way you thought it should, then you effectively forecast the future."

—From Dr. James Meindl, electrical engineering professor at the Georgia Institute of Technology (*Georgia Tech Alumni Magazine Online*, Vol. 72, No. 1, Summer 1995)

3   HOW TO DISCOVER ENGINEERING

Key idea: Discover engineering by talking to engineers.

So how do you learn more about the engineering profession? First, *put down this book.* No words on the page can help you realize the richness and satisfaction of your career. No book can bring alive the dramatic and compelling history of engineering, where two steps forward are invariably followed by one step backward. And no mere textbook can do justice to the triumphs, diversity, and human stories of the engineers themselves.

Textbook authors usually do not tell you to stop reading their text. But engineering is not about textbooks. It is about people: people who learn, people who translate ideas into reality, people who solve problems, people who communicate their ideas to others, and people who behave responsibly. To truly discover engineering, you must talk to engineers. But how do you find them?

PONDER THIS

How can you find engineers to speak with about engineering?

Key idea: Learn more about your future career by finding engineers at a university.

The best place to find engineers is at your university. Almost all engineering faculty are trained engineers,* and many have work experience outside of the university. Find a faculty member to help you understand the profession. Many universities have freshman mentoring programs, where freshmen are assigned faculty mentors or advisors. If your school does not have such a program, read the departmental brochures or Internet information and find a professor in an area that interests you. Call him or her for an appointment. Be persistent: the faculty are as busy as you are.

Engineering societies are another great source of information about this practice. These societies are professional organizations; some societies are general in scope, while others focus on a specific discipline. The major discipline-specific engineering societies are listed in Table 1. Other discipline-specific organizations are listed in Table 2. Table 3 lists the main engineering societies that are not associated with a specific engineering field. In Table 4, engineering societies focused on increasing the diversity of engineers are shown. For more information about any of these organizations, search on the Internet. For a story about historical diversity in engineering, see *Focus on Diversity in Engineering: The Real McCoy?*

TABLE 1   Major Discipline-Specific Engineering Societies

Name	Date Started	Number of Members
American Institute of Chemical Engineers (AIChE)	1908	58,000
American Society of Civil Engineers (ASCE)	1852	120,000
American Society of Mechanical Engineers (ASME)	1880	125,000
Institute of Electrical and Electronics Engineers (IEEE)[a]	1884	330,000
Institute of Industrial Engineers (IIE)	1948	24,000

[a]The American Institute of Electrical Engineers (founded in 1884) and the Institute of Radio Engineers merged in 1962 to form IEEE.

---

*You must be a registered professional engineer to use the title "professional engineer." Almost all engineering faculty have received training as engineers, but not all faculty are registered professional engineers.

TABLE 2 Other Discipline-Specific Engineering Societies

Name	Discipline[a]
American Academy of Environmental Engineers (AAEE)	civil
American Ceramic Society (ACerS)	several
American Institute for Medical and Biological Engineering (AIMBE)	several
American Institute of Aeronautics and Astronautics (AIAA)	mechanical
American Institute of Mining, Metallurgical, and Petroleum Engineers (AIME)	several
American Nuclear Society (ANS)	several
American Public Works Association (APWA)	civil
American Society for Quality (ASQ)	industrial
American Society of Agricultural Engineers (ASAE)	civil
American Society of Heating, Refrigerating and Air Conditioning Engineers (ASHRAE)	mechanical
American Society of Naval Engineers (ASNE)	several
American Society of Safety Engineers (ASSE)	several
Associated General Contractors of America (AGC)	civil
Association for Facilities Engineering (AFE)	industrial
Biomedical Engineering Society (BMES)	several
Human Factors and Ergonomics Society (HFES)	industrial
National Association of Power Engineers (NAPE)	several
Society of American Military Engineers (SAME)	several
Society of Automotive Engineers (SAE)	mechanical
Society of Fire Protection Engineers (SFPE)	several
Society of Manufacturing Engineers (SME)	several
Society of Petroleum Engineers (SPE)	chemical
Society of Plastics Engineers (SPE)	chemical
SPIE—The International Society for Optical Engineering[b]	several

[a]"Discipline" refers to the major engineering area(s) (chemical, civil, electrical, industrial, and mechanical engineering) targeted by the society.
[b]Originally, this was the Society of Photo-Optical Instrumentation Engineers.

TABLE 3 General Engineering Societies

Name	Date Founded
American Association of Engineering Societies (AAES)	1979
American Consulting Engineers Council (ACEC)	1910
American Society of Engineering Education (ASEE)	1893
Junior Engineering Technical Society (JETS)	1957[a]
National Council of Examiners for Engineering/Surveying (NCEES)	1920
National Society of Professional Engineers (NSPE)	1934
Tau Beta Pi[b] (ΤΒΠ)	1885

[a]JETS was established in 1950 and incorporated in 1957.
[b]Tau Beta Pi is the national engineering honor society. Several disciplines have their own national honor societies (e.g., Sigma Gamma Tau for aerospace engineering and Eta Kappa Nu for electrical engineering).

TABLE 4 Engineering Societies Focused on Diversity in Engineering

Name	Date Founded
American Indian Science and Engineering Societies (AISES)	1977
Mexican American Engineers and Scientists (MAES)	1974
National Action Council for Minorities in Engineering (NACME)	1974
National Society of Black Engineers (NSBE)	1976
National Organization of Gay and Lesbian Scientists and Technical Professionals (NOGLSTP)	1983
Society of Hispanic Professional Engineers (SHPE)	1974
Society of Woman Engineers (SWE)	1950

student chapter: a student-run organization or club associated with a national society.

The easiest way to meet engineers in professional societies is through student chapters. A ***student chapter*** is a student-run organization affiliated with a national society. Student chapters of engineering societies typically have a faculty advisor and a practicing engineer who serves as a liaison to the parent society. Most of the organizations listed in Tables 1 through 4 have student chapters. The student chapters may invite practicing engineers to share their experiences with students. Look for opportunities to speak with the presenters.

Another way to learn from engineers in professional societies is through participation in National Engineers Week. National Engineers Week was established by the National Society of Professional Engineers in 1951 to increase public awareness of the profession. It is held each year during the week of George Washington's birthday (February 22) to acknowledge Washington's contributions as a surveyor. The local activities during National Engineers Week will provide a great opportunity to learn from professional engineers.

Key idea: To learn more, speak with professionals at engineering firms or engineering departments.

Finally, practicing engineers are a wonderful source of information. Many offices, departments of large companies, and government departments offer office tours and internship programs. Summer jobs and co-op programs provide good opportunities to ask questions. The telephone book and Internet are useful guides to engineering practice in your area. In addition, ask the career planning staff at your university to help locate practicing engineers who have volunteered to act as student mentors.

4 ENGINEERING EDUCATION: WHAT YOU SHOULD EXPECT

For many engineers, the discovery of engineering begins with their college years. To see what is in store for you as you begin your engineering education, it is instructive to look back in time. Engineering education has a long history in the United States. Engineering education, as with engineering itself, began with military applications.

In the United States, the first formal training program for engineers began in 1794, when Congress added the rank of cadet to the Corps of Artillerists and Engineers. The Corps was assigned to the garrison at West Point. A four-year degree program began at West Point in 1817, under the direction of Sylvanus Thayer (1785–1872). Civilian education in engineering began in 1820 at the American Literary, Scientific, and Military Academy (now Norwich University) in Norwich, Vermont, under the guidance of Alden Partridge (1785–1854).

The work of Thayer and Partridge expanded the traditional university curriculum to educate soldiers and citizen-soldiers about the applied sciences. A different approach was developed by Amos Eaton and Stephen Van Rensselaer. In 1824, they founded the Rensselaer School (now called Rensselaer Polytechnic Institute in Troy, New York) to "teach the application of science to the common purposes of life" (Griggs, 1997).

FOCUS ON DIVERSITY IN ENGINEERING: THE REAL MCCOY?

BACKGROUND

Engineering has made great strides in becoming more diverse and increasing the participation of previously underrepresented groups. Few people realize that one of the most productive engineers of the post–Civil War era was African-American. Elijah McCoy was born in Colchester, Ontario, on May 2, 1844. McCoy's parents were former slaves who fled from Kentucky before the outbreak of the Civil War. (In fact, McCoy's wife was born in 1846 at an Underground Railway station.) After receiving training as a mechanical engineer in Scotland, McCoy moved to Detroit and obtained a job as a fireman on the Michigan Central Railroad.

THE PROBLEM AND ITS SOLUTION

In his job, McCoy became aware of a problem that plagued the railroads and other industries that relied on steam engines. Steam engines required lubrication, which, in the mid-19th century, was usually accomplished by hand. Hand lubrication meant that the machinery had to be turned off or idled to be oiled. McCoy realized that a well-designed automatic lubricator would solve the problem and allow equipment to be run continuously.

McCoy's solution was to improve the hydrostatic lubricator based on a drip cup. In a steam engine, steam from the boiler fills the cylinder and pushes the piston back. In the McCoy lubricator, a small portion of the steam was used to pressurize the lubricator body containing the oil. The pressurized oil drips continuously into the cylinder, thus lubricating the cylinder and piston. The steam condenses into water inside the lubricator body and the oil floats on top. Eventually, the water drains off and the oil is replenished.

The device was patented in 1872. With McCoy's improved lubricator, the continuous operation of steam engines was easier and the transcontinental railroad (completed in 1869) was exploited.

MCCOY'S CONTRIBUTIONS

Elijah McCoy's contributions to lubrication have been exaggerated by some historians and underemphasized by others. While McCoy did not invent the hydrostatic lubricator, he contributed significantly to its optimization and usage. In fact, McCoy's original patent was titled "*Improvement* in Lubricators for Steam-Engines" (emphasis added). Elijah McCoy was a prolific inventor. He was eventually responsible for 57 patents, most involving lubrication equipment. One of his greatest contributions to the field was the graphite lubricator. By suspending graphite in oil, McCoy developed a device to lubricate the then-emerging superheated steam engines.

As with many inventors, McCoy had to assign a number of his patents to investors in his companies. As a result, he did not reap great financial benefits from his inventions. McCoy died at age 85 and was inducted into the National Inventors Hall of Fame in 2001.

IS HE THE "REAL MCCOY"?

The story goes that McCoy's device was prized for its performance, even above the many other automatic lubrication devices that were patented later. Engineers were purported to have asked if their machinery was equipped with "the real McCoy."

Elijah McCoy

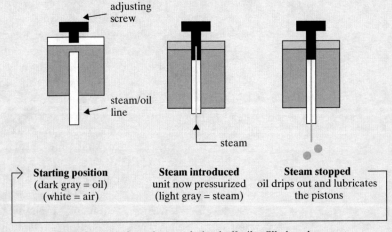

adjusting screw

steam/oil line

steam

Starting position
(dark gray = oil)
(white = air)

Steam introduced
unit now pressurized
(light gray = steam)

Steam stopped
oil drips out and lubricates
the pistons

Water from condensed steam drained off, oil refilled, cycle restarts

Charles "Kid" McCoy

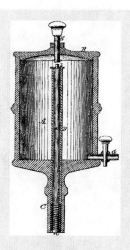

McCoy's lubricator

Did Elijah McCoy's inventions contribute to the popularization of the phrase "the real McCoy"? This question may be impossible to answer. Several people (and objects) from the mid-19th century could be the source of the phrase. Explanations range from Elijah's lubricator to boxer Norman Selby (the Light Heavyweight Champion of the World in 1904, who fought under the name "Kid McCoy") to Mssrs. Mackay's whiskey (made in Edinburgh and marketed as "the real Mackay.")

Regardless of the etymology of "the real McCoy," it is remarkable that a black railroad fireman could have a significant impact on railroad operations within a dozen years of the end of the Civil War. Elijah McCoy stands as a testament to problem solving, perseverance, and intelligence. In these characteristics, he truly was a real McCoy.

Amos Eaton based the program on five rules of education. Eaton's rules are reproduced next, with the original spelling and punctuation (Griggs, 1997). Although the engineering profession and engineering education have changed greatly in almost 200 years,° Eaton's rules are still meaningful today. In this section, Eaton's rules shall be interpreted for the 21st-century engineering curriculum.

4.1   Eaton's First Rule: " . . . make practical applications of all the sciences . . . "

Key idea: Discover engineering through problem solving and hands-on work.

"Let the student make practical applications of all the sciences, with the immediate direction and shewing [showing] of the teacher, before studying any elementary rules. For example, shew him in taking the courses and distances around a field with the compass and chain, before he studies any of the rules of surveying—let him measure a pile of wood and attempt to calculate it before teaching him duo-decimals; let him use optical instruments, under the teacher's shewing, before studying optics, let him give an experimental course on chemistry, before reading any work on chemistry; excepting a textbook of experimental description while in the course of experimenting."

Engineering education must be a marriage of fundamental science and practical applications. *Let the applied problem serve as your introduction to and motivation for theory and analysis.* As Amos Eaton might have put it: engage the hands first and the mind will follow.

°For example, Eaton speaks of students using only the pronouns "he" and "him," since women engineers were rare in the late 19th century. In addition, the original engineering program at the Rensselaer School could be completed in one year!

4.2   Eaton's Second Rule: " ... take the place of the teacher ... [in] exercises."

"Let the student always take the place of the teacher on his exercises. He must make every subject his own and then teach his fellow and the schoolmaster, as though there were not a book in the world which treated on this subject, and he was the very oracle of science. Extemporaneous lectures on Tuesday, Wednesday, Thursday, and Friday, and written lectures on Mondays, is a good exercise for that student, in the acquisition of knowledge. He must not speak without a specimen in hand, or the apparatus before him."

Key idea: Learn by teaching others.

Teaching others is a valuable learning strategy. To master engineering fundamentals, practice explaining your reasoning to faculty and fellow students. Most professors feel that teaching deepens their understanding and appreciation of any material. In the last sentence of the quote, note again Eaton's emphasis on the practical problem.

4.3   Eaton's Third Rule: " ... attend to but one branch of learning at the same time."

"Let a student attend to but one branch of learning at the same time. Personal exercise in the afternoon, at surveying, engineering, collecting plants and minerals, inspecting factories, machines, and agricultural operations, may be permitted. For, although reflection is required, such exercises call such different faculties into action, that the mind is not thereby burdened or fatigued."

Unfortunately, engineering curricula usually do not allow the luxury of immersing the students in only one subject at a time. In fact, the modern engineering curriculum ensures that the courses you will take are integrated together and build on one another. However, *you can focus on one topic at a time*. A key to success in engineering is mastering the material from one lecture or set of readings before the next lecture occurs.

Key idea: Take the time to master material before new concepts are presented.

It is absolutely critical that you give yourself time to master the material. As Eaton said, "reflection is required." In high school, you may have been able to master some material by sitting passively in class and listening to your teacher. In your engineering courses, you will need to think and talk about the material *outside* of the classroom. You must give yourself the time to think, to make mistakes, and to explore. In reading this text, use the *Ponder This* questions as a springboard for reflection.

In this rule, Eaton once again urges you to return to practice. Talking to professionals, going on field trips at every opportunity, and searching the Internet are some 21st-century versions of Eaton's "personal exercises" (see also Section 2).

Finally, Eaton's advice about the importance of using "different faculties" of the mind should serve as a guide to your college education. Use liberal arts and social science courses to exercise the different parts of your brain. These courses are every bit as valuable as your technical courses.

4.4   Eaton's Fourth Rule: "Let the amusements and recreation of students be of a scientific character."

"Let the amusements and recreation of students be of a scientific character. Collecting and preserving minerals and plants, surveying, and engineering, are good amusement."

Eaton's idea of amusement may not jibe with *your* idea of amusement, but the sentiment is important. Eaton's comment focuses on how you spend your time away from the classroom. In modern times, this rule should remind you to get involved with

Key idea: Join student clubs and enter student engineering contests.

student clubs and student engineering contests. In addition, consider getting involved in service-oriented organizations (such as Habitat for Humanity) where your engineering skills can be used to help others immediately. Also, look for engineering in your everyday life—from the automatic teller machine to the roller coaster at your local amusement park to your cell phone.

Eaton also is speaking about commitment. To be a successful engineer, it is **not** necessary to spend every waking moment with your nose in a technical journal. However, *you must make a commitment to getting your degree* or graduation day will never come. Success in engineering is all about using your time wisely to achieve your goals. Start now: make earning an engineering degree a high priority in your life.

4.5   Eaton's Fifth Rule: "Let every student daily criticize those whose exercise he has attended."

Key idea: Challenge your instructors and respect the value of good technical communication skills.

"Let every student daily criticize those whose exercise he has attended. Such as to point out all errors in language, gesture, position, and manner of performing experiments, etc. The teacher must always preside during the hour of criticism. No exercise sharpens the faculty of discrimination like this, while it causes each student to be perpetually on his guard."

Give constructive feedback to your instructors. Challenge them as they challenge you. Learning requires two-way communication, giving you the responsibility to interact with your instructors. Eaton's fifth rule is also a reminder of the importance in the engineering profession of both *technical communications* (i.e, avoiding "errors in language, gesture, position") and *data collection* (i.e., avoiding errors in the "manner of performing experiments").

5   SUMMARY

Your discovery of engineering has begun. It is sincerely hoped that your sense of discovery will be just as keen 40 years from now as it is today. Although you may have some trepidation as you begin your exploration of engineering, know that engineering is the place for you if you are curious, have a strong work ethic, wish to help other people, and respect and enjoy math and science. Discover engineering by talking with engineers, including your professors, members of professional societies (and the student chapters of professional societies), and practicing engineers. Consider the wisdom of Amos Eaton when discovering engineering in your classes.

SUMMARY OF KEY IDEAS

- Engineering is the right place for people who have curiosity, a strong work ethic, a desire to help other people, and a deep respect for math and science.
- Discover engineering by talking to engineers.
- Learn about your future career by finding engineers at a university.
- To learn more, speak with professionals at engineering firms or engineering departments.
- Discover engineering through problem solving and hands-on work.
- Learn by teaching others.
- Take the time to master material before new concepts are presented.
- Join student clubs and enter student engineering contests.
- Challenge your instructors and respect the value of good technical communication skills.

Problems

1. Find and record the Internet home page of each society listed in Table 1. Organizations often write a mission statement that succinctly states their goals and aspirations. Read the mission statement of each organization.

2. Using Table 1, pick two societies that interest you the most and explain why they interest you.

3. Summarize the purpose and goals of three societies listed in Tables 2 through 4.

4. Using the library and the Internet, write a short essay on the contributions to engineering education from Sylvanus Thayer, Alden Partridge, Amos Eaton, or any other pioneering educator in a technical field.

5. Devise a way to teach a high school student about a technical topic using the approach suggested in Eaton's first rule. Pick a topic that you learned about in high school or are learning about now. Possible topics might be Newton's laws of motion, Boyle's law, or Ohm's law.

6. State an applied problem that interests you. Looking at the curriculum for your field of study, list the courses that you think will help you solve this problem.

7. How can you use the ideas in Eaton's second rule to study engineering?

8. Write a paragraph on the opportunities at your university to teach others.

9. Make a list of the liberal arts and social science courses that you plan to take and explain why they interest you.

10. Ask an engineering professor how teaching deepens his or her understanding and appreciation of engineering.

11. Make a list of "amusements and recreation … of a scientific character" in your community. Pick an activity to participate in this year.

12. Attend a meeting of a service-oriented organization in your community. Write a short paragraph about how you might use your engineering training to help the organization.

13. Attend a meeting of an engineering student club. Write a short paragraph about the plans of the student club for the year.

14. Make a list of local engineering firms in the discipline of most interest to you. Visit a local office and report on your visit.

2

What Is Engineering?

1   INTRODUCTION

The question posed by the title of this chapter may seem a bit strange. After all, you do not have to ask the meaning of brain surgery, soccer, or veterinary science—and there are many more engineers in the world than brain surgeons, professional soccer players, or veterinarians. Your familiarity with engineered *systems* (highways, buildings, computers, and factories, to name a few) does not tell you much about the *process* that made those systems. The process is engineering. In this chapter, you will explore the characteristics that engineers and engineering disciplines have in common.

2   DEFINING ENGINEERING

What is engineering? This simple question has a very complex answer. Engineering is a diverse collection of professions, academic disciplines, and skills. You can start your exploration of engineering with the dictionary. Your ego may be boosted to learn that the word "engineering" stems from the Latin *ingenium*, meaning skill. (Other words sharing this Latin root include "ingenious" and "ingenuity.") Engineers are skilled at what they do. But what do they do? The dictionary offers you further insight. The Latin root *ingenium* comes from *in + gignere*, meaning to produce or beget (also the source of the words "generate" and "kin"). Thus, engineers are skilled producers or creators of things.

This exercise in word origins does not do justice to the field of engineering. Many definitions of "engineering" and "engineer" are possible. Most definitions have some elements in common.

OBJECTIVES

After reading this chapter, you will be able to:

- identify the elements that all engineering disciplines have in common;
- describe how engineers help others.

Based on your experiences, what is your definition of engineering?

Key idea: Engineers are professionals who apply science and mathematics to useful ends, solve problems creatively, optimize, and make reasoned choices.

Common elements in the definitions include the following:

- Engineers apply science and mathematics to useful ends.
- Engineers solve problems creatively.
- Engineers optimize.
- Engineers make choices.
- Engineers help others.
- Engineering is a profession.

You will examine each of these elements in more detail in this chapter.

3   ENGINEERING AS AN APPLIED DISCIPLINE

3.1   Knowledge Generation versus Knowledge Implementation

Almost everyone would agree that engineering is the application of science and mathematics to practical ends. Indeed, the emphasis on practice and application always is in the mind of the engineer. They care more about *using* basic knowledge than *generating* basic knowledge. They care more about converting basic science into technology and converting technology into useful products than in expanding basic science.

However, the emphasis on application tells only part of the story of engineering. The pure engineer may be concerned only with practice, just as the pure scientist is concerned only with generating new knowledge. In reality, both practicing scientists and engineers contribute to the complicated and rewarding process of converting ideas into reality. The pure scientist and the pure engineer are extremes of a spectrum of skills required to make new things.

3.2   The Role of Engineering

The role of the engineer in turning ideas into usable ideas or objects° is illustrated in Figure 1. Both scientists and engineers use mathematics and natural sciences as their tools. Engineers focus on answering the questions that lie on the more applied side of the spectrum. In your career as an engineer, it is likely that you will help develop and implement technology. You will likely work from the middle to the right side of the spectrum

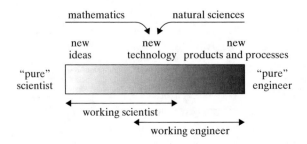

Figure 1. Spectrum of Skills in Engineering and Science.

°Engineers develop both *products* (e.g., ballpoint pens, toasters, microprocessors, and satellites) and *processes* (e.g., better ways to stock inventory, new approaches to manufacturing compact discs, and innovative ways to treat wastewater).

in Figure 1. As an engineer, you will acquire a pool of skills required to translate new knowledge into usable ideas.

You are urged to return to Figure 1 throughout your career. It may help you remember that knowledge generation and product design are two ends of the same spectrum. Neither skill is useful without the other.

Figure 1 is a good road map for getting the most out of your courses. For example, if you are suffering from motivational problems in your science and mathematics courses, think about how the material can be applied. Speak to your science and mathematics professors about the practical use of the material. Ask engineering mentors how they use basic science and mathematics in their everyday professional lives.

EXAMPLE 1: APPLICATION OF SCIENTIFIC PRINCIPLES

In your high school or freshman chemistry course, you may have learned about the unit of chemical concentration called the *mole*. At first glance, the use of molar units of concentration may seem very theoretical and not applied. Give an example of how each main engineering discipline can use this concept.

SOLUTION

Lithium iodine batteries as small as 4 mm thick have been used in implantable cardiac pacemakers for over 20 years (Photo courtesy of Greatbatch, Inc.)

Engineers use different sets of units to solve different kinds of problems. Molar units express the proportions in which chemicals combine. Therefore, they are very useful for solving problems involving *combining proportions*.

Almost every engineering discipline uses molar units for some applications. For example, a civil engineer (in the environmental engineering specialty) might use molar units for determining doses of chemicals to react with pollutants and solve pollution problems. A chemical engineer may use moles to determine the ratios of chemicals used to synthesize polymers on a commercial scale. An electrical engineer would use molar units to determine the number of electrons per time (also called the current) produced by an electrochemical cell (such as a battery). Molar units could be used by an industrial engineer to design monitoring devices to make the workplace safer. Mechanical engineers use the concept of the mole to optimize material properties. All engineers may work together to use molar units to design sensors capable of detecting chemical or biological agents.

4 ENGINEERING AS CREATIVE PROBLEM SOLVING

4.1 Solving Problems

Engineers solve problems. These three simple words have far-reaching ramifications on the life of an engineer. First, since engineers solve problems, engineering work is usually motivated by a concern or roadblock. This idea may conjure up an image of lone warriors furiously performing dense calculations in a cubicle under a green-shaded desk lamp.

No image of engineering could be more incorrect. In reality, engineers often solve other people's problems. Thus, engineers must be able to *listen to a concern* and *map out a solution.* Whether the problem is to make cars that pollute less or to make oil refining more efficient or to reduce the manufacturing cost of a child's toy, engineers must be able to understand problems that their clients face. In this way, engineering is a very people-oriented profession.

4.2 Standard Approaches to Solving Problems

Second, engineers must be skilled in using standard approaches to solve problems. We all respect the brilliant physician who can leap to a diagnosis using intuition and experience. We marvel at the aircraft mechanic who spots the mechanical problem by "feel."

However, we also know that *every* physician must be able to follow standard diagnostic procedures and *every* mechanic must be familiar with the inspection checklist. Similarly, engineers must know the well-established protocols used in solving many problems.

4.3 Creative Approaches to Solving Problems

Key idea: The solution to engineering problems involves both standard and creative approaches.

Third, engineers must be creative in solving problems. Just like the physician and aircraft mechanic, engineers must supplement the standard solution methods with creativity and insight. Engineering is a highly creative profession. As Theodore von Kármán (1881–1963), a well-known Hungarian-born specialist in fluid mechanics and aerodynamics, put it, "The scientist describes what is; the engineer creates what never was" (Mackay, 1991). This quotation should not be interpreted as minimizing the creativity of scientists. Rather, it points out that engineers must have vision to create something that did not previously exist.

5   ENGINEERING AS CONSTRAINED OPTIMIZATION

5.1   Constraints

constrained optimization: determining the best solution to a problem, given limitations on the solution

Key idea: Engineering solutions are often constrained.

Engineering, like life, is about **constrained optimization**. In high school, it was likely that you did not strive to be the *best* student you could be. Rather, you strived to be the best student you could be *given that* you had to work part-time or you had family obligations or you were active in community groups. In other words, your time available for studying was *constrained* by other activities.

Similarly, engineers always face constraints in solving problems. As an example, electrical engineers rarely seek to design the fastest computer chip. To be useful, computer chips must exhibit other characteristics as well.

PONDER THIS

> **List some constraints on computer chip design.**

We could list the various constraints on computer chip design, but a better goal is just to say that we seek to develop the fastest computer chip of sufficiently small size with adequate heat dissipation characteristics that can be mass-produced at a reasonable cost.

Is it *ever* valuable to build the fastest chip? Absolutely! An electrical engineer specializing in the research side of research and development (R&D) may, in fact, seek to design the fastest computer chip. Some major breakthroughs in engineering have been generated by engineers and scientists who ignored constraints. However, most engineers seek to put ideas into practice. This means taking the real world and its constraints into account when designing engineered systems.

Key idea: Engineering solutions must take into account the probability of failure.

One aspect of the constrained nature of engineering is that engineers live in a probabilistic world. In other words, engineers must consider the *chances* of certain events occurring, including the probability of failure. A civil engineer does not design a bridge that will never fall down. Such a bridge would be infinitely expensive. Rather, the civil engineer examines the probabilities that certain loads will occur on the bridge from traffic, earthquakes, and wind. A bridge is designed to perform acceptably for a specified period of time under the anticipated loads and stresses. Similarly, an environmental engineer does not design a drinking water treatment plant to remove *all* pollutants completely. Such a plant is probably not possible (and if it was possible, the drinking water it produced would be unaffordable). Instead, engineers design treatment plants to meet water quality standards and minimize risk at a socially acceptable cost.

Due to constrained optimization in a probabilistic world, engineers must constantly ask: How strong is strong enough? How clean is clean? Have I thought of everything that could go wrong?* An example of extremely constrained optimization is given in the *Focus on Constrained Optimization: A Square Peg in a Round Hole*.

5.2   Feasibility

The ability of an engineering project to meet its constraints is often expressed in terms of feasibility. There are several aspects of feasibility, which will be introduced here. *Technical* (or engineering) *feasibility* measures whether or not a project meets its technical goals. It addresses several questions, such as "Does the new road handle the traffic?" and "Is the upgraded electrical transmission system more efficient?"

Key idea: To be successful, engineering projects must be technically, economically, fiscally, socially, politically, and environmentally feasible.

Most of your undergraduate course work is focused on technical feasibility. However, it is not sufficient for an engineering project to be technically feasible. Engineering projects also must be economically feasible. *Economic feasibility* addresses whether the project benefits outweigh the project costs. In the examples above, economic feasibility addresses whether the road benefits (e.g., tolls collected, elimination of slowdowns, and increased safety) are greater than the road construction and maintenance costs or whether the money saved from the more efficient transmission systems will pay for the upgrade work. Sometimes, the benefits and costs are difficult to quantify. What is the value of a five-minute reduction in commuting time or one less incidence of cancer for every one million people? To answer these questions, engineers may seek the advice of social scientists and economists.

Another factor to consider is *fiscal feasibility*. Fiscal feasibility measures whether sufficient funds can be generated to build the project. Many engineering projects would be profitable (i.e., are economically feasible), but are not built because start-up money cannot be acquired. The difference between economic and fiscal feasibility is important. For large, multimillion-dollar engineering projects, obtaining money through loans or bonds to achieve fiscal feasibility may be the critical step. Engineers who ignore fiscal feasibility will never see their ideas translated into reality.

The last type of feasibility is social, political, and environmental feasibility. Engineers cannot work in a vacuum. Engineering projects must be socially acceptable, have political backing, and result in an acceptable environmental impact. Many engineering projects remain only on paper because societal and political support was lacking. Should you, as an engineer, be upset because some projects die due to nontechnical issues? No. It should remind you that engineers are part of the fabric of society. The public cares about the impact of engineering projects. As a result, you must consider the social consequences of your proposal along with the technical details.

FOCUS ON CONSTRAINED OPTIMIZATION: A SQUARE PEG IN A ROUND HOLE

BACKGROUND

Engineering is about constrained optimization. The need to "make the best with what you have" is demanding when the constraints are the most severe. For example, a space vehicle located 200,000 nautical miles from Earth presents some of the most severe constraints that an engineer will face.

Such was the case with *Apollo 13*, launched April 11, 1970. The crew of the spacecraft—Commander James A. Lovell, Lunar Module Pilot Fred W. Haise, Jr., and Command Module Pilot John L. Swigert, Jr.—was hard at work and enjoying the ride. Suddenly, about 56 hours into the flight, the crew heard a loud noise (which is never a good sign in a spacecraft). The pressure in Cryogenic Oxygen Tank 2 had begun to rise

---

*For an insightful and entertaining discussion of this question as it pertains to civil engineering, see Petroski (1992).

Launch of Apollo 13, Saturday, April 11, 1970

very quickly. Within two minutes, the tank lost pressure. Why did this matter? Electricity on *Apollo 13* was generated by a fuel cell, where oxygen and hydrogen were combined. No oxygen meant no power—and no way to return to Earth.

PROBLEMS AND SOLUTIONS

The ground crew quickly assessed the situation. The three people in space required three things to return to Earth alive: power, water (to drink and to cool the equipment), and oxygen. With the fuel cells virtually inoperable, the only source of power was the batteries in the Lunar Module (LM, the *Aquarius*). It became clear that the LM, with its own ample oxygen supplies, would become the lifeboat for the crew. But the LM had its own problems. Its batteries would need to be recharged to provide enough power for the journey home. However, there was no direct electrical connection between the Command Service Module (CSM, the *Odyssey*) and the LM to recharge the batteries. Engineers on the ground discovered a way to leak current slowly from the CSM to the batteries. By turning off nonessential equipment,

the crew limped home with an amazing 20% of the LM power left.

The problem with water could be addressed only by drinking less. The crew cut its water ration to 200 milliliters per person per day (a little over one-half of a soft drink can). The crew lost a collective 31 pounds on the trip home, arriving in poor health and with 10% of the water supply remaining.

The LM had a sufficient oxygen supply, but the ground crew soon realized that *another* air supply problem would threaten the astronauts: the build-up of carbon dioxide (CO_2) exhaled by the crew. The CO_2 was removed by lithium hydroxide (LiOH) canisters through a chemical reaction. The LM was designed to transport two members of the crew from lunar orbit to the surface of the Moon. It had a sufficient canister capacity to remove the CO_2 produced by two people for about 30 hours, not the CO_2 exhaled by three people for the long trip back to Earth. Even by allowing the CO_2 levels to rise a little, the canisters could operate for only about 187 person-hours, when at least 288 person-hours would be needed. The solution? The CSM had its own LiOH canisters. But as luck would have it, the CSM canisters had *square* connectors that would not fit in the *round* fittings of the LM.

CONSTRAINED OPTIMIZATION

In a brilliant feat of constrained optimization, the ground crew had to develop an interface between the square CSM canisters and the round LM fittings from material available to the astronauts. (The near-impossibility of this task is shown dramatically in a famous scene from the movie *Apollo 13*.) The adapter, called the "mailbox," was designed by ground engineer Ed Smylie. (In NASA-speak, the adapter is known officially as the "supplemental carbon dioxide removal system.") It was made of two CSM canisters, a space suit exhaust hose, cardboard from instructional cue cards in the LM, plastic stowage bags from liquid-cooled undergarments, and one roll of duct tape. (Ironically, much of this material would have been otherwise unused by the astronauts. The cue cards contained instructions for lifting off from the moon and the undergarments were to be worn on moonwalks.)

Timeline for the Apollo 13 Carbon Dioxide Crisis
(all times are Central Standard Time for Houston, TX)

**Deke Slayton displays
the prototype**

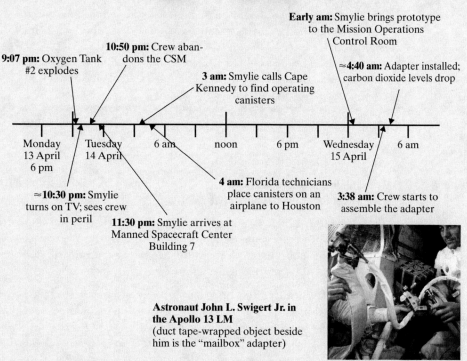

Early am: Smylie brings prototype
to the Mission Operations
Control Room

10:50 pm: Crew aban-
dons the CSM

9:07 pm: Oxygen Tank
#2 explodes

≈4:40 am: Adapter installed;
carbon dioxide levels drop

3 am: Smylie calls Cape
Kennedy to find operating
canisters

| Monday 13 April 6 pm | Tuesday 14 April | 6 am | noon | 6 pm | Wednesday 15 April | 6 am |

≈10:30 pm: Smylie
turns on TV; sees crew
in peril

4 am: Florida technicians
place canisters on an
airplane to Houston

3:38 am: Crew starts to
assemble the adapter

11:30 pm: Smylie arrives at
Manned Spacecraft Center
Building 7

**Astronaut John L. Swigert Jr. in
the Apollo 13 LM**
(duct tape-wrapped object beside
him is the "mailbox" adapter)

The efforts of engineer Ed Smylie, the other Houston personnel, and the astronauts were truly unbelievable. Only about 30 hours elapsed between the time Smylie turned on his television set to learn of *Apollo 13*'s problems and the time that the astronauts finished building the mailbox in space. (See the accompanying timeline.) Smylie and his assistant, Jim Correale, had no operational LiOH canisters to test the interface. Working canisters from Florida (intended for *Apollo 14* or *Apollo 15*) were airlifted to Houston to enable testing of the device. After testing on the ground, the ground crew issued about an hour's worth of instructions by radio so that the astronauts could construct the adapter in space.

The *Apollo 13* flight had a very happy ending, due to the bravery of the astronauts and the ingenuity of the engineers. When faced with an overwhelmingly constrained problem, the engineers created a solution that saved the lives of three American heroes.

6   ENGINEERING AS MAKING CHOICES

Key idea: Engineers make recommendations by selecting from a list of feasible alternatives.

feasibility assessment: evaluation of the feasibility of an engineering project

The discussion thus far has centered on what engineering *is* rather than what engineers *do*. So what *does* an engineer do? Engineers listen carefully to the problem. (See Section 4.1.) Using accepted and creative methods (see Sections 4.2 and 4.3), they develop a list of feasible solutions or alternatives. Here, "feasible" means that each solution is technically, economically, fiscally, and socially/politically/environmentally feasible. (Evaluating whether a project is feasible is called a ***feasibility assessment***. See Example 2 for an example.) Finally, engineers select an alternative from among the feasible solutions and recommend it to their client.

In a real sense, engineering is about generating alternatives and selecting feasible solutions. The selection step sets engineers apart from other professionals (e.g., technicians and designers) who may be trained to do the calculations and run the software, but may not be trained to make recommendations. To recommend an alternative, an engineer has to balance the technical, economic, fiscal, and social/political/environmental issues. A person trained only to crunch numbers will fail in this critical decision-making task. A person trained only to crunch numbers is not an engineer.

EXAMPLE 2: FEASIBILITY ASSESSMENT

Conduct a feasibility assessment for buying a used car to commute to a part-time job.

SOLUTION

A feasibility assessment determines the technical, economic, fiscal, and social/political/environmental feasibility of an alternative.

Technical feasibility: Technical feasibility probes whether the alternative will solve the problem. In this case, you need to ask whether buying the car will allow you to commute to work safely and reliably. Perhaps the car you can afford will not be sufficiently reliable. Perhaps other more reliable alternatives exist, such as public transportation.

Economic feasibility: Economic feasibility questions whether the benefits of the alternative exceed its costs. The costs of car ownership include depreciation, financing, insurance, taxes and fees, fuel, maintenance, and repairs. For a used 2000 Honda Accord two-door LX coupe in Buffalo, New York, the purchase and ownership costs average about $7,570 per year for the first five years (as determined by the cost calculator at www.edmunds.com). The benefits include your ability to get to your part-time job and the freedom and convenience that car ownership engenders. Other alternatives (such as a monthly bus pass) may have lower costs, but they do not have the freedom and convenience of car ownership.

Fiscal feasibility: Fiscal feasibility probes whether you can get the start-up funds to finance the project. In this example, purchasing the car is fiscally feasible if you can qualify for a reasonable car loan.

Social/political/environmental feasibility: In this example, social/political/environmental feasibility centers on environmental impact. In spite of the large social, political, and environmental costs of reliance on the internal combustion engine, car ownership remains socially acceptable in North America. You could consider, as an alternative, a car with lower environmental impact. (Buying a new Toyota Prius has about twice the purchase + interest + depreciation costs of the Honda, but about half the fuel + maintenance + repair costs.)

7   ENGINEERS AS HELPING OTHERS

Professions can be characterized in many ways. Some people are attracted to the so-called caring professions.

PONDER THIS

Make a list of caring professions.

Caring professions include medicine, nursing, social work, and teaching. Did your list include engineering?

Engineering is also one of the caring professions. Why? Nearly every project that an engineer completes satisfies a need or concern of the public. For example, if you become an electrical engineer, you may develop sensors to make more powerful neonatal incubators. Perhaps as a civil engineer, you may work on earthquake-resistant buildings or develop drinking-water treatment systems for less developed countries. (Water-related diseases, the leading cause of death globally, is responsible for 14,000 deaths *per day* because more than one billion people on the planet lack access to safe drinking water.) Maybe you will become a chemical engineer and work on ways to mass-produce HIV medications, making such drugs affordable to every HIV-positive person in the world. Perhaps you will go into industrial engineering and devise systems to help nonprofit organizations better serve their clients. (Volunteers from several professional and student chapters of the Institute of Industrial Engineers recently helped make a women's shelter in Pittsburgh become more efficient to save resources.) Or maybe you will become a mechanical engineer and develop a robust heart valve for premature infants. Whatever field of engineering interests you, know that you can use your training to make the world a better place and to make people's lives healthier and more fulfilling.

8   ENGINEERING AS A PROFESSION

Finally, engineering is a profession. This means, of course, that engineers get paid for what they do. In addition, it means that to be called an engineer, you must meet certain requirements. Just as the public must be assured that a person called a dentist or lawyer is fully certified, so the public must know that a person using the title "engineer" has been trained properly. The process of meeting the requirements is called *registration*. A registered engineer holds the title *professional engineer*, or PE.

All professions have ethical standards. Engineers, as professionals, must meet high standards of professional ethics.

9   SUMMARY

The dictionary tells us that engineers give birth to things creatively. In particular, the work of engineers is characterized by six elements. First, engineers apply science and mathematics to useful ends. Second, engineers solve problems using both standard and creative approaches. Third, engineers optimize solutions subject to the constraints of the real world. The constraints are often grouped under the headings of technical feasibility (will the system perform the task for which it was designed?), economic feasibility (do benefits outweigh costs?), fiscal feasibility (are start-up funds available?), and social/political/environmental feasibility. Fourth, engineers make reasoned choices. They select and recommend feasible alternatives. Fifth, engineers help others. Without a public to serve, engineering as a profession would not exist. Finally, engineers are professionals. This means that engineers may seek professional registration and must meet ethical standards.

<table>
<tr><td>

SUMMARY OF KEY IDEAS

</td><td>

- Engineers are professionals who apply science and mathematics to useful ends, solve problems creatively, optimize, and make reasoned choices.
- The solution to engineering problems involves both standard and creative approaches.
- Engineering solutions are often constrained.
- Engineering solutions must take into account the probability of failure.
- To be successful, engineering projects must be technically, economically, fiscally, socially, politically, and environmentally feasible.
- Engineers make recommendations by selecting from a list of feasible alternatives.
- Engineering is a profession and engineers have ethical responsibilities.

</td></tr>
</table>

Problems

1. What are the six main elements of engineering?

2. Some pharmaceuticals are manufactured by genetically engineered bacteria to produce the drug. Discuss the role of the engineer (if any) in the following steps of the development of a new drug:
   - Synthesis of the drug for animal tests
   - Genetic engineering of the bacteria
   - Mass production through bacterial synthesis
   - Clinical trials
   - Development of the time-release capsules and transdermal patches
   - Efficiency study of the manufacturing process, and
   - Design of the marketing strategy

3. Explain the differences in the contributions to society of scientists and engineers. Which contribution appeals more to you and why?

4. Give an example of constrained optimization in an engineering problem.

5. For Problem 4, what is a possible solution, given the constraints? How would the solution change if the constraints were different?

6. From your local newspaper, find an example of an engineering project that was not implemented because it was not economically or fiscally feasible.

7. Explain the difference between economic feasibility and fiscal feasibility.

8. Give an example of an engineering project that is economically feasible, but not fiscally feasible. Give an example of an engineering project that is fiscally feasible, but not economically feasible.

9. From your local newspaper, find an example of an engineering project that was not implemented because it was not socially, politically, or environmentally feasible.

10. For your answer in Problem 9, how would you change the project to make it feasible?

11. Talk with an engineer in government service (e.g., a town, city, or county engineer) about the difference between economic and fiscal feasibility. Illustrate the difference with an example from your community.

12 Two towns are separated by a river and wish to exchange goods. List several alternative solutions to this problem. Perform a feasibility assessment and rank the alternatives according to their feasibility. (Be sure to include all types of feasibility.) Recommend a solution to the problem.

13. Make a list of the professions that are licensed by your state. What do the professions have in common? Which licenses are in technical fields?

14. Which agency in your state licenses engineers? (Try searching the Internet for your state name and the phrase "professional engineer.") How many engineers are licensed in your state?

15. How do engineers in your area participate in public service?

3

Engineering Careers

1   INTRODUCTION

You have learned about the activities and approaches common to many engineers. This chapter explores the kinds of careers for which an engineering education prepares you. Engineering jobs will be discussed in general terms in this chapter. Jobs specific to each engineering discipline will be presented elsewhere.

2   ENGINEERING JOBS

2.1   Availability of Jobs

What do engineering students do when they graduate? Fortunately, they have the opportunity to work in their field if they wish. In a recent study, a sample of the 109,200 people receiving baccalaureate degrees in engineering in 1999 and 2000 were surveyed to find out what they were doing in 2001. Ninety-three percent of the recent graduates were working. Of those employed, 84% found jobs in engineering and science (NSF, 2003; see Figure 1). Most of the employed engineers (68%) found jobs in the same discipline as their degree. The bottom line? Trained engineers can usually find jobs as engineers.

2.2   Introduction to Engineering Jobs

Where are engineers employed? The range of jobs performed by engineers is truly amazing. They have optimized devices as simple as the pencil and developed systems as complex as the Space Shuttle.° For example, some engineers work on systems as small as very large scale integration (VLSI)

OBJECTIVES

After reading this chapter, you will be able to:

- list the types of jobs available to engineers;
- explain why job satisfaction is high in engineering;
- describe the future of engineering employment.

°The Space Shuttle *Endeavour*, built to replace the Space Shuttle *Challenger*, was first flown in May 1992. This Space Shuttle has several hundreds of thousands of parts, and it was constructed with the assistance of over 250 subcontractors at a cost of approximately $1.7 billion.

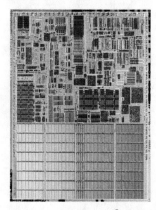

Intel Corp.'s Itanium® 2 microprocessor contains 221 million transistors in an area less
than a square inch (421 mm²).

Arecibo observatory (photo
courtesy of the NAIC-Areci-
bo Observatory, a faculty of
the NSF)

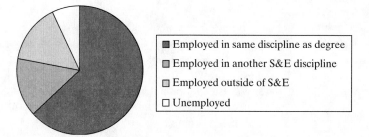

Figure 1. Employment Statistics for Baccalaureate Engineers (S&E = science and
engineering)

chips, with millions of transistors and other circuits on each 0.25-inch square speck of
silicon. Engineers are helping to develop *nanomachines:* futuristic mechanical devices
consisting of only a few thousand atoms. Others work on systems as large as the 305-
meter (1,000-foot) radio telescope near Arecibo, Puerto Rico.

Engineers have done work as helpful as creating assistive devices for the disabled
and inventing innovative approaches to clean polluted air. In fact, engineers work on systems as controversial as nuclear weapons and nerve gases.

With such a range of experiences, how can you make sense of engineering jobs? It
is instructive to examine the distribution of engineering jobs in various economic sectors. In 2002, about 1,769,000 engineers were employed in the United States (BLS,
2004), including about 611,000 computer software engineers. About half of these jobs
were in manufacturing industries. A little more than one-quarter of the jobs were in service industries. Government agencies at all levels (federal, state, and local governments)
employed about 12% of all engineers in 2000.

2.3   Engineers in Industry

Engineers in industry are involved mainly with the manufacture of products. In 2001,
there were 1,000 engineers making toys and sporting goods and 57,000 engineers involved in manufacturing electronic components and accessories. Manufacturing accounts for about half of engineering jobs. Most of these jobs are in transportation
equipment (mainly motor vehicles and aircraft), electrical and electronic equipment,
and industrial equipment (including computing equipment). Other engineers in industry work in nonmanufacturing areas such as construction and mining.

2.4   Engineers in Service

Engineers in service act as consultants, contribute to product marketing and sales, or
conduct research. The service sector accounts for about 28% of engineering jobs, mostly
in engineering and architecture, business services (mainly computer/data processing
and personnel supply services), and research and testing services.

Most engineering companies are small. In 2001, 59% of engineering firms had fewer
than 5 employees, and 35% of the firms employed 5 to 50 people (Rosenbaum, 2002). It is
not uncommon to find very small "mom-and-pop" engineering consulting firms.

Consulting engineers may own their own business. About 43,000 engineers in
2000 were self-employed. Most of these engineers worked as consultants.

2.5   Engineers in Government

Government engineers may be employed by federal, state, or local agencies. The military also employs both civilian and active-duty engineers. Government engineers work

Key idea: About 12% of engineers work for government agencies.

for a wide range of agencies, from city engineering offices to the U.S. Army Corps of Engineers to the Peace Corps.

As stated in Section 2.2, about one out of every eight engineering jobs is in government. Over half of these jobs are in the federal government, primarily in such agencies as the Departments of Defense, Transportation, Agriculture, Interior, and Energy and in the National Aeronautics and Space Administration (NASA) (BLS, 2004). Engineers employed by state and local governments typically work in highway and public works departments.

2.6   Other Engineering Jobs

Transportation and public utilities account for another 5% of engineering jobs. Most of these jobs are with electric and telephone utilities. The remaining engineering jobs are mainly in wholesale/retail trade and construction.

2.7   Engineering Education as a Route to Other Fields

Key idea: An engineering education is excellent preparation for many non-engineering professions.

An engineering education provides a strong background in quantitative skills and problem solving. Such tools are highly valued in many fields. Thus, an engineering education is a good start for many nonengineering professions. Trained engineers are well suited to pursue professional degrees in other fields, including law, medicine, business, and education. For example, an engineering background is very desirable for patent and environmental law. Engineers can go on to medical school and contribute to such fields as biomechanics and neurobiology. Many business schools encourage potential students to pursue technical degrees at the undergraduate level. An engineering degree is a fine route to a teaching career in secondary or higher education.

The tools and approaches learned in engineering classes have led to successful careers in other fields. U.S. Presidents Herbert Hoover (mining) and Jimmy Carter (nuclear) were trained as engineers. Other engineers that became politicians include John Sununu (mechanical), Yasser Arafat (civil), Leonid Brezhnev (metallurgical), and Boris Yeltsin (civil).

Several famous entertainers started out as engineers. For example, both *Star Trek* creator Gene Roddenberry (aeronautical) and Academy Award-winning director Frank Capra (chemical) had engineering degrees. Other engineers who landed in entertainment-oriented careers include film directors and Roger Corman (industrial) and Alfred Hitchcock (studied at the School of Engineering and Navigation in London), jazz musician Herbie Hancock (electrical), talk show host Montel Williams (general), and television star Bill Nye, "The Science Guy" (mechanical). For another interesting story of an engineering entertainer, see the *Focus on Nonengineers*.

Engineering careers are not limited to Earth. Nearly all the early astronauts in the Mercury, Gemini, and Apollo programs were engineers. All but four of the 39 U.S. astronaut pilots in the Space Shuttle program in 2004 had engineering degrees.

Herbert Hoover

3   JOB SATISFACTION IN ENGINEERING

3.1   What Does "Job Satisfaction" Mean to You?

As discussed in Section 2.1, people trained as engineers can generally obtain jobs as engineers. Thus, you are not just pursuing a *degree* in engineering, but you are also traveling the road towards a *career* in engineering. One measure of a successful career is a love for the jobs you will have as you progress in your chosen field.

FOCUS ON NONENGINEERS: "IT'S NOT HEDY, IT'S HEDLEY"

Fans of Mel Brooks's notoriously crude movie *Blazing Saddles* (1974) will recognize the title of this section. The crooked attorney general Hedley Lamarr (played outrageously by Harvey Korman) repeatedly has to remind everyone how to pronounce his name: "It's not Hedy, it's Hedley."

Hedy Lamarr (photo courtesy of Anthony Loder).

So who was Hedy Lamarr, the source of the attorney general's confusion? And what does she have to do with engineering? Hedy Lamarr was born as Hedwig Eva Maria Kiesler in Vienna in 1913. She made dozens of movies, including the 1933 Austrian–Czech film *Ecstasy*, which featured one of the first nude scenes in a movie. Lamarr married arms manufacturer Fritz Mandl in 1933. To escape the Nazi regime and her domineering husband, Lamarr escaped to London in 1938. There, she met movie mogul Louis B. Mayer. Mayer gave her the stage name we know now and took her to Hollywood. She became a famous actress and pin-up girl in World War II, and she was active in the sale of millions of dollars in war bonds.

But Hedy Lamarr was not just a glamorous film star of Hollywood's Golden Age. In fact, Lamarr had the temperament, if not the education, of an engineer. At a dinner party shortly after the onset of World War II, Lamarr was talking with her friend, composer George Antheil. Using the analogy of a player piano, Lamarr and Antheil reasoned that communication between a submarine and a torpedo could be made secret if the information was scrambled by hopping it between frequencies. The pair eventually patented the idea. It became U.S. Patent Number 2,292,387, filed June 10, 1941, and issued August 11, 1942, to Hedy Kiesler Markey (her legal name at the time) and George Antheil for a "Secret Communications System."

The U.S. military decided that the idea of "frequency hopping" was impractical. In fact, given the technology of the time, frequency hopping probably was nearly impossible to implement. The idea, however, would revolutionize communication. The patent expired in 1959 and the concept was generalized as "spread spectrum technology."° Soon, the technology caught up with the idea. Spread spectrum technology has been used in military applications from the Cuban Missile Crisis to the 1991 Gulf War. It was released to the public domain in the 1980s and is now used in applications as diverse as pagers and traffic signals.

Spread spectrum communication is the basis for the operation of garage door openers, cell phones, and wireless Internet communication. Why? In addition to the security of the signal, spread spectrum technology has a number of advantages. By spreading the signal across a number of frequencies, this communication tool makes efficient use of the clogged radio frequency band. In addition, because the devices transmit only for a short time at any one frequency, the signals appear as background noise rather than interfering with existing transmissions at that frequency. This property allows spread spectrum devices (for example, digital spread spectrum [DSS] cordless telephones) to operate at a higher power (and hence, have a longer range) and with less interference.

It is not an exaggeration to say that Lamarr and Antheil's idea for defeating Nazism is the cornerstone of modern digital communication. Not bad for a glamorous actress and avant-garde composer. Hedy Lamarr and George Antheil were honored with an International Pioneer Award in 1997 from the Electronic Frontier Foundation. Hedy Lamarr died in 2000, remembered as an actress and inventor.

°The term "spread spectrum technology" refers to any technology where information is distributed over a wide signal bandwidth according to a pattern independent of the data transmitted. One way to accomplish this is to use the frequency-hopping approach of Hedy Lamarr and George Antheil.

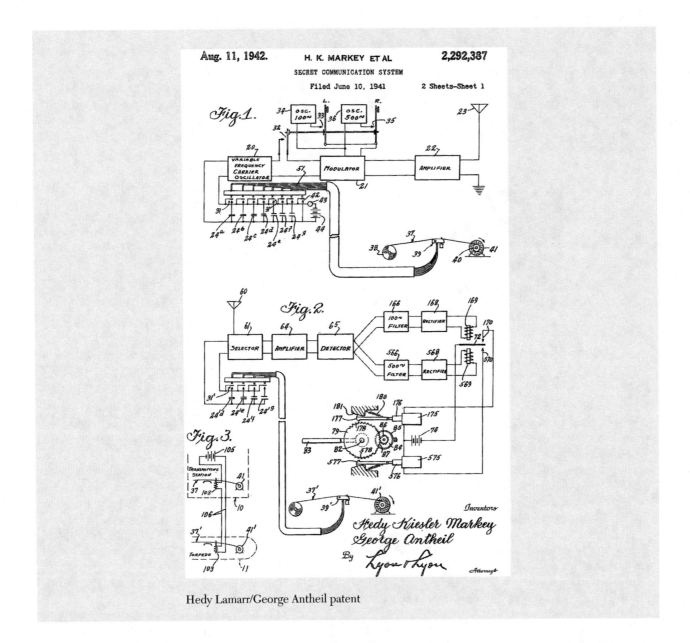

Hedy Lamarr/George Antheil patent

PONDER THIS

When you get your first engineering job, how are you going to measure your own job satisfaction?

Most people measure their job satisfaction in three categories:

- Accomplishments: what they have contributed to society
- Work environment: independence, responsibility, the degree to which they are challenged by their work, and where they work
- Monetary issues: salary, benefits, and opportunities for promotion

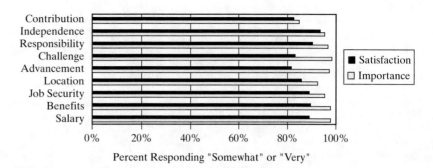

Figure 2.   Importance in Job Selection and Level of Satisfaction of Recent Engineering Graduates

Key idea: Job satisfaction includes contributions to society, degree of independence, level of responsibility, intellectual challenge, opportunities for promotion, benefits, and salary.

Key idea: Job satisfaction among engineers is very high.

Key idea: Engineers are well compensated, with salaries varying by discipline, educational level, and experience.

Key idea: Employers expect to receive more value from you than you are paid.

It is not uncommon for people to have very high expectations of their future careers, only to have their visions squashed by reality. Entry-level engineers also have high expectations. In 2001, the National Science Foundation (NSF) surveyed 1999 and 2000 engineering graduates about their job satisfaction (NSF, 2003). The elements of job satisfaction included contribution to society, degree of independence, level of responsibility, intellectual challenge, opportunities for advancement, location, job security, benefits, and salary. As shown in the gray bars in Figure 2, most factors were very important to the recent engineering graduates. (Figure 2 shows the percentage of respondents that said the factor was "very important" or "somewhat important" to them.)

The good news is that their level of job satisfaction was high. The average job satisfaction rating for the nine factors was 88%. (For scientists in the same survey, the average job satisfaction was 82%.) The entry-level engineers were particularly satisfied with the degree of independence and level of responsibility provided in their jobs.

3.2   Engineering Salaries

Compared with other fields, engineers are paid well. Salaries vary by discipline, educational level, and experience. So how much do engineers make? It would be misleading to list detailed salary data here. Information about salaries can become outdated very quickly and should be interpreted with caution. It is almost impossible to know the true average salary of any group as large as the engineering community. Salary surveys invariably cover different populations and may or may not include some benefits. In general, engineers have and continue to be valued in our society. Compensation is expected to remain good for the foreseeable future.

While the higher salaries of engineers are an attraction, avoid choosing a profession (or engineering discipline) strictly on the basis of salary. Your job satisfaction will be low (and your life miserable) if you go for the bucks without listening to your heart.

One final note on salaries: The higher salaries of engineers come with some expectations.

PONDER THIS

What do employers expect of you when they offer you, say, $45,000 as a starting salary?

It means that they expect to receive more than $45,000 worth of value from you. For a company to make money, it must receive more value (in sales or client fees) from you than you are being paid. Remember this fact when you interview for jobs: salaries create an obligation to work responsibly, diligently, and ethically.

4   FUTURE OF ENGINEERING EMPLOYMENT

Key idea: Engineering jobs are expected to grow over 7% from 2002 to 2012, with over about 5% growth in the major engineering disciplines.

The future is good for the employment of engineers. In total, 109,000 engineering job openings are expected from 2002 to 2012. Most of the major engineering disciplines are predicted to show over about 5% growth in that period, with engineering as a whole having a 7.3% job growth. According to the best estimates of the economists, engineers trained today should have reasonable expectations of a job tomorrow.

5   SUMMARY

The present and future states of engineering employment are strong, and students should expect to find jobs in their fields. Engineering jobs may be found in manufacturing (e.g., mainly motor vehicles, aircraft, electrical and electronic equipment, and industrial equipment and computing equipment), services (e.g., consulting services, marketing and sales, and research), government, and other areas (e.g., transportation, public utilities, wholesale/retail trade, and construction).

Engineers are paid well, with salaries varying by discipline and increasing with educational level and experience. While engineering salaries are good, never forget that employers expect you to contribute in value to the company more than they pay you. Job availability and salaries are expected to increase in the future. Finally, an engineering education can lead to rich and rewarding careers in nonengineering fields.

SUMMARY OF
KEY IDEAS

- People trained as engineers generally can find jobs as engineers.
- About half of all engineers work in manufacturing, producing motor vehicles, aircraft, electrical and electronic equipment, and industrial or computing equipment.
- About 28% of engineers work in the service sector, primarily as consulting engineers.
- Many engineers are small business owners.
- About 12% of engineers work for government agencies.
- An engineering education is excellent preparation for many nonengineering professions.
- Job satisfaction includes contributions to society, degree of independence, level of responsibility, intellectual challenge, opportunities for promotion, benefits, and salary.
- Job satisfaction among engineers is very high.
- Engineers are well compensated, with salaries varying by discipline, educational level, and experience.
- Employers expect to receive more value from you than you are paid.
- Engineering jobs are expected to grow over 7% from 2002 to 2012, with over about 5% growth in the major engineering disciplines.

Problems

1. For an engineering discipline of your choice (chemical, civil, electrical, industrial, or mechanical engineering), list two jobs from each job sector in Section 2. Which job sector appeals to you and why?

2. Interview practicing engineers from two job sectors listed in Section 2. Write a paragraph explaining how the engineers you interviewed got from their baccalaureate degree to their current job.

3. Which of the job satisfaction criteria discussed in Section 3.1 is most important to you?

4. Describe your ideal engineering job. As a guideline, use the job satisfaction criteria discussed in Section 3.1.

5. Using the Internet, research jobs in the discipline of most interest to you. How closely do the jobs align with the ideal engineering job you described in Problem 4?

6. You have received two job offers: one from Technolico, Inc., at $44,000 per year and one from Engionics at $46,000 per year. What criteria should you use in deciding which job to take?

7. List four questions you would like to ask during an engineering job interview.

8. A small consulting firm wishes to expand. If they hire an entry-level engineer, they can increase their revenue by $4,750 per month. The annual salary for an entry-level engineer in their community is $47,000. Benefits (e.g., health insurance and contributions to retirement accounts) cost 25% of the employee's salary. Can the firm afford to hire an entry-level engineer at the going rate?

9. How much would revenues have to grow for a small consulting firm to justify hiring an entry-level engineer? Assume that the typical annual salary for an entry-level engineer is $48,500 and benefits amount to 30% of the employee's salary.

10. Ask a practicing engineer whether a master's degree in engineering is desirable for engineers in your area.

11. Ask a practicing engineer whether an MBA (master of business administration) is desirable for engineers in your area.

4

Engineering Disciplines

1   INTRODUCTION

Earlier, you were given some advice: to discover engineering, put down this book and talk to an engineer. Similarly, to find out more about any particular engineering discipline, speak to an engineer engaged in that discipline. Only a practitioner can give you the depth, history, and potential future of a field. Only an engineer can impart the excitement, challenges, and occasional frustrations of working in a given area. Only a working engineer can tell you what he or she does every day on the job.

So why read the rest of this chapter? The remainder of the chapter is devoted to giving you a brief taste of each of the major engineering disciplines. Its purpose is to whet your appetite rather than answer all your questions about a field of particular interest to you. This chapter is intended to motivate you to seek out engineers in the fields that pique your interest.

There are dozens of specific fields, each with dozens of types of engineers. Section 2 discusses how the many types of engineers can be organized into a small number of primary disciplines and emerging fields.

The other sections in the chapter are devoted to a general description of each of the principal engineering disciplines. The primary *technical areas* will also be presented to shed light on the core of each discipline. These technical areas are the tools that define what makes a chemical, civil, electrical/computer, industrial, or mechanical engineer. The technical areas are combined into *applications*, which show the fields in which each type of engineer works and illustrate the diversity of the engineering discipline. Finally, unique elements of the *curriculum* leading to an engineering degree in each discipline will be discussed. Only the typical core coursework is presented. For further information,

SECTIONS

OBJECTIVES

After reading this chapter, you will be able to:

- list the principal engineering disciplines;
- discuss the technical areas, applications, and curricula for chemical, civil, electrical and computer, industrial, and mechanical engineering;
- explain how new engineering disciplines emerge.

Key idea: To learn about a specific discipline, speak with an engineer working in that discipline.

investigate the Web page of the pertinent engineering department at any major university. It is important that you have a general knowledge of all engineering disciplines, since engineers of different backgrounds frequently work together to solve problems.

2   HOW MANY ENGINEERING DISCIPLINES EXIST?

To answer this question, consider a seemingly unrelated question: how long is the coastline from Portland, Maine, to Miami, Florida? To estimate the coastline length, you might start with a globe and measure the distance with a straight ruler. This would be a crude estimate of the distance. You could refine your measurement by using a road map of the eastern United States. Now your measurement would take into account more details, such as the fishhook of Cape Cod and the coastline of the Chesapeake Bay. As a result, your measurement would likely be larger than the estimate from the globe. If you used state or local road maps, your measurement would continue to be refined and continue to grow. If, in desperation, you crawled the entire trip, measuring around each grain of sand, you would come up with a different (and larger) value.°

Key idea: The five principal engineering disciplines are chemical, civil, electrical and computer, industrial, and mechanical engineering.

Counting engineering disciplines is like measuring the distance along a coastline: as the scale narrows, the number of disciplines increases. One of the broadest views on the number of disciplines looks at the number of accredited engineering programs in the United States. The number of accredited programs is shown in Figure 1. In this text, the top five engineering disciplines (chemical, civil, electrical and computer, industrial, and mechanical engineering) will be called the *principal engineering disciplines.*

The engineering profession defines an engineer as someone eligible for professional registration. The Fundamentals of Engineering Examination (FE Exam) is required for professional registration as a licensed professional engineer. The specialty portion of the FE Exam is offered in the five principal engineering disciplines plus environmental engineering.

Using professional registration as a guide, your list of engineering fields can be expanded by examining the areas in which it is possible to take the Principles and Practice

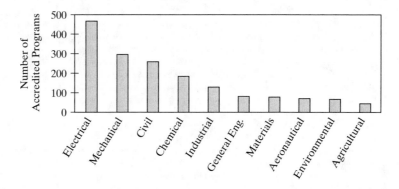

Figure 1.   Number of Accredited Engineering Programs in the United States by Discipline (*Electrical* includes electrical and computer engineering; other disciplines include related fields. Data obtained from www.abet.org.)

°An object that looks the same at every degree of magnification (or, formally, exhibits self-similarity across scales) is said to be *fractal*. Fractal analysis is used in signal processing to analyze anything from Internet traffic data to biomedical data.

Examination (PP Exam). The PP Exam is the last step in the professional registration process. The 17 different PP Exams are listed in Table 1.

Examining engineering disciplines on a smaller scale, you could make a list of relatively common engineering fields. A good list is shown in Table 2, with most fields listed under their closest principal engineering disciplines.

TABLE 1 Several Lists of Major Engineering Disciplines

Principal Disciplines	Fundamentals of Engineering Exam Areas	Principles and Practices Exam Areas
		Agricultural
		Architectural
Chemical	Chemical	Chemical
Civil	Civil	Civil
		Control Systems
Electrical/Computer	Electrical	Electrical and Computer
	Environmental	Environmental
		Fire Protection
Industrial	Industrial	Industrial
Mechanical	Mechanical	Mechanical
		Metallurgical
		Mining and Mineral
		Naval Architecture and Marine
		Nuclear
		Petroleum
		Structural (I and II)

Note: The manufacturing engineering FE Exam was discontinued after October 2003.

TABLE 2 Common Engineering Fields by Principal Discipline

Chemical	Civil	Electrical and Computer
Biological	Architectural	Control Systems
Biomedical	Construction	Electronics
Ceramic	Environmental	Signal Processing
Control Systems	Geotechnical	
Petroleum	Sanitary	
Plastics	Structural	
Polymer	Transportation	

Industrial	Mechanical	Other
Human Factors	Aeronautical	Agricultural
Operations Research	Aerospace	Fire
Production Systems	Automotive	Military
	Biomechanical	Mining
	Heating	Naval
	Manufacturing	Nuclear
	Materials	Ocean
	Metallurgical	Plant
	Robotics	Safety

Note: The "other" category contains unique or multidisciplinary fields.

A more complete list of engineering jobs has been developed by the Bureau of Labor Statistics (BLS). They list an unbelievable 431 engineering jobs, from absorption engineering to mud engineering to zoning engineering.[*]

So how can you make sense of all these disciplines, fields, subfields, and subsubfields? In this text, the five principal engineering disciplines will be discussed in Sections 3 through 7. The major subdisciplines will be explored in Section 8. The process of how new disciplines evolve will be discussed in Section 9.

3   CHEMICAL ENGINEERING

3.1   Technical Areas

Key idea: Chemical engineers work with the transformation of chemicals to form useful products or processes.

Chemical engineers work with the transformation of chemicals to form useful products or processes. The main technical areas are catalysis and reaction engineering, heat transfer and energy conversion, and separations. As you can see by these areas (and the name of the discipline), chemical engineers tend to have a strong interest in chemistry.

Reaction engineering and catalysis refers to the design and construction of engineered systems to bring about chemical change. In catalytic processes, materials are added to make the chemistry proceed more quickly. This can make the difference between an economically feasible and an economically infeasible process.

Chemical changes are driven by energy. Some chemical engineers specialize in *heat transfer*. Other chemical engineers focus on the conversion of energy from one form to another (especially in the presence of chemical transformations).

In the field of *separations*, chemical engineers assist in product purification. Examples of products benefiting from separation systems designed by chemical engineers range from perfume to gasoline to beer.

3.2   Applications

chemical process industry: any industry where chemicals are extracted, isolated, or combined (the primary application of chemical engineering)

Chemical engineers apply their technical skills to almost every industry. The primary application is in the **chemical process industries**—that is, any industry where chemicals are extracted, isolated, or combined. The main industries employing chemical engineers manufacture agricultural chemicals; food; industrial gases; petrochemicals and petroleum products; pharmaceuticals and personal care products; polymers (including plastics and rubber); pulp and paper; soaps and other fats; and synthetic fibers.

Other areas where chemical engineers work include biotechnology, environmental engineering, nuclear engineering, and advanced materials. Biotechnology is the synthesis of new products by using living organisms. Chemical engineers have teamed with scientists to develop new approaches to product development through biotechnology. From the development of artificial skin and blood to the biosynthesis of pharmaceuticals, chemical engineers are at the forefront of biotechnology. In fact, many chemical engineering departments have changed names from "chemical engineering" to "chemical and biological engineering."

pollution prevention: a contribution of chemical engineers, where industrial processes are modified to minimize pollution

Chemical engineers specializing in the environmental area often work with industry to make industrial processes cleaner (called **pollution prevention**). Chemical engineers also have contributed to nuclear engineering in its various forms (e.g., power generation, propulsion, and commercial uses). Chemical engineers have led the development of new materials with highly specialized properties for the aerospace, automotive, and photographic industries, as well as many others.

---

[*]To be fair, most of the BLS jobs are not engineering positions because they employ people who are not eligible for professional registration.

3.3   Curriculum

Chemical engineering students usually take engineering courses in thermodynamics; conservation and transport of mass, momentum, and energy; unit operations (i.e., industrial processes such as separations); and design. Science courses in organic chemistry and biochemistry frequently are required.

4   CIVIL ENGINEERING

4.1   Technical Areas

Key idea: Civil engineers are involved in the analysis, design, and construction of public works.

Civil engineering takes its name from Latin *civis*, meaning citizen. As with many technological fields, engineering once had a mainly military focus. As engineering applications broadened, engineering was divided into two areas: military engineering and civil (i.e., nonmilitary) engineering. The other four principal engineering disciplines eventually split off, leaving what we now know as civil engineering. As a result, civil engineering is one of the broadest engineering disciplines. In a nutshell, civil engineers are involved in the analysis, design, and construction of public works.

solid mechanics: the behavior of solids at rest and in motion

Although diverse, civil engineering shares the core technical area of engineering mechanics. This core is divided into three areas: solid mechanics, fluid mechanics, and soil mechanics. **Solid mechanics** refers to the behavior of solids at rest and in motion. It is the primary tool used to analyze the structural integrity of structures both large (such as buildings, roads, and bridges) and small (such as printed circuit boards). *Fluid mechanics* is used to understand the behavior of water and air in both natural systems (such as rivers and the atmosphere) and engineered systems (such as pipes and blowers). *Soil mechanics* studies the behavior of soils in response to stress. It is an important tool in the design of foundations and earthen structures (such as landfills).

4.2   Applications

The main applications of civil engineering are construction, environmental, geotechnical, structural, transportation, and water resources engineering. In the *construction engineering* area, civil engineers optimize the use of materials, money, and people in construction projects. *Environmental engineers* develop and design treatment processes for a variety of pollutants and follow the fate of pollutants in the environment (see Section 8.4). The **geotechnical** specialty in civil engineering is concerned with the design of foundations, embankments, retaining walls, and landfills. *Structural engineering* is one of the largest specialties in civil engineering. Structural engineers focus on the design of buildings, bridges, dams, and other systems. *Transportation engineers* study both traffic patterns and construction materials to maintain and improve transportation and other delivery systems. In the *water resources* area, civil engineers plan, manage, and design systems for the use and management of lakes, rivers, groundwater, storm water, and reservoirs. Examples include irrigation systems, dams, and storm water retention ponds.

geotechnical engineering: a specialty of civil engineering concerned with the design of foundations, embankments, retaining walls, and landfills

4.3   Curriculum

The civil engineering curriculum reflects both the core area of mechanics and the wide variety of applications. Civil engineering students generally take engineering courses in statics, mechanics (usually separate courses in solid mechanics, fluid mechanics, and soil mechanics), materials, structures, transportation, and environmental engineering. Often, courses in project management and foundation engineering are required.

5   ELECTRICAL AND COMPUTER ENGINEERING

5.1   Technical Areas

Key idea: Electrical engineers focus on the transmission and use of electrons and photons.

Electrical engineers focus on the transmission and use of *electrons* and *photons*. This simple statement does not do justice to the richness of electrical engineering. We use electric power through many different types of communication, computational, industrial, and consumer devices. Electrical engineering often includes the related field of *computer engineering*. In addition, electric energy is often transformed prior to use. Examples include alternating and direct current conversions, analog and digital transformations, and the interconversion of electricity and magnetism, sound, and light.

physical electronics: the study of solid-state electronic devices, such as transistors

electromagnetics: the study of the complex relationships between electricity and magnetism

The core technical areas of electrical engineering include circuits, physical electronics, signal processing, and electromagnetics. *Analog and digital circuits* are fundamental tools of the electrical engineer. The circuits area involves the analysis of networks, power delivery, specialized circuits (alternating current, radio frequency, and microwave circuits), and circuit design. **Physical electronics** includes the understanding of solid-state electronic devices, such as transistors. *Signal processing* (information engineering) involves the interpretation of time-dependent voltages and currents. **Electromagnetics**, the complex relationship between electricity and magnetism, is the theory that underlies much of modern-day electrical engineering.

5.2   Applications

To appreciate the far-reaching applications of electrical engineering, you only have to look around your home, office, or school. Electronic devices surround you. The diversity in the field is shown by the fact that the main professional society in electrical engineering (the Institute of Electrical and Electronics Engineers or IEEE) contains 38 technical societies and councils. To simplify this broad branch of engineering, consider four basic applications: communications, digital electronics, microelectronics and photonics, and power systems.

The *communications* area includes applications as varied as communications theory, telecommunications, and optical communications systems. Electrical engineers specializing in *digital electronics* focus on digital circuit design and instrumentation, control systems, image processing, and computationally efficient architectures. In the *microelectronics and photonics* area, electrical engineers develop microprocessor architecture, work with machine- and assembly-language programming, and develop systems with optical fibers using lasers and other light sources. The field of *power systems* includes the generation, transmission, and distribution of electrical power.

5.3   Curriculum

Electrical engineering students usually take courses in analog and digital circuit analysis and design, microprocessors, signal processing, electromagnetics, and programming. Common electives include power systems and communications.

6   INDUSTRIAL ENGINEERING

6.1   Technical Areas

Industrial engineers seek to analyze, design, model, and optimize complex systems. The traditional role of industrial engineers has been in the manufacturing sector. However, industrial engineering also is applied to areas as diverse as transportation, service industries (e.g., hospitals and banks), and supply and distribution problems.

The core technical areas in industrial engineering are simulation, statistics, and engineering economics. *Simulation* is important to the industrial engineer, because many improvements in manufacturing or other systems must be simulated (usually through

Key idea: Industrial engineers seek to analyze, design, model, and optimize complex systems.

computer models) before they are accepted and implemented. *Statistics* plays a large role because of the random nature of errors and disruptions in the work environment. More than the other engineering branches, industrial engineers address economic feasibility in their work with manufacturing and service industries.

6.2   Applications

ergonomics: relationships between people and the jobs they perform (now commonly called human factors engineering)

operations research: optimization of complex systems to meet one or more goals

The tools of industrial engineering are combined and applied in three basic areas: human factors engineering, operations research, and production systems engineering. *Human factors engineering* (or **ergonomics**, literally the management of work) concerns the relationship between people and the things they use or the jobs they perform. **Operations research** deals with the optimization of complex systems to meet one or more goals (called *objective functions*). In *production systems engineering*, the industrial engineer focuses on optimizing both the physical facilities (e.g., plant layout and materials handling) and production scheduling.

6.3   Curriculum

Industrial engineers typically take courses in probability and statistics; engineering economics; human factors; production systems and facilities planning; operations research; and simulation. Electives in economics, computer science, and psychology are common. Since knowledge of the manufacturing site is at the heart of industrial engineering, many industrial engineering programs offer cooperative experiences (co-ops) or internships in industry.

7   MECHANICAL ENGINEERING

7.1   Technical Areas

Mechanical engineering is synonymous with machinery. In fact, the words "mechanical" and "machine" both come from the Greek *mechos*, meaning expedient (because mechanized devices are often the most efficient way to carry out a task). Mechanical engineers develop, design, and manufacture machines.

Key idea: Mechanical engineers develop, design, and manufacture machines.

The primary technical areas in mechanical engineering are mechanics and thermodynamics. In mechanical engineering, the fields of *solid mechanics* and *fluid mechanics* are applied to machines rather than to structures (as they are in civil engineering). Since machines use, generate, or transmit power, mechanical engineers are interested in the use of energy and its loss as heat. Thus, *thermodynamics* is a primary tool of the mechanical engineer.

7.2   Applications

Mechanical engineers generally specialize in one or more of the following areas: applied mechanics, bioengineering, fluids engineering, heat transfer, tribology, and aeronautics. Using *applied mechanics*, engineers analyze and design machines. In *bioengineering*, mechanical engineers apply the principles of mechanics to solve problems with human anatomy (e.g., prosthetic and assistive devices) and physiology (e.g., devices to improve heart and lung function). *Fluids engineering* refers to the flow of fluids (e.g., air, ink, or blood) in mechanical systems. Mechanical engineers specializing in fluids engineering may perform complex calculations to predict fluid flow, a subspecialty called *computational fluid dynamics*. *Heat transfer* involves the study of heat transport by conduction, convection, and radiation. The study of heat transfer is critical, since all processes lose energy as heat. **Tribology** (from the Greek *tribein*, to rub) concerns friction, wear, and lubrication. Aeronautics and astronautics are major subdisciplines of mechanical engineering. (See Section 8.3.)

tribology: the study of friction, wear, and lubrication

Robotic arm on the Mars rover *Spirit* reaches out to a rock called Adirondack. Placing a rover on Mars required experts in nearly all fields of mechanical engineering (as well as other types of engineers). (Image credit: NASA/JPL.)

7.3   Curriculum

In accordance with the technical fields and primary applications, mechanical engineers usually take courses in machines, fluid mechanics, thermodynamics, instrumentation, materials, systems engineering, and design. Common technical electives include applied mathematics, aeronautics, and biomechanics.

8   MAJOR ENGINEERING SUBDISCIPLINES

Key idea: The major engineering subdisciplines are materials, aeronautical/aerospace, environmental, agricultural, and biomedical engineering.

8.1   Introduction

As shown in Figure 1, there are a number of accredited engineering programs in the United States outside of the principal engineering disciplines. The major subdisciplines—materials, aeronautical/aerospace, environmental, agricultural, and biomedical engineering—may exist as separate departments in universities, but more frequently are found within departments representing the five principal disciplines. Each major subdiscipline will be discussed in more detail in this section.

8.2   Materials Engineering

Materials engineers contribute to all aspects of materials used for engineering purposes, from the origin of a material (extraction or synthesis), through its transformations (processing, design, and manufacture), to its applications. Often called *material science and engineering*, the field emphasizes the science behind the properties of materials.

Materials engineering programs often are housed in mechanical engineering departments. However, the home department sometimes depends on the materials. For example, the materials engineering aspects of metals and their alloys often are taught in mechanical engineering departments (sometimes under the heading *metallurgical engineering*). *Polymers, ceramics,* and *biomaterials* may be the purview of chemical engineers. Civil engineers have been making more use of *composite materials*, while electrical engineers study and use *semiconductors*.

8.3   Aeronautical, Astronautical, and Aerospace Engineering

The fields of aeronautical and astronautical engineering are related subdisciplines of mechanical engineering. Aeronautics (from the Greek *aero*, air, + *nautes*, sailor) is the study of mechanized flight. Astronautical engineering, on the other hand, deals with mechanized flight beyond the Earth's atmosphere. (The term *aerospace*, first used in 1958, refers to both the atmosphere and outer space.)

One way to look at the diversity in aerospace engineering is to examine its largest professional society, the American Institute of Aeronautics and Astronautics (AIAA). The AIAA has over 60 technical committees, covering issues from lighter-than-air systems to modeling and simulation to space colonization.

8.4   Environmental Engineering

As stated in Section 4.2, environmental engineers both design treatment processes and model the fate of pollutants in the environment. Environmental engineering (previously called sanitary engineering) is traditionally part of civil engineering. However, some areas are associated with other principal engineering disciplines (e.g., pollution prevention with chemical engineering).

In the water treatment area, environmental engineers develop and design treatment facilities for drinking water, wastewater, and industrial wastes. Environmental engineers also work with treatment systems for air and contaminated soil. In the modeling area, environmental engineers track everything from global warming (caused, in part, by carbon dioxide emissions to the atmosphere) to leaking underground storage tanks at your neighborhood gas station.

8.5   Agricultural Engineering

Agricultural engineering (sometimes called food, biological, bioresource, or biosystems engineering) involves the solution of problems in the production and processing of food, fiber, timber, and renewable energy sources. Agricultural engineers seek to produce agricultural products from natural resources efficiently, while minimizing environmental impact. The major areas of agricultural engineering are food engineering, power systems and machinery design, and forest engineering.

8.6   Biomedical Engineering

Biomedical engineers use engineering and scientific principles to solve problems in medicine and biology. Two of the largest areas in this diverse field are biomaterials engineering and biomechanical engineering. In the biomaterials area, engineers (typically with training in chemical engineering) develop implants from both living tissue and artificial materials. Biomaterials engineers have contributed significantly to the development of artificial skin and artificial blood. In the biomechanical engineering area, engineers study fluid flow and materials properties in the human body. Biomechanical engineers have contributed greatly to the development of the artificial heart and artificial joint replacements. Electrical and computer engineers specializing in the biomedical engineering area have contributed to new imaging and surgical technologies, such as CAT (computer-aided tomography) scans and remote surgery.

9   HOW DO EMERGING ENGINEERING DISCIPLINES EVOLVE?

Key idea: New engineering fields can be formed by the budding off of existing disciplines or by the creation of interdisciplinary fields.

9.1   Introduction

A cursory glance at engineering curricula in the United States reveals that new types of engineering programs are constantly being developed. *Engineering disciplines evolve over time.* Why? If problems emerge that require more specialization, then new engineering fields will evolve to address the challenges. But how do new engineering disciplines form?

Engineering fields form in two ways. First, new engineering disciplines are created by *splitting off* from existing disciplines. Second, new engineering disciplines form when two or more fields *combine*.

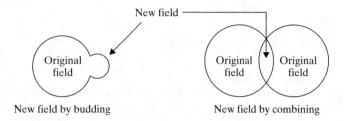

New field by budding   New field by combining

9.2   Creation of New Field by Budding

In some engineering fields, a subfield will mature and split off to form its own discipline like an amoeba reproducing. In fact, each of the five principal engineering disciplines formed in this way. The first split occurred when "engineering" (once used almost exclusively for warfare) divided into military engineering and "civilian" (civil) engineering. Subsequently, the other disciplines we know today budded off from civil engineering.

More recently, a number of engineering disciplines have been created by budding off of existing fields. From mechanical engineering, the field of robotic engineering has developed some independence. Photonic engineering is in the process of separating itself from electrical engineering. Photonic engineers use photons for useful purposes just as electrical engineers use electrons for useful purposes. Civil engineering has produced the developing discipline of renewal engineering. Renewal engineering is the study of the aging of engineered systems and the specification of repairs. Only time will tell if robotic, photonic, and renewal engineering will blossom into separate engineering disciplines or whether they will remain subfields of existing disciplines.

9.3   Creation of New Fields by Merging

Other new engineering disciplines are created as *interdisciplinary* fields. This occurs when skills from many different fields must be applied to a problem. In fact, *a great deal of the progress in science and engineering occurs where fields intersect.* Examples of emerging interdisciplinary engineering fields are bioengineering and nanoengineering. Nanoengineering is discussed in more detail in the *Focus on Emerging Disciplines: So You Want to Be a Nanoengineer?*

FOCUS ON EMERGING DISCIPLINES: SO YOU WANT TO BE A NANOENGINEER?

As stated in this chapter, engineering is a constantly evolving field. Advances in technology have opened up opportunities that would have been impossible to pursue even a few years ago. One of the most recent emerging fields is nanoengineering. The concept of nanoengineering was first described by Nobel laureate physicist Richard Feynmann in 1959. The prefix "nano-" (from the Greek *nanos*, dwarf) often refers to 10^{-9}. Thus, a nanometer is 10^{-9} m. How big is the nanometer scale? The hydrogen–oxygen bond length in water is about 0.1 nm. Thus, nanoengineering refers to building objects from the atomic level up.

To get an idea of the length scales possible with nanotechnology, the picture that follows shows the URL of the National Nanotechnology Initiative in letters written with a carbon nanotube tip. The letters are about 7 to 8 nm thick and 20 nm tall. The diameter of a carbon atom is about 0.15 nm, so each letter is about 50 carbon atoms thick and 130 carbon atoms tall.

Nanolithography: writing on the nanometer scale

Working on the atomic or molecular scale changes the nature of engineering. For example, a biomedical engineer may look at the transport of red blood cells (about 2.5 μm or 2,500 nm in size), while a nanoengineer might consider the mechanical manipulation of DNA (about 2.5 nm in size). In addition, nano-sized systems often exhibit unique characteristics.

To illustrate the potential of nanoengineering, three existing product classes will be discussed: nanoparticles, nanostructured polymer films, and quantum dots. Nanoparticles are particles with diameters on the nanometer scale. Such particles have a great deal of surface area per gram of material. As a result, nanoparticles make very efficient catalysts. They are now being used in oil refining and to remove oxides of nitrogen in automobile exhaust.

Nanostructured polymer films are being used to make displays for a wide array of digital consumer devices (e.g., cell phones and digital cameras). The polymers are formed into organic light-emitting diodes (OLEDs) to produce brighter, lighter displays.

To illustrate the potential impact of nanoengineering, consider quantum dots. Quantum dots are nano-sized semiconductors that can trap a small number of electrons. These structures may someday be used to compute on a single-electron scale (called *quantum computing*). Quantum dots in the form of nanocrystals can be used to image biological processes. They can be designed to emit certain wavelengths based on their size. (For example, a 3-nm cadmium selenide particle

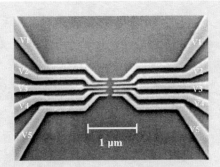

Quantum Dots. The small wires in this picture are 50 nm wide. They form two quantum dots (center of picture) that contain about 20–40 electrons. In the future, isolated electrons in the dots may be used for computers based on the behavior of single electrons. (Photo courtesy of Dave Umberger.)

emits at 520 nm—green light—while a 5.5-nm cadmium selenide particle emits at 630 nm—red light.) By using a variety of particle sizes, an array of biological processes can be imaged.

Engineers of your generation will certainly contribute to harvesting the potential of nanoengineering. Perhaps you will major in nanoengineering. (This is possible: the first undergraduate nanoengineering program was started by the University of Toronto in the fall of 2001.) Nanoengineering is an emerging, interdisciplinary engineering field with the potential to revolutionize the way we think about the world.

10   SUMMARY

This chapter focused on the five principal engineering disciplines: chemical, civil, electrical and computer, industrial, and mechanical engineering. For each branch, a general description of the discipline was presented, along with the major technical areas, applications, and curricula. Several major subdisciplines (materials, aeronautical/aerospace, environmental, agricultural, and biomedical engineering) were also explored.

Engineering is not static. New engineering fields evolve by splitting off of the major disciplines or by bringing together a variety of skills to address emerging challenges or to explore new opportunities.

This chapter ends with the same advice given in its beginning: to find out more about any particular engineering discipline, speak to an engineer engaged in that discipline.

SUMMARY OF KEY IDEAS

- To learn about a specific discipline, speak with an engineer working in that discipline.
- The five principal engineering disciplines are chemical, civil, electrical and computer, industrial, and mechanical engineering.
- Chemical engineers work with the transformation of chemicals to form useful products or processes.
- Civil engineers are involved in the analysis, design, and construction of public works.
- Electrical engineers focus on the transmission and use of electrons and photons.
- Industrial engineers seek to analyze, design, model, and optimize complex systems.
- Mechanical engineers develop, design, and manufacture machines.
- The major engineering subdisciplines are materials, aeronautical/aerospace, environmental, agricultural, and biomedical engineering.
- New engineering fields can be formed by the budding off of existing disciplines or by the creation of interdisciplinary fields.

Problems

1. Describe your interest in two technical areas from two different engineering disciplines. Are there common elements in the two technical areas that interest you?

2. Discuss how *each* of the five principal engineering disciplines can contribute to the following applications:
   a. Development of a manned space station
   b. Design and production of an electric car
   c. Design of a new artificial heart valve
   d. Development of a motorized scooter aimed at the 16–25-year-old market

3. A company wishes to develop and sell a new ultracaffeinated beverage. Which principal engineering discipline(s) would be involved in the design of each of the following?
   a. Syrup formulation
   b. Syrup–water mixing apparatus
   c. Carbonation system
   d. Bottling line
   e. Bottling plant

4. Using the Internet, find two jobs performed by chemical engineers. Explain how the jobs use the technical areas listed in Section 3.

5. Using the Internet, find two jobs performed by civil engineers. Explain how the jobs use the technical areas listed in Section 4.

6.   Using the Internet, find two jobs performed by electrical and computer engineers. Explain how the jobs use the technical areas listed in Section 5.

7.   Using the Internet, find two jobs performed by industrial engineers. Explain how the jobs use the technical areas listed in Section 6.

8.   Using the Internet, find two jobs performed by mechanical engineers. Explain how the jobs use the technical areas listed in Section 7.

9.   Explain how new engineering disciplines form. Interview a professor to find how new fields are formed in his or her field of research. Summarize your findings in a short paragraph.

10.   Summarize the state of the field of robotic, photonic, or renewal engineering.

5

Introduction to Engineering Problem Solving and the Scientific Method

1 INTRODUCTION

1.1 Engineering Problems

Engineers are problem solvers. So how do engineers solve problems? In some ways, you know the answer to that question, since you have been solving problems all your life. In recent years, it is likely that you toiled long hours to solve problems given by your teachers. You probably approached those problems with several assumptions. First, you likely assumed that the problem *could be solved* and probably had *one correct answer*. Second, you may have assumed that you were given all the information you needed to solve the problem. Third, you probably started working on the problem in a way similar to that used by your teacher in class.

Solving engineering problems is a bit different: at least one of the three assumptions usually is not true. In some cases, engineers do not know if a suitable solution to an engineering problem exists. In many other cases, multiple solutions are available. If multiple solutions are possible, then your job as an engineer becomes to develop alternatives and recommend one answer.

Engineers almost never encounter problems for which they have all the information needed for a solution. In fact, a major element in engineering problem solving is collecting the required information.

Finally, engineers may face problems that no one has attempted to answer before. What do you do if faced with a unique problem? You can make good progress by becoming familiar with solution strategies for related problems. However, engineering problems often are unique enough that you cannot use a canned approach to solve them.

OBJECTIVES

After reading this chapter, you will be able to:

- compare the three main approaches to engineering problem solving;
- list the steps in the scientific method;
- solve engineering problems using the scientific method.

Key idea: Engineering problems may have one, many, or no solutions and often require data gathering to obtain the information needed to solve the problem.

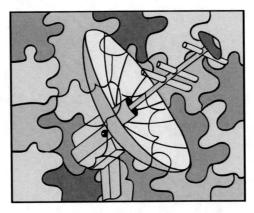

Does a unique solution exist?

Do you have all the information you need?

Key idea: Engineering problems are solved by a combination of science (knowledge of the principles of mathematics, chemistry, physics, mechanics, and other technical subjects) and art (creativity, judgment, experience, and common sense).

1.2   The Art and Science of Engineering Problem Solving

Good problem-solving skills are essential characteristics for a successful engineer. Early in your engineering education, you must develop the ability to solve and present the solutions of both simple and complex problems in an orderly, logical, and systematic way. Solving engineering problems involves a combination of *science* and *art*. *Science* refers to a knowledge of the principles of mathematics, chemistry, physics, mechanics, and other technical subjects you will learn during the first two or three years of your engineering studies. These principles become some of the tools of your profession.

However, science is not enough. Engineering problem solving is also an art. *Art* means the creativity, judgment, experience, and common sense to use the scientific tools to solve real-life problems effectively. You must learn how to translate a real-world problem to a form that can be solved using scientific tools. Successful problem solving also requires good judgment; you must know whether the result is a reasonable solution to the original problem. The art of problem solving depends on experience and common sense. However, the art is more effective if approached in a logical and organized manner.

Key idea: Engineering problems should be approached in a logical and organized manner.

1.3   Engineering Solution Methods

No problem-solving strategy fits all engineering problems, so engineers use several types of solution methods. To meet the wide variety of challenges in engineering, three common problem-solving techniques are used: the scientific method, the engineering analysis method, and the engineering design method. While the procedures for solving different types of problems vary, all three problem-solving techniques are step-by-step processes. In this chapter, differences between the scientific, analysis, and design methods are explored. The scientific method is then discussed in more detail.

Key idea: Engineers use the scientific method, engineering analysis method, and engineering design method to solve problems.

2   APPROACHES TO ENGINEERING PROBLEM SOLVING

2.1   Introduction

To illustrate the different methods of engineering problem solving, consider the following example. Suppose you are a chemical engineer at a large specialty chemical company. The management staff wishes to increase the production of an enzyme used in the synthesis of an anti-cancer agent. You are charged with answering the following three questions:

- Will an increase in operating pressure increase enzyme production significantly?
- What are the optimal operating conditions for the enzyme production line?
- Are any alternative production processes superior to the existing process?

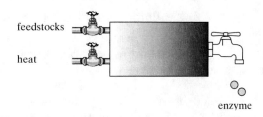

feedstocks

heat

enzyme

Would you use the same problem-solving approach to answer each of the three questions?

It is likely that a practicing engineer would use several *different* approaches to solve these three questions. Each question will be discussed in more detail later in this section.

2.2   Scientific Method

Key idea: The scientific method involves generating and testing hypotheses.

The first question (whether an increase in operating pressure would increase production) can be translated into a hypothesis. A hypothesis (discussed further in Section 3) is a trial statement about the behavior of a system. Hypotheses can be tested. The formulation, testing, and acceptance or rejection of hypotheses are at the heart of the scientific method.

How could you test the hypothesis that an increase in operating pressure will increase enzyme production significantly? There are many approaches. The simplest test would be to increase the operating pressure and observe the production rate. But this approach might be difficult in practice: the equipment may not tolerate the higher pressure or, more likely, the company may not be able to accept the downtime required to perform the tests.

numerical experiments: experiments performed with mathematical models rather than laboratory equipment

Alternatively, you might create a *mathematical model* from the known chemistry of the system. By including the effects of pressure on the chemical reactions, you could test the hypothesis with computer-based experiments (sometimes called **numerical experiments**).

Finally, you might build a scale model (called a *physical model*) of the critical chemical reactor and test it separately to elucidate the effects of operating pressure. The use of models to test hypotheses is discussed in another chapter.

2.3   Engineering Analysis Method

What about the question regarding the optimal operating conditions of the enzyme production line? This question is much more complicated, since now you are being asked to examine *all* aspects of the production line (e.g., pressure, temperature, chemical feed rates, energy consumption, and heat transfer efficiency). The question requires the analysis method. With this method, the problem is defined, data gathered, analysis tools selected, and a solution calculated.

In the example at hand, you might use a combination of mathematical models and physical models to probe the effects of operating conditions on production efficiency. Before starting the analysis, you must develop a quantitative indicator of success. Are you trying to produce as much enzyme as possible, regardless of cost? Are you trying to produce the enzyme at the lowest cost per kilogram? Is the demand for the enzyme constant or do you favor a production line that runs intermittently (say, two shifts per day)? These questions need to be translated into mathematical statements called *objective functions* (mathematical statements of the state of the project). You may be able to develop mathematical models that allow you to calculate the pressure, temperature, and other operating conditions satisfying the objective functions.

2.4   Engineering Design Method

Key idea: Design problems require the generation of alternatives.

A different approach would be needed to develop and evaluate alternative production lines (as in the third question in Section 2.1). This is a design problem, requiring the engineering design method to develop a recommendation. In the engineering design method, you define the problem carefully, collect data, generate alternatives, analyze and select a solution, implement the solution, and evaluate the solution.

A key to the solution of design problems is defining the problem. Are you free to evaluate *any* alternative production lines? Are you limited by the availability of certain chemicals, certain equipment, or the reaction conditions?

After collecting the pertinent data, you must generate ideas for alternative production lines. How do engineers create new ideas? Perhaps you would select people with the required expertise and hold a brainstorming session.

After generating alternative production lines, you might repeat your analysis from Section 2.3 with each alternative. This would allow you to select the most *feasible* solution.

Even if the recommended solution is deemed to be acceptable, your job is not over. You must now *implement* the solution; in other words, you must build and operate the new production line. One of the most enjoyable aspects of engineering is watching your ideas take physical form. After the new line is built, you need to evaluate its performance to ensure that the anticipated benefits are being realized.

2.5   Need for Innovation

On some occasions, the traditional analysis and design methods fail to take into account the realities of the marketplace. Innovative design approaches are needed to ensure that product manufacturing, marketing, and disposal are considered in the design process. In addition, engineers sometimes get stuck using analysis and design approaches that are no longer valid for the situation at hand. In these events, innovative methods are required.

3   INTRODUCTION TO THE SCIENTIFIC METHOD

3.1   Introduction

Key idea: The scientific method is used to evaluate explanations of observed phenomena.

Key idea: Solve problems by using the scientific method: define the problem, formulate a hypothesis, and reject or conditionally accept the hypothesis.

Of the methods of inquiry used by engineers, the scientific method is probably the most familiar to you. This method is used to evaluate explanations or trial statements of observed phenomena. The explanations are called *hypotheses*.

Engineers employ the scientific method in several settings. Research engineers use it to extend our knowledge of engineered systems. For example, they may use the scientific method to test the idea that a new semiconductor will outperform existing materials. Practicing engineers use the scientific method to confirm the underlying causes of observed behavior. For example, a chemical engineer may operate a lab-scale distillation facility at several temperatures to test the idea that certain operating temperatures will improve separation of the marketable product from unwanted reaction byproducts.

3.2   Scientific Problem-Solving Process

The following four-step process can be used to apply the scientific method:

1. Define the problem
2. Formulate a hypothesis

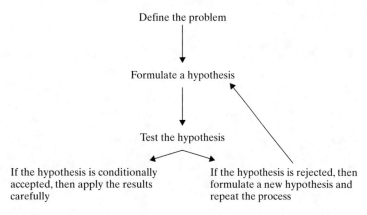

Figure 1. Steps in the Scientific Method.

3. Test the hypothesis
4. Reject or conditionally accept the hypothesis

If the hypothesis is rejected, then a new hypothesis might be developed. Using the scientific method in this iterative mode is shown in Figure 1. Each of the steps in the scientific problem-solving method will be described in more detail.

4   PROBLEM DEFINITION

4.1   Introduction

Problem definition is the first step in all problem-solving methods. Defining the problem, often in the form of a question, is a key step in the scientific method. However, there is a tendency to think of the problem definition phase as trivial and unimportant. But if the problem is not well defined, then you are doomed to expending considerable effort to eliminate extraneous factors and focus on the root problem. If the problem is not well defined, then you may spend significant time and effort solving the wrong problem!

Key idea: Problem definitions must be specific.

How can you decide if your problem definition is useful? Problem definitions must be *specific*. A specific problem definition is one that includes all relevant solutions, but excludes irrelevant solutions.

4.2   Inclusive and Exclusive Definitions

As stated in Section 4.1, problem definitions should be *inclusive* (to include all relevant solutions or hypotheses) and *exclusive* (to exclude irrelevant solutions or hypotheses). Suppose you are conducting a study of severe accidents caused by double-wide tractor trailers.

PONDER THIS

Evaluate the following problem definition: "Do trucks cause most of the severe highway accidents?"

This problem definition is not inclusive enough, since *all* severe traffic accidents (not just highway accidents) are of interest. It is also not exclusive enough, since the study is focused only on double-wide tractor trailers (and not *all* trucks). A better problem definition would be: "Do double-wide tractor trailers cause most of the severe traffic accidents?"

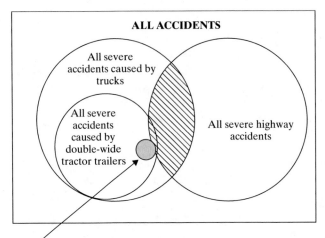

All accidents caused by double-wide tractor trailers on Route 34 in Thayer
County between January 1, 2002 and December 31, 2004

Figure 2. Problem Definitions for the Accident Example.

Key idea: Problem definitions should include the constraints of the problem.

To be even more specific, the problem definition should include the constraints of the problem. For example, it is likely that the truck problem has both temporal (time) and spatial (geographic) constraints. Thus, an even better problem definition would be "Did double-wide tractor trailers cause most of the severe traffic accidents on Route 34 in Thayer County between January 1, 2002, and December 31, 2004?"

The increasing specificity of the problem definition is illustrated in the Venn diagram in Figure 2. The problem definition in the *Ponder This* ("Do trucks cause most of the severe highway accidents?") is shown by the shaded area. The gray circle represents the most constrained problem definition.

4.3   Disadvantages of Definitions that Are Not Specific

If the problem definition is too inclusive, then the answer might be incorrect. As an example, suppose you wish to improve the efficiency of combustion in the internal combustion engine of an automobile. If you define the problem too broadly, then you may fail to take into account the differences in engine type. For example, conventional engines ignite the air–fuel mixture with a spark plug, while diesel engines ignite fuel with hot, compressed air. Also, the "cylinders" differ in shape (rectangular cross section for conventional, domed for the HEMI design, and oval for rotary engines). As this example shows, the answer you get may depend on the problem definition.

Key idea: Problem definitions should not limit the solutions.

Excessively exclusive problem definitions also can be misleading. One common way in which design problems are defined inappropriately is when the *needs* to be satisfied are confused with possible *solutions*. Needs should be broadly defined. When the needs are expressed in terms of solutions, the problem definition may inappropriately constrain the solution.

For example, a common problem in hotel management is the limitation on the transport of guests to the upper floors. In the past, this problem was defined as the need to add an additional elevator shaft and elevator.

PONDER THIS

How could the hotel problem be redefined to open up additional solutions?

When the problem was redefined as a requirement for additional transport capacity, an elegant solution—the outside elevator—became possible and has become quite popular. Previously, the *need* (transport capacity) was confused with a *solution* (elevator shaft and elevator), thus confining the solution to indoor elevators.

Key idea: Problem definitions should quantify the objectives.

Problem definitions should also quantify the objectives. In the transport capacity example, it is not sufficient to seek to "increase the transport capacity for guests." It is unlikely that the project would be successful if it allows the transport of only one additional guest per week to the penthouse suite. A more complete problem definition would be: "Transport at least 200 additional guests per day from the lobby to the top five floors with a project that must be completed in 18 months with a budget of $1 million." Another example of a problem definition is shown in Example 1.

EXAMPLE 1: PROBLEM DEFINITION

You have been charged with designing a new type of family automobile. The new car should combine the passenger capacity of a minivan with the sportiness of a sport utility vehicle (SUV). Evaluate the following design problem definitions:

1. Design an automobile with a length halfway between a minivan and SUV.
2. Redesign a minivan with a more attractive front grille.

SOLUTION

The first definition is **too constrained**. It assumes that the length of the new car will be the average of the lengths of the minivan and SUV. The second definition confuses the problem definition with a solution. **It assumes that the front grille limits the sportiness of the minivan**.

A better problem definition is: **design a family automobile with the passenger capacity of a minivan and the sportiness of an SUV**.

---

5   FORMULATE A HYPOTHESIS

5.1   Introduction

A hypothesis (from the Greek *hypo-* + *tithenai*, to put under or suppose) is an educated guess of the reason for observed phenomena. While problem definitions are usually questions, hypotheses are usually statements. Thus, a problem statement might be: "Why did the Space Shuttle *Discovery* disintegrate upon reentry on February 1, 2003?" A hypothesis concerning this topic would be a statement of an educated guess: "The Space Shuttle *Discovery* disintegrated upon reentry because falling foam hit the leading edge of the wing and damaged the heat-resistant tile."

Hypotheses generally come from the science behind the engineering. In other words, science tells you how the system should behave if you have identified all pertinent features of the system.

5.2   Hypotheses as Testable Statements

The most important characteristic of a hypothesis is that it is testable. For example, the hypothesis "Removal of control rods will result in the core meltdown of a nuclear power facility" is not testable under any reasonable system of ethics (except through mathematical models). The hypothesis "Cam shaft misalignment causes vibrations at vehicle speeds above 50 miles per hour" is testable. If you cannot test it, then your statement is not a hypothesis.

Key idea: Hypotheses must be capable of being tested.

6   TEST THE HYPOTHESIS

6.1   Testing a Hypothesis by Experiment

Key idea: Hypotheses can be tested by experiment or analysis.

An important step in the scientific method is testing the hypothesis. This step can be achieved in several ways. Most commonly, hypotheses are tested by conducting experiments. In this context, an *experiment* is the probing of an engineered system. For example, to test whether a new inventory system improves throughput, you might isolate a production line and try out the new system. Experiments often are performed with smaller scale models of a system or with mathematical models.

6.2   Hypothesis Testing by Analysis

On other occasions, a hypothesis might be tested by using the analysis techniques of the engineering analysis method. Suppose you wish to design a disinfection device for the treatment of water after a natural disaster (such as a tsunami or an earthquake). Water flows continuously through the device and is well mixed, with bacteria killed by a disinfectant inside. You hypothesize that the fraction of surviving bacteria decreases proportionally with the residence time in the device. (The residence time is the average time spent by the bacteria in the device.) In other words, if you double the residence time, then the fraction of surviving bacteria decreases by one-half.

You could, of course, test this hypothesis experimentally. You might also test it by analysis. Performing a balance on the number of bacteria and assuming that no bacteria stay in the water purifier, you know that

rate of bacteria going into the device = rate of surviving bacteria exiting the device

+ rate of kill of bacteria   (1)

The rate of bacteria going into the device (in number per second) is equal to the flow Q (in L/s) multiplied by the number concentration of bacteria going into the device, N_0 (in number/L). Similarly, the rate of bacteria exiting the device is equal to QN, where N is the number concentration of surviving bacteria exiting the device. The rate of kill commonly is modeled as kNV, where k is a disinfection rate constant and V is the volume of the device. Thus, the number balance in Eq. (1) becomes

$$QN_0 = QN - kNV$$

Rearranging terms, we find that the fraction of surviving bacteria $(=N/N_0)$ is given by

$$\frac{N}{N_0} = \frac{1}{1 + k\theta}$$

where $\theta = V/Q$ = residence time in the device.

This analysis tells you that the hypothesis is not completely correct: if you double the residence time, the fraction of surviving organisms will decrease by a factor of $(1 + k\theta)/(1 + 2k\theta)$, not by a factor of one-half. For example, if k was 0.1 per minute, then increasing the residence time from two to four minutes would decrease the fraction surviving from $1/[1 + (0.1 \text{ min}^{-1})(2 \text{ min})] = 0.83$ to $1/[1 + (0.1 \text{ min}^{-1})(4 \text{ min})] = 0.71.$[*] Thus, analysis can be used to test hypotheses.

---

[*]Note that the fraction of surviving organisms will decrease by a factor approaching $^1/_2$, as hypothesized, only when $k\theta \gg 1$.

7   DRAWING CONCLUSIONS FROM HYPOTHESIS TESTING

7.1   Rejecting a Hypothesis

Based on the results of the tests, a hypothesis may be rejected or conditionally accepted. If the data collected through experiments do not support the hypothesis, then the hypothesis is rejected. For example, suppose you are trying to improve engine performance by increasing the engine cooling capacity. You hypothesize that a new antifreeze formulation will increase the engine cooling capacity. The experiments you conduct in a test facility reveal that the new antifreeze *decreases* fuel mileage by 10–25% over a large number of test conditions. You may reasonably reject the hypothesis that the new formulation improves fuel efficiency.

7.2   Conditionally Accepting a Hypothesis

If tests conducted under two conditions show that the new antifreeze *increases* fuel efficiency, you would not reject the hypothesis. You might conclude that the new antifreeze formulation shows promise and should be evaluated in greater detail.

Key idea: Accept hypotheses only for the conditions under which they were tested.

Be very careful about *accepting* a hypothesis. In all cases, accept a hypothesis only for the conditions under which the hypothesis was tested. Usually, we say that we "conditionally accept" a hypothesis; that is, we accept the hypothesis under the conditions tested until more data are collected.

A classic example of the conditional acceptance of a hypothesis was developed by the British philosopher Karl Popper (1902–1994). He asked his readers to consider the hypothesis: "All swans are white." How many white swans would you have to see to accept this hypothesis? 10? 100? 1,000? Your answer may depend on your patience with counting swans. No matter how many white swans you count, you can only conditionally accept the hypothesis: seeing *one* black swan disproves the hypothesis.°

Similarly, in your engineering career, you may find yourself conditionally accepting hypotheses until they are proven false. For example, you may conclude that temperature does not affect the gear assembly in a snowmobile. One day during testing, the temperature may drop to a certain point where the mechanical properties of the metal change precipitously and the gears seize. You now reject a hypothesis that you previously accepted conditionally (namely, you reject the hypothesis that temperature does not affect the gear assembly).

8   EXAMPLES OF THE USE OF THE SCIENTIFIC METHOD

Two examples will illustrate the use of the scientific method. Suppose you wish to explore whether human activities have led to global warming. The issues involved in understanding global warming are very broad, but a problem can be defined for a very focused question based on science.

Suppose you formulate the following problem definition: "Does the Earth's temperature depend on the composition of the atmosphere?" A corresponding hypothesis might be "The average global temperature of the Earth depends on the composition of the atmosphere."

°European scientists were convinced that all swans were white, until black swans were observed in Australia by Dutch explorers in 1697. Black swans live in Australia, New Zealand, and Tasmania.

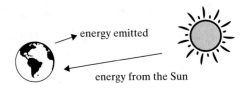

This hypothesis can be tested by analysis. The key scientific concept to test this hypothesis is the energy balance: the energy input from the Sun to the Earth must equal the energy emitted from the Earth (called *back-radiation*).

The energy input from the Sun is given by

energy input from the Sun = (cross-sectional area of the Earth)
$$\times \text{ (solar output)}(1 - \text{reflectivity of the Earth)}$$

or

$$\text{energy input from the Sun} = (\pi R^2)S(1 - A) \tag{2}$$

where R = Earth's radius, S = solar output (also called the solar *constant*) = 1,367 W/m^2 (watts per square meter), and A = reflectivity (also called the albedo) of the Earth = 0.31. The energy emitted from the Earth is given by

energy emitted from the Earth = (constant)(surface area of the Earth)
$$\times \text{ (fraction of back-radiation that escapes}$$
$$\text{the atmosphere of the Earth)}$$
$$\times \text{ (temperature of the Earth)}^4$$

or

$$\text{energy emitted from the Earth} = \sigma(4\pi R^2)eT^4 \tag{3}$$

where σ = Stefan–Boltzmann constant = 5.5597×10^{-8} W/m^2-K^4 (watts per square meter per Kelvin to the fourth power), e = fraction of back-radiation that escapes the atmosphere of the Earth (also called the emissivity), and T = temperature of the Earth in K. (Recall that K = °C + 273.16.) Equation (3) is called the *Stefan–Boltzmann equation*. To perform the energy balance, set Eq. (2) equal to Eq. (3):

$$(\pi R^2)S(1 - A) = \sigma(4\pi R^2)eT^4$$

Solving for temperature yields

$$T = \left[\frac{S(1 - A)}{4e\sigma}\right]^{1/4}.$$

Substituting in the values given for S, A, and σ, and assuming that $e = 1$ (all energy escapes the atmosphere) gives $T = 255$ K or -18°C. Clearly, the average temperature of the Earth is not -18°C. (If it were this cold, then all fresh water would freeze.)

In fact, the atmosphere *retains* some of the back-radiated energy. This process is called the *greenhouse effect* and is due mainly to water vapor and carbon dioxide in the atmosphere. From the natural levels of water vapor and carbon dioxide in the atmosphere (i.e., before human activity), the value of e is about 0.615 (i.e., about 38.5% of the energy is trapped and 61.5% of the energy is transmitted through the atmosphere). Recalculating with $e = 0.615$ yields $T = 288$°K or $+15$°C.

This model predicts the actual long-term average global temperature of the Earth fairly well. The long-term average temperature is 13.9°C. The average global temperature in 2003 was 0.56°C above the long-term average. This represents about a 1%

decrease in e. This analysis shows that the average global temperature depends on e and e depends on the atmospheric composition. Thus, you would conditionally accept the hypothesis that "The average global temperature of the Earth depends on the composition of the atmosphere."

Another example of the use of the scientific method is given in Example 2.

EXAMPLE 2: APPLICATION OF THE SCIENTIFIC METHOD

Using the scientific method, analyze why some photographs exhibit "red eye" (i.e., red-colored pupils in the subjects).

SOLUTION

First, define the question. In this case, the question is obvious from the problem statement: why do some photographs exhibit red eye? Second, formulate a hypothesis. (You may wish to formulate your own hypothesis at this point.) One hypothesis states that red eye is caused by reddish color in the camera's flash. Third, test the hypothesis. The preceding hypothesis could be tested by using different filters on the flash and observing whether red eye is related to the wavelengths of light reaching the subject.

Note: Experiments would show that the stated hypothesis is false and should be rejected. An alternative hypothesis for red eye is discussed in Problem 2.

---

9   SUMMARY

Engineers solve problems. Engineering problems are solved by a combination of science (knowledge of the principles of mathematics, chemistry, physics, mechanics, and other technical subjects) and art (creativity, judgment, experience, and common sense). Engineering problems involving the testing of hypotheses are solved by the scientific method. In the scientific method, you define the problem, pose a hypothesis, test the hypothesis, and reject or conditionally accept the hypothesis.

An important step in all of the problem-solving methods is defining the problem. Problem definitions must be specific, should include the constraints of the problem, and should quantify the objectives. In addition, problem definitions should not limit the solutions. In other words, the problem definition should not overly constrain possible solutions.

Once the problem is defined, hypotheses can be generated. Hypotheses must be capable of being tested, usually by experiment or analysis. In interpreting the results of hypothesis testing, be sure to accept hypotheses only for the conditions under which they were tested.

SUMMARY OF KEY IDEAS

- Engineering problems may have one, many, or no solutions and often require data gathering to obtain the information needed to solve the problem.
- Engineering problems are solved by a combination of science (knowledge of the principles of mathematics, chemistry, physics, mechanics, and other technical subjects) and art (creativity, judgment, experience, and common sense).
- Engineering problems should be approached in a logical and organized manner.
- Engineers use the scientific method, engineering analysis method, and engineering design method to solve problems.
- The scientific method involves generating and testing hypotheses.

- Design problems require the generation of alternatives.
- The scientific method is used to evaluate explanations of observed phenomena.
- Solve problems by using the scientific method: define the problem, pose a hypothesis, test the hypothesis, and reject or conditionally accept the hypothesis.
- Problem definitions must be specific.
- Problem definitions should include the constraints of the problem.
- Problem definitions should not limit the solutions.
- Problem definitions should quantify the objectives.
- Hypotheses must be capable of being tested.
- Hypotheses can be tested by experiment or analysis.
- Accept hypotheses only for the conditions under which they were tested.

Problems

1. State whether you would use the scientific method, engineering analysis method, or engineering design method to solve each of the following engineering problems. Explain your reasoning in each case.

   a. Find the best cylinder arrangement to maximize the output of a racing car engine.

   b. Decide whether temperature influences the performance of an electromagnet.

   c. Determine the response of a building to an earthquake.

2. An alternative hypothesis for red eye (see Example 2) is that red eye is caused by the reflection of light from the flash off of the blood vessels at the back of the retina. If the flash is rapid, then the pupil remains dilated and the surface area for reflection is relatively large. If the angle formed by the flash, subject's eye, and camera lens (see accompanying figure) is too small, then the light is reflected back to the camera. Restate this information as a hypothesis and discuss how you would test it. Research red-eye reduction techniques on the Internet to verify your hypothesis-testing ideas.

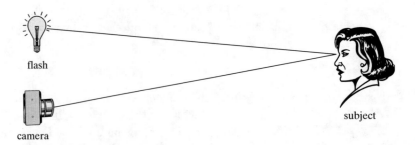

flash

camera

subject

3. A traffic signal was designed to turn red for cars every time the "Walk" button is pressed. The traffic engineers are considering a change in the traffic signal operation. In the new system, the traffic signal will turn red for cars every minute. Develop a problem statement and hypothesis regarding the effects of the traffic signal operation on the average wait time of a car.

4. Develop a problem statement and hypothesis regarding the effects of current on the power output of a resistive heater. Assume that the resistive heater has constant resistance. Test the hypothesis using the following equations: power = current × voltage and voltage = current × resistance.

5. List the characteristics of a good problem definition. Illustrate with a proper problem definition and problem definitions that are deficient.

6. The television show *MythBusters* tests urban myths. Watch an episode or visit their Web site (http://dsc.discovery.com/fansites/mythbusters/mythbusters.html) and select three myths they have tested. Evaluate their problem statements, hypotheses, and testing methodologies. Did they have sufficient evidence to accept or reject their hypotheses?

7. Does tapping on the side of a soda can prevent it from foaming over when you open it? Develop a problem statement, hypothesis, and testing methodology. Test your hypothesis and explain why you reject or conditionally accept the hypothesis.

8. The problem described in Problem 7 was evaluated at the Web site http://www.snopes.com/science/sodacan.htm. Evaluate their problem statement, hypothesis, and testing methodology. Did they have sufficient evidence to accept or reject their hypothesis?

9. Do toilets flush clockwise in the northern hemisphere and counterclockwise in the southern hemisphere? Develop a problem statement, hypothesis, and testing methodology. Test your hypothesis and explain why you reject or conditionally accept the hypothesis.

10. Do eelskin wallets made from electric eels demagnetize credit cards? Develop a problem statement, hypothesis, and testing methodology. Test your hypothesis and explain why you reject or conditionally accept the hypothesis.

6

Engineering Analysis Method

1   INTRODUCTION

1.1   Introduction to Engineering Analysis

Analysis is the application of mathematical and scientific principles to solve a technical problem. The word analysis comes from the Greek *ana-* + *lyein*, literally to loosen or break up. You analyze problems by breaking them up into parts.

In an ***analysis problem***, the system has been defined and your job is to determine specific characteristics of the system. Just about every homework problem you have done in the past is an analysis problem. A typical analysis problem might read: "Given a, b, and c, determine x, y, and z."

Analysis problems have two important characteristics. First, the system and problem context are usually well defined. Second, analysis problems usually have only one solution. Think back to the homework assignments in your high school physics class. You might have been given an object's acceleration and been asked to determine its position at some time. The system is well defined (i.e., you know exactly what to calculate) and has only one solution. (In this case, the position is given by $x = \frac{1}{2}at^2$, where a = acceleration and t = time. For each value of t, this is only one possible value of x.) Example engineering analysis problems include determining the stresses in a truss for a proposed bridge design, calculating the thrust needed to propel a satellite into orbit, or estimating the reliability of a computer network.

You have so much experience with analysis problems that you may wonder whether *all* engineering problems are well defined with one possible answer. In fact, a large number of engineering problems (called design problems) have *many* solutions. Consider two problems: (1) Determine the force on a pulley, and (2) devise wheelchair controls to be operated by a quadriplegic person. Clearly, the pulley problem

OBJECTIVES

After reading this chapter, you will be able to:

- list the steps in the engineering analysis method;
- identify the kinds of engineering problems for which the engineering analysis method is appropriate;
- solve engineering problems using the engineering analysis method.

analysis: application of mathematical and scientific principles to solve technical problems

analysis problem: a problem where the system is well defined and system characteristics must be determined

Key idea: Analysis problems are usually well defined and have only one solution.

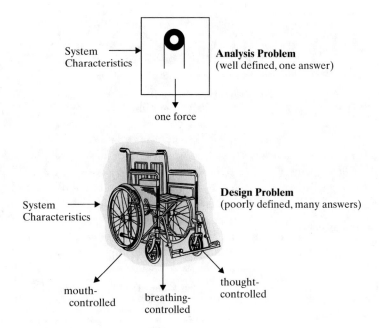

Figure 1. Illustration of Analysis and Design Problems

has one answer (one force), but many wheelchair-control designs are possible (see Figure 1). Design problems are addressed by the engineering design method.

1.2   Solving Analysis Problems

The process used to solve analysis problems is called the *engineering analysis method*. The engineering analysis method uses established mathematical and scientific principles. The analysis method is more science than art. The following six-step process should be used for solving analysis problems:

Key idea: Solve analysis problems by defining the problem, gathering data and verifying data accuracy, selecting the analysis methods, estimating the solution, solving the mathematical expressions, and checking the results.

1.   Define the problem
2.   Gather data and verify the accuracy of the data
3.   Select the analysis method(s)
4.   Estimate the solution
5.   Solve the problem
6.   Check the results

The last five steps in the engineering analysis method will be described in more detail next.

2   GATHERING DATA

2.1   Introduction

Before you continue in the solution process, you must collect and substantiate all data pertinent to the problem. These quantities may include physical data (e.g., dimensions, voltages, currents, temperatures, or velocities) or data from interviews. Some problems require that problem definition and data gathering steps be done separately. In other problems, defining the problem may automatically provide some or all of the data.

2.2   Data Collection

Engineers gather data in two ways. First, *laboratory-scale* (also called *bench-scale*) or *pilot-scale* experiments° can be performed to mimic full-scale systems. System variables can be varied and the output recorded. Experiments conducted at a scale smaller than full scale represent physical models of all or part of the system of interest.

Second, measurements can be taken in the field. Engineering measurements are as diverse as engineering itself. Measured values may range from stresses in beams to stray currents to worker's opinions of a new touch-screen layout.

Key idea: Data are gathered through experiments and field measurements.

Key idea: Test all data for reasonableness.

In all cases, it is important to verify the reasonableness of the data. For measured values, look to see if the values seem reasonable and remeasure if you have questions. For data taken from other sources, look closely at the sources of data. For example, it is not always clear whether data available on the Internet come from a disinterested party or from a company wishing to sell a particular product or service. (Data sources that have not been verified independently sometimes are called *gray literature*.) Similarly, when interviewing people about a problem, be sure to note whether their statements are backed up by data or whether they have made assumptions about the on-site conditions. It is useful to ask three questions: What do you know? What do you *not* know? and What do you *think* you know?

3   SELECTING THE ANALYSIS METHOD

3.1   Introduction

Key idea: To select an analysis method, first select the physical laws and then translate the physical laws into mathematical equations.

The selection of an analysis method is a two-step process. First, you must select the fundamental laws or principles that apply to the system. The laws or principles typically come from mathematics and science. For example, Newton's second law of motion (force = mass × acceleration or $F = ma$) can be combined with a force balance to solve many problems in statics, where system components are not moving. Equations generated from the fundamental laws are used to solve the problem.

Key idea: Engineers need quantifiable relationships between variables.

The second step is to translate the physical laws into mathematical statements (also called *mathematical models*). Engineering is a quantitative field. As an engineer, you will frequently develop mathematical models of the physical world. You may need to know how voltage depends on current, or the relationship between heat capacity and temperature, or the effects of a delay in a concrete delivery on a construction schedule. *Simply knowing that one variable depends on another is not enough.* To analyze systems that interact with the physical world, it is necessary to have *quantifiable* relationships between variables. As an engineer, you will develop and use mathematical models for relationships between variables.

3.2   Selection of Physical Laws

physical law: a description of nature assumed to be true

As stated in Section 3.1, you generally begin with a ***physical law***. In engineering and science, laws are propositions about nature that are assumed to be true.

PONDER THIS

How do you *know* the laws are true?

In fact, you do not know if the laws are true! Laws are unprovable because they relate the values of real, physical properties. Due to experimental imprecision, no matter

---

°For etymology fans, the word "experiment" comes from the Latin *experiri* (to try). Small-scale experiments (smaller than full scale, but larger than laboratory scale) sometimes are called *pilot-scale* experiments. Here, the word "pilot" is used in the sense "to guide." Pilot-scale experiments guide engineers in the design and operation of full-scale engineered systems just as a pilot guides a ship or airplane.

how carefully you measure the physical properties, you cannot confirm that the values are *exactly* as stated in the law. It may seem strange that so much engineering work is based on some unproven assumptions, but these assumptions have withstood the test of time in engineered systems.

The vast majority of engineering calculations start with one of a small handful of physical laws. Three kinds of physical laws are important in engineering: laws of conservation, laws of motion, and constitutive laws. You will learn about these laws over the next few semesters. The laws will be introduced briefly here to demonstrate how physical laws are used in the engineering analysis method.

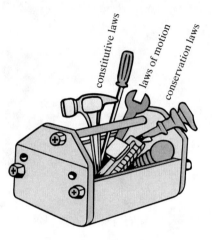

Conservation laws, laws of motion, and constitutive laws will be some of the most important tools in your engineering toolbox.

laws of conservation: the statements that mass, momentum, energy, and charge (among other properties) are unchanged for different states of a system

The first class of important laws consists of the **laws of conservation**. It often is assumed that several key physical parameters remain unchanged in engineered systems. Specifically, engineers assume that mass, momentum (mass × velocity), angular momentum, energy (the entity that allows the system to do work), and charge are conserved. The statement of the conservation of energy is sometimes called the *First Law of Thermodynamics*. Conserved properties will *balance* (i.e., be unchanged for different states of the engineered system).

mass in
momentum in
angular momentum in
energy in

mass out
momentum out
angular momentum out
energy out

The conservation laws are behind many engineering calculations.[*] A chemical engineer might use an energy balance to design a refrigeration system. A mechanical engineer uses a momentum balance to calculate ink flow in an ink-jet printer. An industrial engineer's complex parts routing system ultimately must be based on a mass balance of the parts stored.

The conservation laws are summarized in Table 1. As noted in Table 1, some other statements called "laws" stem from the conservation laws.

Other common laws serving as starting places for engineering calculations are the *laws of motion*. Isaac Newton (1643–1727) proposed three laws of motion. The First Law of Motion (also called the *law of inertia*) states that objects at rest will remain at rest unless acted upon by an unbalanced force. (It also states that objects in motion will remain in a straight-line motion at constant speed unless acted upon by an unbalanced force.)

laws of motion:

statements about the motion of objects in response to applied forces

Newton's First Law of Motion (velocity is constant if the sum of the "forward" forces is equal to the sum of the "reverse" forces)

TABLE 1   Common Laws of Conservation

Property Conserved	Example of the Conservation Law	Other Laws Based on Conservation of the Property
Mass (m)	Determining the chemical doses required for an industrial process	*Continuity equation*: for a flow of constant density, the sum of the flows in and out of a node is zero
Momentum (mv)	Determining the initial velocity of a baseball after being hit by a bat	
Angular momentum (mvr)	Determining the rotational velocity of a fan	*Kepler's Second Law*: a line between the Sun and a planet sweeps out equal areas in equal time intervals
Energy (E) (First Law of Thermodynamics)	Determining the amount of lift generated by an airplane wing	*Bernoulli Equation*: the relationship between pressure, velocity, and elevation of a fluid
		Kirchhoff's Voltage Law: the net voltage drop around any closed path must be zero
Charge (z)	Determining the pH of acid rain	*Kirchhoff's Law*: the sum of the currents in and out of a node is zero

v = velocity, r = radial distance

Namesakes of the laws and equations: Daniel Bernoulli (1700–1782), Johannes Kepler (1571–1630), and Gustav Robert Kirchhoff (1824–1887).

---

[*]You may know that Albert Einstein (1879–1955) showed that mass (m) and energy (E) are interchangeable according to $E = mc^2$, where c = speed of light. For a vast majority of engineered systems, it is still useful to write separate conservation statements for mass and energy.

Newton's second law of motion states that force (F) equals mass (m) multiplied by acceleration (a), or $F = ma$. Finally, the Third Law of Motion (also called the *law of action and reaction*) states that for every force, there is an equal and opposite force (in other words, the forces that two objects exert on each other are equal but in opposite directions).

$F = ma$

Newton's Second Law of Motion

Newton's Third Law of Motion

An electrical engineer would use Newton's first law of motion to describe the motion of electrons in a magnetic field. An aerospace engineer starts with Newton's second law of motion when designing a novel propulsion system. A civil engineer uses Newton's third law of motion to understand that a concrete floor pushes against the force exerted by a person standing on it. The laws of motion are summarized in Table 2.

A third class of laws consists of the relationships between the measurable properties of a system and is called ***constitutive laws***. The constitutive laws are empirical; that is, they are based on observations rather than theory. Three important constitutive laws are

> *Hooke's law* (after Robert Hooke, 1635–1703): the force exerted by a spring (F) is proportional to the displacement of the spring (x), or $F = kx$, where k is the spring stiffness
>
> *Ohm's law* (after Georg Simon Ohm, 1789–1854): the voltage (V) equals current (I) × resistance (R), or $V = IR$
>
> *Ideal gas law*:° pressure × volume = number of moles × ideal gas constant × temperature, or $PV = nRT$

constitutive laws:

relationships (usually empirical) between the measurable properties of a system

TABLE 2   Newton's Laws of Motion

Law of Motion	Statement of Law
First Law (Law of inertia)	An object at rest will remain at rest and an object in motion will remain in motion at constant speed, unless either object is acted upon by an unbalanced force
Second Law	Force (F) equals mass (m) × acceleration (a): $F = ma$
Third Law (Law of action and reaction)	For every force, there is an equal and opposite force

°The ideal gas law is consistent with Boyle's Law (pressure is proportional to 1/volume at constant temperature and amount of material, after Robert Boyle, 1627–1691) and Charles's Law (volume is proportional to temperature at constant pressure and amount of material, after Jacques Charles, 1746–1823).

A civil engineer might use a version of Hooke's Law to relate the stress in a beam (stress = force/area) to the strain (displacement/length). An electrical engineer might use Ohm's Law to determine voltage drops in electrical transmission systems. A mechanical engineer would start with the ideal gas law to determine the required thickness of a new material for storing liquid oxygen.

How do you decide which physical laws to select? In general, *seek a relationship between the components of the system that you know and the system components you are trying to calculate.* If you want to know the velocity of a crash dummy's head after a collision with a wall, you might pick the conservation of momentum statement. It will contain elements that you know (masses and initial velocities) and elements that you wanted to determine (namely, the velocity of the dummy's head). Other examples of how to select physical laws are given in Example 1.

EXAMPLE 1 SELECTING PHYSICAL LAWS	Select the physical law from Tables 1 and 2 to model the following phenomena: the pressure exerted by a waterbed mattress on the floor, the escape velocity of a rocket, and the operation of an ionization smoke detector. (You may need to use the Internet to learn how a smoke detector works.)
SOLUTION	Pressure is force divided by area. Thus, a pertinent analysis method for the waterbed problem is **Newton's Second Law of Motion**. Newton's Second Law can be used to relate what you want (force/area) with what you know (system properties of mass, acceleration, and waterbed area).

The escape velocity of a rocket is described by **conservation of energy**. The kinetic energy of the rocket is balanced by the gravitational energy pulling it back to Earth.

The ionization smoke detector works by **conservation of charge**. The detector contains about 200 μg of the radioactive element americium 241. The alpha particles released by the americium form ions from the components of air, which are trapped on charged plates to produce a background current. (The smoke detector battery charges the plates.) The current (charges per unit time) is reduced when ions adsorb to smoke particles.

Note: The waterbed and rocket problems are evaluated further in Example 2.

3.3   Translation into Mathematical Expressions

Physical laws do not help in a calculation unless you can translate the physical law into a mathematical expression involving the parameters you wish to determine. The second step in performing an engineering calculation is the *translation of the physical law into a mathematical statement.* For example, suppose that you are analyzing a household electric circuit, where the electric supply is split into two subcircuits at a node. If you know the supply current and the current of one subcircuit, how do you find the current in the other subcircuit? You need an expression that relates the currents in a circuit. Kirchhoff's Current Law will do (see Table 1). It states that the sum of the currents flowing into a circuit node must be equal to the sum of the currents leaving the node. In this case:

supply current = current in subcircuit #1 + current in subcircuit #2

You now have a mathematical expression involving the known and the unknown quantities. You can solve for the parameter of interest. An example of translating physical laws into mathematical expressions is given in Example 2.

EXAMPLE 2 TRANSLATING PHYSICAL LAWS INTO MATHEMATICAL EXPRESSIONS

From Example 1, calculate the escape velocity of a rocket. Assume that the rocket stops moving when it is infinitely far from Earth. Also, from Example 1, determine whether your waterbed mattress violates the building code loading of 100 pounds of force per square foot (4,780 Pa, where 1 Pa = 1 N/m^2 and 1 N = 1 newton = 1 kg-m/s^2; so the building code is 4,780 N/m^2 = 4780 kg/m-s^2). The dimensions of the mattress are 5.0 ft × 7.0 ft × 0.75 ft (1.5 m × 2.1 m × 0.23 m).

SOLUTION

Rocket problem:

At take-off, the rocket's net energy is the kinetic energy of the rocket minus the gravitational energy pulling it back to Earth. When the rocket stops infinitely far from the Earth, its total energy is zero. An energy balance reveals several factors:

$$\text{energy at take-off} = \text{energy infinitely far away from Earth}$$

$$\text{kinetic energy} - \text{gravitational energy} = 0$$

So

$$\text{kinetic energy} = \text{gravitational energy}$$

The kinetic energy at take-off is $\frac{1}{2}mv^2$, where m = rocket mass and v = escape velocity. The gravitational energy is mGM/R, where G = universal gravitational constant = 6.672×10^{-11} N-m^2/kg^2 = 6.672×10^{-11} m^3/kg-s^2, M = Earth's mass = 5.98×10^{24} kg, and R = Earth's radius = 6.37×10^6 m. The energy balance becomes

$$\tfrac{1}{2}mv^2 = mGM/R \quad \text{or} \quad v = (2GM/R)^{1/2}$$

Substituting in the values, we find that

$$v = \text{escape velocity} = \sqrt{\frac{GM}{R}}$$

$$= \sqrt{\frac{2\left(6.67 \times 10^{-11}\dfrac{\text{m}^3}{\text{kg} - \text{s}^2}\right)(6.98 \times 10^{24}\ \text{kg})}{6.37 \times 10^6\ \text{m}}}$$

$$= \textbf{11,200 m/s} \text{ (about 24,000 mph)}$$

Waterbed problem:

For the waterbed, the force from Newton's Second Law of Motion is $F = ma = mg$ (g = acceleration due to the Earth's gravity = 9.8 m/s^2). The pressure P is $F/A = mg/A$, where A is the area of the mattress in contact with the floor. The mass of the waterbed is mainly the mass of the water: mass = (density)(volume) = ρV. The density of water is about 1,000 kg/m^3. Therefore,

$$P = mg/A = \rho V g/A = (1{,}000\ \text{kg/m}^3)(1.5 \times 2.1 \times 0.23\ \text{m}^3)(9.8\ \text{m/s}^2)/(1.5 \times 2.1\ \text{m}^2)$$

$$= 2{,}300\ \text{kg/m-s}^2$$

The pressure exerted by the waterbed is 2,300 kg/m-s^2 (about 47 pounds of force per square foot). Therefore, **the mattress does not violate the code of 4,780 kg/m-s^2** (100 pounds of force per square foot).

4   ESTIMATING THE SOLUTION

4.1   Introduction

An important, but often ignored, step in solving an analysis problem is developing a "ballpark" estimate of the solution. In many cases, mistakes in analysis can be caught by making an order-of-magnitude guess of the solution. Estimation serves as a check on the calculations and also helps in the development of engineering intuition. Of course, the result of the calculation may be surprising; in fact, it may be significantly different from your estimate. Still, estimation is a good "reality check" on engineering calculations.

Even in this age of speedy personal computers, some engineers still lament the passing of the **slide rule**. (Do you know what a slide rule is? Search on the Internet to learn more.) Slide rules are fairly primitive calculators, but they have one interesting feature: they do not indicate the decimal place of the answer. If you multiply 71.2 by 46.3 on a slide rule, you get the answer: 330. Is this 3.30? 33.0? 330? 3,300? With a slide rule, you have to estimate the location of the decimal place.

slide rule: a ruler scaled logarithmically with a movable centerpiece typically used for performing multiplication and division (phrase was coined in 1663)

PONDER THIS

> **Take a moment to estimate the product of 71.2 × 46.3. Is it closest to 3.30, 33.0, 330, or 3,300?**

You might guess that $71.2 \times 46.3 \approx 70 \times 50 = 3,500$, so the answer from the slide rule is 3,300. Slide rules help to develop intuition in engineering calculations. Even with electronic calculators and spreadsheets, it is useful to estimate the location of the decimal place as a way to check the calculation. This is called an *order-of-magnitude estimation*.

terminal velocity: a constant velocity sometimes achieved by falling objects (hence, the acceleration is zero)

4.2   Example

As an example of estimation, suppose you are planning to take your first skydiving lesson and you wish to know how fast you will be falling. You remember that your diving instructor talked about reaching **terminal velocity**.

PONDER THIS

> **Estimate your terminal velocity during skydiving. Is it 1 mile per hour (mph)? 10 mph? 100 mph? 1,000 mph?**

Your intuition probably tells you the terminal velocity will be greater than 10 mph but smaller than 1,000 mph. What is your estimate? Something in the 50 to 150 mph range sounds about right.

You can calculate the terminal velocity more accurately. Recall that the terminal velocity is a constant velocity. Thus, the acceleration (change in velocity with respect to time) is zero at the terminal velocity.

PONDER THIS

> **If terminal velocity means that you are not accelerating, what net force are you experiencing? Why?**

If your acceleration is zero, the net force on you will also be zero (since, from Newton's Second Law of Motion, force = mass × acceleration: $F = ma$). Two forces act on you: a force from gravitational acceleration ($F_g = mg$) and a drag force ($F_d = $

$\frac{1}{2}C_d A\rho v_t^2$). The drag force depends on the drag coefficient C_d (approximately 0.22 in this example); the cross-sectional area of your falling body, A ($\approx$0.8 m^2 if you curl up in a ball); the density of air, ρ; and the terminal velocity v_t.

If the net force is zero, then

$$0 = F_g - F_d = mg - \frac{1}{2}C_d A\rho v_t^2$$

Solving for the terminal velocity yields

$$v_t = \sqrt{\frac{2mg}{C_D A\rho}}$$

If you weigh 60 kg, then your terminal velocity is

$$\sqrt{\frac{2(60 \text{ kg})\left(9.8\frac{\text{m}}{\text{s}^2}\right)}{(0.22)(0.8 \text{ m}^2)\left(1,000\frac{\text{kg}}{\text{m}^3}\right)}} = 2.6 \text{ m/s} = 5.8 \text{ mph}$$

Did the answer 5.8 mph match your estimate? No, this answer seems *much* too small. Can you find the error in the equation? The density of water (1 kg/L = 1,000 kg/m^3) was used inadvertently instead of the density of air (1.225 kg/m^3 at 15°C). Substituting the correct density, the terminal velocity turns out to be 74 m/s or 165 miles per hour. This probably fits your preconceived notion more closely.* Another estimation example is shown in Example 3.

**EXAMPLE 3
ESTIMATING
THE SOLUTION**

In the waterbed scenario from Examples 1 and 2, you can estimate the pressure from the "rule of thumb" that a 2.3-foot column of water exerts a pressure of 1 pound of force per square inch (1 psi). (This relationship is derived easily from the density of water.)

SOLUTION

The 0.75-foot "column" of water in the waterbed is about one-third of 2.3 feet; thus, it would exert about $\frac{1}{3}$ psi or about ($\frac{1}{3}$ psi) (144 square inches/square foot) $\approx$ 50 pounds of force per square foot. With this estimate, you might conclude that the calculated value of 47 pounds of force per square foot seems reasonable.

---

5   SOLVING THE PROBLEM

5.1   Solving Mathematical Expressions by Isolating the Unknown

Key idea: Manipulate expressions (i.e., rearrange terms) to solve for the variable of interest.

expression: any relationship between variables (if the relationship is an equality, the expression is called an **equation**)

If the previous steps result in a mathematical expression, it is normally solved by application of mathematical theory. The key to solving mathematical expressions is to isolate the unknown on one side of the expression. Always be aware of which variables you seek to calculate: "Keep your eyes on the prize."

By convention, you usually try to isolate the parameter or variable of interest on the left-hand side of the expression. The term **expression** refers to any relationship between variables. An expression can be an inequality (e.g., $y > x^2$) or an equality (e.g., $y = mx + b$). Equality expressions are called **equations**. A few simple rules will come to your aid in manipulating expressions.

---

*Does this analysis mean that your terminal velocity falling in water is 2.6 m/s? No—estimation should tell you that 2.6 m/s seems too fast. In water, a third force is important: buoyancy. Your buoyancy in water makes your settling velocity in water less than 2.6 m/s.

5.2   "Golden Rule" of Expression Manipulation

Key idea: The "Golden Rule" of expression manipulation is as follows: "Do to one side of the expression that which you did to the other side."

First, obey the ***"Golden Rule" of expression manipulation***: Do to one side of the expression that which you did to the other side. Suppose you wish to know how the acetone concentration in the feedstock of an industrial process changes with time. Suppose your mathematical model yields the following relationship between the feedstock concentration C and time t:

$$C = C_0 e^{-kt} \qquad (1)$$

where C_0 is the initial feedstock concentration and k is a rate constant (C_0 and k are always positive here). Suppose you want to find the time (called the *half life*, $t_{1/2}$) at which the feedstock concentration falls to one-half its initial value; in other words, find $t = t_{1/2}$ when $C = \frac{1}{2}C_0$. You would proceed by dividing *both sides* of Eq. (1) by C_0. Since $C = \frac{1}{2}C_0$, it follows that

$$C/C_0 = \frac{1}{2} = e^{-kt}$$

Using the "Golden Rule" and taking the natural log *of both sides* yields

$$\ln(\tfrac{1}{2}) = \ln(e^{-kt}) = -kt \qquad [\text{recall that } \ln(e^x) = x]$$

Dividing *both sides* by k gives

$$t_{1/2} = -\ln(\tfrac{1}{2})/k \qquad (2)$$

Thus, employing the "Golden Rule" and performing the same operations on both sides of the equation tells you that $t_{1/2} = -\ln(\frac{1}{2})/k$.

5.3   Manipulating Inequalities

Key idea: Remember to reverse the inequality sign when multiplying or dividing both sides by a negative number.

The second rule of manipulating equations states that inequality signs are reversed when multiplying or dividing both sides by a negative number. Suppose you are interested in reaction times greater than the half life: $t > t_{1/2}$. Is C greater than or less than $\frac{1}{2}C_0$ at $t > t_{1/2}$? Equation (2) becomes

$$t > t_{1/2} = -\ln(\tfrac{1}{2})/k$$

or

$$t > -\ln(\tfrac{1}{2})/k$$

Multiplying by $-k$ (a negative quantity) yields

$$-kt < \ln(\tfrac{1}{2})$$

Notice that the "greater than" sign became a "less than" sign when you multiply the inequality by the negative value $-k$. Exponentiating *both sides* gives the following: $e^{-kt} < \frac{1}{2}$. From Eq. (1), $e^{-kt} = C/C_0$, so $e^{-kt} < \frac{1}{2}$ means that $C/C_0 < \frac{1}{2}$. Multiplying both sides by C_0 (a positive quantity) gives

$$C < \tfrac{1}{2}C_0$$

(Note that you do not change the inequality sign, since C_0 is positive.) Thus, if $t > t_{1/2}$, then $C < \frac{1}{2}C_0$. In other words, at times greater than the half life, the feedstock concentration is less than half the initial feedstock concentration.

5.4   Hints for Manipulating Equations

Key idea: Solve for the unknowns with symbols (by isolating the unknowns on one side of the expression) and *then* substitute in numbers ("chug" before you "plug").

A common problem encountered when manipulating equations is the tendency to substitute numbers for symbols too early in the process. *Always substitute numbers for symbols only in the last step of the calculation.* Inserting values into an expression is commonly called "plugging and chugging." However, it is important to "chug" (i.e., manipulate the expression) ***before*** you "plug" (i.e., substitute values for symbols).

Say, for example, you want to find the current (in amperes or A) required to achieve a heating power of 1,000 watts (1,000 W) in a resistive heating device (for example, a space heater) if the resistance is 10 ohms ($= 10 \ \Omega$). The relationship between power (P), current (I), and resistance (R) is

$$P = I^2 R$$

(Recall that $1 \ \mathrm{A}^2 \times 1 \ \Omega = 1 \ \mathrm{W}$.) Many people make the mistake of substituting in the known values first and then solving for the unknown:

$$(1,000 \ \mathrm{W}) = I^2 (10 \ \Omega),$$

or

$$I^2 = (1,000 \ \mathrm{W})/(10 \ \Omega) \text{ and } I = (1,000 \ \mathrm{W}/10 \ \Omega)^{1/2} = 10 \ \mathrm{A}$$

What is the problem with this approach? If you want to calculate the current at *another* resistance (say, 20 Ω), then you must start the calculation over again.

It is much more efficient to *solve for the unknown with symbols and then substitute in numbers during the last step in the calculation.* Thus, from $P = I^2 R$, you can derive

$$I = \sqrt{\frac{P}{R}}$$

This equation can be used to calculate the current for *any* power and resistance. The bottom line: manipulate symbols to solve for the unknown, and *then* substitute in the values of the known quantities. Another example of manipulating equations is shown in Example 4.

EXAMPLE 4: MANIPULATING EXPRESSIONS

Two resistors in series (with resistances R_1 and R_2) give an overall resistance R, with $1/R$ equal to $1/R_1 + 1/R_2$. Find the overall resistance for 1-Ω and 2-Ω resistors in series and for 2-Ω and 10-Ω resistors in series.

SOLUTION

Manipulate symbols *first*, and then plug in numbers. Thus, we begin with

$$\frac{1}{R} = \frac{1}{R_1} + \frac{1}{R_2}$$

Inverting *both* sides gives

$$R = \frac{1}{\dfrac{1}{R_1} + \dfrac{1}{R_2}} = \frac{R_1 R_2}{R_1 + R_2}$$

Plugging in values then produces the following result: **The overall resistance is 0.67 Ω for 1-Ω and 2-Ω resistors in series and 1.7 Ω for 2-Ω and 10-Ω resistors in series.**

6   CHECKING THE RESULTS

Key idea: Answers to engineering calculations almost always have physical meaning.

Key idea: Check engineering calculations by logic, estimation, and checking units.

6.1   Introduction

It is tempting to stop after computing an answer and assume that the solution is correct. However, determining *a* solution and determining the *correct* solution are two very different things: obtaining a solution does not mean that the solution is correct or even realistic.

In almost all engineering calculations, the result is a physical quantity. You are computing *something* and not just calculating for the sake of calculation. This fact puts constraints on the answers you obtain as an engineer: answers represent tangible quantities in the real world. In engineering calculations, *numbers almost always have physical meaning.* As a result, there are three tools you can use to check engineering calculations: logic, estimation, and checking units.

6.2   Use Logic to Avoid Aphysical Answers

aphysical: not physically possible

Key idea: Use logic to eliminate aphysical answers: always ask if your answers make sense.

Since answers in engineering calculations represent physical quantities, you must employ logic to eliminate nonsensical results. Such results are sometimes call **aphysical**, because they are physically impossible answers. One of the best ways to avoid reporting errors is to ask yourself a simple question: *does the answer make sense?* Never leave an engineering calculation without thinking about whether the answer is reasonable. In many ways, this is the most important step in the engineering calculation process.

As an example of using logic to weed out aphysical answers, suppose you and your studymates ponder the possibility of bungee jumping off the top of Ye Olde Administration Building. In a moment of clarity, you decide it would be prudent to determine if you would hit the ground at the bottom of the first bounce.

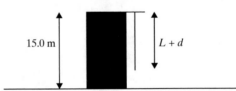

You want to know if the distance you will fall is greater than the height of the building.° At the bottom of your jump, you will have fallen a distance equal to the length of the unstretched bungee cord (L, say, 9.0 m) plus the length that the bungee cord has stretched (d). Thus, you want to know if $L + d$ is greater than the building height (say, 15.0 m). Since you know $L = 9.0$ m, you really just need to know if $d > 15.0$ m $-$ $9.0\ m = 6.0\ m$. So the question to be answered is simple: is d > 6.0 m?

PONDER THIS

Without performing a potentially tragic experiment on an unsuspecting classmate, how would you decide whether you would hit the ground?

potential energy: energy associated with the position in a field (for a gravitational field, potential energy = mass × gravitational acceleration × height)

Conservation of energy reveals that the loss of **potential energy** at the bottom of the jump should equal the energy stored in the bungee cord. Your loss in potential energy is $mg(L + d)$, where m = your mass (assume 70 kg), g = gravitational acceleration = 9.8 m/s², and $L + d$ = the distance you have fallen. The bungee cord is like a spring. Thus, the energy stored in the bungee cord is equal to $\frac{1}{2}kd^2$, where k = spring stiffness (say, 150 N/m = 150 kg/s²). Thus,

$$\text{potential energy lost} = \text{energy stored in the bungee cord}$$
$$mg(L + d) = \tfrac{1}{2}kd^2$$

°Assume you are standing in a loop at the end of the bungee cord, so that your height does not affect the calculation.

Rearranging terms yields

$$\tfrac{1}{2}kd^2 - mgd - mgL = 0 \tag{3}$$

quadratic equation:
if $ax^2 + bx + c = 0$, then

$$x = \frac{b \pm \sqrt{b^2 - 4ac}}{2a}$$

You and your studymates realize immediately that you can solve Eq. (3) for d by using the **quadratic equation** (see definition). In Eq. (3), the symbols in the quadratic equation are

$$a = \tfrac{1}{2}k, b = -mg, \text{ and } c = -mgL$$

So

$$d = \frac{mg \pm \sqrt{m^2g^2 - 2kmgL}}{k} \tag{4}$$

The total distance you would fall is

$$L + d = L + \frac{mg}{k} \pm \frac{\sqrt{m^2g^2 - 2kmgL}}{k} \tag{5}$$

Substituting the preceding values of m, g, L, and k into Eq. (5) gives

$$L + d = 9.0 \text{ m} + 4.6 \text{ m} \pm 10.2 \text{ m} = 3.4 \text{ m or } 23.7 \text{ m}$$

There are two solutions. If you fall 3.4 m, you *may* be safe. However, a fall of 23.7 m from a height of 15.0 m would be disastrous!

How do you decide which is the right answer? Remember: *The answer must have physical meaning.* From Eq. (4),

$$d = 4.6 \text{ m} \pm 10.2 \text{ m} = -5.6 \text{ m or } 14.7 \text{ m}$$

Clearly, d must be 14.7 m: it does not make much sense for you to "fall" 5.6 m *up* if you jump off a building! Thus, d must be 14.7 m and $L + d$ is 23.7 m. The moral of the story: *use logic to eliminate aphysical answers* (and don't bungee-jump off buildings on campus).

6.3   Using Logic to Check Expression Manipulation

Key idea: Use logic to check whether one variable changes as expected with changes in the other variables.

Logic also can help you check your manipulation of mathematical expressions. One way to do this is to check whether one variable changes as expected when other variables change. In other words, you can check the predicted trends of your expressions. For example, consider a common property of matter: the ratio of the surface area of an object to its volume (called the surface-to-volume ratio or S/V). The S/V is an important quantity in engineering. It controls the functioning of objects from ball bearings to industrial catalysts to the human lung. For simple shapes, S/V is easy to calculate. For a sphere of radius r,

$$V = 4\pi r^3/3 \text{ and } S = 4\pi r^2 \text{ }^\circ$$

Thus,

$$S/V = 3/r \tag{6}$$

Does this equation make sense? One way to see if it makes sense is to look at the trend in S/V with the independent variable (r).

$^\circ$If you have knowledge of calculus, you can show that, for a sphere, $S = dV/dr = d(4\pi r^3/3)/dr = 4\pi r^2$.

PONDER THIS

How should the surface-to-volume ratio change with the particle size?

To see how the surface-to-volume ratio changes with the particle size, compare a 3 cm by 3 cm by 3 cm cube with twenty-seven 1 cm by 1 cm by 1 cm cubes.

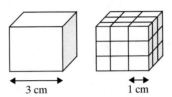

3 cm   1 cm

The large cube has the same volume as the small cubes together. However, the surface area of the large cube (1 cube × 6 faces/cube × 3 cm × 3 cm = 54 cm^2) is three times less than the surface area of the small cubes together (27 cubes × 6 faces/cube × 1 cm × 1 cm = 162 cm^2, after the small cubes are separated). The S/V of the large cube is 2 cm^{-1}, and the S/V of the small cubes is 6 cm^{-1}. Thus, you might expect the surface-to-volume ratio to *increase* with *decreasing* particle size. Equation (6) is consistent with this notion: as r decreases, $S/V(= 3/r)$ increases. The use of logic does not *prove* that you manipulated the equations correctly. However, it is a useful check on manipulations that will catch *some* errors.

Key idea: Use logic to check whether one variable is predicted correctly for extreme values of the other variables.

Another way to use logic to check mathematical expressions is to make sure the variable on the left side of the equation is predicted correctly for *extreme values* of the variables on the right side of the equation. As an example, consider the flight of a champagne cork. If the champagne bottle is at an angle θ with the ground and the cork has an initial velocity out of the bottle of v_0, then (ignoring air resistance) the cork will travel a distance equal to

$$\text{distance} = (2v_0^2/g)\sin(\theta)\cos(\theta) \tag{7}$$

Does the dependency of the distance shot on the angle in Eq. (7) make sense? Try looking at extreme values of the angle. For $\theta = 0°$ (when the bottle is lying on the ground), the cork will hit the ground immediately and the distance traveled should be zero. For $\theta = 90°$ (when the bottle is vertical), the cork will go straight up and down and the horizontal distance traveled should also be zero.

Equation (7) predicts that the distance is equal to zero for $\theta = 0°$ and $\theta = 90°$. Thus, Eq. (7) matches your thoughts about the values of the distance traveled at extreme values of the angle of the bottle to the ground.° An example of using logic to check expressions is given in Example 5.

°Remember from trigonometry that $\sin(\theta)\cos(\theta) = \frac{1}{2}\sin(2\theta)$. Thus, the distance traveled is $(2v_0^2/g)\sin(\theta)\cos(\theta) = (v_0^2/g)\sin(2\theta)$. The distance is maximized when $\sin(2\theta)$ is maximized; that is, at $\theta = 45°$. To shoot a champagne cork the farthest, hold it 45° to the ground.

**EXAMPLE 5:
USING LOGIC
TO CHECK
EXPRESSIONS**

You are helping a friend move. A box of books is sliding down the ramp of the moving van. You push against the box to hold it in place, and you remember that the force needed to stop an object from sliding down an inclined plane is

$$F = W[\sin(\alpha) - \mu\cos(\alpha)]$$

where W = weight of the object, α = angle of the inclined plane, and μ = coefficient of friction = $\tan(\varphi)$, where φ is the angle of the inclined plane at which the box starts to slide back by itself. Evaluate this formula using logic.

SOLUTION

The required force is $W[\sin(\alpha) - \tan(\varphi)\cos(\alpha)]$. Checking extremes, it is logical that the required force is zero when $\alpha = \varphi$ (the ramp is at the angle where the box starts to slide). The equation implies that the required force at $\alpha = \varphi$ is $W[\sin(\varphi) - \tan(\varphi)\cos(\varphi)] = W[\sin(\varphi) - \sin(\varphi)] = 0$, which is consistent with the logic [recall that $\tan(\varphi)\cos(\varphi) = \sin(\varphi)$].

It is also logical that the required force is W when $\alpha = 90°$ (when the ramp is straight up), since this ramp angle is equivalent to holding the box in your arms. The equation implies that the required force at $\alpha = 90°$ is $W[\sin(90°) - \tan(\varphi)\cos(90°)] = W[1 - 0] = W$, which is again consistent with the logic. **Thus, the equation checks at the extremes.**

Checking the dependency of the required force on the weight of the box, ramp angle, and coefficient of friction, it is logical that the required force should increase as the weight of the box (W) increases and as the angle increases. It is also logical that the required force should decrease as the coefficient of friction decreases. **The equation is consistent with these predictions.**

6.4   Using Estimation to Check Solutions

Key idea: Use estimation to reveal errors in the mathematical model.

The use of estimation was discussed in Section 4. Estimations can be used to check the solutions. Estimations can also reveal errors in the mathematical model. As an example, say you are a chemical engineer growing bacteria to synthesize a new pharmaceutical product. You know the bacterial population doubles in 20 minutes. If you start with one bacterium, what will be the mass of the organisms after three days of growth?

PONDER THIS

Based on your everyday experiences (e.g., that funny growth in your refrigerator), estimate the bacterial mass after three days. A few grams? A few kilograms? A few metric tons?

doublings: here, the number of times a population doubles (a population doubles three times when growing from 1 to 8: 1 to 2, 2 to 4, and 4 to 8)

You need to determine how many times the bacterial population will double. The number of **doublings** is equal to the time divided by the doubling time. Now, three days is (3 days) (24 hours/day) (60 minutes/hour) = 4,320 minutes or (4,320 minutes)/ (20 minutes per doubling time) = 216 doublings. A moment of reflection will confirm that the number of bacteria after n doublings is 2^n. Thus, you will have $2^{216} = 1.05 \times 10^{65}$ bacteria after three days.

You need to convert the number of bacteria into the mass of bacteria:

$$\text{total mass} = (\text{number of bacteria})(\text{mass per bacterium})$$

You can estimate the mass of a bacterium by its volume multiplied by its density (mass = volume × density). The volume of a bacterium can be found by approximating the organism as a sphere with diameter = 5 μm = 5×10^{-6} m (or a radius, r = diameter/2 = 2.5×10^{-6} m). Thus, the volume of one bacterium is about

$$(4/3)\pi r^3 = (4/3)\pi(2.5 \times 10^{-6} \text{ m})^3 = 6.54 \times 10^{-17} \text{ m}^3$$

A bacterium has a density near water (1,000 kg/m^3). Thus, after three days, the bacterial mass is

$$(1.05 \times 10^{65} \text{ bacteria})(6.54 \times 10^{-17} \text{ m}^3/\text{bacterium}) \times (1,000 \text{ kg/m}^3) = 6.9 \times 10^{51} \text{ kg}$$

This value of almost 7×10^{51} kg is probably far greater than your estimate. In fact, *this mass is about 10^{27} times the mass of the Earth*! Something must be amiss. A check of the calculations reveals no errors. In this case, the mathematical model is incorrect: bacteria do **not** double at a constant time interval at their maximum growth rate for such a large number of doublings. (Doubling at a fixed time interval is called *exponential growth*.) In reality, bacteria run out of resources (i.e., food, water, or space) or are killed off by a build-up of their waste products and natural decay processes. In this calculation, a "reality check" spurred by estimation uncovered an error in the model. For other examples of estimation, see John Harte's delightful books on problem solving (Harte, 1988 and 2001).

6.5   Using Units to Check Solutions

Checking units is an important tool in evaluating the solutions to mathematical expressions. Units are discussed in Section 7.

7   UNITS

7.1   Introduction

Most of the numbers you will deal with as an engineer have *units*. A voltmeter does not measure 6.2; it measure 6.2 *millivolts*. An old personal computer does not operate at 900; it operates at 900 *megahertz*. A successful engineering calculation results in not only the right value, but also the right *units* for that value. An example of a very expensive unit error is shown in *Focus on Units: The Multimillion-Dollar Units Mistake.*

The units for many physical properties have been standardized. The standardized system of units is called the **Système Internationale d'Unités** or **SI units**. A list of SI units appears in Table 3.

7.2   Dimensional Analysis

One tool for checking the units of an expression is **dimensional analysis**. Dimensional analysis refers to the manipulation of units without numbers. This technique can be used to determine the units of a result of an engineering calculation. In the skydiving example shown in Section 4.2, the terminal velocity was given by $v_t = \sqrt{\dfrac{2mg}{C_D A \rho}}$. To check the validity of this equation, you can perform a dimensional analysis. Substitute the units of each term and check to see that the terminal velocity has units of velocity (i.e., length/time). If you denote the units of X by $\{X\}$, then

$$\{v_t\} = \sqrt{\frac{\{2\}\{m\}\{g\}}{\{C_D\}\{A\}\{\rho\}}} = \sqrt{\frac{()(\text{kg})\left(\dfrac{\text{m}}{\text{s}^2}\right)}{()(\text{m}^2)\left(\dfrac{\text{kg}}{\text{m}^3}\right)}} = \sqrt{\frac{\text{m}^2}{\text{s}^2}} = \frac{\text{m}}{\text{s}}$$

(Note that the number 2 and the drag coefficient C_D are **dimensionless**; that is, they have no units.) According to the equation, the units of the terminal velocity are meters per second. These are proper units for a velocity.

Please note that there are limitations to dimensional analysis. Just because the units check, does that mean the equation is valid? No. Proper units are *necessary*, but not *sufficient*, for a valid equation. For example, the units check for $v_t = \pi\sqrt{\dfrac{2mg}{C_D A \rho}}$, but this equation is **not** correct.

Dimensional analysis also can be used to determine the units of an unknown variable. Do you sometimes forget the units of force? Since $F = ma$, it follows that

$$\{F\} = \{m\}\{a\} = (\text{kg})(\text{m/s}^2) = \text{kg-m/s}^2$$

(Remember that 1 kg-m/s^2 is called 1 newton = 1 N; see Table 3.)

As a more complex example, determine the units of viscosity. Viscosity refers to the property of a fluid offering resistance to flow. It is formally defined as the ratio of the shearing stress to the shear.° The shearing stress is a force per unit area and the shear is the change in the velocity with respect to distance. Thus,

---

°If the viscosity is independent of the shearing stress, then the fluid is called a *Newtonian fluid*. Other fluids are called *non-Newtonian fluids*. For example, certain paints are made to spread more easily when you apply more pressure to the brush. These paints are non-Newtonian fluids. Fluids like these paints, where the viscosity decreases as the shearing stress increases, are called *thixotropic* fluids.

$$\{\text{viscosity}\} = \frac{\{\text{shearing stress}\}}{\text{shear}} = \frac{\left(\dfrac{\{\text{force}\}}{\{\text{area}\}}\right)}{\left(\dfrac{\{\text{velocity}\}}{\{\text{distance}\}}\right)}$$

$$= \frac{\left(\dfrac{\left[\dfrac{\text{kg} - \text{m}}{\text{s}^2}\right]}{\text{m}^2}\right)}{\left(\dfrac{\left[\dfrac{\text{m}}{\text{s}}\right]}{\text{m}}\right)}$$

$$= \frac{\text{kg}}{\text{m} - \text{s}}$$

The units of viscosity are kg per m per s. (Common units of viscosity are centipoise = cp = 0.01 g/cm-s. The viscosities of water, chocolate syrup, and peanut butter at room temperature are about 1 cp, 6×10^4 cp, and 2×10^5 cp.)

TABLE 3 SI Units (adapted from Wright, 1993)

Quantity	Unit(s)	Symbol and/ or Formula
Base Units		
Length	meter	m
Mass	kilogram	kg
Time	second	s
Electric current	ampere	A
Temperature	kelvin	K
Amount of substance	mole	mol
Luminous intensity	candela	cd
Supplementary Units		
Plane angle	radian	rad
Solid angle	steradian	sr
Common Derived Units with Special Names		
Frequency	hertz	Hz (s^{-1})
Force	newton	N (kg-m/s^2)
Pressure or stress	pascal	Pa (N/m^2)
Energy or work	joule	J (N-m)
Power	watt	W (J/s)
Quantity of electricity	coulomb	C (A-s)
Electric potential	volt	V (W/A)
Capacitance	farad	F (C/V)
Electric resistance	ohm	Ω (V/A)
Conductance	siemens	S (A/V)

TABLE 3 (Continued)

Quantity	Unit(s)	Symbol and/ or Formula
Magnetic flux	weber	Wb (V-s)
Magnetic flux density	tesla	T (Wb/m^2)
Inductance	henry	H (Wb/A)
Luminous flux	lumen	lm (cd-sr)
Illuminance	lux	lx (lm/m^2)
Common Derived Units without Special Names		
Area	m^2	
Volume	m^3	
Velocity	m/s	
Acceleration	m/s^2	
Density	kg/m^3	
Specific volume	m^3/kg	
Entropy	J/K	
Radiant intensity	W/sr	
Bending moment (or torque)	N-m	
Heat capacity	J/kg-K	

FOCUS ON UNITS: THE MULTIMILLION-DOLLAR UNITS MISTAKE

BACKGROUND

In 1993, the National Aeronautics and Space Administration (NASA) initiated the Mars Surveyor Program. The Mars Surveyor Program consisted of three missions: the *Mars Global Surveyor* (MGS, launched in 1997), the *Mars Climate Orbiter* (MCO, launched in 1998), and the *Mars Polar Lander* (MPL, launched in 1999). The Mars Surveyor Program, together with the Discovery Program's *Mars Pathfinder* lander, constituted NASA's efforts for a robotic exploration of Mars.

(Image credit: NASA/JPL.)

MCO launched from Cape Canaveral Air Force Station Space Launch Complex 17 on December 11, 1998, on a Boeing Delta II 7425 rocket. The 338-kg spacecraft consisted of a main bus (2.1 m tall by 1.6 m wide by 2 m deep) and a solar array (with a wingspan of 5.5 m). MCO's mission was threefold: provide support for the MPL, carry out scientific studies of the Martian atmosphere and climate, and serve as a relay for communication with future Mars landers.

A PRIMER ON SPACECRAFT CONTROL

Guiding a spacecraft across interplanetary space on a $9\frac{1}{2}$-month journey to Mars is no small task. To keep on course, the thrusters must be fired periodically. Data from the spacecraft were sent to the ground. The "impulse bit" (force × time) was calculated from the firing time and used to determine the change in spacecraft velocity (Δv). About four months into the flight, it was clear that the ground-based software was not modeling Δv correctly. The extent of the errors was unknown, because the thrust events occurred mainly perpendicular to the line-of-sight from the Earth. (Imagine the difficulty in determining the acceleration of a distant car moving away from you as it rounds a curve.)

THE PROBLEM

As MCO approached Mars, three steps were planned to reach the final circular orbit. First, a final trajectory correction burn would prepare the spacecraft for orbit. Second, the main Mars orbital burn (Mars orbit insertion, or MOI) would establish a highly elliptical orbit with a point of closest approach to Mars of 226 km. Finally, friction with the upper Martian atmosphere would ease MCO into a circular orbit in a process called *aerobraking*. After the final trajectory correction burn (but before the planned MOI), NASA navigators realized that the point of closest approach was going to be much smaller than anticipated—perhaps 150–170 km. As MOI grew nearer, the Martian gravitational effects increased and were included in the calculations. About one hour before MOI, navigators determined that the point of closest approach would be about 110 km, dangerously close to the minimum survivable distance of 80 km. About four minutes after the MOI burn began, MCO entered the Martian shadow (49 seconds earlier than anticipated) and communication with the spacecraft ceased. The signal was never reacquired.

THE UNITS PROBLEM

What happened? Subsequent calculations showed that the actual point of closest approach to Mars was a mere 57 km. Six days after the MOI burn, the MCO team realized that the calculated Δv values were low by a factor of 4.45. Can you account for a factor of 4.45 mistake in calculating velocity from force $\times$ time? It turns out that the computer software had been programmed to calculate forces (used to determine Δv) in units of *pounds of force*, rather than the expected unit of *newtons*. (You may wish to verify that 1 lb of force = 4.45 N.)

An error in units resulted in the loss of hundreds of millions of dollars worth of orbiter, spacecraft development, launch, and mission operations costs. Never forget: ***units are important!***

7.3   Units and Functions

Dimensional analysis leads to four rules when you perform an operation on a number. First, you can add or subtract numbers only when they have the same units. You can use this fact to check equations: additive terms *must* have the same units.

Key idea: Add or subtract terms only if they have the same units.

Key idea: If you multiply, divide, or exponentiate terms, apply the same operation to their units.

Second, when you multiply, divide, or exponentiate (i.e., raise a number to an exponent), you must perform the same operation on the units of the number. An example was shown in Section 7.2 for determining the units of viscosity.

Third, some mathematical functions can operate only on dimensionless parameters. Examples of such functions include the exponential, logarithmic, and trigonometric functions. For the functions e^{ax}, $\log(y/b)$, and $\cos(2\pi\omega)$, you know that the terms ax, y/b, and $2\pi\omega$ must be dimensionless.

Key idea: Certain functions (e.g., exponential, logarithmic, and trigonometric functions) only operate on and only produce dimensionless values.

Fourth (a corollary to the third rule), exponential, logarithmic, and trigonometric functions also *produce* dimensionless results. In other words, the values produced by the functions e^{ax}, $\log(y/b)$, and $\cos(2\pi\omega)$ are dimensionless.

As before, dimensional analysis can be used to check units or determine units, since the collection of terms operated on and produced by exponential, logarithmic, and trigonometric functions must be dimensionless. For example, in first-order chemical reactions, concentrations decrease over time by $e^{-k_1 t}$, where k_1 is called the first-order rate constant and t is time.

PONDER THIS

In the expression $e^{-k_1 t}$, what is the unit of k_1?

The exponent, $-k_1t$, **must** be dimensionless. If the unit of time is the second, then the first-order rate constant must have the unit of inverse seconds (denoted 1/s or s^{-1}). In other words, first-order rate constants always have the unit of 1/time.

7.4   Units Conversion

English System:
a system of units in common use in the United States

You are entering the engineering profession at a unique time. In spite of numerous efforts to adopt the metric system of units (now codified as SI units), the so-called **English System** of units is still in common use in the United States. Engineers in the United States must be familiar with *both* sets of units and must be able to interconvert units with ease. You will find yourself in your career stating masses in kilograms and pounds in the same sentence. You may need to speak to a client about the power requirements of a turbine in horsepower and then call the vendor to specify the turbine power in kilowatts.

Values can be converted from one set of units to another by *conversion factors*. For example, to convert a length from inches to centimeters (cm), multiply the length in inches by the number of cm per inch:

$$\text{length in cm} = (\text{length in inches})(2.54 \text{ cm/in})$$

Note that the conversion factor here has units of cm/in and that the units in the equation check out.

Here is a more complicated example: If a spring water bottling plant produces 27,000 gallons of bottled water per day, what is the production rate in the SI base units of cubic meters per second (m^3/s)? As with many unit conversion problems, this one is best handled in steps. You can convert gallons to cubic feet and then cubic feet to cubic meters. Simultaneously, you can easily convert days to seconds. The important conversion factors for this problem are as follows: one cubic foot is equivalent to 7.48 gallons (or 1 gallon = 1/7.48 ft^3; in other words, 1/7.48 ft^3/gallon) and one day is (1 day)(24 hours/day)(60 minutes/hour)(60 seconds/minute) = 86,400 seconds (or 1/86,400 day/second). Also, one foot is equal to 0.3048 m (or 0.3048 m/ft), so one cubic foot is equal to $(0.3048 \text{ m/ft})^3 = 0.0283 \text{ m}^3$ (or 0.0283 m^3/ft^3). Thus,

$$\text{flow in ft}^3\text{/s} = (\text{flow in gallons/day})(1/7.48 \text{ ft}^3\text{/gal}) \times (1/86,400 \text{ day/s})$$

and

$$\text{flow in m}^3\text{/s} = (\text{flow in ft}^3\text{/s})(0.0283 \text{ m}^3\text{/ft}^3),$$

so,

$$\text{flow in m}^3\text{/s} = (\text{flow in gallons/day})(1/7.48 \text{ ft}^3\text{/gal})$$
$$\times (1/86,400 \text{ day/s})(0.0283 \text{ m}^3\text{/ft}^3)$$
$$= 4.38 \times 10^{-8}(\text{flow in gallons/day})$$

You have calculated the conversion factor: to convert flows from units of gallons per day to units of cubic meters per second, you simply multiply by 4.38×10^{-8}. Note that this conversion factor is **not** dimensionless: it has units of $(m^3$/s)/(gallons/day) or $(m^3$-day)/(gallons-s). Thus,

$$27,000 \text{ gallons per day} = (27,000 \text{ gallons/day})$$
$$\times [4.38 \times 10^{-8} \text{ (m}^3\text{/s)/(gallons/day)}]$$
$$= 1.18 \times 10^{-3} \text{ m}^3\text{/s}$$

Another example of using units to check and solve problems is given in Example 6.

**EXAMPLE 6
USING UNITS
TO CHECK
SOLUTIONS**

[Caution: Problem statement may contain errors!]

A great deal of aluminum has been saved by reducing the thickness of aluminum beverage cans. The current thickness of a can side is about 0.08 mm. The thickness is limited by the ability of the can to withstand internal pressures. (For example, beer often is pasteurized in the can.) What is the minimum thickness of an aluminum can? The can thickness is given by $T = \dfrac{DP}{2S}$, where D = the inside diameter of the can, P = the allowable internal pressure, and S = the tensile strength of aluminum = 3.2×10^9 g/cm-s.

SOLUTION

A look at the units reveals an error in the problem statement. Since T and D both have units of length, P and S must have the same units. Pressure is force per unit area or mass $\times$ acceleration/area or $(g)(cm/s^2)/(cm^2)$ or g/cm-s^2. Rechecking the references, the tensile strength of aluminum = 3.2×10^9 g/cm-s^2 (**not** 3.2×10^9 g/cm-s). With $D = 6.6$ cm and $P = 90$ psi = 6.2×10^6 g/cm-s^2, the minimum thickness is about 0.06 mm. Thus, the current thickness is near the minimum thickness required to withstand an internal pressure of 90 psi.

8   AN EXAMPLE OF THE ENGINEERING ANALYSIS METHOD

The steps in the engineering analysis method will be applied to the following problem. You bought a used bed that is missing its legs. You plan to build four new legs out of a long pine dowel. How much will the legs compress if the total mass of the bed plus you is 100 kg? You may wish to do the analysis before reading further.

Before you begin, you should ask yourself: is this an analysis problem? Yes, the problem is amenable to the engineering analysis method, since it is reasonably well defined and one answer is sought. Using the following steps in the analysis process:

1. Define the problem.
    The problem is well defined.
2. Gather data and verify data accuracy.
    You need the dimensions of the legs. Suppose the dowel measures 1.2 m long and 2.5 cm in diameter [so each leg will be (1.2 m)/4 = 0.3 m long].
3. Select the analysis method(s).
    You need a relationship between the data (legs and bed mass) and the desired outcome (compression length). The appropriate relationship is given by the stress–strain relationship (a constitutive law similar to Hooke's Law). A common stress–strain relationship is that stress (i.e., the force applied per unit area) is proportional to strain (i.e., the length of compression divided by the length of the column). The proportionality constant is called *Young's modulus*. In other words,

$$\text{stress} = \text{force per area}$$
$$= F/A$$
$$= E(\text{strain})$$

where E is Young's modulus and strain is the compression length (δ) divided by the length of the leg (L). Rearranging terms yields

$$\delta = \frac{L}{E}\frac{F}{A} \tag{8}$$

The selection of the analysis method leads to more data collection: you need Young's modulus (E) for pine and the applied force. An accepted value for Young's modulus for pine is 12,200 MPa (1 MPa = 10^6 Pa). The net force of the bed plus you can be calculated from the total mass of you and the bed.

4. Estimate the solution.

Only a very small compression of the legs is expected.

5. Solve the problem.

The force is $F = mg = (100 \, \text{kg})(9.8 \, \text{m/s}^2) = 980$ N. The force per area per leg is $(980 \, \text{N})/[(4 \, \text{legs})(\pi r^2)]$, where r = radius of the leg = 0.0125 m. So the pressure per leg is 5.0×10^5 N/m^2 or 0.5 MPa. From Eq. (8),

$$\delta = (L/E)(F/A)$$

$$= [(0.3 \, \text{m})/(12{,}200 \, \text{MPa})](0.5 \, \text{MPa})$$

$$= 1.2 \times 10^{-5} \, \text{m}$$

6. Check the results.

This analysis is simple and no mathematical errors are apparent.

Therefore, each leg will be compressed about 1.2×10^{-5} m or 0.012 mm. This is as small as expected in the estimation step.

9 SUMMARY

The analysis method is useful when the system is well defined and system characteristics can be determined through the application of mathematical and scientific principles. Analysis problems typically have one solution. They are solved by defining the problem, gathering data and verifying data accuracy, selecting analysis methods, estimating the solution, solving the mathematical expressions, and checking the results.

Engineering data can come from many sources, including measurements, interviews, and the Internet. Always remember to verify the reasonableness of the data.

Selecting an analysis method generally means selecting the physical laws that describe the system of interest. Three kinds of physical laws are important in engineering: laws of conservation, laws of motion, and constitutive laws.

It is also important to estimate the solution. Many mistakes in analysis can be caught by making even a crude guess of the solution. Estimation can help you check the calculations and the analysis method.

This chapter also provided an introduction to solving mathematical expressions. Recall that expressions can be manipulated to solve for the unknown of interest. Try to isolate the unknown by manipulating symbols, not numbers (i.e., substitute numbers at the last step of the calculation). As you explore engineering further, remember that the numbers you calculate have physical meaning. You can use logic and estimation to avoid aphysical or unreasonable solutions. Keep in mind that most numbers in engineering have units. Use dimensional analysis (i.e., manipulating units without numbers) to check equations and determine the units of unknown quantities. Remember that many functions operate on and produce only dimensionless values.

Never leave an engineering calculation without checking the results. Engineering results can be validated by logic, estimation, and checking units. Use logic to eliminate aphysical answers, test whether your answer makes sense, and check whether the variables change as expected with changes in the other variables. Use estimation to reveal errors in the mathematical model. Remember that answers must have the correct units.

SUMMARY OF KEY IDEAS

- Analysis problems are usually well defined and have only one solution.
- Solve analysis problems by defining the problem, gathering data and verifying data accuracy, selecting the analysis methods, estimating the solution, solving the mathematical expressions, and checking the results.
- Data are gathered through experiments and field measurements.
- Test all data for reasonableness.
- To select an analysis method, first select the physical laws and then translate the physical laws into mathematical equations.
- Engineers need quantifiable relationships between variables.
- Manipulate expressions (i.e., rearrange terms) to solve for the variable of interest.
- The "Golden Rule" of expression manipulation is as follows: "Do to one side of the expression that which you did to the other side."
- Remember to reverse the inequality sign when multiplying or dividing both sides by a negative number.
- Solve for the unknowns with symbols (by isolating the unknowns on one side of the expression) and *then* substitute in numbers ("chug" before you "plug").
- Answers to engineering calculations almost always have physical meaning.
- Check engineering calculations by logic, estimation, and checking units.
- Use logic to eliminate aphysical answers: always ask if your answer makes sense.
- Use logic to check whether one variable changes as expected with changes in the other variables.
- Use logic to check whether one variable is predicted correctly for extreme values of the other variables.
- Use estimation to reveal errors in the mathematical model.
- Use dimensional analysis to check engineering calculations.
- Use dimensional analysis to determine the units of an unknown quantity.
- Add or subtract terms only if they have the same units.
- If you multiply, divide, or exponentiate terms, apply the same operation to their units.
- Certain functions (e.g., exponential, logarithmic, and trigonometric functions) only operate on and only produce dimensionless values.

Problems

1. Using each step of the engineering analysis process, analyze the following problems.

   a. What is the maximum numbers of hours you should work at a job this semester? [*Hint*: Use the 60-hour rule: for each week, the sum of the hours in class, hours studying (2 × hours in class), and hours working should be less than or equal to 60 hours.]

   b. How much money do you have for entertainment? (*Hint*: Calculate an annual budget.)

    c.   What is the optimal number of sides for a pencil? (*Hint:* Consider comfort and the need to prevent a pencil from sliding down a slanted drafting table.)

2.   List at least four ways to catch errors in engineering calculations.

3.   How can logic be used to screen for calculation errors?

4.   The following questions concern the speed of world-class sprinters.

    a.   Without any data, estimate the speed of world-class sprinters in miles per hour (mph). Is it 1 mph? 10 mph? 100 mph? Higher?

    b.   A young engineer reads that the world record for the 200 m is 19.32 s. The engineer calculates the velocity as follows:

    (Warning: The following derivation may contain one or more errors!)

$$\text{velocity} = \text{distance/time}$$

$$\text{distance} = 200 \text{ m} = (200 \text{ m})(6.21 \times 10^{-4} \text{ miles/m}) = 0.124 \text{ mile}$$

$$\text{time} = 19.32 \text{ s} = (19.32 \text{ s})(2.78 \times 10^{-5} \text{ hours/s}) = 5.37 \times 10^{-4} \text{ hours}$$

$$\text{velocity} = (0.124 \text{ mile})/(5.37 \times 10^{-4} \text{ hours}) = 231 \text{ mph}$$

    Does this answer fit your estimate in part (a)? Identify the errors (if any) in the approach calculation.

5.   What is the volume of your favorite 12-oz beverage in mL? (Recall that 1 gallon = 128 oz = 3.78 L.)

6.   Show that kinetic energy ($\frac{1}{2}mv^2$) has the same unit as potential energy (mgh). In this problem, m = mass, v = velocity, g = gravitational acceleration, and h = height.

7.   You are designing a new desktop computer monitor. To satisfy customer needs, you want the footprint of the monitor to be 400 cm^2 and the length to be 6 cm less than the width. (The footprint is the area of the desktop occupied by the monitor.) Size the unit (i.e., determine its width and height). Indicate where you are performing the same operations on both sides of the pertinent equations.

8.   The following questions concern how high you can jump from a running start.

    a.   Estimate how high you can jump from a running start. Is it 0.1 m? 1 m? 10 m?

    b.   An engineering professor preferred to calculate the jump height rather than measure it. The analysis is shown below:

    (Warning: The following derivation may contain one or more errors!)

    Physical law: energy balance

    kinetic energy (KE) converted to potential energy (PE)

$PE = mgh = KE = mv^2/2$, where $h =$ change in height of center of mass (CM) so

$$h = v^2/(2g)$$

$$g = 9.8 \text{ m/s}^2$$

assume

$$v = 7 \text{ m/s}$$

Thus,

$$h = 2.5 \text{ m}$$

If the CM starts at 1.0 m, then you could jump a height of

$$1.0 + 2.5 = 3.5 \text{ m}$$

Does this answer fit your estimate in part (a)? (The world record for the high jump is 2.45 m.) Identify the errors (if any) in the approach and/or calculation.

9. The metric system is praised in part for the simple relationship between the volume of water and the mass of water: $1 \text{ m}^3 \approx 1 \text{ kg}$. Show that $1 \text{ ft}^3 \approx 1{,}000 \text{ oz}$.

10. Gas mileage in the United States is often expressed in miles per gallon (mpg). What are the equivalent units using only SI base units (see Table 3)? If you get 30 mpg, what is your gas mileage in inverse acres (acre^{-1})?

11. The farthest recorded distance for shooting a champagne cork is about 178 ft. Using the information in Section 6.3, what initial cork velocity (in SI base units) would be required to reach 178 ft, assuming little air resistance and the optimum launch angle?

12. How long would it take for the bacteria described in Section 6.4 to grow to 1 gram? Estimate your answer before solving.

13. For the aluminum can example in Example 6,
    a. Show that the conversion of psi to g/cm-s^2 is correct.
    b. Discuss whether the effects of increasing the can diameter, internal pressure, and tensile strength on the can thickness make sense.

14. The crew of a blimp must know the blimp mass accurately to ensure that the landing velocity is not too large. The blimp mass is determined by allowing the blimp to "settle" and measuring its terminal settling velocity. For Goodyear's *Spirit of America* blimp, a settling velocity of 100 ft/min corresponds to a mass of about 100 pounds greater than the mass of displaced air. Find the drag coefficient for the *Spirit of America* (volume $= 202{,}700 \text{ ft}^3$ and cross-sectional area $= 7{,}540 \text{ ft}^2$). (*Hint*: Modify the force balance in the skydiving example of Section 4.2 to include a buoyancy force. The buoyancy force is equal to g times the mass of displaced air. The blimp mass is the mass of displaced air plus 100 lb.)

7

Dimensions and Units

1   INTRODUCTION

Suppose for a moment that someone asks you to hurry to the grocery store to buy a few items for tonight's dinner. You get in your car, turn the ignition on, and drive down the road. Immediately you notice something strange. There are no numbers or divisions on your speedometer! As you accelerate and decelerate, the speedometer indicator changes position, but you do not know your speed because there are no markings to read. Bewildered, you notice that the speed limit and other road signs between your house and the store also lack numerical information. Realizing that you were instructed to arrive home with the groceries by 6 P.M., you glance at your digital watch only to discover that the display is blank. Now you are really spooked, but you drive on. Upon arriving at the store, you check your list: 1 pound of lean ground beef, 4 ounces of fresh mushrooms, and a 12-ounce can of tomato paste. You go to the meat counter first. As you scan the meat counter, you can't believe your eyes. The label on each package does not indicate the weight of the product. "This can't be," you mutter under your breath. You hastily grab what appears to be a 1-pound package and scurry to the produce section. Scooping up a bunch of mushrooms, you place them on the scale to weigh them. "Oh no! The scale looks like my speedometer:—It has no markings either!" Once again, you estimate. One item is left: the tomato paste. The canned goods aisle is very large and contains many types of canned items: soup, juice, and fruit. Finally, you locate the tomato paste. "Not again!" you exclaim. The label on the can has no numerical information—no weight, no volume, nothing to let you know the amount of tomato paste in the can. Being mystified and shaken by this whole experience, you still make your purchase, drive home, and deliver the items. Later, you somehow manage to consume a large plate of spaghetti.

OBJECTIVES

After reading this chapter, you will have learned

- How to check equations for dimensional consistency
- The physical standards on which units are based
- Rules for proper usage of SI units
- Rules for proper usage of English units
- The difference between mass and weight
- How to do unit conversions between the SI and English unit systems

The preceding Twilight Zone-like story is, of course, fictitious, but it dramatically illustrates how strange our world would be without measures of physical quantities. Speed is a physical quantity that is measured by the speedometers in our automobiles and the radar gun of a traffic officer. Time is a physical quantity that is measured by the watch on our wrist and the clock on the wall. Weight is a physical quantity that is measured by the scale in the grocery store or at the health spa. The need for measurement was recognized by the ancients, who based standards of length on the breadth of the hand or palm, the length of the foot, or the distance from the elbow to the tip of the middle finger (referred to as a cubit). Such measurement standards were both changeable and perishable because they were based on human dimensions. In modern times, definite and unchanging standards of measurement have been adopted to help us quantify the physical world. These measurement standards are used by engineers and scientists to analyze physical phenomena by applying the laws of nature such as conservation of energy, the second law of thermodynamics, and the law of universal gravitation. As engineers design new products and processes by utilizing these laws, they use dimensions and units to describe the physical quantities involved. For instance, the design of a bridge primarily involves the dimensions of length and force. The units used to express the magnitudes of these quantities are usually either the meter and newton or the foot and pound. The thermal design of a boiler primarily involves the dimensions of pressure, temperature, and heat transfer, which are expressed in units of pascal, degrees Celsius, and watt, respectively. Dimensions and units are as important to engineers as the physical laws they describe. It is vitally important that engineering students learn how to work with dimensions and units. Without dimensions and units, analyses of engineering systems have little meaning.

2   DIMENSIONS

To most people, the term dimension denotes a measurement of length. Certainly, length is one type of dimension, but the term dimension has a broader meaning. A **dimension** is a *physical variable that is used to describe or specify the nature of a measurable quantity.* For example, the mass of a gear in a machine is a dimension of the gear. Obviously, the diameter is also a dimension of the gear. The compressive force in a concrete column holding up a bridge is a structural dimension of the column. The pressure and temperature of a liquid in a hydraulic cylinder are thermodynamic dimensions of the liquid. The velocity of a space probe orbiting a distant planet is also a dimension. Many other examples could be given. Any variable that engineers use to specify a physical quantity is, in the general sense, a dimension of the physical quantity. Hence, there are as many dimensions as there are physical quantities. Engineers always use dimensions in their analytical and experimental work. In order to specify a dimension fully, two characteristics must be given. First, the *numerical value* of the dimension is required. Second, the appropriate *unit* must be assigned. A dimension missing either of these two elements is incomplete and therefore cannot be fully used by the engineer. If the diameter of a gear is given as 3.85, we would ask the question, "3.85 what? Inches? Meters?" Similarly, if the compressive force in a concrete column is given as 150,000, we would ask, "150,000 what? Newtons? Pounds?"

Dimensions are categorized as either *base* or *derived*. A **base dimension**, sometimes referred to as a *fundamental* dimension, is a dimension that cannot be broken down or subdivided into other dimensions or a dimension that has been internationally accepted as the most basic dimension of a physical quantity. There are seven base dimensions that have been formally defined for use in science and engineering:

1. length [L]
2. mass [M]

3.   time [t]
4.   temperature [T]
5.   electric current [I]
6.   amount of substance [N]
7.   luminous intensity [i]

A **derived dimension** is obtained by any combination of the base dimensions. For example, volume is length cubed, density is mass divided by length cubed, and velocity is length divided by time. Obviously, there are numerous derived dimensions. Table 1 lists some of the most commonly used derived dimensions in engineering, expressed in terms of base dimensions.

TABLE 1   Derived Dimensions Expressed in Terms of Base Dimensions.

Quantity	Variable Name	Base Dimensions
Area	A	$[L]^2$
Volume	V	$[L]^3$
Velocity	v	$[L][t]^{-1}$
Acceleration	a	$[L][t]^{-2}$
Density	ρ	$[M][L]^{-3}$
Force	F	$[M][L][t]^{-2}$
Pressure	P	$[M][L]^{-1}[t]^{-2}$
Stress	σ	$[M][L]^{-1}[t]^{-2}$
Energy	E	$[M][L]^2[t]^{-2}$
Work	W	$[M][L]^2[t]^{-2}$
Power	P	$[M][L]^2[t]^{-3}$
Mass flow rate	$\dot{m}$	$[M][t]^{-1}$
Specific heat	c	$[L]^2[t]^{-2}[T]^{-1}$
Dynamic viscosity	μ	$[M][L]^{-1}[t]^{-1}$
Molar mass	M	$[M][N]^{-1}$
Voltage	V	$[M][L]^2[t]^{-3}[I]^{-1}$
Resistance	R	$[M][L]^2[t]^{-3}[I]^{-2}$

The single letters in brackets in Table 1 are symbols that designate each base dimension. These symbols are useful for checking the dimensional consistency of equations. Every mathematical relation used in science and engineering must be **dimensionally consistent**, or *dimensionally homogeneous*. This means that the dimension on the left side of the equal sign must be the same as the dimension on the right side of the equal sign. The equality in any equation denotes not only a numerical equivalency but also a dimensional equivalency. To use a simple analogy, you cannot say that five apples equals four apples, nor can you say that five apples equals five oranges. You can only say that five apples equals five apples.

The following examples illustrate the concept of dimensional consistency:

EXAMPLE 1

Dynamics is a branch of engineering mechanics that deals with the motion of particles and rigid bodies. The straight-line motion of a particle, under the influence of gravity, may be analyzed by using the equation

$$y = y_0 + v_0 t - \frac{1}{2}gt^2$$

where

$$y = \text{height of particle at time } t$$
$$y_0 = \text{initial height of particle (at } t = 0)$$
$$v_0 = \text{initial velocity of particle (at } t = 0)$$
$$t = \text{time}$$
$$g = \text{gravitational acceleration}$$

Verify that this equation is dimensionally consistent.

SOLUTION

We check the dimensional consistency of the equation by determining the dimensions on both sides of the equal sign. The heights, y_0 and y, are one-dimensional coordinates of the particle; so these quantities have a dimension of length, [L]. The initial velocity, v_0, is a derived dimension consisting of a length, [L], divided by a time, [t]. Gravitational acceleration, g, is also a derived dimension consisting of a length, [L], divided by time squared, $[t]^2$. Of course, time, [t], is a base dimension. Writing the equation in its dimensional form, we have

$$[\text{L}] = [\text{L}] + [\text{L}][t]^{-1}[t] - [\text{L}][t]^{-2}[t]^2$$

Note that the factor, $\frac{1}{2}$, in front of the gt^2 term is a pure number, and therefore has no dimension. In the second term on the right side of the equal sign, the dimension [t] cancels, leaving length, [L]. Similarly, in the third term on the right side of the equal sign, the dimension [t] cancels, leaving length, [L]. This equation is dimensionally consistent because all terms have the dimension of length, [L].

EXAMPLE 2

Aerodynamics is the study of the performance of bodies moving through air. An aerodynamics analysis could be used to determine the lift force on an airplane wing or the drag force on an automobile. A commonly used equation in aerodynamics relates the total drag force acting on a body to the velocity of the air approaching it. This equation is

$$F_D = \frac{1}{2} C_D A \rho U^2$$

where

$$F_D = \text{drag force}$$
$$C_D = \text{drag coefficient}$$
$$A = \text{frontal area of body}$$
$$\rho = \text{air density}$$
$$U = \text{upstream air velocity}$$

Determine the dimensions of the drag coefficient, C_D.

SOLUTION

The dimension of the drag coefficient, C_D, may be found by writing the equation in dimensional form and simplifying the equation by combining like dimensions. Using the information in Table 1, we write the dimensional equation as

$$[\text{M}][\text{L}][t]^{-2} = C_D[\text{M}][\text{L}]^{-3}[\text{L}]^2[t]^{-2}[\text{L}]^2$$
$$= C_D[\text{M}][\text{L}][t]^{-2}$$

Compare the combination of base dimensions on the left and right sides of the equal sign. They are identical. This can only mean that the drag coefficient, C_D, has no dimension. If it did, the equation would not be dimensionally consistent. Thus, we say that C_D

is *dimensionless*. In other words, the drag coefficient, C_D, has a numerical value, but no dimensional value. This is not as strange as it may sound. In engineering, there are many instances, particularly, in the disciplines of fluid mechanics and heat transfer, where a physical quantity is dimensionless. Dimensionless quantities enable engineers to form special ratios that reveal certain physical insights into properties and processes. In this instance, the drag coefficient is physically interpreted as a "shear stress" at the surface of the body, which means that there is an aerodynamic force acting on the body parallel to its surface that tends to retard the body's motion through the air. If you take a course in fluid mechanics, you will learn more about this important concept.

EXAMPLE 3

For the following dimensional equation, find the dimensions of the quantity k:

$$[M][L][t]^{-2} = k[L][t]$$

SOLUTION

To find the dimensions of k, we multiply both sides of the equation by $[L]^{-1}[t]^{-1}$ to eliminate the dimensions on the right side of the equation, leaving k by itself. Thus, we obtain

$$[M][L][t]^{-2}[L]^{-1}[t]^{-1} = k$$

which, after applying a law of exponents, reduces to

$$[M][t]^{-3} = k$$

A closer examination of the given dimensional equation reveals that it is Newton's second law of motion:

$$F = ma$$

Here F is force, m is mass, and a is acceleration. Referring to Table 1, force has dimensions of $[M][L][t]^{-2}$, which is a mass $[M]$ multiplied by acceleration, $[L][t]^{-2}$.

PRACTICE!

1. For the following dimensional equation, find the base dimensions of the parameter k:
$$[M][L]^2 = k[L][t][M]^2$$
Answer: $[L][M]^{-1}[t]^{-1}$

2. For the following dimensional equation, find the base dimensions of the parameter g:
$$[T]^{-1}[t][L] = g[L]^{-2}$$
Answer: $[L]^3[t][T]^{-1}$

3. For the following dimensional equation, find the base dimensions of the parameter h:
$$[I][t]^{-1}h = [N]$$
Answer: $[I][N]^{-1}[t]^{-1}$

4. For the following dimensional equation, find the base dimensions of the parameter f:
$$[M][M]^{-3} = \cos(f[L])$$
Answer: $[L]^{-1}$

5. For the following dimensional equation, find the base dimensions of the parameter p:
$$[T] = [T]\log([T]^{-2}[t]p)$$
Answer: $[T]^2[t]^{-1}$

3   UNITS

A **unit** is an *arbitrarily chosen size subdivision by which the magnitude of a dimension is expressed*. For example, the dimension length, [L], may be expressed in units of meter (m), feet (ft), mile (mi), millimeter (mm), and many others. The dimension temperature, [T], is expressed in units of degrees Celsius (°C), degrees Fahrenheit (°F), degrees rankine (°R), or kelvin (K). (By convention, the degree symbol (°) is not used for the Kelvin temperature scale.) In the United States, there are two unit systems commonly in use. The first unit system, and the one that is internationally accepted as the standard, is the **SI** (System International d'Unites) **unit system**, commonly referred to as the *metric* system. The second unit system is the **English (or British) unit system**, sometimes referred to as the *United States Customary System (USCS)*. With the exception of the United States, most of the industrialized nations of the world use the SI system exclusively. The SI system is preferred over the English system, because it is an internationally accepted standard and is based on simple powers of 10. To a limited extent, a transition to the SI system has been federally mandated in the United States. Unfortunately, this transition to total SI usage is a slow one, but many American companies are using the SI system to remain internationally competitive. Until the United States makes a complete adaptation to the SI system, U.S. engineering students need to be conversant in both unit systems and know how to make unit conversions.

The seven base dimensions are expressed in terms of SI units that are based on **physical standards**. These standards are defined such that, the corresponding SI units, except the mass unit, can be reproduced in a laboratory anywhere in the world. The reproducibility of these standards is important, because everyone with a suitably equipped laboratory has access to the same standards. Hence, all physical quantities, regardless of where in the world they are measured, are based on identical standards. This universality of physical standards eliminates the ancient problem of basing dimensions on the changing physical attributes of kings, rulers, and magistrates who reigned for a finite time. Modern standards are based on constants of nature and physical attributes of matter and energy.

The seven base dimensions and their associated SI units are summarized in Table 2. Note the symbol for each unit. These symbols are the accepted conventions for science and engineering. The discussion that follows outlines the physical standards by which the base units are defined.

TABLE 2   Base Dimensions and Their SI Units.

Quantity	Unit	Symbol
Length	meter	m
Mass	kilogram	kg
Time	second	s
Temperature	kelvin	K
Electric current	ampere	A
Amount of substance	mole	mol
Luminous intensity	candela	cd

Length

The unit of length in the SI system is the *meter* (m). As illustrated in Figure 1, the meter is defined as the distance traveled by light in a vacuum, during a time interval of 1/299,792,458 s. The definition is based on a physical standard: the speed of light in a vacuum. The speed of light in a vacuum is 299,792,458 m/s. Thus, light travels one

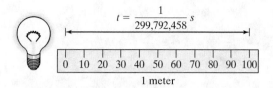

$$t = \frac{1}{299{,}792{,}458}\ s$$

1 meter

Figure 1. The physical standard for the meter is based on the speed of light in a vacuum.

meter during a time interval of the reciprocal of this number. Of course, the unit of time, the *second* (s), is itself a base unit.

Mass

The unit of mass in the SI system is the *kilogram* (kg). Unlike the other units, the kilogram is not based on a reproducible physical standard. The standard for the kilogram is a cylinder of platinum-iridium alloy, which is maintained by the International Bureau of Weights and Measures in Paris, France. A duplicate of this cylinder is kept in the United States by the National Institute of Standards and Technology (NIST). (See Figure 2.)

Mass is the only base dimension that is defined by an artifact. An artifact is a man-made object, not as easily reproduced as the other laboratory-based standards.

Figure 2. A duplicate of the kilogram standard is a platinum-iridium cylinder maintained by NIST. (© Copyright Robert Rathe. Courtesy of the National Institute of Standards and Technology, Gaithersburg, MD)

Time

The unit of time in the SI system is the *second* (s). The second is defined as the duration of 9,192,631,770 cycles of radiation corresponding to the transition between the two hyperfine levels of the ground state of the cesium133 atom. An atomic clock incorporating this standard is maintained by NIST. (See Figure 3.)

Figure 3.   The seventh generation atomic clock maintained by NIST keeps time with an accuracy of five parts in 10^{15}, equivalent to about one second in six million years. (Courtesy of the National Institute of Standards and Technology, Boulder, CO.)

Temperature

The unit of temperature in the SI system is the *kelvin* (K). The kelvin is defined as the fraction 1/273.16 of the temperature of the triple point of water. The triple point of water is the combination of pressure and temperature at which water exists as a solid, liquid, and gas at the same time. (See Figure 4.) This temperature is 273.16 K, 0.01°C, or 32.002°F. Absolute zero is the temperature at which all molecular activity ceases and has a value of 0 K.

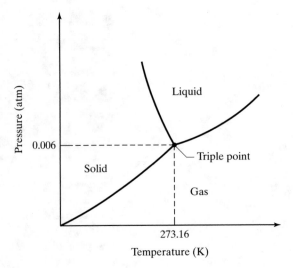

Figure 4.   A phase diagram for water shows the triple point on which the kelvin temperature standard is based.

Electric Current

The unit of electric current in the SI system is the *ampere* (A). As shown in Figure 5, the ampere is defined as the steady current, which, if maintained in two straight parallel wires of infinite length and negligible circular cross section and placed one meter apart in a vacuum, produces a force of 2×10^{-7} newton per meter of wire length. Using Ohm's law, $I = V/R$, one ampere may also be denoted as the current that flows when one volt is applied across a 1-ohm resistor.

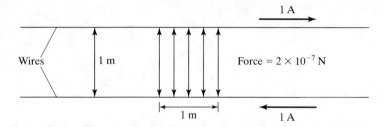

Figure 5. The standard for the ampere is based on the electrical force produced between two parallel wires, each carrying 1 A, located 1 m apart.

Amount of Substance

The unit used to denote the amount of substance is the *mole* (mol). One mole contains the same number of elements as there are atoms in 0.012 kg of carbon-12. This number is called Avogadro's number and has a value of approximately 6.022×10^{23}. (See Figure 6.)

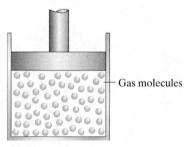

Figure 6. A mole of gas molecules in a piston-cylinder device contains 6.022×10^{23} molecules.

Luminous Intensity

The unit for luminous intensity is the *candela* (cd). As illustrated in Figure 7, one candela is the luminous intensity of a source emitting light radiation at a frequency of 540×10^{12} Hz that provides a power of 1/683 watt (W) per steradian. A steradian is a solid angle, which, having its vertex in the center of a sphere, subtends (cuts off) an area of the sphere equal to that of a square with sides of length equal to the radius of the sphere.

The unit for luminous intensity, the candela, utilizes the steradian, a dimension that may be unfamiliar to most students. The *radian* and *steradian* are called *supplementary*

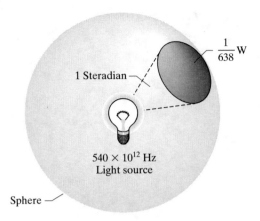

Figure 7. The candela standard for luminous intensity.

dimensions. These quantities, summarized in Table 3, refer to plane and solid angles, respectively. The radian is frequently used in engineering, and it is defined as the plane angle between two radii of a circle that subtends on the circumference an arc equal in length to the radius. From trigonometry, you may recall that there are 2π radians in a circle (i.e., 2π radians equals 360°). Thus, one radian equals approximately 57.3°. The steradian, defined earlier, is used primarily for expressing radiation quantities such as light intensity and other electromagnetic parameters.

TABLE 3 Supplementary Dimensions.

Quantity	Unit	Symbol
Plane angle	radian	rad
Solid angle	steradian	sr

4   SI UNITS

Throughout the civilized world there are thousands of engineering companies that design and manufacture products for the benefit of man. The international buying and selling of these products is an integral part of a global network of industrialized countries, and the economic health of these countries, including the United States, depends to a large extent on international trade. Industries such as the automotive and electronics industries are heavily involved in international trade, so these industries have readily embraced the SI unit system in order to be economically competitive. The general adoption of the SI unit system by U.S. companies has been slow, but global economic imperatives are driving them to fall into step with the other industrialized nations of the world. SI units are now commonplace on food and beverage containers, gasoline pumps, and automobile speedometers. The SI unit system is the internationally accepted standard. In the United States, however, the English unit system is still widely used. Hopefully, it is only a matter of time before all U.S. companies use SI units exclusively. Until that time, the burden is upon you, the engineering student, to learn both unit systems. You will gladly discover, however, that most engineering textbooks emphasize SI units, but provide a list of unit conversions between the SI and English systems.

Table 2 summarizes the seven base dimensions and their SI units, and Table 3 summarizes the supplementary dimensions and their units. Derived dimensions consist of a combination of base and supplementary dimensions. Sometimes, the units of a derived dimension are given a specific name. For example, the derived dimension *force* consists of the SI base units $kg \cdot m \cdot s^{-2}$. This combination of SI base units is called a *newton* and is abbreviated N. Note that the unit name, in honor of Isaac Newton, is not capitalized when spelled out as a unit name. The same rule applies to other units named after people such as hertz (Hz), kelvin (K), pascal (Pa), etc. Another example is the *joule*, the SI unit for energy, work, and heat. The joule unit is abbreviated J and consists of the SI base units $kg \cdot m^2 \cdot s^{-2}$. A summary of the most commonly used SI derived dimensions and the corresponding SI unit names is given in Table 4.

Most derived dimensions do not have specific SI unit names, but their units may contain specific SI unit names. For example, the dimension, *moment of force*, usually

TABLE 4 Derived Dimensions and SI Units with Specific Names.

Quantity	SI Unit	Unit Name	Base Units
Frequency	Hz	hertz	s^{-1}
Force	N	newton	$kg \cdot m \cdot s^{-2}$
Pressure	Pa	pascal	$kg \cdot m^{-1} \cdot s^{-2}$
Stress	Pa	pascal	$kg \cdot m^{-1} \cdot s^{-2}$
Energy	J	joule	$kg \cdot m^2 \cdot s^{-2}$
Work	J	joule	$kg \cdot m^2 \cdot s^{-2}$
Heat	J	joule	$kg \cdot m^2 \cdot s^{-2}$
Power	W	watt	$kg \cdot m^2 \cdot s^{-3}$
Electric charge	C	coulomb	$A \cdot s$
Electric potential (voltage)	V	volt	$kg \cdot m^2 \cdot s^{-3} \cdot A^{-1}$
Electric resistance	Ω	ohm	$kg \cdot m^2 \cdot s^{-3} \cdot A^{-2}$
Magnetic flux	Wb	weber	$kg^{-1} \cdot m \cdot s^{-2} \cdot A^{-1}$
Luminous flux	lm	lumen	$cd \cdot sr$

referred to simply as *moment*, has the SI units $N \cdot m$, a force multiplied by a distance. There is no special name for this unit—we simply call it "newton–meter." Another example is the dimension *mass flow rate*. Mass flow rate is the mass of a fluid that flows past a point in a given time. The SI units for mass flow rate are $kg \cdot s^{-1}$, which we state as "kilograms per second." Note that units that are located in the denominator, that is, those that have a negative sign on their exponent, may also be written using a divisor line. Thus, the units for mass flow rate may be written as kg/s. Caution must be exercised, however, when utilizing this type of notation for some units. For example, the SI units for thermal conductivity, a quantity used in heat transfer, are $W \cdot m^{-1} \cdot K^{-1}$. How do we write these units with a divisor line? Do we write these units as W/m/K? How about $W/m \cdot K$? The first choice can cause some confusion. Does a "watt per meter per kelvin" mean that the kelvin unit is inverted twice and therefore goes above the divisor line? One glance at the units written as $W \cdot m^{-1} \cdot K^{-1}$ tells us that the temperature unit belongs "downstairs" because K has a negative exponent. If the kelvin unit were placed above the divisor line, and the thermal conductivity were used in an equation, a dimensional inconsistency would result. The second choice is the preferred method of writing units when more than one unit is below the divisor line. Because the meter and kelvin units are located to the right of the divisor line and they are separated by a dot, both units are interpreted as being in the denominator. Sometimes, parentheses are used to group units above or below the divisor line. Units for thermal conductivity would then be written as $W/(m \cdot K)$. In any case, a dot or a dash should always be placed between adjacent units to separate them regardless of whether the units are above or below the divisor line. Some derived dimensions and their SI units are given in Table 5.

TABLE 5   Derived Dimensions and SI Units.

Quantity	SI Units
Acceleration	$m \cdot s^{-2}$
Angular acceleration	$rad \cdot s^{-2}$
Angular velocity	$rad \cdot s^{-1}$
Area	m^2
Concentration	$mol \cdot m^{-3}$
Density	$kg \cdot m^{-3}$
Electric field strength	$V \cdot m^{-1}$
Energy	$N \cdot m$
Entropy	$J \cdot K^{-1}$
Heat	J
Heat transfer	W
Magnetic field strength	$A \cdot m^{-1}$
Mass flow rate	$kg \cdot s^{-1}$
Moment of force	$N \cdot m$
Radiant intensity	$W \cdot sr^{-1}$
Specific energy	$J \cdot kg^{-1}$
Surface tension	$N \cdot m^{-1}$
Thermal conductivity	$W \cdot m^{-1} \cdot K^{-1}$
Velocity	$m \cdot s^{-1}$
Viscosity, dynamic	$Pa \cdot s$
Viscosity, kinematic	$m^2 \cdot s^{-1}$
Volume	m^3
Volume flow rate	$m^3 \cdot s^{-1}$
Wavelength	m
Weight	N

When a physical quantity has a numerical value that is very large or very small, it is cumbersome to write the number in standard decimal form. The general practice in engineering is to express numerical values between 0.1 and 1000 in standard decimal form. If a value cannot be expressed within this range, a *prefix* should be used. Because the SI unit system is based on powers of 10, it is more convenient to express such numbers by using prefixes. A prefix is a letter in front of a number that denotes multiples of powers of 10. For example, if the internal force in an I-beam is three million seven hundred and fifty thousand newtons, it would be awkward to write this number as 3,750,000 N. It is preferred to write the force as 3.75 MN, which is stated as "3.75 mega-newtons." The prefix "M" denotes a multiple of a million. Hence, 3.75 MN equals 3.75×10^6 N. Electrical current is a good example of a quantity represented by a small number. Suppose the current flowing in a wire is 0.0082 A. This quantity would be expressed as 8.2 mA, which is stated as "8.2 milliamperes." The prefix "m" denotes a multiple of one-thousandth, or 1×10^{-3}. A term we often hear in connection with personal computers is the storage capacity of hard disks. When personal computers first appeared in the early 1980s, most hard disks could hold around 10 or 20 MB (megabytes) of information. Nowadays, hard disks typically can hold around one thousand times that amount. Perhaps, a few years from now, the typical storage capacity of a personal computer's hard disk will be on the order of TB (terabytes). The standard prefixes for SI units are given in Table 6.

TABLE 6   Standard Prefixes for SI Units

Multiple	Exponential Form	Prefix	Prefix Symbol
1,000,000,000,000	10^{12}	tera	T
1,000,000,000	10^{9}	giga	G
1,000,000	10^{6}	mega	M
1000	10^{3}	kilo	k
0.01	10^{-2}	centi	c
0.001	10^{-3}	milli	m
0.000 001	10^{-6}	micro	μ
0.000 000 001	10^{-9}	nano	n
0.000 000 000 001	10^{-12}	pico	p

As indicated in Table 6, the most widely used SI prefixes for science and engineering quantities come in multiples of one thousand. For example, stress and pressure, which are generally large quantities for most structures and pressure vessels, are normally expressed in units of kPa, MPa, or GPa. Frequencies of electromagnetic waves such as radio, television, and telecommunications are also large numbers. Hence, they are generally expressed in units of kHz, MHz, or GHz. Electrical currents, on the other hand, are often small quantities, so they are usually expressed in units of μA or mA. Because frequencies of most electromagnetic waves are large quantities, the wavelengths of these waves are small. For example, the wavelength range of the visible light region of the electromagnetic spectrum is approximately 0.4 μm to 0.75 μm. It should be noted that the SI mass unit, kilogram (kg), is the only base unit that has a prefix.

Here are some rules on how to use SI units properly that every beginning engineering student should know:

1. A unit symbol is never written as a plural with an "s." If a unit is pluralized, the "s" may be confused with the unit second (s).

2. A period is never used after a unit symbol, unless the symbol is at the end of a sentence.

3. Do not use invented unit symbols. For example, the unit symbol for "second" is (s), not (sec), and the unit symbol for "ampere" is (A), not (amp).

4. A unit symbol is always written by using lowercase letters, with two exceptions. The first exception applies to units named after people, such as the newton (N), joule (J), and watt (W). The second exception applies to units with the prefixes M, G, and T. (See Table 6.)

5. A quantity consisting of several units must be separated by dots or dashes to avoid confusion with prefixes. For example, if a dot is not used to express the units of "meter-second" (m $\cdot$ s), the units could be interpreted as "millisecond" (ms).

6. An exponential power for a unit with a prefix refers to both the prefix and the unit; for example, $\text{ms}^{2} = (\text{ms})^{2} = \text{ms} \cdot \text{ms}$.

7. Do not use compound prefixes. For example, a "kilo MegaPascal" (kMPa) should be written as GPa, because the product of "kilo" (10^{3}) and "mega" (10^{6}) equals "giga" (10^{9}).

8. Put a space between the numerical value and the unit symbol.

9. Do not put a space between a prefix and a unit symbol.

10. Do not use prefixes in the denominator of composite units. For example, the units N/mm should be written as kN/m.

Table 7 provides some additional examples of these rules.

TABLE 7 Correct and Incorrect Ways of Using SI Units.

Correct	Incorrect	Rules
12.6 kg	12.6 kgs	1
450 N	450 Ns	1
36 kPa	36 kPa.	2
1.75 A	1.75 amps	1, 3
10.2 s	10.2 sec	3
20 kg	20 Kg	4
150 W	150 w.	2, 4
4.50 kg/m · s	4.50 kg/ms	5
750 GN	750 MkN	7
6 ms	6 kμs	7
800 Pa · s	800Pa · s	8
1.2 MΩ	1.2 M Ω	9
200 MPa	200 M Pa	9
150 μA	150 μ A	9
6 MN/m	6 N/μm	10

APPLICATION: DERIVING FORMULAS FROM UNIT CONSIDERATIONS

To the beginning engineering student, it can seem as if there is an infinite number of formulas to learn. Formulas contain physical quantities that have numerical values plus units. Because formulas are written as equalities, formulas must be numerically and dimensionally equivalent across the equal sign. Can this feature be used to help us derive formulas that we do not know or have forgotten? Suppose that we want to know the mass of gasoline in an automobile's gas tank. The tank has a volume of 70 L, and a handbook of fluid properties states that the density of gasoline is 736 kg/m^3. Thus, we write

$$\rho = 736 \text{ kg/m}^3 \quad V = 70 \text{ L} = 0.070 \text{ m}^3$$

If the tank is completely filled with gasoline, what is the mass of the gasoline? Suppose that we have forgotten that density is defined as mass per volume, $\rho = m/V$. Because our answer will be a mass, the unit of our answer must be kilogram (kg). Looking at the units of the input quantities, we see that if we multiply density, ρ, by volume, V, the volume unit (m^3) divides out, leaving mass (kg). Hence, the formula for mass in terms of ρ and V is

$$m = \rho V$$

so the mass of gasoline is

$$m = (736 \text{ kg/m}^3)(0.070 \text{ m}^3) = 51.5 \text{ kg}$$

PROFESSIONAL SUCCESS: USING SI UNITS IN EVERYDAY LIFE

The SI unit system is used commercially to a limited extent in the United States, so the average person does not know the highway speed limit in kilometers per hour, his or her weight in newtons, atmospheric pressure in kilopascals, or the outdoor air temperature in kelvin or degrees Celsius. It is ironic that the leading industrialized nation on earth has yet to embrace this international standard. Admittedly, American beverage containers routinely show the volume of the liquid

product in liters (L) or milliliters (mL), gasoline pumps often show liters of gasoline delivered, speedometers may indicate speed in kilometers per hour (km/h), and automobile tires indicate the proper inflation pressure in kilopascals (kPa) on the sidewall. On each of these products, and many others like them, a corresponding English unit is written along side the SI unit. The beverage container shows pints or quarts, the gasoline pump shows gallons, speedometers show miles per hour, and tires show pounds per square inch. Dual labeling of SI and English units on U.S. products are supposed to help people learn the SI system, "weaning" them from the antiquated English system in anticipation of the time when a full conversion to SI units occurs. This transition is analogous to the process of incrementally quitting smoking. Rather than quitting "cold turkey," we employ nicotine patches, gums, and other substitutes until our habit is broken. So, you may ask, "Why don't we make the total conversion now? Is it as painful as quitting smoking suddenly?" It probably is. As you might guess, the problem is largely an economic one. A complete conversion to SI units may not occur until we are willing to pay the price in actual dollars. People could learn the SI unit system fairly quickly if the conversion were done suddenly, but an enormous financial commitment would have to be made.

As long as dual product labeling of units is employed in the United States, most people will tend to ignore the SI unit and look only at the English unit, the unit with which they are most familiar. In U.S. engineering schools, SI units are emphasized. Therefore, the engineering student is not the average person on the street who does not know, or know how to calculate, his or her weight in newtons. So, what can engineering students in the United States do to accelerate the conversion process? A good place to start is with yourself. Start using SI units in your everyday life. When you make a purchase at the grocery store, look only at the SI unit on the label. Learn by inspection how many milliliters of liquid product are packaged in your favorite sized container. Abandon the use of inches, feet, yards, and miles as much as possible. How many kilometers lie between your home and school? What is 65 miles per hour in kilometers per hour? What is the mass of your automobile in kilograms? Determine your height in meters, your mass in kilograms, and your weight in newtons. How long is your arm in centimeters? What is your waist size in centimeters? What is the current outdoor air temperature in degrees Celsius? Most fast-food restaurants offer a "quarter pounder" on their menu. It turns out that 1 N = 0.2248 lb, almost a quarter pound. On the next visit to your favorite fast-food place, order a "newton burger" and fries. (See Figure 8.)

Figure 8. An engineering student orders lunch (art by Kathryn Hagen).

PRACTICE!

1. A structural engineer states that an I-beam in a truss has a design stress of "five million, six hundred thousand pascals." Write this stress, using the appropriate SI unit prefix.

    Answer: 5.6 MPa

2. The power cord on an electric string trimmer carries a current of 5.2A. How many milliamperes is this? How many microamperes?

    Answer: 5.2×10^3 mA, 5.2×10^6 μA

3. Write the pressure 13.8 GPa in scientific notation.

    Answer: 13.8×10^9 Pa

4. Write the voltage 0.00255 V, using the appropriate SI unit prefix.

    Answer: 2.55 mV

5. In the following list, various quantities are written using SI units incorrectly. Write the quantities, using the correct form of SI units.
    a. 4.5 mw
    b. 8.75 M pa
    c. 200 Joules/sec
    d. 20 W/m^2 K
    e. 3 Amps

    Answer:
    a. 4.5 mW
    b. 8.75 MPa
    c. 200 J/s
    d. 20 W/m$^2 \cdot$ K
    e. 3 A

5   ENGLISH UNITS

The English unit system is known by various names. Sometimes it is referred to as the United States Customary System (USCS), the British System or the Foot-Pound-Second (FPS) system. The English unit system is still used extensively in the United States even though the rest of the industrialized world, including Great Britain, has adopted the SI unit system. English units have a long and colorful history. In ancient times, measures of length were based on human dimensions. The foot started out as the actual length of a man's foot. Because not all men were the same size, the foot varied in length by as much as three or four inches. Once the ancients started using feet and arms for measuring distance, it was only a matter of time before they began using hands and fingers. The unit of length that we refer to today as the inch was originally the width of a man's thumb. The inch was also once defined as the distance between the tip to the first joint of the forefinger. Twelve times that distance made one foot. Three times the length of a foot was the distance from the tip of a man's nose to the end of his outstretched arm. This distance closely approximates what we refer to today as the yard. Two yards equaled a fathom, which was defined as the distance across a man's outstretched arms. Half a yard was the 18-inch cubit, which was called a span. Half a span was referred to as a hand.

The pound, which uses the symbol *lb*, is named after the ancient Roman unit of weight called the libra. The British Empire retained this symbol into modern times. Today, there are actually two kinds of pound units, one for mass and one for weight and force. The first unit is called pound-mass (lb$_m$), and the second is called pound-force (lb$_f$). Because mass and weight are not the same quantity, the units lb$_f$ and lb$_m$ are different.

As discussed previously, the seven base dimensions are length, mass, time, temperature, electric current, amount of substance, and luminous intensity. These base dimensions, along with their corresponding English units, are given in Table 8. As with SI units, English units are not capitalized. The slug, which has no abbreviated symbol, is the mass unit in the English system, but the pound-mass (lb_m) is frequently used. Electric current is based on SI units of meter and newton, and luminous intensity is based on SI units of watt. Hence, these two base dimensions do not have English units per se, and these quantities are rarely used in combination with other English units.

TABLE 8 Base Dimensions and Their English Units.

Quantity	Unit	Symbol
Length	foot	ft
Mass	slug[1]	slug
Time	second	s
Temperature	rankine	°R
Electric current	ampere[2]	A
Amount of substance	mole	mol
Luminous intensity	candela[2]	cd

(1) The unit pound-mass (lb_m) is also used. 1 slug = 32.174 lb_m.
(2) There are no English units for electrical current and luminous intensity. The SI units are given here for completeness only.

Recall that derived dimensions consist of a combination of base and supplementary dimensions. Table 9 summarizes some common derived dimensions expressed in English units. Note that Table 9 is the English counterpart of the SI version given by Table 5. The most notable English unit with a special name is the British thermal unit (Btu), a unit of energy. One Btu is defined as the energy required to change the temperature of 1 lb_m of water at a temperature of 68°F by 1°F. One Btu is approximately the energy released by the complete burning of a single kitchen match. The magnitudes of the kilojoule and Btu are almost equal (1 Btu = 1.055 kJ). Unlike the kelvin (K), the temperature unit in the SI system, the rankine (°R) employs a degree symbol as do the Celsius (°C) and Fahrenheit (°F) units. The same rules for writing SI units apply for English units with one major exception: *Prefixes are generally not used with English units*. Thus, units such as kft (kilo-foot), Mslug (megaslug), and GBtu (gigaBtu) should not be used. Prefixes are reserved for SI units. Two exceptions are the units ksi, which refers to a stress of 1000 psi (pounds per square inch), and kip, which is a special name for a force of 1000 lb_f (pound-force).

There are some non-SI units that are routinely used in the United States and elsewhere. Table 10 summarizes some of these units and provides an equivalent value in the SI system. The inch is a common length unit, being found on virtually every student's ruler and carpenter's tape measure in the United States. There are exactly 2.54 centimeters per inch. Inches are still used as the primary length unit in many engineering companies. The yard is commonly used for measuring cloth, carpets, and loads of concrete (cubic yards), as well as ball advancement on the American football field. The ton is used in numerous industries, including shipping, construction, and transportation. Time subdivisions on clocks are measured in hours, minutes, and seconds. Radians and degrees are the most commonly used units for plane angles, whereas minutes and seconds are primarily used in navigational applications when referring to latitude and longitude on the earth's surface. The liter has made a lot of headway into the American culture, being found on beverage and food containers and many gasoline pumps. Virtually every American has seen the liter unit on a product, and many know that there are about four liters in a gallon (actually, 1 gal = 3.7854 L), but fewer people know that 1000 L = 1 m^3.

TABLE 9 Derived Dimensions and
English Units.

Quantity	English Units
Acceleration	$ft \cdot s^{-2}$
Angular acceleration	$rad \cdot s^{-2}$
Angular velocity	$rad \cdot s^{-1}$
Area	ft^2
Concentration	$mol \cdot ft^{-3}$
Density	$slug \cdot ft^{-3}$
Electric field strength	$V \cdot ft^{-1}$
Energy	Btu
Entropy	$Btu \cdot slug^{-1} \cdot {}^{\circ}R^{-1}$
Force	lb_f
Heat	Btu
Heat transfer	$Btu \cdot s^{-1}$
Magnetic field strength	$A \cdot ft^{-1}$
ass flow rate	$slug \cdot s^{-1}$
Moment of force	$lb_f \cdot ft$
Radiant intensity	$Btu \cdot s^{-1} \cdot sr^{-1}$
Specific energy	$Btu \cdot slug^{-1}$
Surface tension	$lb_f \cdot ft^{-1}$
Thermal conductivity	$Btu \cdot s^{-1} \cdot ft^{-1} \cdot {}^{\circ}R$
Velocity	$ft \cdot s^{-1}$
Viscosity, dynamic	$slug \cdot ft^{-1} \cdot s^{-1}$
Viscosity, kinematic	$ft^2 \cdot s^{-1}$
Volume	ft^3
Volume flow rate	$ft^3 \cdot s^{-1}$
Wavelength	ft

TABLE 10 Non-SI Units Commonly Used in the United States.

Quantity	Unit Name	Symbol	SI Equivalent
Length	inch	in	0.0254 m[1]
	yard	yd	0.9144 m (36 in)
Mass	metric ton	t	1000 kg
	short ton	t	907.18 kg (2000 lb_m)
Time	minute	min	60 s
	hour	h	3600 s
	day	d	86,400 s
Plane angle	degree	°	$\pi/180$ rad
	minute	'	$\pi/10,800$ rad
	second	"	$\pi/648,000$ rad
Volume	liter	L	10^{-3} m³
Land area	hectare	ha	10^4 m²
Energy	electron-volt	eV	1.602177×10^{-19} J

[1]Exact conversion

6   MASS AND WEIGHT

The concepts of *mass* and *weight* are fundamental to the proper use of dimensions and units in engineering analysis. Mass is one of the seven base dimensions used in science and engineering. Mass is a base dimension because it cannot be broken down into more fundamental dimensions. **Mass** is defined as a *quantity of matter*. This simple definition of mass may be expanded by exploring its basic properties. All matter possesses mass. The magnitude of a given mass is a measure of its resistance to a change in velocity. This property of matter is called *inertia*. A large mass offers more resistance to a change in velocity than a small mass, so a large mass has a greater inertia than a small mass. Mass may be considered in another way. Because all matter has mass, all matter exerts a gravitational attraction on other matter. Shortly after formulating his three laws of motion, Sir Isaac Newton postulated a law governing the gravitational attraction between two masses. Newton's law of universal gravitation is stated mathematically as

$$F = G\frac{m_1 m_2}{r^2} \tag{1}$$

where

F = gravitational force between masses (N)
G = universal gravitational constant = 6.673×10^{-11} m^3/kg·s^2
m_1 = mass of body 1 (kg)
m_2 = mass of body 2 (kg)
r = distance between the centers of the two masses (m)

According to Equation (1), between any two masses there exists an attractive gravitational force whose magnitude varies inversely as the square of the distance between the masses. Because Newton's law of universal gravitation applies to *any* two masses, let's apply Equation (1) to a body resting on the surface of the earth. Accordingly, we let $m_1 = m_e$, the mass of the earth and $m_2 = m$, the mass of the body. The distance, r, between the body and the earth may be taken as the mean radius of the earth, r_e. The quantities m_e and r_e have the approximate values

$$m_e = 5.979 \times 10^{24}\,\text{kg} \qquad r_e = 6.378 \times 10^6\,\text{m}$$

Thus, we have

$$F = G\frac{m_e m}{r_e^2}$$

$$= \frac{(6.673 \times 10^{-11}\,\text{m}^3/\text{kg·s}^2)(5.979 \times 10^{24}\,\text{kg})}{(6.378 \times 10^6\,\text{m})^2}\,m$$

$$= (9.808\,\text{m/s}^2)\,m$$

We can see that upon substituting values, the term Gm_e/r_e^2 yields a number of approximately 9.81 m/s^2, the standard acceleration of gravity on the earth's surface. Redefining this term as g, and letting $F = W$, we express the law of universal gravitation in a special form as

$$W = mg \tag{2}$$

where

W = weight of body (N)
m = mass of body (kg)
g = standard gravitational acceleration = 9.81 m/s^2

This derivation clearly shows the difference between mass and weight. We may therefore state the definition of **weight** as *a gravitational force exerted on a body by the earth*. Because mass is defined as a quantity of matter, the mass of a body is independent of its location in the universe. A body has the same mass whether it is located on the earth, the moon, Mars, or in outer space. The weight of the body, however, depends on its location. The mass of an 80 kg astronaut is the same whether or not he is on earth or in orbit about the earth. The astronaut weighs approximately 785 N on the earth, but while in orbit he is "weightless." His weight is zero while he orbits the earth, because he is continually "falling" toward earth. A similar weightless or "zero-g" condition is experienced by a skydiver as he free falls prior to opening the parachute.

The greatest source of confusion about mass and weight to the beginning engineering student is not the physical concept, but the units used to express each quantity. To see how units of mass and weight relate to each other, we employ a well-known scientific principle, **Newton's second law** of motion. Newton's second law of motion states that *a body of mass, m, acted upon by an unbalanced force, F, experiences an acceleration, a, that has the same direction of the force and a magnitude that is directly proportional to the force*. Stated mathematically, this law is

$$F = ma \qquad\qquad (3)$$

where

F = force (N)
m = mass (kg)
a = acceleration (m/s^2)

Note that this relation resembles Equation (2). Weight is a particular type of force, and acceleration due to gravity is a particular type of acceleration, so Equation (2) is a special case of Newton's second law, given by Equation (3). In the SI unit system, the newton (N) is *defined* as the force that will accelerate a 1-kg mass at a rate of 1 m/s^2. Hence, we may write Newton's second law dimensionally as

$$1\text{ N} = 1\text{ kg} \cdot \text{m/s}^2$$

In the English unit system, the pound-force (lb$_f$) is *defined* as the force that will accelerate a 1-slug mass at a rate of 1 ft/s^2. Hence, we may write Newton's second law dimensionally as

$$1\text{ lb}_f = 1\text{ slug} \cdot \text{ft/s}^2$$

See Figure 9 for an illustration of Newton's second law. Confusion arises from the careless interchange of the English mass unit, pound-mass (lb$_m$), with the English force unit, pound-force (lb$_f$). These units are not the same thing! In accordance with our definitions of mass and weight, pound-mass refers to a quantity of matter, whereas pound-force refers to a force or weight. In order to write Newton's second law in terms of pound-mass instead of slug, we rewrite Equation (3) as

$$F = \frac{ma}{g_c} \qquad\qquad (4)$$

where g_c is a constant that is required to make Newton's second law dimensionally consistent when mass, m, is expressed in lb$_m$, rather than slug. As stated previously, the English unit for force is lb$_f$, the English unit for acceleration is ft/s^2, and, as indicated in

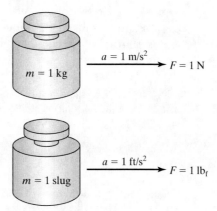

Figure 9. Definitions of the force units newton (N) and pound-force (lb_f).

Table 8, 1 slug $= 32.174$ lb_m. Thus, the constant g_c is

$$g_c = \frac{ma}{F}$$

$$= \frac{(32.174 \ lb_m)(ft/s^2)}{lb_f}$$

$$= 32.174 \frac{lb_m \cdot ft}{lb_f \cdot s^2}$$

This value is usually rounded to

$$g_c = 32.2 \frac{lb_m \cdot ft}{lb_f \cdot s^2}$$

Note that g_c has the same numerical value as g, the standard acceleration of gravity on the earth's surface. Newton's second law as expressed by Equation (4) is dimensionally consistent when the English unit of mass, lb_m, is used.

To verify that Equation (4) works, we recall that the pound-force is defined as the force that will accelerate a 1-slug mass at a rate of 1 ft/s². Recognizing that 1 slug $= 32.2$ lb_m, we have

$$F = \frac{ma}{g_c}$$

$$= \frac{(32.2 \ lb_m)(1 \ ft/s^2)}{32.2 \frac{lb_m \cdot ft}{lb_f \cdot s^2}} = 1 \ lb_f$$

Note that in this expression, all the units, except lb_f, cancel. Hence, the pound-force (lb_f) is *defined* as the force that will accelerate a 32.2-lb_m mass at a rate of 1 ft/s². Therefore, we may write Newton's second law dimensionally as

$$1 \ lb_f = 32.2 \ lb_m \cdot ft/s^2$$

To have dimensional consistency when English units are involved, Equation (4) *must* be used when mass, m, is expressed in lb_m. When mass is expressed in slug, however, the use of g_c in Newton's second law is not required for dimensional consistency because 1 lb_f is already defined as the force that will accelerate a 1-slug mass at a rate of 1 ft/s². Furthermore, because 1 N is already defined as the force that will accelerate a 1-kg mass at a rate of 1 m/s², the use of g_c is not required for dimensional consistency in the SI unit system. *Thus, Equation (3) suffices for all calculations, except for those in which mass is expressed in lb_m; in that case, Equation (4) must be used.* However, Equation (4) may be universally used when recognizing that the numerical value and units for g_c can be defined such that any consistent unit system will work. For example, substituting $F = 1$ N, $m = 1$ kg, and $a = 1$ m/s² into Equation (4) and solving for g_c we obtain

$$g_c = \frac{1 \text{ kg} \cdot \text{m}}{\text{N} \cdot \text{s}^2}$$

Since the numerical value of g_c is 1, we can successfully use Equation (3) as long as we recognize that 1 N is the force that will accelerate a 1-kg mass at a rate of 1 m/s².

Sometimes, the units pound-mass (lb_m) and pound-force (lb_f) are casually interchanged because a body with a mass of 1 lb_m has a weight of 1 lb_f (i.e., the mass and weight are *numerically equivalent*). Let's see how this works: By definition, a body with a mass of 32.2 lb_m (1 slug) when accelerated at a rate of 1 ft/s² has a weight of 1 lb_f. Therefore, using Newton's second law in the form, $W = mg$, we can also state that a body with a mass of 1 lb_m, when accelerated at a rate of 32.2 ft/s² (the standard value of g), has a weight of 1 lb_f. Our rationale for making such a statement is that we maintained the same numerical value on the right side of Newton's second law by assigning the mass, m, a value of 1 lb_m and the gravitational acceleration, g, the standard value of 32.2 ft/s². The numerical values of the mass and weight are equal even though a pound-mass and a pound-force are conceptually different quantities. It must be emphasized, however, that mass in pound-mass and weight in pound-force are numerically equivalent only when the standard value, $g = 32.2$ ft/s², is used. See Figure 10 for an illustration. The next example illustrates the use of g_c.

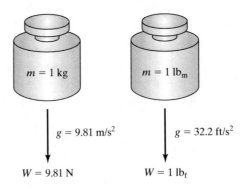

Figure 10. Definitions of weight for the standard value of gravitational acceleration.

EXAMPLE 4

Find the weight of some objects with the following masses:

(a) 50 slug

(b) 50 lb_m

(c) 75 kg

SOLUTION

To find weight, we use Newton's second law, where the acceleration, a, is the standard acceleration of gravity, $g = 9.81$ m/s^2 = 32.2 ft/s^2.

(a) The mass unit, slug, is the standard unit for mass in the English unit system. The weight is

$$W = mg$$
$$= (50 \text{ slug})(32.2 \text{ ft/s}^2) = 1{,}610 \text{ lb}_f$$

(b) When mass is expressed in terms of lb$_m$, we must use Equation (4):

$$W = \frac{mg}{g_c} = \frac{(50 \text{ lb}_m)(32.2 \text{ ft/s}^2)}{32.2 \dfrac{\text{lb}_m \cdot \text{ft}}{\text{lb}_f \cdot \text{s}^2}} = 50 \text{ lb}_f$$

Note that the mass and weight are numerically equivalent. This is true only in cases where the standard value of g is used, which means that an object with a mass of x lb$_m$ will always have a weight of x lb$_f$ on the earth's surface.

(c) The mass unit, kg, is the standard unit for mass in the SI unit system. The weight is

$$W = mg$$
$$= (75 \text{ kg})(9.81 \text{ m/s}^2) = 736 \text{ N}$$

Alternatively, we can find weight by using Equation (4):

$$W = \frac{mg}{g_c} = \frac{(75 \text{ kg})(9.81 \text{ m/s}^2)}{1 \dfrac{\text{kg} \cdot \text{m}}{\text{N} \cdot \text{s}^2}} = 736 \text{ N}$$

∎

Now that we understand the difference between mass and weight and know how to use mass and weight units in the SI and English systems, let's revisit the astronaut we discussed earlier. (See Figure 11.) The mass of the astronaut is 80 kg, which equals about 5.48 slug. His mass does not change, regardless of where he ventures. Prior to departing

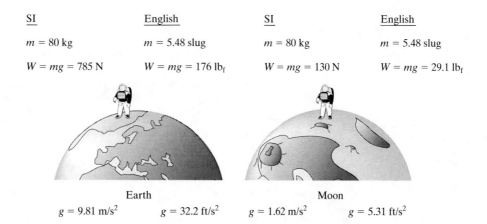

SI	English	SI	English
$m = 80$ kg	$m = 5.48$ slug	$m = 80$ kg	$m = 5.48$ slug
$W = mg = 785$ N	$W = mg = 176$ lb$_f$	$W = mg = 130$ N	$W = mg = 29.1$ lb$_f$

Earth		Moon	
$g = 9.81$ m/s^2	$g = 32.2$ ft/s^2	$g = 1.62$ m/s^2	$g = 5.31$ ft/s^2

Figure 11. An astronaut's mass and weight on the earth and moon.

on a trip to the moon, he weighs in at 785 N (176 lb$_f$). What is the mass of the astronaut in pound-mass? Three days later, his vehicle lands on the moon, and he begins constructing a permanent base for future planetary missions. The mass of the moon is about one-sixth that of the earth, so the value of the gravitational acceleration on the moon is only 1.62 m/s^2(5.31 ft/s^2). The astronaut's mass is still 80 kg, but his weight is only 130 N (29.1 lb$_f$) due to the smaller value of g. Is the mass and weight of the astronaut in pound-mass and pound-force numerically equivalent? No, because the standard value of g is not used.

EXAMPLE 5

Special hoists are used in automotive repair shops to lift engines. As illustrated in Figure 12, a 200-kg engine is suspended in a fixed position by a chain attached to the cross member of an engine hoist. Neglecting the weight of the chain itself, what is the tension in portion AD of the chain?

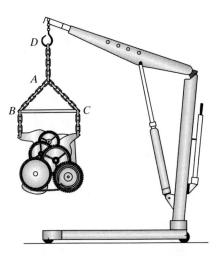

Figure 12.   Engine hoist for Example 5.

SOLUTION

This example is a simple problem in engineering statics. Statics is the branch of engineering mechanics that deals with forces acting on bodies at rest. The engine is held by the chain in a fixed position, so clearly the engine is at rest; that is, it is not in motion. This problem can be solved by recognizing that the entire weight of the engine is supported by portion AD of the chain. (The tension in portions AB and AC could also be calculated, but a thorough equilibrium analysis would be required.) Hence, the tension, which is a force that tends to elongate the chain, is equivalent to the weight of the engine. Using Equation (2), we have

$$F = mg$$

$$= (200 \text{ kg})(9.81 \text{ m/s}^2) = 1962 \text{ N}$$

Therefore, the tension in portion AD of the chain is 1962 N, the weight of the engine.

PRACTICE!

1. It has been said that you do not fully understand a basic technical concept, unless you can explain it in terms simple enough that a second grader can understand it. Write an explanation of the difference between mass and weight for a second grader.

2. Which is larger, a slug or a pound-mass?

   Answer: slug

3. Consider a professional linebacker who weighs 310 lb_f. What is his mass in slugs?

   Answer: 9.63 slug

4. A rock ($\rho = 2300$ kg/m^3) is suspended by a single rope. Assuming the rock to be spherical, with a radius of 15 cm, what is the tension in the rope?

   Answer: 319 N

7   UNIT CONVERSIONS

Although the SI unit system is the international standard, English units are in widespread use in the United States. Americans as a whole are much more familiar with English units than SI units. Students of science and engineering in U.S. schools primarily use SI units in their course work because most textbooks and the professors who teach out of them, stress SI units. Unfortunately, when students of these disciplines go about their day-to-day activities outside of the academic environment, they tend to slip back into the English unit mode along with everyone else. It seems as if students have a "unit switch" in their brains. When they are in the classroom or laboratory, the switch is turned to the "SI position." When they are at home, in the grocery store, or driving their car, the switch is turned to the "English position." Ideally, there should be no unit switch at all, but as long as science and engineering programs at colleges and universities stress SI units and American culture stresses English units, our cerebral unit switch toggles. In this section, a systematic method for converting units between the SI and English systems is given.

A **unit conversion** enables us to convert from one unit system to the other by using **conversion factors**. A conversion factor is an equivalency ratio that has a *unit value* of 1. Stated another way, a conversion factor simply relates the same physical quantity in two different unit systems. For example, 0.0254 m and 1 in are equivalent length quantities because 0.0254 m = 1 in. The ratio of these two quantities has a unit value of 1 because they are physically the same quantity. Obviously, the numerical value of the ratio is not 1, but depends on the numerical value of each individual quantity. Thus, when we multiply a given quantity by one or more conversion factors, we alter only the numerical value of the result and not its dimension. Table 11 summarizes some common conversion factors used in engineering analysis. A more extensive listing of unit conversions is given in Appendix B.

A systematic procedure for converting a quantity from one unit system to the other is as follows:

Unit Conversion Procedure

1. Write the given quantity in terms of its numerical value and units. Use a horizontal line to divide units in the numerator (upstairs) from those in the denominator (downstairs).

2. Determine the units *to* which you want to make the conversion.

TABLE 11   Some Common SI-to-English Unit Conversions

Quantity	Unit Conversion
Acceleration	$1 \text{ m/s}^2 = 3.2808 \text{ ft/s}^2$
Area	$1 \text{ m}^2 = 10.7636 \text{ ft}^2 = 1550 \text{ in}^2$
Density	$1 \text{ kg/m}^3 = 0.06243 \text{ lb}_m/\text{ft}^3$
Energy, work, heat	$1055.06 \text{ J} = 1 \text{ Btu} = 252 \text{ cal}$
Force	$1 \text{ N} = 0.22481 \text{ lb}_f$
Length	$1 \text{ m} = 3.2808 \text{ ft} = 39.370 \text{ in}$
	$0.0254 \text{ m} = 1 \text{ in}^{(1)}$
Mass	$1 \text{ kg} = 2.20462 \text{ lb}_m = 0.06852 \text{ slug}$
Power	$1 \text{ W} = 3.4121 \text{ Btu/h}$
	$745.7 \text{ W} = 1 \text{ hp}$
Pressure	$1 \text{ kPa} = 20.8855 \text{ lb}_f/\text{ft}^2 = 0.14504 \text{ lb}_f/\text{in}^2$
Specific heat	$1 \text{ kJ/kg} \cdot {}^\circ\text{C} = 0.2388 \text{ Btu/lb}_m \cdot {}^\circ\text{F}$
Temperature	$T(\text{K}) = T({}^\circ\text{C}) + 273.16 = T({}^\circ\text{R})/1.8 = [T({}^\circ\text{F}) + 459.67]/1.8$
Velocity	$1 \text{ m/s} = 2.2369 \text{ mi/h}$

$^{(1)}$ Exact conversion

3. Multiply the given quantity by one or more conversion factors that, upon cancellation of units, leads to the desired units. Use a horizontal line to divide the units in the numerator and denominator of each conversion factor.

4. Draw a line through all canceled units.

5. Perform the numerical computations on a calculator, retaining infinite decimal place accuracy until the end of the computations.

6. Write the numerical value of the converted quantity by using the desired number of significant figures (three significant figures is standard practice for engineering) with the desired units.

Examples 6, 7, and 8 illustrate the unit conversion procedure.

EXAMPLE 6

An engineering student is late for an early morning class, so she runs across campus at a speed of 9 mi/h. Determine her speed in units of m/s.

SOLUTION

The given quantity, expressed in English units, is 9 mi/h, but we want our answer to be in SI units of m/s. Thus, we need a conversion factor between mi and m and a conversion factor between h and s. To better illustrate the unit conversion procedure, we will use two length conversion factors rather than one. Following the procedure outlined, we have

$$9\,\frac{\cancel{\text{mi}}}{\cancel{\text{h}}} \times \frac{5280\,\cancel{\text{ft}}}{1\,\cancel{\text{mi}}} \times \frac{1\,\text{m}}{3.2808\,\cancel{\text{ft}}} \times \frac{1\,\cancel{\text{h}}}{3600\,\text{s}} = 4.02\,\frac{\text{m}}{\text{s}}$$

given quantity   conversion factors   answer

The key aspect of the unit conversion process is that the conversion factors must be written such that the appropriate units in the conversion factors cancel those in the given quantity. If we had inverted the conversion factor between ft and mi, writing it instead as 1 mi/5280 ft, the mi unit would not cancel and our unit conversion exercise would not work, because we would end up with units of mi^2 in the numerator. Similarly, the conversion factor between m and ft was written such that the ft unit canceled the ft unit in the first conversion factor. Also, the conversion factor between h and s was written such that the h unit canceled with the h unit in the given quantity. Writing conversion factors with the units in the proper locations, "upstairs" or "downstairs," requires some practice, but after doing several conversion problems, the correct placement of units will become second nature to you. Note that our answer is expressed in three significant figures.

EXAMPLE 7

Lead has one of the highest densities of all the pure metals. The density of lead is 11,340 kg/m^3. What is the density of lead in units of lb_m/in^3?

SOLUTION

A direct conversion factor from kg/m^3 to lbm/in^3 may be available, but to illustrate an important aspect of converting units with exponents, we will use a series of conversion factors for each length and mass unit. Thus, we write our unit conversion as

$$11{,}340 \frac{kg}{m^3} \times \frac{(1\ m)^3}{(3.2808\ ft)^3} \times \frac{(1\ ft)^3}{(12\ in)^3} \times \frac{2.20462\ lb_m}{1\ kg} = 0.410\ lb_m/in^3$$

We used two length conversion factors, one factor between m and ft and the other between ft and in. But the given quantity is a density than has a volume unit. When performing unit conversions involving exponents, *both* the numerical value and the unit must be raised to the exponent. A common error that students make is to raise the unit to the exponent, which properly cancels units, but to forget to raise the numerical value also. Failure to raise the numerical value to the exponent will lead to the wrong numerical answer even though the units in the answer will be correct. Using the direct conversion factor, we obtain the same result:

$$11{,}340\ kg/m^3 \times \frac{(3.6127 \times 10^{-5}\ lb_m/in^3)}{1\ kg/m^3} = 0.410\ lb_m/in^3$$

EXAMPLE 8

Specific heat is defined as the energy required to raise the temperature of a unit mass of a substance by one degree. Pure aluminum has a specific heat of approximately 900 $J/kg \cdot °C$. Convert this value to units of $Btu/lb_m \cdot °F$.

SOLUTION

By following the unit conversion procedure, we write the given quantity and then multiply it by the appropriate conversion factors, which can be found in Appendix B:

$$\frac{900\ J}{kg \cdot °C} \times \frac{1\ Btu}{1055.06\ J} \times \frac{1\ kg}{2.20462\ lb_m} \times \frac{1°C}{1.8°F} = 0.215\ Btu/lb_m \cdot °F$$

The temperature unit, °C, in the original quantity has a unique interpretation. Because specific heat is the energy required to raise a unit mass of a substance by one degree, the temperature unit in this quantity denotes a temperature *change*, not an absolute temperature value. A temperature change of 1°C is equivalent to a temperature change of 1.8°F. Stated another way, a change of one degree on the Fahrenheit scale is 1.8 times a change of one degree on the Celsius scale, as given by the temperature difference conversion factor, $\Delta T(°C) = \Delta T(°F)/1.8$. Other thermal properties, such as thermal conductivity, involve the same temperature change interpretation. See problem 39, at the end of this chapter, for reference.

This example can also be done by applying a single conversion factor 1 $kJ/kg \cdot °C$ = 0.2388 $Btu/lb_m \cdot °F$, which yields the same result.

PROFESSIONAL SUCCESS: UNIT CONVERSIONS AND CALCULATORS

Scientific pocket calculators have evolved from simple electronic versions of adding machines to complex portable computers. Today's high-end scientific calculators have numerous capabilities, including programming, graphing, numerical methods, and symbolic mathematics. Most scientific calculators also have an extensive compilation of conversion factors either burned into a chip within the calculator itself or available as a plug-in application module. Why, then, should students learn to do unit conversions by hand when calculators will do the work? This question lies at the root of a more fundamental question: Why should students learn to do *any* computational task by hand when calculators or computers will do the work? Is it because "in the old days" students and practicing engineers did not have the luxury of highly sophisticated computational tools, so professors, who perhaps lived in the "old days," force their students to do things the old fashioned way? Not really.

Students will always need to learn engineering by *thinking* and *reasoning* their way through a problem, regardless of whether that problem is a unit conversion or a stress calculation in a machine component. Computers, and the software that runs on them, do not replace the thinking process. The calculator, like the computer, should never become a "black box" to the student. A black box is a mysterious device whose inner workings are largely unknown, but that, nonetheless, provides output for every input supplied. By the time you graduate with an engineering degree, or certainly by the time you have a few years of professional engineering practice under your belt, you will come to realize that a calculator program or computer software package exists for solving almost any conceivable type of engineering problem. This does not mean that you need to learn every one of these programs and software packages. It means that you should become proficient in the use of those computational tools that pertain to your particular engineering field *after* learning the underlying basis for each. By all means, use a calculator to perform unit conversions, but *first* know how to do them by hand, so you gain confidence in your own computational skills and have a way of verifying the results of your calculator.

PRACTICE!

1. A microswitch is an electrical switch that requires only a small force to operate it. If a microswitch is activated by a 0.25-oz force, what is the force in units of N that will activate it?

   Answer: 0.0695 N

2. At room temperature, water has a density of about 62.4 lb_m/ft^3. Convert this value to units of $slug/in^3$ and kg/m^3.

   Answer: 1.12×10^{-3} $slug/in^3$, 999.5 kg/m^3

3. At launch, the Saturn V rocket that carried astronauts to the moon developed five million pounds of thrust. What is the thrust in units of MN?

   Answer: 22.2 MN

4. Standard incandescent light bulbs produce more heat than light. Assuming that a typical house has twenty 60-W bulbs that are continuously on, how much heat in units of Btu/h is supplied to the house from light bulbs if 90 percent of the energy produced by the bulbs is in the form of heat?

   Answer: 3685 Btu/h

5. Certain properties of animal (including human) tissue can be approximated by using those of water. Using the density of water at room temperature, $\rho = 62.4$ lb_m/ft^3, calculate the weight of a human male by approximating him as a cylinder with a length and diameter of 6 ft and 1 ft, respectively.

   Answer: 294 lb_f

6. The standard frequency for electrical power in the United States is 60 Hz. For an electrical device that operates on this power, how many times does the current alternate during a year?

   Answer: 1.89×10^9

KEY TERMS

base dimension

conversion factors

derived dimension

dimension

dimensionally consistent

English unit system

mass

Newton's second law

physical standards

SI unit system

unit

unit conversion

weight

REFERENCES

Cardarelli, F., *Encyclopaedia of Scientific Units, Weights and Measures: Their SI Equivalences and Origins*, 3d ed., NY: Springer-Verlag, 2003.

Lewis, R., *Engineering Quantities and Systems of Units*, NY: Halsted Press, 1972.

Lide, D.R., Editor, *CRC Handbook of Chemistry and Physics*, 84th ed. Boca Raton, FL: CRC Press, 2003.

Problems

1. For the following dimensional equations, find the base dimensions of the parameter K:

    a. $[M][L][t]^{-2} = k[M][L]^{-1}[t]^{-2}$

    b. $[M][L][t]^{-2}[L]^{-1} = k[L][t]^{-3}$

    c. $[L]^2[t]^{-2} = k[M]^4[T]^2$

    d. $[M][L]^2[t]^{-3} = k[L][T]$

    e. $[N][L][L]^3 k = [T]^2[M]^{-2}[L]$

    f. $[M][I]^2 k = [N][T][M]^{-3}[L]^{-1}$

    g. $[I][L]^2[t] = k^2[M]^4[t]^2$

    h. $k^3[T]^6[M]^3[L]^{-5} = [T]^{-3}[t]^{-6}[L]$

    i. $[T]^{-1/2}[L]^{-1}[I]^2 = k^{-1/2}[t]^4[T]^{-5/2}[L]^{-3}$

    j. $[M][L][t]^{-2} = [M][L][t]^{-2} \sin(k[L]^{-2}[M]^{-1})$

    k. $[T]^2[N] = [T]^2[N] \ln(k[N][T]^{-1})$

2. Is the following dimensional equation dimensionally consistent? Explain.

    $$[M][L] = [M][L] \cos([L][t])$$

3. Is the following dimensional equation dimensionally consistent? Explain.

    $$[t]^2[L][T] = [t][L][T] \log([t][t]^{-1})$$

4. Is the following dimensional equation dimensionally consistent? Explain.

    $$[T][N][T] = [T][N][T] \exp([M][M]^{-1})$$

5. In the following list, various quantities are written using SI units incorrectly: Write the quantities, using the correct form of SI units.

    a. 10.6 secs

    b. 4.75 amp

    c. 120 M hz

d.   2.5 kw

e.   0.00846 kg/μs

f.   90 W/m^2 K

g.   650 mGPa

h.   25 MN.

i.   950 Joules

j.   1.5 m/s/s

6.   The dimension *moment*, sometimes referred to as *torque*, is defined as a force multiplied by a distance and is expressed in SI units of newton-meter (N · m). In addition to moment, what other physical quantities are expressed in SI units of N · m? What is the special name given to this combination of units?

7.   Consider a 60-W light bulb. A watt (W) is defined as a joule per second (J/s). Write the quantity 60 W in terms of the units newton (N), meter (m), and second (s).

8.   A commonly used formula in electrical circuit analysis is $P = IV$, power (W) equals current (A) multiplied by voltage (V). Using Ohm's law, write a formula for power in terms of current [I] and resistance [R].

9.   A particle undergoes an average acceleration of 5 m/s^2 as it travels between two points during a time interval of 2 s. Using unit considerations, derive a formula for the average velocity of a particle in terms of average acceleration and time interval. Calculate the average velocity of the particle for the numerical values given.

10.   A crane hoists a large pallet of materials from the ground to the top of a building. In hoisting this load, the crane does 100 kJ of work during a time interval of 5 s. Using unit considerations, derive the formula for power in terms of work and time interval. Calculate the power expended by the crane in lifting the load.

11.   A spherical tank with a radius of 0.25 m is filled with water ($\rho = 1000$ kg/m^3). Calculate the mass and the weight of the water in SI units.

12.   A large indoor sports arena is roughly cylindrical in shape. The height and diameter of the cylinder are 120 m and 180 m, respectively. Calculate the mass and weight of air contained in the sports arena in SI units if the density of air is $\rho = 1.20$ kg/m^3.

13.   A 90-kg astronaut biologist searches for microbial life on Mars where the gravitational acceleration is g $= 3.71$ m/s^2. What is the weight of the astronaut in units of N and lb$_f$?

14.   A 90-kg astronaut biologist places a 4-lb$_m$ rock sample on two types of scales on Mars in order to measure the rock's weight. The first scale is a beam balance, which operates by comparing masses. The second scale operates by the compression of a spring. Calculate the weight of the rock sample in units of lb$_f$ using (a) the beam balance and (b) the spring scale.

15.   A stainless steel plate measuring 1.2 m × 0.8 m × 3 mm has a density of $\rho = 8000$ kg/m^3. Find the mass and weight of the plate in SI units.

16.   A circular tube of polyethylene plastic ($\rho = 930$ kg/m^3) has an inside radius of 1.2 cm and an outside radius of 4.6 cm. If the cylinder is 40 cm long, what is the mass and weight of the cylinder in SI units?

17.   The density of porcelain is $\rho = 144$ lb$_m$/ft^3. Approximating a porcelain dinner plate as a flat disk with a diameter and thickness of 9 in and 0.2 in, respectively,

find the mass of the plate in units of slug and lb_m. What is the weight of the plate in units of lb_f?

18. In an effort to reduce the mass of an aluminum bulkhead for a spacecraft, a machinist drills an array of holes in the bulkhead. The bulkhead is a triangular-shaped plate with a base and height of 2.5 m and 1.6 m, respectively, and a thickness of 8 mm. How many 5-cm diameter holes must be drilled clear through the bulkhead to reduce its mass by 8 kg? For the density of aluminum, use $\rho = 2800$ kg/m^3.

19. A world-class sprinter can run 100 m in a time of 10 s, an average speed of 10 m/s. Convert this speed to mi/h.

20. A world-class mile runner can run 1 mi in a time of 4 min. What is the runner's average speed in units of mi/h and m/s?

21. The typical home is heated by a forced-air furnace that burns natural gas or fuel oil. If the heat output of the furnace is 120,000 Btu/h, what is the heat output in units of kW?

22. Calculate the temperature at which the Celsius (°C) and Fahrenheit (°F) scales coincide.

23. A large shipping container of ball bearings is suspended by a cable in a manufacturing plant. The combined mass of the container and ball bearings is 2500 lb_m. Find the tension in the cable in units of N.

24. A typical human adult loses about 65 Btu/h · ft^2 of heat while engaged in brisk walking. Approximating the human adult body as a cylinder with a height and diameter of 5.8 ft and 1.1 ft, respectively, find the total amount of heat lost in units of J if the brisk walking is maintained for a period of 2 h. Include the two ends of the cylinder in the surface area calculation.

25. A symmetric I-beam of structural steel ($\rho = 7860$ kg/m^3) has the cross section shown in Figure 25. Calculate the weight per unit length of the I-beam in units of N/m and lb_f/ft.

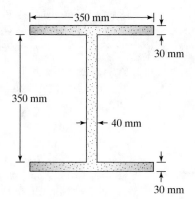

Figure 25.

26. A sewer pipe carries waste away from a commercial building at a mass flow rate of 5 kg/s. What is this flow rate in units of lb_m/s and slug/h?

27. The rate at which solar radiation is intercepted by a unit area is called solar heat flux. Just outside the earth's atmosphere, the solar heat flux is approximately 1350 W/m^2. Determine the value of this solar heat flux in units of Btu/h · ft^2.

28.   During a typical summer day in the arid southwest regions of the United States, the outdoor air temperature may range from 115°F during the late afternoon to 50°F several hours after sundown. What is this temperature range in units of °C, K, and °R?

29.   An old saying is "an ounce of prevention is worth a pound of cure." Restate this maxim in terms of the SI unit newton.

30.   How many seconds are there in a leap year?

31.   What is your approximate age in seconds?

32.   A highway sign is supported by two posts as shown in Figure 32. The sign is constructed of a high-density pressboard material ($\rho = 900 \text{ kg/m}^3$) and its thickness is 2 cm. Assuming that each post carries half the weight of the sign, calculate the compressive force in the posts in units of N and lb_f.

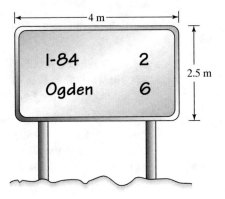

Figure 32.

33.   A boiler is a vessel containing water or other fluid at a high temperature and pressure. Consider a boiler containing water at a temperature and pressure of 250°C and 5 MPa, respectively. What is the temperature and pressure in units of K and psi, respectively?

34.   A pressure gauge designed to measure small pressure differences in air ducts has an operating range of 0 to 16 inch H_2O. What is this pressure range in units of Pa and psi?

35.   Resistors are electrical devices that retard the flow of current. These devices are rated by the maximum power they are capable of dissipating as heat to the surrounding area. How much heat does a 25-W resistor dissipate in units of Btu/h if the resistor operates at maximum capacity? Using the formula $P = I^2R$, what is the current flow, I, in the resistor if is has a resistance, R, of 100 Ω?

36.   Chemical reactions can generate heat. This type of heat generation is often referred to as volume heat generation because the heat is produced internally by every small parcel of chemical. Consider a chemical reaction that generates heat at the rate of 50 MW/m^3. Convert this volume heat generation to units of $\text{Btu/h} \cdot \text{ft}^3$.

37.   A sport-utility vehicle has an engine that delivers 250 hp. How much power does the engine produce in units of kW and Btu/h?

38. An underground pipe carries culinary water to a home at a volume flow rate of 5 gal/min. Determine the flow rate in units of m^3/s and ft^3/h.

39. Thermal conductivity is a property that denotes the ability of a material to conduct heat. A material with a high thermal conductivity readily transports heat, whereas a material with a low thermal conductivity tends to retard heat flow. Fiberglass insulation and silver have thermal conductivities of 0.046 W/m · °C and 429 W/m · °C, respectively. Convert these values to units of Btu/h · ft · °F.

40. A standard incandescent 75-W light bulb has an average life of 1000 h. What is the total amount of energy that this light bulb produces during its lifetime? Express the answer in units of J, Btu, and cal.

41. A steam power plant produces 400 MW of power. How much energy does the power plant produce in a year? Express your answer in units of J and Btu.

42. It is estimated that about 50 million Americans go on a new diet each year. If each of these people cuts 300 cal from their diets each day, how many 100-W light bulbs could be powered by this energy?

43. The standard acceleration of gravity at the earth's surface is $g = 9.81$ m/s^2. Convert this acceleration to units of ft/h^2 and mi/s^2.

44. At room temperature, air has a specific heat of 1.007 kJ/kg · °C. Convert this value to units of J/kg · K and Btu/lb$_m$ · °F.

45. The yield stress for structural steel is approximately 250 MPa. Convert this value to units of psi.

8

Analysis Methodology

1   INTRODUCTION

One of the most important things an engineering student learns during his or her program of study is how to approach an engineering problem in a systematic and logical fashion. In this respect, the study of engineering is somewhat similar to the study of science in that a science student learns how to think like a scientist by employing the scientific method. The scientific method is a process by which hypotheses about the physical world are stated, theories formulated, data collected and evaluated, and mathematical models constructed. The **engineering method** may be thought of as a problem-solving process by which the needs of society are met through design and manufacturing of devices and systems. Engineering analysis is a major part of this problem-solving process. Admittedly, engineering and science are not the same, because they each play a different role in our technical society. Science seeks to explain how nature works through fundamental investigations of matter and energy. The objective of engineering is more pragmatic. Engineering, using science and mathematics as tools, seeks to design and build products and processes that enhance our standard of living. Generally, the scientific principles underlying the function of any engineering device were derived and established *before* the device was designed. For example, Newton's laws of motion and Kepler's orbital laws were well established scientific principles long before spacecraft orbited the earth or the other planets. Despite their contrasting objectives, both engineering and science employ tried-and-true methodologies that enable people working in each field to solve a variety of problems. To do science, the scientist must know how to employ the scientific method. To do engineering, the engineer must know how to employ the "engineering method."

SECTIONS

1   Introduction
2   Numerical Calculations
3   General Analysis Procedure
4   The Computer as an Analysis Tool

OBJECTIVES

After reading this chapter, you will have learned

- How to make order-of-magnitude calculations
- The proper use of significant figures
- How to perform an analysis systematically
- The proper method of analysis presentation
- Advantages and disadvantages of using computers for analysis

Engineering analysis is the solution of an engineering problem by using mathematics and principles of science. Because of the close association between analysis and design, analysis is one of the key steps in the design process. Analysis also plays a major role in the study of engineering failures. The engineering method for conducting an analysis is a logical, systematic procedure characterized by a well-defined format. This procedure, when consistently and correctly applied, leads to the successful solution of any analytical engineering problem. Practicing engineers have been using this analysis procedure successfully for decades, and engineering graduates are expected to know how to apply it upon entering the technical workforce. Therefore, it behooves the engineering student to learn the analysis methodology as thoroughly as possible. The best way to do so is to practice solving analytical problems. As you advance in your engineering course work, you will have ample opportunities to apply the analysis methodology outlined in this chapter. Courses such as statics, dynamics, strength of materials, thermodynamics, fluid mechanics, heat and mass transfer, electrical circuits, and engineering economics are analysis intensive. These courses, and others like them, focus almost exclusively on solving engineering problems that are analytical in nature. That is the character of these engineering subjects. The analysis methodology presented here is a *general* procedure that can be used to solve problems in any analytical subject. Clearly, engineering analysis heavily involves the use of numerical calculations.

2   NUMERICAL CALCULATIONS

As a college student, you are well aware of the rich diversity of academic programs and courses offered at institutions of higher learning. Because you are an engineering major, you are perhaps more familiar with the genre of engineering, science, and mathematics courses than liberal arts courses such as sociology, philosophy, psychology, music, and languages. The tenor of liberal arts is vastly different than that of engineering. Suppose for a moment that you are enrolled in a literature class, studying Herman Melville's great book, *Moby Dick*. While discussing the relationship between the whale and Captain Ahab, your literature professor asks the class, "What is your impression of Captain Ahab's attitude toward the whale?" As an engineering major, you are struck by the apparent looseness of this question. You are accustomed to answering questions that require a quantitative answer, not an "impression." What would engineering be like if our answers were "impressions"? Imagine an engineering professor asking a thermodynamics class, "What is your impression of the superheated steam temperature at the inlet of the turbine?" A more appropriate question would be, "What *is* the superheated steam temperature at the inlet of the turbine?" Obviously, literature and the other liberal arts disciplines operate in a completely different mode than engineering. By its very nature, engineering is based on specific, quantitative information. An answer of "hot" to the second thermodynamics question would be quantitative, but not specific, and therefore insufficient. The temperature of the superheated steam at the inlet of the turbine could be calculated by conducting a thermodynamic analysis of the turbine, thereby providing a *specific* value for the temperature; 400°C, for example. The analysis by which the temperature was obtained may consist of several numerical calculations involving different thermodynamic quantities. Numerical calculations are mathematical operations on numbers that represent physical quantities such as temperature, stress, voltage, mass, flow rate, etc. In this section, you will learn the proper numerical calculation techniques for engineering analysis.

2.1   Approximations

It is often useful, particularly during the early stages of design, to calculate an approximate answer to a given problem when the given information is uncertain or when little information is available. An approximation can be used to establish the cursory aspects of a design and to determine whether a more precise calculation is required. Approximations are usually based on assumptions, which must be modified or eliminated during the latter stages of the design. Engineering approximations are sometimes referred to as "guesstimates," "ballpark calculations," or "back-of-the-envelope calculations." A more appropriate name for them is **order-of-magnitude** calculations. The term order of magnitude means a *power of* 10. Thus, an order-of-magnitude calculation refers to a calculation involving quantities whose numerical values are estimated to within a factor of 10. For example, if the estimate of a stress in a structure changes from about 1 kPa to about 1 MPa, we say that the stress has changed by three orders of magnitude, because 1 MPa is one thousand (10^3) times 1 kPa. Engineers frequently conduct order-of-magnitude calculations to ascertain whether their initial design concepts are feasible. Order-of-magnitude calculations are therefore a useful decision-making tool in the design process. Order-of-magnitude calculations do not require the use of a calculator because all the quantities have simple power-of-10 values, so the arithmetic operations can be done by hand with pencil and paper or even in your head. The example that follows illustrates an order-of-magnitude calculation.

EXAMPLE 1

A warehouse with the approximate dimensions 200 ft $\times$ 150 ft $\times$ 20 ft is ventilated with 12 large industrial blowers. In order to maintain acceptable air quality in the warehouse, the blowers must provide two air changes per hour, meaning that the entire volume of air within the warehouse must be replenished with fresh outdoor air two times per hour. Using an order-of-magnitude analysis, find the required volume flow rate that each blower must deliver, assuming the blowers equally share the total flow rate.

SOLUTION

To begin, we estimate the volume of the warehouse. The length, width, and height of the warehouse is 200 ft, 150 ft, and 20 ft, respectively. These lengths have order-of-magnitude values of 10^2, 10^2, and 10^1, respectively. Two air changes per hour are required. Thus, the total volume flow rate of air for the warehouse, including the factor of two air changes per hour, is

$$Q_t \approx (10^2 \text{ ft})(10^2 \text{ ft})(10^1 \text{ ft})(2 \text{ air changes/h}) = 2 \times 10^5 \text{ ft}^3/\text{h}$$

(Note that "air changes" is not a unit, so it does not appear in the answer.) The number of blowers (12) has an order-of-magnitude value of 10^1. Based on the assumption that each blower delivers the same flow rate, the flow rate per blower is the total volume flow rate divided by the number of blowers:

$$Q = Q_t/N = (2 \times 10^5 \text{ ft}^3/\text{h})(10^1 \text{ blowers}) = 2 \times 10^4 \text{ ft}^3/\text{h} \cdot \text{blower}$$

Our order-of-magnitude calculation shows that each blower must supply $2 \times 10^4 \text{ ft}^3/\text{h}$ of outdoor air to the warehouse.

How does our order-of-magnitude answer compare with the exact answer? The exact answer is

$$Q = (200 \text{ ft})(150 \text{ ft})(20 \text{ ft})(2 \text{ air changes/h})/(12 \text{ blowers}) = 1 \times 10^5 \text{ ft}^3/\text{h} \cdot \text{blower}$$

By dividing the exact answer by the approximate answer, we see that the approximate answer differs from the exact answer by a factor of five, which is within an order of magnitude.

2.2   Significant Figures

After order-of-magnitude calculations have been made, engineers conduct more precise calculations to refine their design or to more fully characterize a particular failure mode. Accurate calculations demand more of the engineer than simply keeping track of powers of 10. Final design parameters must be determined with as much accuracy as possible to achieve the optimum design. Engineers must determine how many digits in their calculations are significant. A **significant figure** or *significant digit* in a number is defined as *a digit that is considered reliable as a result of a measurement or calculation*. The number of significant figures in the answer of a calculation indicates the number of digits that can be used with confidence, thereby providing a way of telling the engineer how accurate the answer is. No physical quantity can be specified with infinite precision because no physical quantity is *known* with infinite precision. Even the constants of nature such as the speed of light in a vacuum, c, and the gravitational constant, G, are known only to the precision with which they can be measured in a laboratory. Similarly, engineering material properties such as density, modulus of elasticity, and specific heat are known only to the precision with which these properties can be measured. A common mistake is to use more significant figures in an answer than are justified, giving the impression that the answer is more accurate than it really is. No answer can be more accurate than the numbers used to generate that answer.

How do we determine how many significant figures (colloquially referred to as "sig figs") a number has? A set of rules has been established for counting the number of significant figures in a number. (All significant figures are underlined in the examples given for each rule.)

Rules for Significant Figures

1.   All digits *other than zero* are significant. Examples: 8.936, 456, 0.257.

2.   All zeroes *between* significant figures are significant. Examples: 14.06, 5.0072.

3.   For nondecimal numbers greater than one, all zeroes placed *after* the significant figures are *not* significant. Examples: 2500, 8,640,000. These numbers can be written in scientific notation as 2.5×10^3 and 8.64×10^6, respectively.

4.   If a decimal point is used *after* a nondecimal number larger than one, the zeroes are significant. The decimal point establishes the precision of the number. Examples: 3200., 550,000.

5.   Zeroes placed *after* a decimal point that are *not necessary* to set the decimal point are significant. The additional zeroes establish the precision of the number. Examples: 359.00, 1000.00.

6.   For numbers smaller than one, all zeroes placed *before* the significant figures are *not* significant. These zeroes only serve to establish the location of the decimal point. Examples: 0.0254, 0.000609

Do not confuse the number of significant figures with the number of decimal places in a number. The number of significant figures in a quantity is established by the precision with which a measurement of that quantity can be made. The primary exception to this are numbers such as π and the Naperian base, e, that are derived from mathematical relations. These numbers are accurate to an infinite number of significant figures.

Let's see how the rules for significant figures are used in calculations.

EXAMPLE 2

We wish to calculate the weight of a 25-kg object. Using Newton's second law, $W = mg$, find the weight of the object in units of N. Express the answer, by using the appropriate number of significant figures.

SOLUTION

We have $m = 25$ kg and $g = 9.81$ m/s^2. Suppose that our calculator is set to display six places to the right of the decimal point. We then multiply the numbers 25 and 9.81. In the display of the calculator, we see the number 245.250000. How many digits in this answer are we justified in writing? The number in the calculator's display implies that the answer is accurate to six decimal places (i.e., to within one-millionth of a newton). Obviously, this kind of accuracy is not justified. The rule for significant figures for *multiplication* and *division* is that *the product or quotient should contain the number of significant figures that are contained in the number with the fewest significant figures.*

Another way to state this rule is to say that the quantity with the fewest number of significant figures *governs* the number of significant figures in the answer. The mass, m, contains two significant figures, and the acceleration of gravity, g, contains three. Therefore, we are only justified in writing the weight by using two significant figures, which is the fewest number of significant figures in our given values. Our answer can be written in two ways. First, we can write the weight as 250 N. According to rule 3, the zero is not significant, so our answer contains two significant figures, the "2" and the "5." Second, we can write the weight by using scientific notation as 2.5×10^2 N. In this form, we can immediately see that two significant figures are used without referring to the rules. Note that in both cases we *rounded* the answer *up* to the nearest tens place, because the value of the first digit dropped is 5 or greater. If our answer had been lower than 245 N, we would have rounded *down* to 240 N. If our answer had been precisely 250 N, the rules of rounding suggest rounding up, so our answer would again be 250 N.

The preceding example shows how significant figures are used for multiplication or division, but how are significant figures used for *addition* and *subtraction*?

EXAMPLE 3

Two collinear forces (forces that act in the same direction) of 875.4 N and 9.386 N act on a body. Add these two forces, expressing the result in the appropriate number of significant figures.

SOLUTION

The best way to show how significant figures are used in addition or subtraction is to do the problem by hand. We have

$$
\begin{array}{r}
875.4 \ \text{N} \\
+ \quad 9.356 \ \text{N} \\
\hline
884.786 \ \text{N}
\end{array}
$$

Both forces have four significant figures, but the first force reports one place past the decimal point, whereas the second force reports three places past the decimal point. The answer is written with six significant figures. Are six significant figures justified? Because addition and subtraction are arithmetic operations that require decimal point alignment, the rule for significant figures for *addition* and *subtraction* is different than for multiplication and division. For addition and subtraction, the answer should show *significant figures only as far to the right as is seen in the least precise number in the calculation.* The least precise number in the calculation is the 875.4-N force, because it reports accuracy to the first decimal place, whereas the second force, 9.386 N, reports accuracy to the third decimal place. We are not justified in writing the answer as 884.786 N. We may only write the answer by using the same number of places past the decimal point as seen in the least precise force. Hence, our answer, reported to the appropriate number of significant figures, is 884.8 N. Once again, we rounded the answer up because the value of the first digit dropped is 5 or greater.

In *combined* operations where multiplication and division are performed in the same operation as addition and subtraction, the multiplications and divisions should be performed first, establishing the proper number of significant figures in the intermediate answers, perform the additions and subtractions, and then round the answer to the proper number of significant figures. This procedure, while applicable to operations performed by hand, should not be used in calculator or computer applications, because intermediate rounding is cumbersome and may lead to a serious error in the answer. Perform the entire calculation, letting the calculator or computer software manage the numerical precision, and then express the final answer in the desired number of significant figures:

> It is standard engineering practice to express final answers in three (or sometimes four) significant figures, because the given input values for geometry, loads, material properties, and other quantities are typically reported with this precision.

Calculators and computer software such as spreadsheets and equation solvers keep track of and can display a large number of digits. How many digits will your calculator display? The number of digits displayed by a scientific calculator can be set by fixing the decimal point or specifying the numerical format. For example, by fixing the number of decimal places to one, the number 28.739 is displayed as 28.7. Similarly, the number 1.164 is displayed as 1.2. Because the first digit dropped is greater than 5, the calculator automatically rounds the answer up. Small and large numbers should be expressed in scientific notation. For example, the number 68,400 should be expressed as 6.84×10^4, and the number 0.0000359 should be expressed as 3.59×10^{-5}. Scientific calculators also have an *engineering notation* display setting because SI unit prefixes are primarily defined by multiples of one thousand (10^3). In engineering notation, the number 68,400 may be displayed as 68.4×10^3, and the number 0.0000359 may be displayed as 35.9×10^{-6}. Regardless of how numbers are displayed by calculators or computers, the engineering student who uses these computational tools must understand that significant figures have a physical meaning based on our ability to measure engineering and scientific quantities. The casual or sloppy handling of significant figures in engineering analysis may lead to solutions that are inaccurate at best and completely wrong at worst.

APPLICATION: CALCULATING VISCOSITY BY USING THE FALLING-SPHERE METHOD

You know by experience that some fluids are thicker or more "gooey" than others. For example, pancake syrup and motor oil are thicker than water and alcohol. The technical term we use to describe the magnitude of a fluid's thickness is *viscosity*. Viscosity is a fluid property that characterizes the fluid's resistance to flow. Water and alcohol flow more readily than pancake syrup and motor oil under the same conditions. Hence, pancake syrup and motor oil are more viscous than water and

alcohol. Gases have viscosities, too, but their viscosities are much smaller than those of liquids.

One of the classical techniques for measuring viscosities of liquids is called the *falling-sphere method*. In the falling-sphere method, the viscosity of a liquid is calculated by measuring the time it takes for a small sphere to fall a prescribed distance in a large container of the liquid, as illustrated in Figure 1. As the sphere falls in the liquid under the influence of gravity, it accelerates

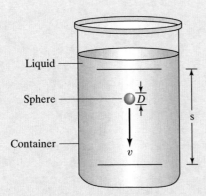

Figure 1. Experimental setup of the falling-sphere method for measuring viscosity.

until the downward force (the sphere's weight) is exactly balanced by the buoyancy force and drag force that act upward. From this time forward, the sphere falls with a constant velocity, referred to as terminal velocity. The buoyancy force, which is equal to the weight of the liquid displaced by the sphere, is usually small compared with the drag force, which is caused directly by viscosity. The terminal velocity of the sphere is inversely proportional to viscosity, since the sphere takes longer to fall a given distance in a very viscous liquid, such as motor oil, than in a less viscous liquid, such as water. By employing a force balance on the sphere and invoking some simple relations from fluid mechanics, we obtain the formula

$$\mu = \frac{(\gamma_s - \gamma_f)D^2}{18v}$$

where

μ = dynamic viscosity of liquid (Pa·s)
γ_s = specific weight of sphere (N/m³)
γ_f = specific weight of liquid (N/m³)
D = sphere diameter (m)
v = terminal velocity of sphere (m/s)

Note that the quantity *specific weight* is similar to *density*, except that it is a weight per volume, rather than a mass per volume. The word *dynamic* is used to avoid confusion with another type of viscosity known as *kinematic* viscosity.

Using the falling-sphere method, let's calculate the viscosity of glycerine, a very viscous liquid used to make a variety of chemicals. We set up a large glass cylinder

and place two marks, spaced 200 mm apart, on the outside surface. The marks are placed low enough on the cylinder to assure that the sphere will achieve terminal velocity before reaching the top mark. For the sphere, we use a steel (γ_s = 76,800 N/m³) ball bearing with a diameter of 2.381 mm (measured with a micrometer). From a previous measurement, the specific weight of the glycerin is γ_f = 12,400 N/m³. Now, we hold the steel sphere above the surface of the glycerin at the center of the cylinder and release the sphere. As accurately as we can determine with our eye, we start a handheld stopwatch when the sphere reaches the top mark. Similarly, we stop the watch when the sphere reaches the bottom mark. Our stopwatch is capable of displaying hundredths of a second, and it reads 11.32 s. Even though the stopwatch is capable of measuring time to the second decimal place, our crude visual timing method does not justify using a time interval with this precision. Sources of uncertainty such as human reaction time and thumb response do not justify the second decimal place. Thus, our time interval is reported as 11.3 s, which has three significant figures. We know that terminal velocity is distance divided by time:

$$v = \frac{s}{t} = \frac{0.200 \text{ m}}{11.3 \text{ s}} = 0.0177 \text{ m/s}$$

The distance was measured to the nearest millimeter, so the quantity, s, has three significant figures. Thus, terminal velocity may be written in three significant figures. (Remember that the zero, according to rule 6, is not significant.) Values of the given quantities for our calculation are summarized as follows:

$$\gamma_s = 76,800 \text{ N/m}^3 = 7.68 \times 10^4 \text{ N/m}^3$$
$$\gamma_f = 12,400 \text{ N/m}^3 = 1.24 \times 10^4 \text{ N/m}^3$$
$$v = 0.0177 \text{ m/s} = 1.77 \times 10^{-2} \text{ m/s}$$
$$D = 2.381 \text{ mm} = 2.381 \times 10^{-3} \text{ m}$$

Each quantity, with the exception of D, which has four significant figures, has three significant figures. Upon substituting values into the equation for dynamic viscosity, we obtain

$$\mu = \frac{(\gamma_s - \gamma_f)D^2}{18v}$$
$$= \frac{(76,800 - 12,400)\text{N/m}^3 (2.381 \times 10^{-3} \text{ m})}{18(0.0177 \text{ m/s})}$$
$$= 1.1459 \text{ Pa·s}$$

(Where did the pressure unit, Pa, come from?) According to the rules of significant figures for multiplication and division, our answer should contain the same number of significant figures as the number with the fewest significant figures. Our answer should therefore have three significant figures, so the dynamic viscosity of glycerin, expressed in the proper number of significant figures, is reported as

$$\mu = 1.15\ \text{Pa}\cdot\text{s}$$

Note that, because the value of the first digit dropped is 5, we rounded our answer up.

PROFESSIONAL SUCCESS: LEARN HOW TO USE YOUR CALCULATOR

As an engineering student, your best friend is your scientific calculator. If you do not yet own a quality scientific calculator, purchase one as soon as you can and begin learning how to use it. You cannot succeed in school without one. Do not scrimp on cost. You will probably only need one calculator for your entire academic career, so purchase one that offers the greatest number of functions and features. Professors and fellow students may offer advice on which calculator to buy. Your particular engineering department or college may even require that you use a particular calculator because they have heavily integrated calculator usage into the curriculum, and it would be too cumbersome to accommodate several types of calculators. Your college bookstore or local office supply store carry two or three name brands that have served engineering students and professionals for many years. Today's scientific calculators are remarkable engineering tools. A high-end scientific calculator has hundreds of built-in functions a large storage capacity graphics capabilities, and communication links to other calculators or personal computers.

Regardless of which scientific calculator you own or plan to purchase, *learn how to use it*. Begin with the basic arithmetic operations and the standard mathematical and statistical functions. Learn how to set the number of decimal places in the display and how to display numbers in scientific and engineering notation. After you are confident with performing unit conversions by hand, learn how to do them with your calculator. Learn how to write simple programs on your calculator. This skill will come in handy numerous times throughout your course work. Learn how to use the equation solving functions, matrix operations and calculus routines. By the time you learn most of the calculator's operations, you will probably have devoted a few hundred hours. The time spent mastering your calculator is perhaps as valuable as the time spent attending lectures, conducting experiments in a laboratory, doing homework problems, or studying for exams. Knowing your calculator thoroughly will help you succeed in your engineering program. Your engineering courses will be challenging enough. Do not make them an even bigger challenge by failing to adequately learn how to use your principal computational asset, your calculator.

PRACTICE!

1. Using an order-of-magnitude analysis, estimate the surface area of your body in units of m^2.

2. Using an order-of-magnitude analysis, estimate the number of hairs on your head.

3. Use an order-of-magnitude analysis to estimate the number of telephones in use in the United States.

4. Use an order-of-magnitude analysis to estimate the electrical energy in kWh used by your city in one month.

5. Underline the significant figures in the following numbers (the first number is done for you):
   a. 0.00<u>254</u>
   b. 29.8
   c. 2001
   d. 407.2

e. 0.0303

f. 2.006

Answer: b. <u>29</u>.8   c. <u>2001</u>   d. <u>407.2</u>   e. 0.0<u>303</u>   f. <u>2</u>.006

6. Perform the following calculations, reporting the answers with the correct number of significant figures:

a. 5.64/1.9

b. 500./0.0025

c. $(45.8 - 8.1)/1.922$

d. $2\pi/2.50$

e. $(5.25 \times 10^4)/(100 + 10.5)$

f. $0.0008/(1.2 \times 10^{-5})$

Answer: a. 3.0   b. 2.0×10^5 c. 19.6   d. 3   e. 473   f. 70

7. A ball bearing is reported to have a radius of 3.256 mm. Using the correct number of significant figures, what is the weight of this bearing in units of N if its density is $\rho = 1675$ kg/m^3?

Answer: 2.38×10^{-3} N

8. The cylinder of an internal combustion engine is reported to have a diameter of 4.000 in. If the stroke (length) of the cylinder is 6.25 in, what is the volume of the cylinder in units of in^3? Write the answer by using the correct number of significant figures.

Answer: 25.0 in^3

3   GENERAL ANALYSIS PROCEDURE

Engineers are problem solvers. In order to solve an engineering analysis problem thoroughly and accurately, engineers employ a solution method that is systematic, logical, and orderly. This method, when consistently and correctly applied, leads the engineer to a successful solution of the analytical problem at hand. The problem-solving method is an integral part of a good engineer's thought process. To the engineer, the procedure is second nature. When challenged by a new analysis, a good engineer knows precisely how to approach the problem. The problem may be fairly short and simple or extremely long and complex. Regardless of the size or complexity of the problem, the same solution method applies. Because of the *general* nature of the procedure, it applies to analytical problems associated with *any* engineering discipline: chemical, civil, electrical, mechanical, etc. Practicing engineers in all disciplines have been using the **general analysis procedure** in one form or another for a long time, and the history of engineering achievements is a testament to its success. While you are a student, it is vitally important that you learn the steps of the general analysis procedure. After you have learned the steps in the procedure and feel confident that you can use the procedure to solve problems, apply it in your analytical course work. Apply it religiously. Practice the procedure over and over again until it becomes a habit. Establishing good habits while still in school will make it that much easier for you to make a successful transition into professional engineering practice.

General Analysis Procedure

The general analysis procedure consists of the following seven steps:

1. PROBLEM STATEMENT

The problem statement is a written description of the analytical problem to be solved. It should be written clearly, concisely, and logically. The problem statement summarizes the given information, providing all necessary input data to solve the problem. The problem statement also states what is to be determined by performing the analysis.

2. DIAGRAM

The diagram is a sketch, drawing or schematic of the system being analyzed. Typically, it is a simplified pictorial representation of the actual system, showing only those aspects of the system that are necessary to perform the analysis. The diagram should show all given information contained in the problem statement such as geometry, applied forces, energy flows, mass flows, electrical currents, temperatures, or other physical quantities as required.

3. ASSUMPTIONS

Engineering analysis almost always involves some assumptions. Assumptions are special assertions about the physical characteristics of the problem that simplify or refine the analysis. A very complex analytical problem would be difficult or even impossible to solve without making some assumptions.

4. GOVERNING EQUATIONS

All physical systems may be described by mathematical relations. Governing equations are those mathematical relations that specifically pertain to the physical system being analyzed. These equations may represent physical laws, such as Newton's laws of motion, conservation of mass, conservation of energy, and Ohm's law; or they may represent fundamental engineering definitions such as velocity, stress, moment of force, and heat flux. The equations may also be basic mathematical or geometrical formulas involving angles, lines, areas, and volumes.

5. CALCULATIONS

In this step, the solution is generated. First, the solution is developed algebraically as far as possible. Then numerical values of known physical quantities are substituted for the corresponding algebraic variables. All necessary calculations are performed, using a calculator or computer, to produce a numerical result with the correct units and the proper number of significant figures.

6. SOLUTION CHECK

This step is crucial. Immediately after obtaining the result, examine it carefully. Using established knowledge of similar analytical solutions and common sense, try to ascertain whether the result is reasonable. However, whether the result seems reasonable or not, double-check every step of the analysis. Flush out defective diagrams, bad assumptions, erroneously applied equations, incorrect numerical manipulations, and improper use of units.

7. DISCUSSION

After the solution has been thoroughly checked and corrected, discuss the result. The discussion may include an assessment of the assumptions, a summary of the main conclusions, a proposal on how the result may be verified experimentally in a laboratory, or a parametric study, demonstrating the sensitivity of the result to a range of input parameters.

Now that the seven-step procedure has been summarized, further discussion of each step is warranted:

1. Problem statement   In your engineering textbook, the problem statement will generally be supplied to you in the form of a problem or question at the end of each chapter. These problem statements are written by the textbook authors, professors or practicing engineers, who have expertise in the subject area. The great majority of end-of-chapter problems in engineering texts are well organized and well written, so you do not have to fret too much about the problem statement. Alternatively, your engineering professor may give you problem statements from sources outside your textbook or from his or her own engineering experience. In either case, the problem statement should be well posed, contain all the necessary input information, and clearly state what is to be determined by the analysis. What is known and what is unknown in the problem should be clearly identified. If the problem statement is flawed in any way, a meaningful analysis is impossible.

2. Diagram   The old saying, "One picture is worth a thousand words," is certainly applicable to engineering analysis. A complete diagram of the system being analyzed is critical. A good diagram helps the engineer visualize the physical processes or characteristics of the system. It also helps the engineer identify reasonable assumptions and the appropriate governing equations. A diagram might even reveal flaws in the problem statement or alternative methods of solution. Engineers use a variety of diagrams in their analytical work. One of the most widely used diagrams in engineering is the *free-body diagram*. Free-body diagrams are used to solve engineering mechanics (statics, dynamics, strength of materials) problems. These diagrams are called "free-body" diagrams because they represent a specific body, isolated from all other bodies that are in physical contact with, or that may be in the vicinity of, the body in question. The influences of nearby bodies are represented as external forces acting on the body being analyzed. Hence, a free-body diagram is a sketch of the body in question, showing all external forces applied to the body. A free-body diagram is a pictorial representation of a "force balance" on the body. Diagrams are also used in the analysis of thermal systems. Unlike a free-body diagram, which shows forces applied to the body, a diagram of a thermal system shows all the various forms of energy entering and leaving the system. This type of diagram is a pictorial representation of an "energy balance" on the system. Another type of diagram represents a system that transports mass at known rates. Common examples include pipe and duct systems, conveyors and storage systems. A diagram for these systems shows all the mass entering and leaving the system. This type of diagram is a pictorial representation of a "mass balance" on the system. Still another type of diagram is an electrical circuit schematic. Electrical schematics show how components are connected and the currents, voltages and other electrical quantities in the circuit. Some examples of diagrams used in analysis are given in Figure 2.

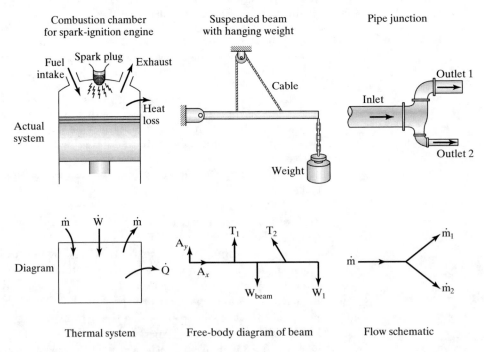

Figure 2.   Examples of typical diagrams used in engineering analysis.

3. Assumptions   I attended a lecture given by a physicist who referred to himself as an "atmospheric scientist" who studied various processes that occur in the upper atmosphere. He recounted an accomplishment that seemed truly remarkable. After convincing the audience that atmospheric processes are some of the most complex phenomena in physics, he boasted that he had developed, over the space of a few months, an analytical model of the upper atmosphere that contained *no* assumptions. There was only one problem: His model had no solution either. By including every physical mechanism to the minutest detail in the model, his analysis was so mathematically convoluted that it could not generate a solution. Had he made some simplifying assumptions, his atmospheric model could have worked even though the results would have been approximate.

Engineers and scientists routinely employ assumptions to simplify a problem. As my story illustrates, an approximate answer is better than no answer at all. Failure to invoke one or more simplifying assumptions in the analysis, particularly a complex one, can increase the complexity of the problem by an order of magnitude, leading the engineer down a very long road, only to reach a dead end. How do we determine which assumptions to use and whether our assumptions are good or bad? To a large extent, the application of good assumptions is an acquired skill, a skill that comes with engineering experience. However, you can begin to learn this skill in school through repeated application of the general analysis procedure in your engineering courses. As you apply the procedure to a variety of engineering problems, you will gain a basic understanding of how assumptions are used in engineering analysis. Then, after you graduate and accept a position with an engineering firm, you can refine this skill as you apply the analysis procedure to solve problems that are specific to the company. Sometimes, a problem can be overly constrained by assumptions such that the problem is simplified to the point where it becomes grossly inaccurate or even meaningless. The engineer must therefore be able to apply the proper *number* as well as the proper *type* of assumptions in a given analysis. A common assumption made in the stress analysis of a column is shown in Figure 3.

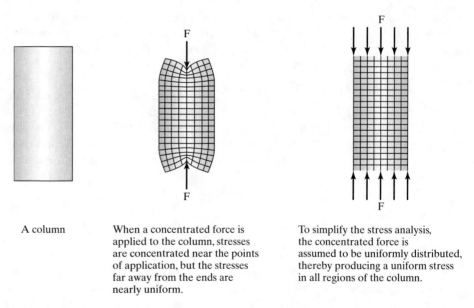

| A column | When a concentrated force is applied to the column, stresses are concentrated near the points of application, but the stresses far away from the ends are nearly uniform. | To simplify the stress analysis, the concentrated force is assumed to be uniformly distributed, thereby producing a uniform stress in all regions of the column. |

Figure 3. A common assumption made in the stress analysis of a column.

4. *Governing equations*   The governing equations are the "workhorses" of the analysis. To a very limited extent, we may be able to afford some sloppiness in the other steps in the analysis procedure, but not in the governing equations. The governing equations are either right or they are wrong—there is no middle ground. They either describe the physical problem at hand, or they do not. If the wrong governing equations are used, the analysis will most certainly lead to a result that does not reflect the true physical nature of the problem, or the analysis will not be possible at all because the governing equations are not in harmony with the problem statement or assumptions. When using a governing equation to a solve a problem, the engineer must ascertain that the equation being used *actually* applies to the specific problem at hand. As an extreme (and probably absurd) example, imagine an engineer attempting to use Newton's second law, $F = ma$, to calculate the heat loss from a boiler? How about trying to apply Ohm's law, $V = IR$, to find the stress in a concrete column that supports a bridge deck? The problem of matching governing equations to the problem at hand is usually more subtle. In thermodynamics, for example, the engineer must determine whether the thermal system is "closed" or "open" (i.e., whether the system allows mass to cross the system boundary). After the type of thermal system has been identified, the thermodynamic equations which apply to that type of system are chosen, and the analysis proceeds. Governing equations must also be consistent with the assumptions. It is counterproductive to invoke simplifying assumptions if the governing equations do not make allowances for them. Some governing equations, particularly those that are experimentally derived, have built-in restrictions that limit the use of the equations to specific numerical values of key variables. A common mistake made in the application of a governing equation in this situation is failing to recognize the restrictions by forcing the equation to accept numerical values that lie outside the equation's range of applicability.

5. Calculations   A common practice, particularly among beginning students, is to substitute numerical values of quantities into equations *too early* in the calculations. It seems that students are more comfortable working with *numbers* than *algebraic variables*, so their first impulse is to substitute numerical values for all parameters at the beginning of the calculation. Avoid this impulse. To the extent that it is practical, develop the solution *analytically* prior to assigning physical quantities their numerical values. Before rushing to "plug" numbers into equations, carefully examine the equations to see if they can be mathematically manipulated to yield simpler expressions. A variable from one equation can often be substituted into another equation to reduce the total number of variables. Perhaps an expression can be simplified by factoring. By developing the solution analytically first, you might uncover certain physical characteristics about the system or even make the problem easier to solve. The analytical skills you learned in your algebra, trigonometry and calculus courses are meant to be used for performing mathematical operations on *symbolic* quantities, not numbers. When doing engineering analysis, do not put your mathematics skills on a shelf to collect dust—*use* them.

The calculations step demands more of an engineer than the ability to simply "crunch numbers" on a calculator or computer. The numbers have to be meaningful, and the equations containing the numbers must be fully understood and properly used. All mathematical relations must be dimensionally consistent, and all physical quantities must have a numerical value plus the correct units. Here is a tip concerning units that will save you time and help you avoid mistakes: *If the quantities given in the problem statement are not expressed in terms of a consistent set of units, convert all quantities to a consistent set of units before performing any calculations.* If some of the input parameters are expressed as a mixture of SI units and English units, convert all parameters to either SI units or English units, and then perform the calculations. Students tend to make more mistakes when they attempt to perform unit conversions *within* the governing equations. If all unit conversions are done prior to substituting numerical values into the equations, unit consistency is assured throughout the remainder of the calculations, because a consistent set of units is established at the onset. Dimensional consistency should still be verified, however, by substituting all quantities along with their units into the governing equations.

6. *Solution check*   This step is perhaps the easiest one to overlook. Even good engineers sometimes neglect to thoroughly check their solution. The solution may "look" good at first glance, but a mere glance is not good enough. Much effort has gone into formulating the problem statement, constructing diagrams of the system, determining the appropriate number and type of assumptions, invoking governing equations and performing a sequence of calculations. All this work may be for naught if the solution is not carefully checked. Checking the solution of an engineering analysis is analogous to checking the operation of an automobile immediately following a major repair. It's always a good idea if the mechanic checks the overhauled transmission to verify that it works before returning the vehicle to its owner.

There are two main aspects of the solution check. First, the result itself should be checked. Ask the question, "Is this result reasonable?" There are several ways to answer this question. The result must be consistent with the information given in the problem statement. For example, suppose you wish to calculate the temperature of a microprocessor chip in a computer. In the problem statement, the ambient air temperature is given as 25°C, but your analysis indicates that the chip temperature is only 20°C. This result is not consistent with the given information because it is physically impossible for a heat-producing component, a microprocessor chip in this case, to have a lower temperature than the surrounding environment. If the answer had been 60°C, it is at least consistent with the problem statement, but it may still be incorrect. Another way to check the result is to compare it with that of similar analyses performed by you or other engineers. If the result of a similar analysis is not available, an alternative analysis that utilizes a different solution approach may have to be conducted. In some cases, a laboratory test may be needed to verify the solution experimentally. Testing is a normal part of engineering design anyway, so a test to verify an analytical result may be customary.

The second aspect of the solution check is a thorough inspection and review of each step of the analysis. Returning to our microprocessor example, if no mathematical or numerical errors are committed, the answer of 60°C may be considered correct insofar as the calculations are concerned, but the answer could still be in error. How? By applying bad assumptions. For example, suppose that the microprocessor chip is air cooled by a small fan, so we assert that forced convection is the dominant mechanism by which heat is transferred from the chip. Accordingly, we assume that conduction and radiation heat transfer are negligible, so we do not include these mechanisms in the analysis. A temperature of 60°C seems a little high, so we revise our assumptions. A second analysis that includes conduction and radiation reveals that the microprocessor chip is much cooler, about 42°C. Knowing whether assumptions are good or bad comes through increased knowledge of physical processes and practical engineering experience.

7. *Discussion*   This step is valuable from the standpoint of communicating to others what the results of the analysis mean. By discussing the analysis, you are in effect writing a "minitechnical report." This report summarizes the major conclusions of the analysis. In the microprocessor example given earlier, the main conclusion may be that 42°C is below the recommended operating temperature for the chip, and therefore, the chip will operate reliably in the computer for a minimum of 10,000 hours before failing. If the chip temperature was actually measured at 45°C shortly after performing the analysis, the discussion might include an examination of why the predicted and measured temperatures differ and particularly why the predicted temperature is lower than the measured temperature. A brief parametric study may be included that shows how the chip temperature varies as a function of ambient air temperature. The discussion may even include an entirely separate analysis that predicts the chip temperature in the event of a fan failure. In the discussion step, the engineer is given one last opportunity to gain additional insights into the problem.

Engineering programs strive to give students a sense of what is it like to actually practice engineering in the "real world." But *studying* engineering in school and *practicing* engineering in the real world are not the same thing. One difference is amply illustrated by considering the origins of problem statements for analysis. In school, problem statements are typically found at the end of each chapter of your engineering texts. (The answers to many of these problems are even provided at the back of the book.) Sometimes your professors obtain problem statements from other texts or invent new ones (especially for exams). In any case, problem statements are supplied to you in a nice, neat little package all ready for you to tackle the problem. If textbooks and professors supply problem statements to students in school, who or what supplies problem statements to practicing engineers in industry? Real-world engineering problems are not typically found in textbooks (answers are never found in the back of the book, either), and

your engineering professors are not going to follow you around after you graduate. So, where do the real-world problem statements come from? They are *formulated* by the engineer who is going to perform the analysis. As stated before, analysis is an integral part of engineering design. As a design matures, quantitative parameters that characterize the design begin to emerge. When an analysis is called for, these parameters are woven into a problem statement from which an analysis may be conducted. The engineer must be able to formulate a coherent, logical problem statement from the design information available. Because engineering design is an iterative process, the values of some or all of the input parameters may be uncertain. The engineer must therefore be able to write the problem statement in such a way as to allow for these uncertainties. The analysis will have to be repeated several times until the parameters are no longer in a state of flux, at which time the design is complete.

The seven-step procedure for performing an engineering analysis is a time-tested method. In order to effectively communicate an analysis to others, the analysis must be presented in a format that can be readily understood and followed. Engineers are known for their ability to present analyses and other technical information with clarity in a thorough, neat, and careful manner. As an engineering student, you can begin to develop this ability by consistently applying the analysis procedure outlined in this section. Your engineering professors will insist that you follow the procedure, or a procedure similar to it, in your engineering courses. You will probably be graded not only on how well you perform the analysis itself, but how well you *present* the analysis on paper. This grading practice is meant to convince students of the importance of presentation standards in engineering and to assist them in developing good presentation skills. An engineering analysis is of little value to anyone unless it can be read and understood. A good analysis is one that can be easily read by others. If your analysis resembles "hen scratchings" or "alien hieroglyphics" that require an interpreter, the analysis is useless. Apply the presentation guidelines given in this section to the point where they become second nature. Then, after you graduate and begin practicing engineering, you can hone your presentation skills as you gain industrial experience.

The 10 guidelines that follow will help you present an engineering analysis in a clear and complete manner. These guidelines are applicable to analysis work in school as well as industrial engineering practice. It should be noted that the guidelines apply specifically to analyses performed by hand with the use of pencil and paper, as opposed to computer-generated analyses.

Analysis Presentation Guidelines

1. A standard practice of engineers who do analysis is to use a special type of *paper*. This paper is usually referred to as "engineer calculation pad" or "engineer's computation paper." The paper is light green in color, and should be available in your college or university bookstore. The back side of the paper is ruled horizontally and vertically with five squares per inch, with only heading and margin rulings on the front side. The rulings on the back side are faintly visible through the paper to help the engineer maintain the proper position and orientation for lettering, diagrams and graphs. (See Figure 4) All work is to be done on the *front* side of the paper. The back side is not used. The paper usually comes prepunched with a standard three-hole pattern at the left edge for placement in a three-ring binder.

Front side   Back side

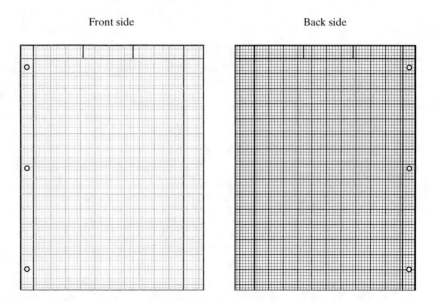

Figure 4. Engineer's computation paper is standard issue for analysis work.

2. No more than *one* problem should be placed on a page. This practice helps maintain clarity by keeping different problems separate. Even if a problem occupies a small fraction of a page, the next problem should be started on a separate page.

3. The *heading* area at the top of the page should indicate your name, date, course number, and assignment number. The upper right corner of the heading area is usually reserved for page numbers. To alert the reader to the total number of pages present, page numbers are often reported, for example, as "1/3", which is read as "page 1 of 3." Page 1 is the current page, and there are a total of three pages. When multiple pages are used, they should be stapled in the upper left corner. Each page should nonetheless be identified with your name, in the unlikely event the pages become separated.

4. The *problem statement* should be written out completely, not summarized or condensed. All figures that accompany the problem statement should be shown. If the problem statement originates from a textbook, it should be

written *verbatim* so the reader does not have to refer back to the textbook for the full version. One way to do this is to photocopy the problem statement, along with any figures given, and then cut and paste it by using rubber cement directly beneath the heading area on the engineer's computation paper. The problem statement could also be electronically scanned and printed directly onto the paper.

5. Work should be done in *pencil*, not ink. Everyone makes mistakes. If the analysis is written in pencil, mistakes can be easily erased and corrected. If the analysis is written in ink, mistakes will have to be crossed out, and the presentation will not have a neat appearance. To avoid smudges, use a pencil lead with the appropriate hardness. All markings should be dark enough to reproduce a legible copy if photocopies are needed. If you still use a standard wooden pencil, throw it out. Mechanical pencils are superior. They do not require sharpening, contain several months worth of lead, have replaceable erasers, produce no waste, and come in a range of lead diameters to suit your own writing needs. Mechanical pencils are also durable. (I have been using the same mechanical pencil since 1977!)

6. Lettering should be *printed*. The lettering style should be consistent throughout.

7. Correct *spelling* and *grammar* must be used. Even if the technical aspects of the presentation are flawless, the engineer will lose some credibility if the writing is poor.

8. There are seven steps in the general analysis procedure. These steps should be sufficiently *spaced* so that the reader can easily follow the analysis from problem statement to discussion. A horizontal line drawn across the page is one way of providing this separation.

9. Good *diagrams* are a must. A straight edge, drawing templates and other manual drafting tools should be used. All pertinent quantitative information such as geometry, forces, energy flows, mass flows, electrical currents, pressures, etc., should be shown on the diagrams.

10. Answers should be *double underlined* or *boxed* for ready identification. To enhance the effect, colored pencils may be used.

These 10 guidelines for analysis presentation are recommended to the engineering student. You may find that your particular engineering department or professors may advocate guidelines that are slightly different. By all means, follow the guidelines given to you. Your professors may have special reasons for teaching their students certain methods of analysis presentation. Methods may vary somewhat from professor to professor, but should still reflect the major points contained in the guidelines given in this section.

The next four examples illustrate the general analysis procedure and the recommended guidelines for analysis presentation. Each example represents a basic analysis taken from the subject areas of statics, electrical circuits, thermodynamics, and fluid mechanics. You probably have not yet taken courses in these subjects, so do not be overly concerned if you do not understand all the technical aspects of the examples. Therefore, do not focus on the theoretical and mathematical details. Focus instead on how the general analysis procedure is used to solve problems from different engineering areas and the systematic manner in which the analyses are presented.

EXAMPLE 4

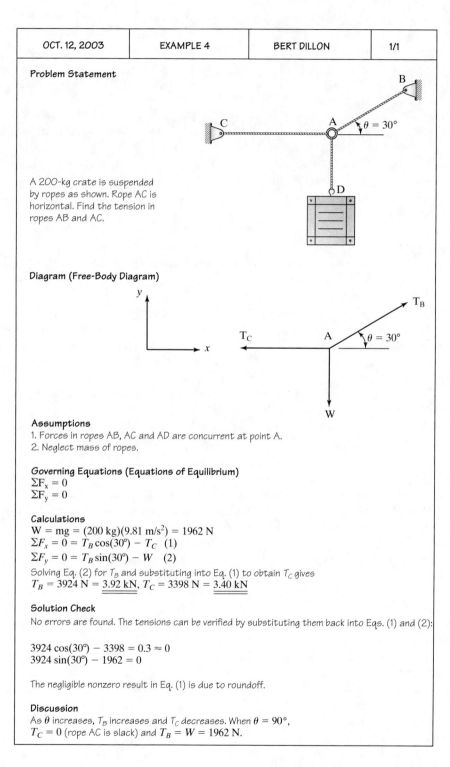

| OCT. 12, 2003 | EXAMPLE 4 | BERT DILLON | 1/1 |

Problem Statement

A 200-kg crate is suspended by ropes as shown. Rope AC is horizontal. Find the tension in ropes AB and AC.

Diagram (Free-Body Diagram)

Assumptions
1. Forces in ropes AB, AC and AD are concurrent at point A.
2. Neglect mass of ropes.

Governing Equations (Equations of Equilibrium)
$\Sigma F_x = 0$
$\Sigma F_y = 0$

Calculations
$W = mg = (200 \text{ kg})(9.81 \text{ m/s}^2) = 1962 \text{ N}$
$\Sigma F_x = 0 = T_B \cos(30°) - T_C$ (1)
$\Sigma F_y = 0 = T_B \sin(30°) - W$ (2)
Solving Eq. (2) for T_B and substituting into Eq. (1) to obtain T_C gives
$T_B = 3924 \text{ N} = \underline{3.92 \text{ kN}}, T_C = 3398 \text{ N} = \underline{3.40 \text{ kN}}$

Solution Check
No errors are found. The tensions can be verified by substituting them back into Eqs. (1) and (2):

$3924 \cos(30°) - 3398 = 0.3 \approx 0$
$3924 \sin(30°) - 1962 = 0$

The negligible nonzero result in Eq. (1) is due to roundoff.

Discussion
As θ increases, T_B increases and T_C decreases. When $\theta = 90°$,
$T_C = 0$ (rope AC is slack) and $T_B = W = 1962 \text{ N}$.

EXAMPLE 5

JAN. 03, 2004	EXAMPLE 5	MARIE NORTON	1/2

Problem Statement

Two resistors with resistances of $5\,\Omega$ and $50\,\Omega$ are connected in parallel across a $10\,\text{V}$ battery. Find the current in each resistor.

Diagram (Electrical Schematic)

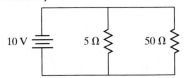

Assumptions

1. Neglect resistance of wires.
2. Battery voltage is a constant $10\,\text{V}$.

Governing Equations (Ohm's law)

$$V = IR$$

V = Voltage (V)
I = Current (A)
R = Resistance (Ω)

Calculations

Rearranging Ohm's law: $I = \dfrac{V}{R}$.

Define: $R_1 = 5\,\Omega$, $R_2 = 50\,\Omega$
Because resistors are connected in parallel with battery,
$V = V_1 = V_2 = 10\,V$.

$$\therefore I_1 = \frac{V_1}{R_1} = \frac{10\,V}{5\,\Omega} = \underline{\underline{2\,\text{A}}}, I_2 = \frac{V_2}{R_2} = \frac{10\,V}{50\,\Omega} = \underline{\underline{0.2\,\text{A}}}$$

Solution Check (no errors found)

JAN. 03, 2004	EXAMPLE 5	MARIE NORTON	2/2

Discussion

Current flow in a resistor is inversely proportional to the resistance.
Total current is split according to the ratio of resistances:

$$\frac{I_1}{I_2} = \frac{R_2}{R_1} = \frac{2\,\text{A}}{0.2\,\text{A}} = \frac{50\,\Omega}{5\,\Omega} = 10$$

Total current:

$$I_T = I_1 + I_2 \\ = 2\,\text{A} + 0.2\,\text{A} = 2.2\,\text{A}$$

Total current may also be found by finding total resistance and then using Ohm's law.

Resistors in parallel as follows:

$$R_T = \frac{1}{\dfrac{1}{R_1} + \dfrac{1}{R_2}} = \frac{1}{\dfrac{1}{5} + \dfrac{1}{50}}$$

$$R_T = 4.5455\,\Omega$$

$$I_T = \frac{V}{R_T} = \frac{10\,V}{4.5455\,\Omega} = 2.2\,\text{A}$$

EXAMPLE 6

MAR. 24, 2004	EXAMPLE 6	CY BRAYTON	1/2

Problem Statement

A classroom occupied by 50 students is to be air conditioned with window-mounted air conditioning units with a 4-kW rating. There are 20 florescent lights in the room, each rated at 60 W. While sitting at their desks, each student dissipates 100 W. If the heat transfer to the classroom through the roof, walls and windows is 5 kW, how many air conditioning units are required to maintain the classroom at a constant temperature of 22°C?

Diagram (Thermodynamic System)

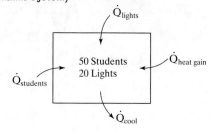

Assumptions

1. Classroom is a closed system, i.e., no mass flows.
2. All heat flows are steady.
3. No other heat sources in classroom such as computers, TVs, etc.

Governing Equations (Conservation of Energy)

$$\dot{E}_{in} - \dot{E}_{out} = \Delta E_{system}$$

Calculations

$$\dot{E}_{in} = \dot{Q}_{students} + \dot{Q}_{lights} + \dot{Q}_{heat\ gain}$$
$$= (50)(100\ W) + (20)(60\ W) + 5000\ W = 11,200\ W = 11.2\ kW$$

$\Delta E_{system} = 0$ (*Classroom is maintained at constant temperature*)

$$\dot{E}_{in} - \dot{E}_{out} = \dot{Q}_{cool}$$

Number of A.C. units required $= \dfrac{\dot{Q}_{cool}}{4\ kW} = \dfrac{11.2\ kW}{4\ kW} = 2.8$

Fractions of A.C. units are impossible, so round up answer to next integer.

MAR. 24, 2004	EXAMPLE 6	CY BRAYTON	2/2

Number of A.C. units required $= \underline{\underline{3}}$.

Solution check (no errors found)

Discussion

The classroom temperature of 22°C was not used in the calculation because this temperature, as well as the outdoor air temperature, are inferred in the given heat gain by a prior heat transfer analysis.

Suppose that the classroom was a computer lab containing 30 computers each dissipating 250 W. We eliminate assumption 3 by including heat input by the computers.

$$\dot{Q}_{cool} = \dot{Q}_{students} + \dot{Q}_{lights} + \dot{Q}_{heat\ gain} + \dot{Q}_{computers}$$
$$= 11,200\ W + 30(250\ W) = 18,700\ W = 18.7\ kW$$

Number of A.C. units required $= \dfrac{\dot{Q}_{cool}}{4\ kW} = \dfrac{18.7\ kW}{4\ kW} = 4.7$

Number of A.C. units required $= \underline{\underline{5}}$.

This example illustrates the effect computers have on air-conditioning requirements.

EXAMPLE 7

MAY 17, 2004	EXAMPLE 7	EDDIE POWERS	1/2

Problem Statement

Water enters a pipe junction at a mass flow rate of 3.6 kg/s. If the mass flow rate in the small branch is 1.4 kg/s, what is the mass flow rate in the large pipe branch? If the inside diameter of the large pipe branch is 5 cm, what is the velocity in the large pipe branch?

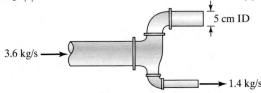

3.6 kg/s →

5 cm ID

→ 1.4 kg/s

Diagram (Flow Schematic)

$\dot{m} = 3.6$ kg/s →

$\dot{m}_2$

$\dot{m}_1 = 1.4$ kg/s

Assumptions
1. Steady, incompressible flow
2. Density of water: $\rho = 1000$ kg/m^3

Governing Equations

Conservation of mass: $\dot{m}_{in} = \dot{m}_{out}$ $\dot{m}$ = mass flow rate (kg/s)
mass flow rate: $\dot{m} = \rho A v$ ρ = fluid density (kg/m^3)
          A = flow cross-sectional area (m^2)
          v = velocity (m/s)

Calculations

$\dot{m} = \dot{m}_1 + \dot{m}_2$
$\dot{m}_2 = \dot{m} - \dot{m}_1 = 3.6$ kg/s $- 1.4$ kg/s
$\qquad = 2.2$ kg/s

MAY 17, 2004	EXAMPLE 7	EDDIE POWERS	2/2

$$\dot{m}_2 = \rho A_2 v_2 = \rho \frac{\pi D_2^2}{4} v_2$$

$$v_2 = \frac{4\,\dot{m}_2}{\pi \rho D_2^2} = \frac{4\,(2.2 \text{ kg/s})}{\pi (1000 \text{ kg/m}^3)(0.05 \text{ m})^2}$$

$$= \underline{\underline{1.12 \text{ m/s}}}$$

Solution check (no errors found)

Discussion

The velocity calculated is an average value because there is a velocity profile across the pipe. The velocity profile is caused by viscosity. If the flow condition is laminar, the velocity profile is parabolic, as shown in the following sketch.

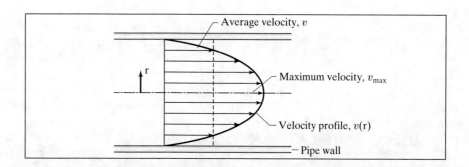

A good engineer is a person who solves an engineering analysis problem by reasoning through it, rather than simply following a prepared "recipe" consisting of step-by-step instructions written by someone else. Similarly, a good engineering student is a person who learns engineering analysis by thinking conceptually about each problem, rather than simply memorizing a collection of disjointed solution sequences and mathematical formulas. This "cookbook" learning approach is a detour on the road of engineering education. Furthermore, the cookbook learning style promotes fragmented rather than integrative learning. A student who embraces this type of learning method will soon discover that it will be difficult and take a long time to solve new engineering problems, unless identical or very similar problems have been previously solved by using an established recipe. An analogy may be drawn from the familiar maxim "Give a man a fish, and you have fed him for a day. Teach a man to fish, and you have fed him for a lifetime." A recipe enables a student to solve only one specific type of problem, whereas a more general conceptual-based learning approach enables a student to solve many engineering problems.

PRACTICE!

Use the general analysis procedure to solve the following problems (present the analysis by using the guidelines for analysis presentation covered in this section):

1. Radioactive waste is to be permanently encased in concrete and buried in the ground. The vessel containing the waste measures 30 cm × 30 cm × 80 cm. Federal regulations dictate that there must be a minimum concrete thickness of 50 cm surrounding the vessel on all sides. What is the minimum volume of concrete required to safely encase the radioactive waste?
   Answer: 2.97 m^3

2. An elevator in an office building has an operating capacity of 15 passengers with a maximum weight of 180 lb_f each. The elevator is suspended by a special pulley system with four cables, two of which support 20 percent of the total load and two of which support 80 percent of the total load. Find the maximum tension in each elevator cable.
   Answer: 270 lb_f, 1080 lb_f

3. A technician measures a voltage drop of 25 V across a 100-Ω resistor by using a digital voltmeter. Ohm's law states that $V = IR$. What is the current flow through the resistor? How much power is consumed by the resistor? (*Hint*: $P = I^2R$.)
   Answer: 250 mA, 6.25 W

4. Air flows through a main duct at a mass flow rate of 4 kg/s. The main duct enters a junction that splits into two branch ducts, one with a cross section of

> 20 cm × 30 cm and one with a cross section of 40 cm × 60 cm. If the mass
> flow rate in the large branch is 2.8 kg/s, what is the mass flow rate in the small
> branch? If the density of air is $\rho = 1.16$ kg/m^3, what is the velocity in each
> branch?
>
> *Answer*: 1.2 kg/s, 10.1 m/s, 17.2 m/s

4   THE COMPUTER AS AN ANALYSIS TOOL

Computers are an integral part of the civilized world. They affect virtually every aspect of our everyday lives, including communications, transportation, financial transactions, information processing, food production, and health care, among others. The world is a much different place today than it was prior to the advent of computers. People use computers for accessing and processing information, word processing, electronic mail, entertainment, and on-line shopping. Like everyone else, engineers use computers in their personal lives in the same ways just mentioned, but they also depend heavily on computers in their professional work. To the engineer, the computer is an indispensable tool. Why do engineers need computers? Without the computer, engineers would not be able to do their work accurately or efficiently. The primary advantage of the computer to engineers is its ability to perform various functions extremely rapidly. For example, a complex sequence of calculations that would take days with a slide rule can be carried out in a few seconds by a computer. Furthermore, the numerical precision of the computer enables engineers to make calculations that are much more accurate. Engineers use computers for computer-aided design (CAD), word processing, communications, information access, graphing, process control, simulation, data acquisition, and, of course, analysis.

The computer is one of the most powerful analysis tools available to the engineer, but the computer does not replace the engineer's thinking. When faced with a new analysis, the engineer must reason through the problem by using sound scientific principles, applied mathematics, and engineering judgement. A computer is only a machine, and, as yet, no machine has been developed that can outthink a human being (except at playing chess, perhaps). A computer can only carry out the instructions supplied to it, but it does so with remarkable speed and efficiency. A computer yields wrong answers just as quickly as it yields right ones. The burden is upon the engineer to supply the computer with correct input. An often-used engineering acronym is *GIGO* (*Garbage In, Garbage Out*), which refers to a situation in which erroneous input data is supplied to a computer, thereby producing erroneous output. When GIGO is at work, the calculations are numerically correct, but the results of those calculations are meaningless, because the engineer supplied the computer with bad input, or the computer program that the engineer wrote is flawed. The computer is capable of accurately performing enormous numbers of computations in a very short time, but it is incapable of composing a problem statement, constructing a diagram of the engineering system, formulating assumptions, selecting the appropriate governing equations, checking the reasonableness of the solution, or discussing and evaluating the results of the analysis. Thus, the only step in the analysis procedure for which a computer is perfectly suited is step 5: calculations. This is not to say that a computer cannot be used to write problem statements, assumptions and equations, as well as draw diagrams. These steps may also be performed by using the computer, but they must be developed by the engineer, whereas calculations are performed automatically once the equations and numerical inputs are supplied.

Engineers use analysis primarily as a design tool and as a means of predicting or investigating failures. Specifically, how does an engineer use the computer to perform an analysis? Steps 1 through 4 and steps 6 and 7 of the analysis procedure are largely unchanged, whether a computer is employed or not. So, exactly how are the calculations in step 5 carried out on a computer? There are basically five categories of computer tools for doing engineering analysis work:

1. Spreadsheets
2. Equation solvers and mathematics software
3. Programming languages
4. Specialty software
5. Finite element software

4.1   Spreadsheets

The term **spreadsheet** originally referred to a special type of paper, divided into rows and columns, for doing financial calculations. The computer-based spreadsheet is a modern electronic version of the paper spreadsheet and was initially used for business and accounting applications. By virtue of their general structure, spreadsheets are useful not only for doing financial calculations, but can also be used for performing a variety of scientific and engineering calculations. Like the original paper version, the computer-based spreadsheet consists of any array of rows and columns. The intersection of a row with a column is called a *cell*. Cells serve as locations for input and output data such as text, numbers, or formulas. For example, a cell may contain an equation representing Newton's second law of motion, $F = ma$. A nearby cell would contain a number for the mass, m, while another cell would contain a number for the acceleration, a. Immediately after entering these two input values in their respective cells, the spreadsheet automatically evaluates the formula, inserting the numerical value of the force, F, in the cell containing the formula for Newton's second law. If the values of the mass or acceleration are changed, the spreadsheet automatically updates the value of the force. This example is very simple, but spreadsheets are capable of doing calculations that involve hundreds or even thousands of variables. Suppose that our analysis involves 100 variables and that we want to know how changing only *one* of those variables affects the solution. We simply change the variable of interest and the entire spreadsheet automatically updates all calculations to reflect the change. The spreadsheet is an excellent analysis tool for rapidly answering "what if" questions. Numerous design alternatives can be efficiently investigated by performing the analysis on a spreadsheet. In addition to numerical functions, spreadsheets also have graphics capabilities. Excel,[1] Quattro Pro,[2] and Lotus 1-2-3[3] are popular spreadsheet products. Figure 3.5 shows a simple example of calculating force using Newton's second law by using Excel.

4.2   Equation Solvers and Mathematics Software

Equation solvers and **mathematics software** packages are general-purpose scientific and engineering tools for solving equations and performing symbolic mathematical operations. Equation solvers are primarily designed for solving problems that involve *numerical* inputs and outputs, whereas mathematics packages are primarily suited for performing *symbolic* mathematical operations much like you would do in a mathematics course. Equation solvers accept a set of equations that represent the mathematical model of the analytical problem. The equations can be linear or nonlinear. The equations may be written in their original form without prior mathematical manipulation to isolate the unknown quantities on one side of the equals sign. For example, Newton's second law would be written in its original form as $F = ma$ even if the unknown quantity was the acceleration a. Solving this problem by hand, however, we would have to write the equation as $a = F/m$ because we are solving for the acceleration. This is not necessary when we use equation solvers.

---

[1] Excel is a registered trademark of Microsoft® Corporation.
[2] Quattro® Pro is a registered trademark of Corel® Corporation.
[3] Lotus 1-2-3 is a registered trademark of Lotus® Development Corporation part of IBM®.

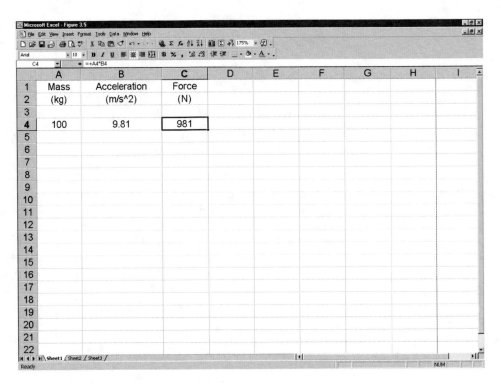

Figure 5. A calculation of Newton's second law using Excel. Note the formula for the force, + A4*B4, entered in cell C4.

After we supply the numerical values for the known quantities, equation solvers solve for the remaining unknown values. Equation solvers have a large built-in library of functions for use in trigonometry, linear algebra, statistics, and calculus. Equation solvers can perform a variety of mathematical operations, including differentiation, integration, and matrix operations. In addition to these mathematical features, equation solvers also do unit conversions. Equation solvers also have the capability of displaying results in graphical form. Programming can also be done within equation solvers. Although all equation solvers have some symbolic capabilities, some have the capacity for data acquisition, image analysis, and signal processing. Popular equation solvers are TK Solver,[4] Mathcad,[5] and Matlab.[6]

The strength of mathematics packages is their ability to perform symbolic mathematical operations. A symbolic mathematical operation is one that involves the manipulation of symbols (variables), using mathematical operators such as the vector product, differentiation, integration, and transforms. These packages are capable of performing very complex and sophisticated mathematical procedures. They also have extensive graphical capabilities. Even though mathematics packages are primarily designed for symbolic operations, they can also perform numerical computations. Mathematica[7] and Maple[8] are popular mathematics software products.

4.3   Programming Languages

Spreadsheets, equation solvers, and mathematics software packages may not always meet the computational demands of every engineering analysis. In such cases, engineers may

---

[4]TK Solver is a registered trademark of Universal Technical Systems, Incorporated.

[5]Mathcad® is a registered trademark of Mathsoft™, Incorporated.

[6]MATLAB® is a registered trademark of The MathWorks, Incorporated.

[7]MATHEMATICA® is a registered trademark of Wolfram Research, Incorporated.

[8]Maple™ is a registered trademark of Maplesoft™, a division of Waterloo Maple, Incorporated.

choose to write their own computer programs with the use of a programming language. **Programming languages** refer to sequential instructions supplied to a computer for carrying out specific calculations. Computer languages are generally categorized according to their level. *Machine language* is a low-level language, based on a binary system of "zeroes" and "ones." Machine language is the most primitive language, because computers are digital devices whose rudimentary logic functions are carried out by using solid state switches in the "on" or "off" positions. *Assembly language* is also a low-level language, but its instructions are written in English-like statements rather than binary. Assembly language does not have many commands, and it must be written specifically for the computer hardware. Computer programs written in low-level languages run very fast because these languages are tied closely to the hardware, but writing the programs is very tedious.

Due to the tediousness of writing programs in low-level languages, engineers usually write programs in high-level languages that consist of straightforward, English-like commands. The most commonly used high-level languages by engineers are Fortran, C, C++, Pascal, Ada, and BASIC. Fortran is the patriarch of all scientific programming languages. The first version of Fortran (FORmula TRANslation) was developed by IBM between 1954 and 1957. Since its inception, Fortran has been the workhorse of scientific and engineering programming languages. It has undergone several updates and improvements and is still in widespread use today. The C language evolved from two languages, BCPL and B, which were developed during the late 1960s. In 1972, the first C program was compiled. The C++ language grew out of C and was developed during the early 1980s. Both C and C++ are popular programming languages for engineering applications because they use powerful commands and data structures. Pascal was developed during the early 1970s and is a popular programming language for beginning computer science students who are learning programming for the first time. The U.S. Department of Defense prompted the development of Ada during the 1970s in order to have a high-level language suitable for embedded computer systems. BASIC (Beginner's All-purpose Symbolic Instruction Code) was developed during the mid-1960s as a simple learning tool for secondary school students as well as college students. BASIC is often included as part of the operating software for personal computers.

Writing programs in high-level languages is easier than writing programs in low-level languages, but the high-level languages utilize a larger number of commands. Furthermore, high-level languages must be written with specific grammatical rules, referred to as *syntax*. Rules of syntax govern how punctuation, arithmetic operators, parentheses, and other characters are used in writing commands. To illustrate the syntactical differences between programming languages, equation solvers and mathematics packages, Table 1 shows how a simple equation is written. Note the similarities and differences in the equals sign, the constant π, and the operator for exponentiation.

TABLE 1   Comparison of Computer Statements for the Equation, $V = 4/3\pi R^3$, the Volume of a Sphere

Computer Tool	Statement
Mathcad	$V := 4/3 {}^* \pi {}^* R^\wedge 3$
TK Solver	$V = 4/3 {}^* \text{pi}() {}^* R^\wedge 3$
MATLAB	$V = 4/3 {}^* \text{pi} {}^* R^\wedge 3;$
MATHEMATICA	$V = 4/3 {}^* \text{Pi} {}^* R^\wedge 3$
maple	$V := 4/3 {}^* \text{pi} {}^* R^\wedge 3;$
Fortran	$V = 4/3 {}^* 3.141593 {}^* R^{**} 3$
C, C++	$V = 4/3 {}^* 3.141593 {}^* \text{pow}(R,3);$
Pascal	$V := 4/3 {}^* 3.141593 {}^* R {}^* R {}^* R;$
Ada	$V := 4/3 {}^* 3.141593 {}^* R^{**} 3;$
BASIC	$V = 4/3 {}^* 3.141593 {}^* R^\wedge 3$

4.4　Specialty Software

Considered as a whole, engineering is a broad field that covers a variety of disciplines and careers. Some of the main engineering disciplines are chemical engineering, civil engineering, electrical and computer engineering, environmental engineering, and mechanical engineering. Primary engineering career fields include research, development, design, analysis, manufacturing, and testing. Given the variety of specific problems that engineers who work in these fields encounter, it comes as no surprise that numerous *specialty software* packages are available to help the engineer analyze specific problems relating to a particular engineering system. For example, specialty software packages are available to electrical engineers for analyzing and simulating electrical circuits. Mechanical and chemical engineers can take advantage of software packages designed specifically for calculating flow parameters in pipe networks. Special software is available to civil and structural engineers for calculating forces and stresses in trusses and other structures. Other specialty software packages are available for performing analyses of heat exchangers, machinery, pressure vessels, propulsion systems, turbines, pneumatic and hydraulic systems, manufacturing processes, mechanical fasteners, and many others too numerous to list. After you graduate and begin working for a company that produces a specific product or process, you will probably become familiar with one or more of these specialty software packages.

4.5　Finite Element Software

Some engineering analysis problems are far too complex to solve using any of the aforementioned computer tools. *Finite element* software packages enable the engineer to analyze systems that have irregular configurations, variable material properties, complex conditions at the boundaries, and nonlinear behavior. The finite element method originated in the aerospace industry during the early 1950s when it was used for stress analysis of aircraft. Later, as the method matured, it found application in other analysis areas such as fluid flow, heat transfer, vibrations, impacts, acoustics, and electromagnetics. The basic concept behind the finite-element method is to subdivide a continuous region (i.e., the system to be analyzed is divided into a set of simple geometric shapes called "finite elements"). The elements are interconnected at common points called "nodes." Material properties, conditions at the system boundaries, and other pertinent inputs are supplied. With the use of an advanced mathematical procedure, the finite element software calculates the value of parameters such as stress, temperature, flow rate, or vibration frequency at each node in the region. Hence, the engineer is provided with a set of output parameters at discrete points that approximates a continuous distribution of those parameters for the entire region. The finite element method is an advanced analysis method and is normally introduced in colleges and universities at the senior level or the first-year graduate level.

PROFESSIONAL SUCCESS: PITFALLS OF USING COMPUTERS

The vital role that computers play in engineering analysis cannot be overstated. Given the tremendous advantages of using computers for engineering analysis, however, it may be difficult to accept the fact that there are also pitfalls. A common hazard that entangles some engineers is the tendency to treat the computer as a "black box," a wondrous electronic device whose inner workings are largely unknown, but that nonetheless provides output for every input supplied. Engineers who treat the computer as a black box are not effectively employing the general analysis procedure and in so doing are in danger of losing their ability to systematically reason their way through a problem. The computer is a remarkable computational machine, but it does not replace the engineer's thinking, reasoning, and judgement. Computers, and the software that runs on them, produce output that *precisely* reflects the input supplied to them. If the input is good, the output will be good. If the input is bad, the output will be bad. Computers are not smart enough to compensate for an engineer's inability to make good assumptions or employ the correct governing equations. Engineers must have a thorough understanding of the physical aspects of the problem at hand and the underlying mathematical principles *before* implementing the solution on the computer. A good engineer understands *what* the computer does when it "crunches the numbers" in the analysis. A good engineer is confident that the input data will result in reasonable output because a lot of sound thinking and reasoning has gone into the formulation of that input.

Can the computer be used too much? In a sense, it can. The tendency of some engineers is to use the computer to analyze problems that may not require a computer at all. Upon beginning a new problem, their first impulse is to set up the problem on the computer without even checking to see whether the problem can be solved by hand. For example, a problem in engineering statics may be represented by the quadratic equation, $x^2 + 4x - 12 = 0$.

This problem can be solved analytically by factoring, $(x + 6)(x - 2) = 0$, which yields the two roots, $x = -6$ and $x = 2$. To use the computer in a situation like this is to rely on the computer as a "crutch" to compensate for weak analytical skills. Continued reliance on the computer to solve problems that do not require a computer will gradually dull your ability to solve problems with pencil and paper. Do not permit this to happen. Examine the equations carefully to see whether a computer solution is justified. If it is, use one of the computer tools discussed earlier. If not, solve the problem by hand. Then, if you have time and wish to check your solution with the use of the computer, by all means do so.

APPLICATION: COMPUTERS FOR NUMERICAL ANALYSIS

Most of the equations that you will encounter in school can be solved analytically; that is, they can be solved by employing standard algebraic operations to isolate the desired variable on one side of the equation. Some equations, however, cannot be solved analytically with standard algebraic operations. These equations are referred to as *transcendental* equations because they contain one or more transcendental functions such as a logarithm or trigonometric function. Transcendental equations occur often in engineering analysis work, and techniques for solving them are known as *numerical methods*. For example, consider the transcendental equation

$$e^x - 3x = 0$$

This equation looks straightforward enough, but try solving it by hand. If we add $3x$ to both sides and take the natural logarithm of both sides to undo the exponential function, we obtain

$$x = \ln(3x) \qquad (a)$$

which, unfortunately, does not isolate the variable, x, because we still have the term $\ln(3x)$ on the right side of the equation. If we add $3x$ to both sides and then divide both sides by 3, we obtain

$$\frac{e^x}{3} = x \qquad (b)$$

The variable, x, is still not isolated without leaving a transcendental function in the equation. Clearly, this equation cannot be solved analytically, so it must be solved numerically. To solve it numerically, we utilize a method called *iteration*, a process by which we repeat the calculation until an answer is obtained.

Before solving this problem by using the computer, we will work it manually to illustrate how iteration works. To begin, we rewrite Equation (a) in the iterative form

$$x_{i+1} = \ln(3x_i)$$

The "i" and the "$i + 1$" subscripts refer to "old" and "new" values of x, respectively. The iteration process requires that we begin the calculation by immediately substituting a number into the iteration formula. This first number constitutes an estimate for the root (or roots) of the variable, x, that satisfy the formula. To keep track of the iterations, we use an iteration table, illustrated in Table 3.2. To start the iterations, we estimate a value of x by letting $x_i = 1$. We now substitute this number into the right side of the formula, yielding a new value of $x_{i+1} = 1.098612$. We then assign this new value of x to the old variable, x_i, and substitute it into the right side of the formula, yielding the second new value, $x = 1.192660$. Substituting this number into the right side of the formula, we obtain the third new value,

TABLE 2 Iteration Table for Finding
One Root of the Equation $e^x - 3x = 0$

Iteration	x_i	x_{i+1}
1	1	1.098612
2	1.098612	1.192660
3	1.192660	1.274798
4	1.274798	1.341400
5	1.341400	1.392326
.		
.		
.		1.512134
41	1.512134	1.512135

$x_{i+1} = 1.274798$. This process is repeated until the value of x stops changing by the desired amount. At this point, we say that the calculation has *converged* to an answer. Table 2 shows the first five iterations and indicates that 41 iterations are required for the calculation to converge to an answer that is accurate to the sixth decimal place. Upon substituting $x = 1.512135$ into the original equation, we see that the equation is satisfied. As this example illustrates, numerous iterations may be required to obtain an accurate solution. The accuracy of the answer depends on how many iterations are taken. Some equations converge to a precise answer in a few iterations, but others, like this one, require several iterations. It is important to note that 1.512135 is not the only root of this equation. The equation has a second root at $x = 0.619061$. If we attempt to find this root by using Equation (a), we discover that our calculation either converges again to 1.512135 or does not converge at all by leading us to an illegal operation; that is, taking the logarithm of a negative number. To find the second root, we iterate on Equation (b), writing it in the iterative form

$$x_{i+1} = \frac{e^{x_i}}{3}$$

With numerical methods, there are often no guarantees that a certain iteration formula will converge rapidly or even converge at all. The success of the iteration formula may also depend on the initial estimate chosen to start the

iterations. If our initial estimate for Equation (a) is less than $\frac{1}{3}$, the new value of x immediately goes negative, leading to an illegal operation. If our initial estimate for Equation (b) is too large, the new value of x grows large very rapidly, leading to an exponential overflow. These and other kinds of numerical difficulties can occur whether the iterations are performed by hand or by using a computer.

As Table 2 suggests, performing iterations by hand can be a long and tedious task. The computer is tailor-made for performing repetitive calculations. The roots of our transcendental equation can readily be found by using one of the computer tools discussed earlier. Figure 6 shows a computer program, written in the BASIC language, for finding the first root, $x = 1.512135$. In the first line the user inputs an initial estimate, which is assigned the variable name XOLD. The program then executes what is referred to as a DO loop that performs the iterations. Each time through the loop, a new value of x is calculated from the old value and an absolute value of the difference between the old and new values is calculated. This value is called DIFF. While DIFF is larger than a preselected convergence tolerance of 0.0000001, the new value of x, XNEW, is reset to the old value, XOLD, and looping continues. When DIFF is less than, or equal to, the convergence tolerance, convergence has been achieved, and looping is halted. The root is then printed. The same program, with the third line replaced with XNEW = EXP(XOLD)/3, could be used to find the second root. There are more sophisticated numerical methods for finding roots than the simple iteration technique illustrated here, and you will study them in your engineering or mathematics courses.

```
INPUT "ESTIMATE = ", XOLD
DO
    XNEW = LOG (3*XOLD)
    DIFF = ABS (XNEW - XOLD)
    XOLD = XNEW
LOOP WHILE DIFF > 0.0000001
PRINT XNEW
END
```

Figure 6. BASIC computer program for finding one root of the equation $e^x - 3x = 0$.

PRACTICE!

Using one of the computer tools discussed in this section, work the following problems:
(Note: These problems are identical to those in Section 3.)

1. Radioactive waste is to be permanently encased in concrete and buried in the ground. The vessel containing the waste measures 30 cm × 30 cm × 80 cm.

Federal regulations dictate that there must be a minimum concrete thickness of 50 cm surrounding the vessel on all sides. What is the minimum volume of concrete required to safely encase the radioactive waste?

Answer: 2.97 m^3

2. An elevator in an office building has an operating capacity of 15 passengers with a maximum weight of 180 lb$_f$ each. The elevator is suspended by a special pulley system with four cables, two of which support 20 percent of the total load and two of which support 80 percent of the total load. Find the maximum tension in each elevator cable.

Answer: 270 lb$_f$, 1080 lb$_f$

3. A technician measures a voltage drop of 25 V across a 100-Ω resistor by using a digital voltmeter. Using Ohm's law, we find that $V = IR$. What is the current flow through the resistor? How much power is consumed by the resistor? (*Hint*: $P = I^2R$.)

Answer: 250 mA, 6.25 W

4. Air flows through a main duct at a mass flow rate of 4 kg/s. The main duct enters a junction that splits into two branch ducts, one with a cross section of 20 cm $\times$ 30 cm and one with a cross section of 40 cm $\times$ 60 cm. If the mass flow rate in the large branch is 2.8 kg/s, what is the mass flow rate in the small branch? If the density of air is $\rho = 1.16$ kg/m^3, what is the velocity in each branch?

Answer: 1.2 kg/s, 10.1 m/s, 17.2 m/s

KEY TERMS

engineering method
equation solver
general analysis procedure
mathematics software

order of magnitude
programming language
significant figure
spreadsheet

REFERENCES

Bahder, T.B., *Mathematica for Scientists and Engineers*, NY: Addison-Wesley, 1995.

Dubin, D., *Numerical and Analytical Methods for Scientists and Engineers Using Mathematica*, NY: John Wiley & Sons, 2003.

Etter, D.M. *Introduction to* C++, Upper Saddle River, NJ: Prentice Hall, 1999.

Etter, D.M. and Kuncicky, D.C. *Introduction to Matlab 6*, Upper Saddle River, NJ: Prentice Hall, 2004.

Ferguson, R.J., *TK Solver for Engineers*, NY: Addison-Wesley, 1996.

Kuncicky, D.C., *Introduction to Excel 2002*, Upper Saddle River, NJ: Prentice Hall, 2003.

Larsen, R.W., *Introduction to Mathcad 11*, Upper Saddle River, NJ: Prentice Hall, 2004.

Nyhoff, L. and S. Leestma, *Introduction to FORTRAN 90*, 2d ed., Upper Saddle River, NJ: Prentice Hall, 1999.

Schwartz, D.I., *Introduction to Maple 8*, Upper Saddle River, NJ: Prentice Hall, 2003.

Problems

1. Using an order-of-magnitude analysis, estimate the number of gallons of gasoline used by all automobiles in the United States each year.

2. Using an order-of-magnitude analysis, estimate the number of 4 ft $\times$ 8 ft plywood sheets required for the floor, roof, and exterior sheathing of a 3000-ft^2 house.

3. Using an order-of-magnitude analysis, estimate the number of basketballs (fully inflated) that would fit in your engineering classroom.

4. Using an order-of-magnitude analysis, estimate the number of spam e-mail messages received by residents of the United States each year.

5. Using an order-of-magnitude analysis, estimate the number of breaths you will take during your lifetime.

6. Use an order-of-magnitude analysis to estimate the number of short tons of human waste produced worldwide each year.

7. The earth has a mean radius of about 6.37×10^6 m. Assuming the earth is made of granite ($\rho = 2770$ kg/m^3), estimate the mass of the earth, using an order-of-magnitude analysis.

8. The solar radiation flux just outside the earth's atmosphere is about 1350 W/m^2. Using an order-of-magnitude analysis, estimate the amount of solar energy that is intercepted by the United States each year.

9. Using an order-of-magnitude analysis, estimate the total textbook expenditure incurred by all engineering majors at your school per year.

10. Underline the significant figures in the following numbers (the first number is done for you):
    a. <u>345</u>0
    b. 9.807
    c. 0.00216
    d. 5000
    e. 7000.
    f. 12.00
    g. 2066
    h. 106.07
    i. 0.02880
    j. 523.91
    k. 1.207×10^{-3}

11. Perform the following calculations, reporting the answers with the correct number of significant figures:
    a. $(8.14)(260)$
    b. $456/4.9$
    c. $(6.74)(41.07)/8.72$
    d. $(10.78 - 4.5)/300$
    e. $(10.78 - 4.50)/300.0$
    f. $(65.2 - 13.9)/240.0$
    g. $(1.2 \times 10^6)/(4.52 \times 10^3 + 988)$
    h. $(1.764 - 0.0391)/(8.455 \times 10^4)$
    i. $1000/(1.003 \times 10^9)$

j. $(8.4 \times 10^{-3})/5000$

k. $(8.40 \times 10^{3})/5000.0$

l. 8π

m. $(2\pi - 5)/10$

12. A 250-kg mass hangs by a cable from the ceiling. Using the standard value of gravitational acceleration, $g = 9.81 \text{ m/s}^2$, what is the tension in the cable? Express your answer with the correct number of significant figures.

13. A 9-slug mass hangs by a rope from the ceiling. Using the standard value of gravitational acceleration, $g = 32.2 \text{ ft/s}^2$, what is the tension in the rope? Express your answer with the correct number of significant figures. Redo the problem, using a mass of 9.00 slug. Is the answer different? Why?

14. A 175 mA current flows through a 62-Ω resistor. Using Ohm's law, $V = IR$, what is the voltage across the resistor? Express your answer with the correct number of significant figures.

15. A rectangular building lot is reported to have the dimensions 200 ft $\times$ 300 ft. Using the correct number of significant figures, what is the area of this lot in units of acre?

For problems 16 through 31, use the general analysis procedure of (1) problem statement, (2) diagram, (3) assumptions, (4) governing equations, (5) calculations, (6) solution check, and (7) discussion.

16. An excavation crew digs a hole in the ground measuring 20 yd $\times$ 30 yd $\times$ 6 yd to facilitate a basement for a small office building. Five dump trucks, each with a capacity of 20 yd^3, are used to haul the material away. How many trips must each truck make to remove all the material?

17. Find the current in each resistor and the total current for the circuit shown in Figure P17.

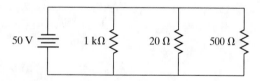

Figure P17.

18. For easy handling, long sheets of steel for manufacturing automobile body panels are tightly rolled up into a cylinder-shaped package. Consider a roll of steel with an inside and outside diameter of 45 cm and 1.6 m, respectively, that is suspended by a single cable. If the length of the roll is 2.25 m and the density of steel is $\rho = 7850 \text{ kg/m}^3$, what is the tension in the cable?

19. In a chemical processing plant, glycerin flows toward a pipe junction at a mass flow rate of 30 kg/s as shown in Figure P3.19. If the mass flow rate in the small pipe branch is 8 kg/s, find the velocity in both branches. The density of glycerin is $\rho = 1260 \text{ kg/m}^3$.

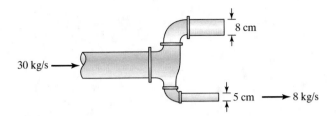

Figure P19.

20.   A portable classroom is heated with small propane heating units with a capacity of 3 kW each. The portable classroom is occupied by 24 students, each dissipating 120 W, and is lighted by 10 light fixtures that dissipate 100 W each. If the heat loss from the portable classroom is 15 kW, how many heating units are required to maintain the classroom at a temperature of 20°C?

21.   A man pushes on a barrel with a force of $P = 80$ lb$_f$ as shown. Assuming that the barrel does not move, what is the friction force between the barrel and the floor? (*Hint:* The friction force acts parallel to the floor toward the man. See Figure P21.)

Figure P21.

22.   The total resistance for resistors connected in series is the arithmetic sum of the resistances. Find the total resistance for the series circuit shown in Figure P22. Because the resistors are connected in series, the current is the same in each resistor. Using Ohm's law, find this current. Also, find the voltage drop across each resistor.

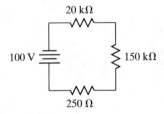

Figure P22.

23.   The pressure exerted by a static liquid on a vertical submerged surface is calculated from the relation

$$P = \rho g h$$

where

P = pressure (Pa)

ρ = density of the liquid (kg/m^3)

g = gravitational acceleration = 9.81 m/s^2

h = height of vertical surface that is submerged (m)

Consider the dam shown in Figure P23. What is the pressure exerted on the dam's surface at depths of 2 m, 6 m, and 20 m? For the density of water, use ρ = 1000 kg/m^3.

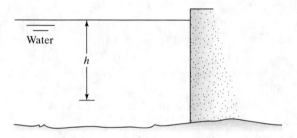

Water

h

Figure P23.

24.   Work Problem 16, using one of the computer tools discussed in this chapter.

25.   Work Problem 17, using one of the computer tools discussed in this chapter.

26.   Work Problem 18, using one of the computer tools discussed in this chapter.

27.   Work Problem 19, using one of the computer tools discussed in this chapter.

28.   Work Problem 20, using one of the computer tools discussed in this chapter.

29.   Work Problem 21, using one of the computer tools discussed in this chapter.

30.   Work Problem 22, using one of the computer tools discussed in this chapter.

31.   Work Problem 23, using one of the computer tools discussed in this chapter.

9

Engineering Design Method

1 INTRODUCTION

1.1 Introduction to Engineering Design

In engineering, a ***design*** is a description of a new or improved device or system. ***Design problems*** are distinguished from analysis problems by the nature of both the problems and the solutions. Design problems usually are more vaguely defined (as contrasted with the more well-defined analysis problems). While analysis problems usually have one solution, there is often no single "correct" solution to a design problem. In fact, design problems *require* you to develop several solutions or alternatives and then use a set of criteria to compare and evaluate the alternatives.

Analysis problem solving is generally more science than art, while design problem solving involves more art. Why? In meeting design challenges, it is necessary to generate new, creative ideas. Evaluating the ideas means repeating the analysis process for each alternative.

Engineering design is as varied as the engineering profession. Engineering design problems have become more complex and challenging, requiring greater specialization and teamwork. It is not uncommon for large engineering projects to be carried out by dozens or even hundreds of engineering specialists. Design problems often are attacked using an ***integrated project team*** (IPT). In the IPT approach, teams of engineers, scientists, and other professionals are grouped by task, not discipline. Each team, consisting of representatives from various engineering, science, and other disciplines, has the responsibility of executing a given task.

OBJECTIVES

After reading this chapter, you will be able to:

- list the steps in the engineering design method;
- identify the kinds of engineering problems for which the engineering design method is appropriate;
- solve engineering problems using the engineering design method.

design: a description of a new or improved device or system

design problem: a problem where the system is often not well defined and more than one (or sometimes no) solution is possible

integrated project team: a management strategy where personnel are organized by task rather than by discipline

1.2   Solving Design Problems

The solution to a design problem does not suddenly appear out of nothing. Most good design solutions are the result of a methodical process. The process may vary from engineer to engineer and problem to problem. The design method described here is quite general and can be adapted to a variety of problems. The six common steps in the engineering design process are

1. Defining the problem.
2. Gathering information.
3. Generating multiple solutions.
4. Analyzing and selecting a solution.
5. Implementing the solution.
6. Evaluating the solution.

Note that just as design is not the same as analysis, the engineering design process differs from the engineering analysis process.

PONDER THIS

What are the differences between the engineering design method and the engineering analysis method?

Key idea: Solve engineering design problems by defining the problem, gathering information, generating multiple solutions, selecting a solution, implementing the solution, and evaluating the solution.

There are three main differences between the analysis and design. In analysis, you seek the *one* solution. In design, you seek to generate *multiple* solutions. In analysis, you *calculate* a solution. In design, you *select* a solution based on some evaluation criteria. Finally, in design, you *implement* the solution.

The overall engineering design method is shown schematically in Figure 1. In this chapter, we discuss the last four steps.

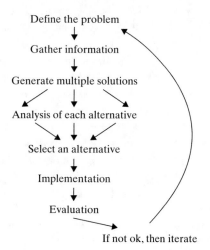

Figure 1. Steps in the Engineering Design Method

2   GENERATING MULTIPLE SOLUTIONS

2.1   Introduction

Once you have defined the problem and gathered information about it, you are ready to begin developing solutions or alternatives. This is when you must think creatively.° Techniques for generating multiple solutions are discussed in this section.

2.2   Brainstorming

brainstorming: a technique for generating possible solutions in a group by recording all spontaneous ideas

Several techniques can be used by groups or individuals to help generate ideas that may lead to solutions. One of the most well-known and effective (but often poorly implemented) techniques for group problem solving is **brainstorming**. The generation of ideas by brainstorming is a freewheeling process. It can be intimidating the first few times you attempt it. Successful brainstorming requires practice. It also requires a commitment to the project that is stronger than the individual egos. The following are some guidelines for a good brainstorming session.

Composition:

1. Small team
   A brainstorming team should have five to ten members to ensure enough new ideas without allowing individuals to hide in the crowd.
2. Diverse team
   Select participants from a diversity of backgrounds, including people with little direct experience with the problem.

Logistics:

1. Short meetings
   Keep brainstorming sessions shorter than one hour.
2. Record meetings
   Record the ideas for evaluation at a future session. Identify one person to record the ideas for evaluation at a future session, using a blackboard, easel, or whiteboard so that all participants may see the ideas generated.

Meeting Protocol:

1. No hierarchy
   Group members must be considered equals.
2. Nonjudgmental
   Accept all ideas without judgment or evaluation, avoiding negative comments (e.g., "That won't work," "That's stupid," "Nobody does it that way," or "We can't solve this problem").
3. Quantity over quality
   Stress the importance of the *quantity* of ideas: *generate as many ideas as possible*.
4. Build ideas
   Create new ideas by combining and building on other ideas.

°The process of looking at challenges in a new way sometimes is called *lateral thinking*.

2.3   Methods for Generating New Ideas

Key idea: Generate multiple solutions through brainstorming, making checklists, listing attributes, and employing forced random relationships.

Brainstorming sessions will stall without new ideas. How do you prevent your brainstorming session from running out of steam? Three popular techniques for generating ideas during a brainstorming session are checklists, attribute listing, and random forced relationships. (Two other methods are presented in Problems 5 and 6.) These techniques also can be used by an individual.

checklist: a tabulation of ways that an objective can be achieved

Checklists are a great way to encourage ideas in a brainstorming session. A **checklist** is a tabulation of ways that an objective can be achieved. For example, suppose you are asked to improve a production line for manufacturing CDs. You might make a checklist that included several concepts: ways the line could be used to produce items other than CDs, ways the line could be reconfigured, ways the line could be made smaller, and so on. Note that the checklist tabulates *ways* in which a device or system could be improved. Once the areas for improvement have been listed, then brainstorming can be used to generate ideas in each area. An example checklist for improving the fuel efficiency of military aircraft is shown in Figure 2.

attribute listing: a technique for generating possible solutions where many attributes of a system are listed

Another technique that can be used by individuals or groups is to create a table of the attributes of the device you are improving and the possible values or solutions for each attribute. This process is called **attribute listing**. For example, in creating ideas for heating a "smart home," you might consider three attributes: energy source (gas, oil, wood, electric, or solar), method of heat transmission (radiant, convection, or forced), and heat transmission medium (air, water, or other liquid).

Key idea: Attribute values can be combined in different ways to generate new ideas.

The attribute values can be combined in different ways to generate new ideas. For example, you could combine attribute values *randomly* to generate a new system (i.e., design a radiant wood-burning stove with no heat transmission medium). In addition, you could combine *every possible solution* for every attribute with every possible solution for every other attribute and create a theoretical listing of every possible solution. This is called **morphological analysis**. In the "smart home" example, the combination of alternatives would generate 5 energy sources $\times$ 3 heat transmission modes $\times$ 3 heat transmission media = 45 ideas. Each idea could undergo further evaluation.

morphological analysis: a technique for generating alternatives where all possible combinations of solutions for all attributes are combined

random forced relationship: a technique for generating possible solutions where attributes from a random word are related to an existing problem

The **random forced relationship** technique is especially useful if you are interested in generating totally new ideas. The idea here is to force a relationship between two normally unrelated objects or words. One of the objects may be your project (or an

---

Checklist: Improving the Fuel Efficiency of Military Aircraft

- Ways to reduce weight
- Ways to make engine more efficient
- Potential alternative fuel mixtures
- Ways to increase lift
- Ways to decrease

Figure 2.   Example of a Checklist

attribute of your project) and the other object is a randomly selected word. This word is used to act as a trigger to change the patterns of thought when a mental roadblock occurs. The random word can be used to generate other words and stimulate the flow of new ideas.

Returning to the "smart home" heating system example, suppose you randomly select "automobile" as a random forced relationship word. This might lead you to consider using antifreeze for the heat transmission medium or putting the heater on wheels to be rolled from room to room or installing a sunroof for solar heat. Clearly, not all of these ideas are reasonable. However, the random forced relationship technique can be useful to generate new ideas when brainstorming is unproductive. An example of using idea-generating techniques in engineering design is given in Example 1.

**EXAMPLE 1
GENERATING
ALTERNATIVES**

Your design team has been asked to develop a new generation of a personal communications device (the cell phone of tomorrow). Your brainstorming session has bogged down. Use checklists and attribute analysis to restart the creative process.

SOLUTION

There are many ways to use checklists and attribute analysis to generate new ideas. A checklist for how to improve the cell phone might include several questions:

Can a cell phone be used for functions other than audio communication?

How can people use a cell phone more effectively?

What needs to happen to wireless communication to eliminate landline telephones completely?

An example attribute listing is given below.

Information Streams	User Interface	Unit Configuration
Audio only	Keypad	Handheld
Still pictures	Detachable keyboard	Wearable
Full-motion video	Voice-activated	Hypodermic implant
Holographic images	Brain wave–activated	

A random sampling might include the following designs: (solid arrows in the table) an audio-only, voice-activated, wearable device or (dashed arrows in the table) a handheld unit with detachable keyboard capable of producing holographic images.

Information Streams	User Interface	Unit Configuration
Audio only	Keypad	Handheld
Still pictures	Detachable keyboard	Wearable
Full-motion video	Voice-activated	Hypodermic implant
Holographic images	Brain wave–activated	

A morphological analysis would include all $4 \times 4 \times 3 = 48$ combinations.

3   ANALYZING ALTERNATIVES AND SELECTING A SOLUTION

3.1   Analyzing Alternatives

Key idea: Evaluate alternatives by applying the engineering analysis method to each alternative.

At this point in the engineering design method, you have defined the problem, gathered the pertinent information, and identified a number of potential solutions. To select the best alternative, the potential solutions must be analyzed and their performance capability must be evaluated. In other words, *you must apply the engineering analysis method to each alternative*. Potential solutions that are not optimal must be discarded, or modified and reevaluated. In light of new information from the evaluation of potential solutions, it may be necessary to redefine the problem, change the constraints, or change the evaluation criteria.

To illustrate the process of analyzing alternatives, suppose you are working with an advocacy group to assist wheelchair-bound people. Your group is designing a portable wheelchair ramp. To meet the requirements of the Americans with Disabilities Act, the ramp must be adjustable to slopes between 1:20 and 1:12 and have a minimum width of 36 inches. In addition, the ramp must be as inexpensive as possible and wheelchair-transportable. Your brainstorming activities result in three candidate designs: an inflatable ramp, a foldable (hinged) stainless steel ramp, and a fiberglass ramp.

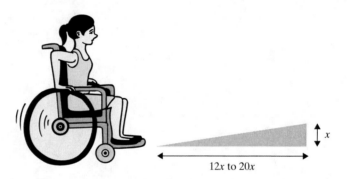

In this case, the analysis might consist of the following questions:

- Can the ramp be made to be adjustable to slopes between 1:20 and 1:12?
- Can the ramp be made with a width of at least 36 inches?
- Can the ramp with the above characteristics be transported on a wheelchair?
- What is the cost of a ramp with all of the above characteristics?

The analysis might result in modified alternatives. Suppose the fiberglass ramp is inexpensive, but too unwieldy to be moved by a wheelchair. You might steal the hinged idea from the second alternative and develop a foldable fiberglass ramp as another alternative to be analyzed.

The analysis of alternative solutions may be simple or very complex. In some cases, a preliminary sketch or a cursory analysis may show that an idea is not worthy of further consideration. In other cases, a component may need to be examined by laboratory tests. In still other cases, a comprehensive research program may be needed to determine the feasibility of a proposed solution. To facilitate the analysis, engineers often rely on models to evaluate the proposed solutions.

3.2   Selecting a Solution

Alternatives should be compared across a common set of criteria.

PONDER THIS

What criteria should you use to compare alternatives?

Key idea: Evaluate alternatives by and select assessing feasibility.

The answer lies in the types of feasibility, namely, technical (or engineering); economic; fiscal; and social, political, and environmental feasibility.

4   IMPLEMENTING THE SOLUTION

Key idea: Implement the solution through planning and action.

Implementation (literally, the act of filling up; from the Latin *in- + plere,* to fill) is the process of producing the product or system. Engineers participate in the implementation step by planning, supporting, and supervising the execution of the selected alternative. For many engineers, implementing the solution is the most satisfying step in the design phase. Finally seeing your ideas in concrete or as an accepted operating procedure on the shop floor is very gratifying and sets engineering apart from many other professions.

analysis paralysis: overanalysis of a problem to the extent that no action is taken

A common malady at this step in the engineering design process is **analysis paralysis**. People may become so involved in evaluating the alternatives that they never select or implement a solution. The analysis should end with a positive statement of the action to be taken to implement the selected alternative.

Implementing a solution to a design problem requires two steps: *planning* and *action.* The most important part of implementation is planning. In the planning stage, you must look at allocations of time and resources, anticipate bottlenecks, and identify a path to the finished product. Every step in the implementation process should be identified and documented. Using mathematical tools, implementation plans can be optimized and the effects of delays on the project schedule can be quantified. Two commonly used tools are the critical path method (CPM) and the program evaluation and review technique (PERT).

Finally, engineers and others involved in the problem-solving process must act on the plans they have formulated. They may execute a design alternative, fabricate a product, prepare a report, or conduct another planning activity. Great care should be taken with this phase, as good planning will not save a poor job of plan execution.

5   EVALUATING THE SOLUTION

continuous improvement: the process of continual reevaluation and redesign to continuously improve a product or process

Nearly all designs can be improved. Often, the deficiencies do not appear until months or years after the design is implemented. For many organizations, complex data systems are used to collect and analyze information from customers. The design team must be ready to repeat the entire design process to solve new problems as they appear. The repetitive design process, called **continuous improvement**, is now recognized as essential for organizations of all types to achieve and maintain leadership positions in their fields.

6   DESIGN EXAMPLE

The world of the automobile has changed significantly since the first Model A rolled off Henry Ford's Detroit assembly line in 1903. However, the power plant (i.e., the internal combustion engine) and powertrain (i.e., transmission) used today would be understood by engineers of Ford's day.

The requirements for today's passenger automobiles are becoming increasingly stringent. Design goals are to meet near-zero emission standards and high fuel efficiency, while satisfying acceleration, safety, handling, comfort, carrying capacity, useful life, and maintenance cost constraints.

Internal combustion engines have three main problems. First, they are complex and therefore expensive to maintain. Second, they are inefficient and inflexible. For example, to satisfy acceleration requirements, their size must be 3 to 10 times greater than the size of engine that will provide the power required for cruising (i.e., power required for operation at constant velocity). Third, they produce air pollutants.

The design example concerns ways to improve vehicle performance.* The focus here is on the generation, evaluation, and selection of alternatives. Suppose your integrated project team conducted a brainstorming session. Three ideas emerged regarding how to optimize vehicle performance:

Alternative 1: Decrease the power requirements.
Alternative 2: Increase the efficiency of energy transfer from the fuel to the wheels.
Alternative 3: Employ complementary propulsion technologies.

In the usual design process, each alternative would be evaluated separately. This example will focus on the ways to decrease the power requirements. You know that automobiles must provide power to satisfy two demands. First, the power provided must overcome resisting forces. The power required to overcome the resisting forces is equal to the sum of the resisting forces multiplied by the velocity (power = force × velocity). Resisting forces include

- the drag force exerted by the car body on the air,
- the component of the gravitational force exerted in the direction of travel if the car is going up a hill,
- the friction forces from the tires meeting the road, and
- the force to accelerate the vehicle (from Newton's Second Law of Motion).

---

*For more information on this design example, see Hyman (2003) and Moore (1996).

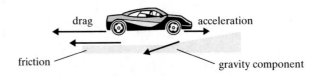

Second, there should be sufficient power to satisfy the electrical systems (sound system, air conditioning, heating, and other accessories). Thus,

$$\text{power required} = (\text{sum of the resisting forces})(\text{velocity}) + \text{other power needs}$$

$$= (\text{drag force} + \text{gravitational force} + \text{friction force}$$

$$+ \text{ force to accelerate the vehicle})v + P_{\text{other}}$$

$$= \left[\tfrac{1}{2}\rho_a C_d A v^2 + mg(\sin\theta) + r_0 mg + ma \right] v + P_{\text{other}} \qquad (1)$$

where [standard values in brackets]

ρ_a = density of air [1.2 kg/m^3]
C_d = drag coefficient [0.3, dimensionless]
A = cross-sectional area of the vehicle [2.1 m^2]
v = vehicle velocity [compare alternatives at 90 km/h = 25 m/s]
m = vehicle mass [585 kg + two 68 kg passengers = 721 kg]
g = gravitational acceleration [9.8 m/s^2]
θ = road grade [compare alternatives at $\theta = 0$ for level cruising]
r_0 = rolling friction coefficient [0.01 dimensionless]
a = vehicle acceleration [compare alternatives at constant velocity cruising, so $a = 0$]
P_{other} = other power requirements (heating, cooling, and accessories) [500 W]

This model includes five ways to reduce the power consumption: reduce the mass, reduce the cross-sectional area, reduce the drag coefficient, reduce the rolling friction coefficient, and/or reduce other power drains. Equation (1) is the analysis tool to assess the impact of changes in the mass, area, drag coefficient, rolling friction coefficient, and other power drains on the power requirements. Equation (1) must be coupled with reality: for example, the mass can be reduced only so much before safety constraints are violated.

The impact of potential changes on the power requirement are summarized in Table 1. With aluminum-based materials, mass reductions of 40% may be possible, with a resulting power savings of 7%. The greatest power savings can be obtained from a decrease in the drag coefficient. Why? At the test velocity (90 km/h), aerodynamic drag is the largest source of power demand. The relative contributions to power demand are shown in Figure 3.

TABLE 1   Impacts of Changes in Vehicle Design on Power Requirements

Parameter	Potential Change	New Value	Power Savings
Vehicle mass	10% reduction[a]	663 kg	1.7%
	40% reduction[a]	487 kg	7.0%
Cross-sectional area	minimum possible[b]	1.9 m^2	6.9%
Drag coefficient	minimum possible[b]	0.20	24%
Rolling friction coefficient	special tires	0.005	11%
Other power needs	50% reduction	250 W	3.1%

[a]Mass reduction in the vehicle without passengers.
[b]Minimum reasonable value consistent with safety, etc.

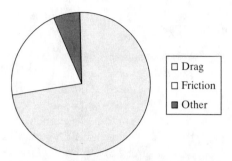

Figure 3. Contributions of Sources to the Power Requirements (calculated with the standard values following Eq. (1), so gravity and acceleration forces are zero)

In addition to reducing power requirements, complementary propulsion technologies (called auxiliary power units, APUs) have been proposed (alternative #3). Candidate APU technologies include fuel cells, gas turbines, and electric systems. To evaluate each APU, engineers have used the analysis process described in this chapter.

The hybrid–electric vehicle (HEV), a dual internal combustion engine/electric propulsion system, has emerged as a leading alternative, in part because it allows for energy recovery from braking. HEVs are favored over battery–electric vehicles (BEVs), because the usable power per unit mass of the batteries is hundreds of times less than the usable power per unit mass of gasoline; an additional pound of gas provides much more energy than an additional pound of battery. An increase in the mass will increase the power requirement (see the previous analysis).

Even if the choice is restricted to HEVs, the number of system configurations is large. Using morphological analysis (see Section 2.3), Steiber and Surampudi (2000) estimated that there are over 27,000 HEV combinations to be evaluated. Thus, the optimization of HEVs is likely to be a formidable design challenge.

Future generations of passenger vehicles must do more than transport people from point A to point B. The increased demands on automobiles require innovative uses of the analysis and design strategies. Relatively simple rules (such as providing sufficient power to meet demands) will be the basis of even the most complex analysis of the most innovative alternatives.

7   DESIGN PARAMETERS

7.1   Introduction

In this chapter, you have seen that analysis and design fit together. In a real sense, the way engineered systems are designed comes from repeated engineering analysis. One of the differences between engineers and engineering technicians is that engineers understand the analysis behind the design.

design parameters:
results of analysis that are used to determine the characteristics of a system

The results of analysis are sometimes summarized in easy-to-use collections of terms called ***design parameters***. Design parameters allow you to calculate key features of the system from known information. Some design parameters can become *code* (i.e., regulatory or legal requirements for design), design specification (i.e., design requirements in a project, also called *design specs*), or informal *rules-of-thumb* used by engineers in design. Using rules-of-thumb (or "seat-of-the-pants" engineering) is also called *heuristics* or *heuristic design* (from the Greek *heuriskein*: to discover).

7.2   Example

As an example, consider the design of a grit chamber. A grit chamber is a basin used to settle out small rocks so that downstream pumps can be protected. How big should such a chamber be? To answer this question, you must analyze the settling of particles. If the particle has a constant settling velocity, its trajectory in the chamber will be a straight line (see Figure 4). For simplicity, assume that if the particle impacts the right wall (path A in Figure 4), then it will be carried out of the chamber. Therefore, the critical trajectory is shown by path B. A particle settling as fast or faster than path B will be completely removed by the chamber. A particle settling slower than path B (e.g., path A) will not be removed by the chamber.

It is possible to calculate the settling velocity of a particle given its physical characteristics. The settling velocity is also related to the geometry of the chamber. Thus, it might be possible to devise a design parameter relating what you know (the settling velocity of the particle) to what you want to design (the dimensions of the chamber).

What is the settling velocity of a particle following path B? You already know that velocity = distance/time. So the settling velocity (v_s) of a particle following path B is

$$v_s = \text{distance/time} = D/(\text{time in the chamber})$$

where D is the chamber depth.

How much time does the particle spend in the chamber? It is pushed out of the chamber only by its horizontal velocity (v_h), so

$$v_h = L/(\text{time in the chamber})$$

where L is the length of the chamber in the direction of flow. Thus,

$$\text{time in the chamber} = L/v_h$$

Now, the horizontal velocity is given by the horizontal flow divided by the cross-sectional area of flow, or

$$v_h = \text{flow}/(WD)$$

where W is the width of the chamber. Thus,

$$\text{time in the chamber} = L/v_h = (LWD)/\text{flow}$$

and

$$\begin{aligned}
v_s &= D/(\text{time in the chamber}) \\
&= D/(LWD/\text{flow}) \\
&= \text{flow}/(LW) \\
&= \text{flow/plan area}
\end{aligned}$$

The plan area is the area of the floor of the chamber.

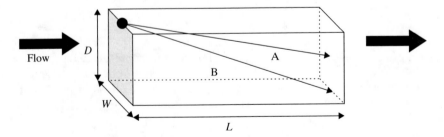

Figure 4. Possible Trajectories of a Settling Particle

Key idea: By specifying a value for the design parameter, you are specifying the performance of the system.

The term flow/plan area is a design parameter and is called the overflow rate.° *By specifying a value for the design parameter, you are specifying the performance of the system.* For example, suppose you want to settle out sand of 0.25 mm in diameter. You can calculate the settling velocity of the sand to be about 4.1 cm/s.[†] If you design a chamber with a flow/plan area = 4.1 cm/s, then all of the sand will be removed. The more common units of overflow rate are volume per time per area (gal/d-ft^2 or m^3/m^2/s). An overflow rate of 4.1 cm/s corresponds to about 87,000 gal/d-ft^2. (You might want to confirm the units conversion on your own.)

7.3   Uses of Design Parameters

Design parameters can be extremely useful for two reasons. First, they relate some measure of system performance with a system characteristic to be designed. In the settling chamber example, the plan area of the chamber was related to the removal of a certain sized sand particle. A design specification for a settling chamber might read: "Design the chamber with an overflow rate of 87,000 gal/d-ft^2." This is another way of saying, "Design the chamber to remove 0.25-mm-diameter sand completely."

Second, design parameters can be used easily to calculate system characteristics. In the settling chamber example, the plan area is calculated readily if the flow is known by plan area = flow/overflow rate. For example, removing sand from a flow of 10 million gallons per day would require $(1 \times 10^7 \text{ gal/day})/(87,000 \text{ gal/d-ft}^2) = 115$ square feet of area.

8   INNOVATIONS IN DESIGN

8.1   Introduction

In the engineering analysis and engineering design methods, you have been provided with lists of steps to be followed. Do not get the impression that analysis and design are cut-and-dried processes. Innovation is the key to success in both engineering analysis and design.

8.2   Need for Innovation

Although the general engineering analysis and engineering design approaches discussed in here have been successful, problems have arisen in using the standard approaches to bring products to the marketplace.

PONDER THIS

> **What problems do you see in using the standard design approach to design new products?**

Key idea: Design times can be very long for new products.

A major problem with the standard approach is that the *design time can be very long*. New products will take a long time to design if engineers and other professionals work independently. This might be called the "throw-it-over-the-wall" design approach:

- The engineering department designs a new product.
- They throw the design over the wall of the cubicle to the marketing department.
- Marketing changes the design to make it more customer friendly.

°It may seem strange that the settling performance appears to be independent of the chamber depth. In fact, if scouring of the particles off the chamber bottom can be ignored, then the depth is not important. Minimum depths usually are used to account for scouring.

†The settling velocity of a particle is given by $v_s = g(\rho_s - \rho)d^2/(18\mu)$, where g = gravitational acceleration = 980 cm/s^2, ρ_s = particle density = 2.65 g/cm^3 for sand, ρ = water density = 0.9997 g/cm^3 at 15°C, d = particle diameter = 0.025 cm, and μ = water viscosity = 1.37×10^{-2} g/cm-s at 15°C.

- Marketing throws design over the wall of the cubicle to the manufacturing unit
- Manufacturing changes the design to make the product easier and cheaper to make
- Manufacturing throws the revised design back to engineering
- Repeat *ad nauseum* until the design is complete

As you can see, this is a very inefficient way to bring a new product to market. It has been estimated that every blueprint page for the design of commercial aircraft in the past was revised 4.5 times, on average.

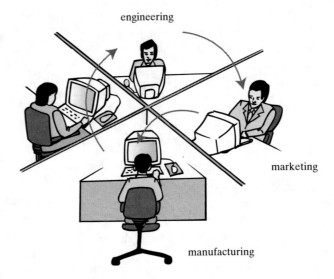

A lengthy design time is not the only problem if engineers and other professionals do not communicate.

PONDER THIS

What other problems arise if engineers develop new products without talking to others?

Key idea: Engineers must take into account the fact that products must be made, sold, used, and disposed of.

concurrent engineering: a design process where the manufacturing, quality control, end-user requirements, user support, and product disposal are considered in the original design

Engineers must take into account the fate of the design once it leaves their desks. First, the *product must be made*. In their design, engineers should take into account the difficulty in manufacturing or assembling products. In addition, the environmental impact of the manufacturing process must be considered. Second, *products must be purchased*, requiring the engineer to think about costs. Third, *products are used*. Thus, the service, maintenance, and support of the product must be considered in the initial design. Finally, the *product must be disposed of*. The environmental impact of products must be minimized. This includes post-consumer environmental impacts that occur when the consumer throws the product away.

8.3   Design Innovation by Concurrent Engineering

To address these problems, engineers have developed new design strategies, including concurrent engineering, reengineering (or redesign), and reverse engineering.

Concurrent engineering, CE, refers to a systematic approach to design, where all elements of product lifecycle are included. Elements include manufacturing, quality

green engineering: a design process where the impact on the environment of the raw materials, manufacturing process, product packing, product use, and product disposal are minimized

control, end-user requirements, user support, and product disposal. Design approaches to achieve CE include design for manufacturing (DFM) and design for the environment (DFE, also called **green engineering**).

A good example of DFM is a toy redesign executed by Mattel in the late 1980s.* In 1987, Mattel obtained the rights to a toy made by a Japanese toy company. The toy, called Color Spin, was designed to entertain and develop motor skills in infants. When the infant activated a roller (on the left in the accompanying picture), colored balls (on the right in the picture) would spin.

Unfortunately, there were several problems with the original Color Spin design. The main problem was that the toy cost too much to manufacture. Mattel's engineers and managers applied the principle of DFM to reduce the cost of the toy. An important aspect in DFM in this case was the idea of **design for assembly** (DFA): making the toy easier and less expensive to assemble. Assembly may not seem too important at first blush, but assembly costs can affect company profits significantly. For example, Mattel has estimated that over one-half million dollars per year could be saved by a *one-cent* reduction in the assembly of Barbie dolls.

There were several important changes in the assembly of the Color Spin toy. First, the total number of parts was reduced from 55 to 27. Second, parts requiring longer assembly times were reduced or eliminated. For example, fasteners (such as screws) require time to put together on an assembly line. The toy design engineers replaced two housing pieces and 10 screws with one piece of housing. (The housing pieces were attached by ultrasonic welding rather than fasteners, removing the construction task from the assembly line.) Third, parts were standardized to reduce the number of different pieces that the assemblers had to manipulate. Examples include the standardization of gears and the redesign of the roller so that the two roller halves were identical. The DFA approach resulted in a 38% reduction in assembly costs and a savings of $700,000 per year.

design for assembly: (DFA): a type of DFM where assembly requirements are considered in the original design

Two other notable changes improved the quality and marketability of the product. Throughput (the number of toys made per day) was limited because of back-ups on the assembly line. Back-ups occurred if an assembly line worker took too long to complete

---

*The background information for this example was taken from "The Mattel Color Spin: A Case Study in Design," created by the Engineering Systems Research Center at the University of California at Berkeley and part of the SYNTHESIS National Engineering Education Coalition (http://bits.me.berkeley.edu/develop/mattel2/welcome.html).

his or her job. Mattel installed storage bins between the workstations, allowing partially completed toys to accumulate. This, in turn, allowed workers to increase the quality of their work without the pressure of holding up the line. (This approach is called the "Pull System" of manufacturing.) Also, design engineers redesigned the packaging to save costs and allow parents to evaluate the toy in the store more effectively. It is believed that the packaging redesign by itself increased sales 5 to 10%.

8.4   Design Innovation by Reengineering

reengineering: the
fundamental rethinking and
radical redesign of a system

Reengineering refers to a fundamental rethinking and radical redesign of a system. The term "reengineering" is used to describe large changes in approaches to engineering, computer software, and business systems. Two examples in computer and electrical engineering can be found in recent "revolutions" proposed by Apple and Microsoft. In August 2000, Apple introduced a very different looking desktop computer, the Power-Mac G4 Cube. It was a very powerful computer. Through impressive engineering design, it fit into an $8'' \times 8'' \times 8''$ cube. Although elegant, the computer was criticized for a lack of expansion slots, limited audio inputs/outputs, and high cost. The design was not a success and was withdrawn in July 2001.

Also in 2000, Microsoft Corporation announced a new approach to business and personal computing: Microsoft .NET technology. The .NET initiative is an Internet-based computing platform promoting services distributed through the Web. Although Microsoft was not the first company to suggest that Web-based computing is the next wave, it has radically redesigned its software to take advantage of Web distribution of information and services. Will the .NET approach revolutionize computing? The answer, as with many initiatives in product engineering, is up to the consumers.

8.5   Design Innovation by Reverse Engineering

reverse engineering:
the process of taking apart
an object or system to see
how it works

Reverse engineering refers to the process of taking apart an object or system to see how it works. You may have performed "reverse engineering" as a child on small household objects as your curiosity in technology grew. Reverse engineering is used in two ways. First, it can be used to obtain new ideas from competitors. Engineering ethics requires that applicable patent and copyright laws be strictly adhered to. Second, reverse engineering can be used to fabricate copies of parts for old equipment (sometimes called *legacy equipment*).

8.6   How to Innovate

How do engineers come up with completely new ideas? To reach a radically different design, you need the ability to think outside the normal constraints. This is frequently illustrated by asking the following:

PONDER THIS

Can you connect the nine dots in Figure 5 with four straight lines without lifting the pencil from the paper?

The solution, shown after the Problems section of this chapter, is to extend the lines *beyond* the constraining "box" formed by the dot array. Based on this puzzle, the ability to think beyond apparent constraints is known as thinking "outside the box."[*] Most people assume incorrectly that the lines may not be extended beyond the dots and are not able to solve the problem.

---

[*]The phrase "thinking outside the box" is overused and has been relegated to the dustbin of outdated business jargon. However, the phrase is a very clear illustration of the need to identify and question artificial constraints in engineering problem solving.

Figure 5. The Nine-Dot Problem

Thinking "outside the box" is described more formally as a *paradigm shift*. A *paradigm* is a model or pattern based on a set of rules that defines boundaries and specifies how to be successful within these boundaries (from the Greek *para-* + *deiknynai*, to show side by side). *Paradigm paralysis* occurs when a person or an organization is frozen with the idea that the rules successful in the past will *always* be successful in the future. Someday, you will hear a person in your organization say, "This is the way we have always done it. Everything seems to be going okay, so why should we change what we are doing?" This person is caught in paradigm paralysis. When a paradigm shifts, a new model based on a new set of rules replaces the old mode. The new rules establish new boundaries and allow solutions to problems that were previously unsolvable.

As an example of paradigm paralysis, American industry was stuck in the paradigm of "quality costs money" until Japanese industry demonstrated that design features that reduce complexity not only reduce cost but also improve quality. Major cost reductions and quality improvements occurred in American-built products in a few years after this new paradigm became accepted.

Similarly, industry has been trapped in the paradigm that "pollution reduction costs money." Only recently has industry recognized that money often can be *saved* by minimizing the amount of pollution discharged to the environment through the reuse and recycling of materials. A new paradigm, "pollution means inefficiency," has worked its way into the business culture.

Success in a new paradigm is only temporary. You must be open to the next new paradigm. For example, many companies that were once leaders in the rapidly changing technology of personal computers fell by the wayside when they failed to adapt to the next challenge.

8.7   Translating Failure into Success through Innovation

Truly innovative solutions that have significantly impacted our lives usually involved risk: risk that the solution will fail or will not be accepted. For example, it is said that Edison had hundreds of failures before finding a suitable filament material for his electric lamp. Even outright failure can result in opportunity if you are open to new ideas. A glue that did not stick well enough and was nearly abandoned became the solution for 3M's Post-it Notes®. As in these examples, engineers sometimes are called upon to translate failure into success.

Solving design problems is often an iterative process (see Figure 1). As the solution to a design problem evolves, you may find yourself continually refining the design. While implementing the solution to a design problem, you may discover that the solution you developed is unsafe, too expensive, or will not work. You then "go back to the drawing board" and change the solution until it works.

Despite the best efforts of engineering designers, designs occasionally fail. Bridges collapse, roofs fall in, and dams fail, potentially causing loss of life and property damage. Although the object of engineering design is to avoid failure, truly foolproof design is usually not economically feasible. One of the ironies of engineering is that failure is often one of the outcomes of success. In the interests of economy, there is a tendency to be more daring in design and to take greater risks. This eventually leads to failure. When a major engineering failure occurs, there is usually pressure to increase factors of safety and generally engage in more conservative engineering practices. Thus, engineering progresses slowly, with failure as an inherent (but sometimes tragic) component. For an example of the upward spiral of success and failure in engineering, see the *Focus on Design: What Comes Around, Goes Around*.

FOCUS ON DESIGN: WHAT COMES AROUND, GOES AROUND

BACKGROUND

Engineers seek to optimize the systems they design. This mentality is summarized in NASA's "faster, better, cheaper" management philosophy introduced in 1992. Sometimes, however, in seeking to make engineered systems less expensive or more attractive, reasonable limits of safety are violated. The result can be catastrophic failure. What happens next? The engineering community usually responds by *overdesigning* the next system (i.e., making the next system safer than necessary). The inevitable result is that the overdesigned systems are gradually reduced in safety to make them faster, better, cheaper, or more aesthetically pleasing—resulting eventually in an *underdesigned* system and failure once again. Like Sisyphus of Greek mythology (forced to eternally roll a stone block up a steep hill, only to have it roll back down), engineers can get locked into this cycle of failure, overdesign, gradual underdesign, and refailure. Engineering practice escapes this "infinite loop" only by a paradigm change to a new design approach.

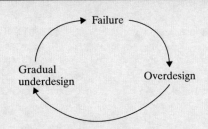

PARADIGM SHIFTS IN BRIDGE DESIGN

One example of how paradigm changes can break the success/failure cycle is in bridge design. It has been argued (Sibly and Walker, 1977) that bridge designs change radically about every 30 years, usually after a series of failures and conservative redesigns. By the 1930s, suspension bridges had become very popular in the United States. Two important features of suspension bridge design are (1) the ratio of the main span length to the bridge width and (2) the ratio of the main span length to the depth of the stiffener. The main span is the part of the bridge suspended between the main towers. The stiffener can be a truss (triangular arrangement of supports) or plate girder (solid structure resembling an I-beam) and is located under the roadway. The stiffener depth is its vertical dimension.

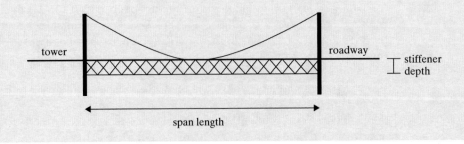

Tacoma Narrows Bridge after the 1940 collapse (note the narrow girder plates) (Photo courtesy of University of Washington Libraries.)

Rebuilt Tacoma Narrows Bridge with deep stiffening trusses (Photo courtesy of Corbis.)

A change in bridge design, the underdesign phase, was beginning in the 1930s. For example, the George Washington Bridge (opened in 1931) and Golden Gate Bridge (opened in 1937) both were wide with very deep (25 and 29 feet deep, respectively) stiffening trusses. However, some bridge designers, including Leon Moissieff, argued that stiff trusses did not dampen the deflections of a suspension bridge very much and that narrow long-span bridges could be successful. For example, the Bronx–Whitestone Bridge (opened in 1939) was built with relatively shallow (11-foot-deep) girder plates.

TACOMA NARROWS BRIDGE

Moissieff got the opportunity to put his ideas into concrete and wire with the Tacoma Narrows Bridge. The Tacoma Narrows is a beautiful, yet windy, passage between the Olympic Peninsula and the Washington mainland in western Washington state. The original design for the Tacoma Narrows span included 25-foot-deep stiffening trusses, but its cost ($11 million) far exceeded the cash available from the federal Public Works Administration and bonds. Moissieff proposed a bridge design that would come in under the available funds: a very narrow bridge with 8-foot-deep girder plates. The resulting bridge was extremely slender and graceful.

Most of the readers of this text already know the end of this sad story. On November 7, 1940, eight weeks after it opened to traffic, the Tacoma Narrows Bridge collapsed catastrophically. Miraculously, the only fatality was a pet dog. The mechanisms behind the failure are complex, but fingers were pointed immediately at the narrow deck and shallow, solid girder plates.

What was the response of the engineering community to the failure? Overdesign. The Bronx–Whitestone Bridge was retrofitted with 14-foot-deep stiffening trusses, decreasing its length-to-stiffening-member depth ratio by a factor of two. The next suspension bridge built after the collapse was, ironically, the *second* Tacoma Narrows Bridge. In length-to-width ratio and length-to-stiffening-truss depth ratio (not plate girders!), it resembled the 1931 George Washington Bridge. The Mackinac Bridge (1957), although narrow relative to its length, also was built with a very conservative length-to-stiffening-truss depth ratio.

Was bridge design doomed to an endless cycle of underdesign, failure, and overdesign? No—a paradigm shift broke the cycle. The paradigm shift in bridge design was the introduction of cable stay bridges in the 1970s. If Sibly and Walker's idea that the bridge designs change radically about every 30 years is accurate, then we are due for a paradigm shift in bridge design soon. Will you be part of the next one?

Postscript: The Bronx–Whitestone Bridge is being retrofitted once again to recapture its original airy profile. The deep stiffening trusses will be removed and replaced with wedge-like structures to allow the wind to flow around the bridge and reduce twisting. And a twin span is planned across the Tacoma Narrows—the third Tacoma Narrows Bridge.

9   SUMMARY

Design results in new or improved devices or systems. In design problems, the system is poorly defined and more than one (or sometimes no) solution is possible. Design problems are solved by defining the problem, gathering information, generating multiple solutions, selecting a solution, implementing the solution, and evaluating the solution. Multiple solutions (i.e., alternative designs) are generated through brainstorming, making checklists, attribute listing (including morphological analysis), and using random forced relationships.

The alternatives are evaluated by assessing their feasibility using the engineering analysis method. Remember that a design is not completed until the solution is implemented (through planning and action) and monitored.

Design parameters are the result of analysis and are used to determine the characteristics of a system. They relate a measure of system performance with some system characteristic to be designed.

Standard analysis and design processes can create problems in product development if engineers work independently from other professionals. Design times can be very long, especially if manufacturing, assembly, marketing, and disposal of products are not considered early in the design process.

One technique for improving design is concurrent engineering, an approach to design where all elements of product lifecycle are included. Examples of concurrent engineering include design for manufacturing, design for assembly, and design for the environment (also called green engineering). A second technique, called reengineering, involves a radical redesign of a system or fundamental rethinking of an engineering problem. Reengineering requires a creative and fluid mind. Third, reverse engineering (the process of taking apart an object or system to see how it works) can be used in specialized situations to improve design.

Finally, watch for barriers to creativity in design, especially paradigm paralysis, where approaches used in the past are assumed to be valid in the present. Be aware, but not afraid, of risk. Remember that solving design problems is often an iterative process.

SUMMARY OF KEY IDEAS

- Solve engineering design problems by defining the problem, gathering information, generating multiple solutions, selecting a solution, implementing the solution, and evaluating the solution.
- Generate multiple solutions through brainstorming, making checklists, listing attributes, and employing forced random relationships.
- Attribute values can be combined in different ways to generate new ideas.
- Evaluate alternatives by applying the engineering analysis method to each alternative.
- Evaluate and select alternatives by assessing feasibility.
- Implement the solution through planning and action.
- By specifying a value for the design parameter, you are specifying the performance of the system.
- Design times can be very long for new products.
- Engineers must take into account the fact that products must be made, sold, used, and disposed of.
- To solve a challenging engineering problem, you may have to go outside the existing paradigm and reengineer the system.
- Design is iterative; failure is an inherent part of engineering progress.

Problems

1. How is the engineering design process different from the engineering analysis process?

2. Using each step in the engineering design process, generate alternatives and select a design for an elevated bed support for a dorm room.

3. Using each step in the engineering design process, generate alternatives and select a design for a fastener that can hold documents that are 2 to 150 pages long.

4. Using each step in the engineering design process, generate alternatives and select a design for a Web page for the online evaluation of engineering courses.

5. Another method for generating new ideas is bionics. The bionics technique uses analogies with the natural world to solve engineering problems. An example is the development of the hook and loop fastener. Swiss inventor George de Mestral observed that cockleburs attached to his wool pants and the fur of his dog; thus, he was inspired to develop Velcro® (named after the French *velour crochet*: velvet hooks). State a design problem and use bionics to generate solutions to the problem.

6. New ideas also can be generated by the method of *inversion*. In the inversion technique, you seek to achieve the opposite of the design goal and then invert the solution for the original design problem. For example, suppose your goal is to develop a very fast switch. Using inversion, you might consider how to make a slow switch (e.g., using high-resistance material) and then invert the solution (e.g., using low-resistance material) in your design. State a design problem and use inversion generate solutions to the problem.

7. Determine two design parameters for bridges from the *Focus on Design: What Comes Around, Goes Around*. Use the Internet to determine the values of the design parameters for two bridges.

8. Discuss an example of a local engineering project that had (or has) implementation challenges. How are engineers and other professions seeking to solve the implementation problems?

9. Write a short paper on how the development of Teflon is an example of a shortcoming turned into a success.

10. Practice thinking outside the proverbial box by solving the 16-dot problem. (Use a 4×4 matrix; Figure 5 shows a 3×3 matrix). Can you think of a strategy to solve the n^2-dot problem ($n \times n$ matrix)?

10

Introduction to Engineering Problem-Solving Tools and Using Data

1   INTRODUCTION

1.1   Engineering Problem-Solving Tools

Engineers use four problem-solving tools. First, engineers collect *data* to test hypotheses, conduct analyses, and do design. Techniques to get the most out of your data are discussed in this chapter. Second, *models* are used. Models are conceptual, mathematical, or physical representations of the engineering system of interest. Engineers use models to verify system performance prior to design. Third, engineers use *computers* to perform calculations and visualize their results. Finally, engineers use feasibility concepts to evaluate alternative designs.

1.2   Using Data

All engineers generate data, use data, and frequently perform calculations involving data. In your engineering curriculum, you will take many classes in mathematics. It is likely that you will take a course or two in probability, statistics, and experimental design. In those courses, you will learn about the characteristics of data and how to manipulate data. In this chapter, a few basic concepts concerning experimental data will be introduced.

2   ACCURACY AND PRECISION

2.1   Introduction

Engineers measure characteristics of the real world. If life were perfect, you could collect data and determine *exactly* the parameter of interest to you. This is almost never the case. As an example, consider a human factors engineering study in which you must determine the distance from a computer user's eyes (modeled by a mannequin) to the computer monitor. The data collection requirements seem

OBJECTIVES

After reading this chapter, you will be able to:

- compare the concepts of accuracy and precision;
- round numbers appropriately;
- report numbers to the proper number of significant figures;
- list the important measures of central tendency and explain when to use them;
- list the important measures of variability and explain when to use them.

simple: you could easily measure the distance with a ruler or other measuring device. Common experience tells you that if you performed the measurement numerous times, you might get different results. If each one of your studymates made the measurement, you would likely get even more variety in the responses. In spite of the variability, there is one true distance (at least, one true distance when measuring at a fixed scale).

2.2   Accuracy

accuracy: a measure of closeness to the true value

How can you describe how closely your measurements are to the true answer? In this section, the relationship between measured and true values will be discussed in a general way. A more quantitative discussion may be found in Sections 4 and 5. The relationship between measurements and the true value is called **accuracy**. A measurement is said to be *accurate* if it is near the true value. For example, if the mannequin's eyes are set at 40.0 cm from the monitor, a measurement of 39.9 cm may be accurate and a measurement of 45.6 cm may be inaccurate (depending on the needs of the study).

2.3   Precision

precision: a measure of similarity in a set of values

The relationship between repeated measurements is called **precision**. A set of measurements is said to be *precise* if the measurements are similar in value. For example, suppose the measurements from the mannequin's eyes to the monitor are 31.6, 31.5, 31.6, and 31.4 cm. This set may be said to be precise (although inaccurate).° An example of accuracy and precision is shown in Example 1.

You may have seen the concepts of accuracy and precision illustrated with a dartboard or archery target. If the goal is to hit the bull's eye, then accurate shots are near the bull's eye and precise shots are clustered together (but not necessarily near the bull's eye). This is shown in Figure 1.

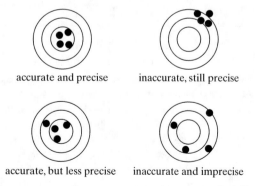

Figure 1.   Accuracy and Precision

°Be careful about the use of the word "precise." In common usage, "precise" is used to mean "exact" ("That is precisely my point."). In scientific work, use "precise" and "precision" only in reference to repeated measures.

EXAMPLE 1 AC-CURACY AND PRECISION

For the human factors example, how would you label the following data sets with regard to accuracy and precision (if the "true" distance from the mannequin's eyes to the monitor is 40.0 cm)?

Set #1 = 40.1, 40.0, 39.8, and 40.0 cm

Set #2 = 39.8, 41.4, 39.4, and 40.9 cm

Set #3 = 35.2, 35.3, 35.3, and 35.1 cm

Set #4 = 36.7, 45.6, 46.2, and 34.9 cm

SOLUTION

The answer depends on the needs of the study. A reasonable answer is as follows:

Set #1 = accurate and precise

Set #2 = accurate, but less precise

Set #3 = less accurate, but precise

Set #4 = much less accurate and much less precise

The data are plotted in the following figure:

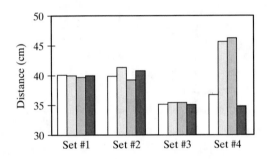

Note that the concepts of accuracy and precision are easy to see in this figure. More quantitative measures of accuracy and precision will be developed in Sections 4 and 5, respectively.

3   ROUNDING AND SIGNIFICANT DIGITS

3.1   Introduction

The concepts of precision and accuracy do not help you to *record* data and data calculations. A particularly troublesome area of data reporting and calculations concerns the number of decimal places to report. In the computer monitor problem, suppose you and a friend measure the distance from the mannequin's eye to the monitor. You use a meter stick and find the distance to be 40.6 cm. Your friend uses a yardstick and finds the distance to be 15 11/16 inches. Your friend realizes that the answer is supposed to be reported in centimeters and performs the following conversion:

$$\text{distance} = (15\ 11/16\ \text{in})(2.54\ \text{cm/in})$$
$$= (15.6875\ \text{in})(2.54\ \text{cm/in})$$
$$= 39.84625\ \text{cm}$$

Thus, your friend reports the distance as 39.84625 cm.

PONDER THIS

Key idea: Do not blindly report the numbers given to you by a calculator or spreadsheet—determine the proper number of digits to report.

significant digits: the number of digits justified by the precision of the data

The answer is, emphatically, *No! Just because your calculator reports five figures after the decimal point does not mean that the measurement is accurate to five figures after the decimal point.**

3.2   Counting the Number of Significant Digits

If reporting all digits is incorrect, how *should* you report measurements and calculation results? To determine the number of decimal places, it is important to understand the idea of **significant digits** (or *significant figures*). Determine the number of significant digits of a number by the following procedure (for numbers containing a decimal place):

1. Starting on the *left* side of the number, move *right* until you encounter the first nonzero digit (ignoring the decimal place). Count this first nonzero digit as "one."

2. Continue moving to the right, counting each digit (still ignoring the decimal place). When you reach the last digit of the number on the right, you have counted the number of significant digits.

As an example, count the number of significant digits in the number 0.0504. It is a good idea to mentally separate each digit, ignoring the decimal place. One way to do this is to put each number in a box:

0.	0	5	0	4

Counting the boxes from left to right, the first box containing a nonzero digit is the third box from the left. Number this box "1" and continue counting from left to right until you run out of digits:

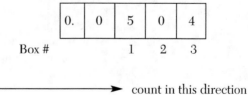

Box #   1   2   3

⟶ count in this direction

The last box is the third numbered box. Thus, 0.0504 has three significant digits. How many significant digits are in the number 120.0? Repeat the procedure by separating each digit (ignoring the decimal place):

1	2	0.	0

*By point of reference, 0.00001 cm = 100 nanometers, about the size of a virus. It is unlikely that a yardstick can measure a distance of about 40 cm to the accuracy of the size of a virus.

Counting the boxes from left to right, the first box containing a nonzero digit is the first box from the left. Number this box "1" and continue counting from left to right until you run out of digits:

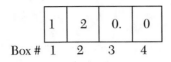

The last box is the fourth numbered box. Thus, 120.0 has four significant digits. See Example 2 for more examples of counting the number of significant digits.

3.3   Exceptions to the Rule: Numbers with No Decimal Point and Exact Numbers

Key idea: Avoid writing numbers without decimal points, because such numbers have an indeterminate number of significant digits.

The procedure in Section 3.2 for counting the number of significant digits works for most numbers. The rule implies that leading zeros to the left of the decimal point are ignored. What about numbers with *no* decimal point? Does the number "8" have the same number of significant digits as "8." or "8.0" or "8.00"? Numbers without decimal places are tricky. It is clear from Section 3.2 that "8.," "8.0," and "8.00" have one, two, and three significant digits, respectively. However, *you do not know how many significant digits there are in the number 8 when it is written without a decimal point*.

To avoid this uncertainty, refrain from writing numbers without decimal points. If you wish to indicate three significant figures with the number seven hundred, write it as "700." not "700" (i.e., write it *with* a decimal point). (In addition, *always* include a leading zero when reporting numbers between 1 and −1. It is much clearer if you write "−0.14" or "0.56" than if you write "−.14" or ".56".)

You also can use scientific notation to show the number of significant digits. Count the number of significant digits in a number in scientific notation by applying the procedure of Section 3.2 to the mantissa.° Thus, the numbers "7. $\times 10^2$", "7.0 $\times 10^2$", and "7.00 $\times 10^2$" have one, two, and three significant digits, respectively. (Again, mantissas without decimal places are tricky: avoid writing numbers such as "7 $\times 10^2$".)

What about *exact* numbers? You may wish to do calculations that involve numbers that are exact. Exact numbers have no variability. For example, there are *exactly* 100 cm in a meter, *exactly* three feet in a yard, and *exactly* eight sides in an octagon. In engineering calculations, you may wish incorporate exact numbers into calculations, such as the number of roads in a city, the number of distillation columns in a factory, or the number of capacitors in a circuit.

PONDER THIS

How many significant digits are there in an exact number?

Exact numbers are treated as if they have an *infinite* number of significant digits. This may seem a little strange at first, but as you shall see in Section 3.5, the number of significant digits in exact numbers is ignored in calculations.

°Numbers in scientific notation have three parts: the base (usually 10), the mantissa (number before the "×" symbol), and the exponent (exponent on the base). Thus, in the number 1.71 $\times 10^5$, the mantissa is 1.71, the base is 10, and the exponent is 5. The word *mantissa* means "an addition of little importance." In some software packages, "×10" is replaced with an uppercase letter "e." Thus, 1.71 $\times 10^5$ = 1.71E5.

**EXAMPLE 2
SIGNIFICANT
DIGITS**

Count the number of significant digits in the following measurements: 43 cm, 4.3 kV, 0.43 Ω, and 0.043 microcurie (0.043 μCi). Count the number of significant digits in the numbers 691, 1.30, and 0.00000500.

SOLUTION

Start with the first nonzero digit from the left and count to the right until encountering the last digits. For example, the measurement "4.3 kV" can be counted as

The number "0.00000500" can be counted as

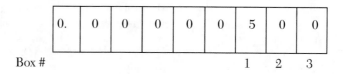

Thus, each number and unit in the set of measurements (43 cm, 4.3 kV, 0.43 Ω, and 0.043 μCi) has two significant digits. Each number in the set of numbers (691, 1.30, and 0.00000500) has three significant digits.

3.4   Reporting Measurements

Key idea: Report one more significant digit than the number of digits you are certain about. The last significant digit is understood to include some uncertainty.

You now know how to *determine* the number of significant digits in numbers. However, the question from Section 3.2 remains: how should you *report* measurements? The usual interpretation of significant digits is as follows: report *one more significant digit than the number of digits you are certain about.* In other words, the last significant digit is understood to be estimated and may include some uncertainty.

An example will help here. Suppose you are weighing concrete test specimens to test the strength of a new concrete formulation. The scale is marked in grams. You interpolate between gram markings to estimate tenths of grams. It would be proper to report a weight of 79.6 g. When another engineer reads this number, he or she will know that there is some uncertainty in the tenths of grams, because it is the last significant digit reported.

3.5   Rounding and Calculations

rounding: adjusting the value of certain digits to comply with the appropriate number of significant digits

Always report your calculations with the number of significant digits consistent with the data. Determining the number of significant digits involves two steps: deciding which digits to drop and deciding what to do with the digits you report. The latter process is called **rounding**.

There are two simple rules for rounding:

1. If the digit to be dropped is less than 5, then write the last digit retained as it is.
2. If the digit to be dropped is greater than or equal to 5, then increase the last digit retained by one.*

---

*Sometimes, a different convention is used if the digit to be dropped is equal to 5. Some people write the last digit retained as the nearest even digit if the digit to be dropped is equal to 5. For example, if you determine that three significant digits are appropriate, you would round 0.6225 to 0.622 and 1.235 to 1.24 in this system.

For example, if you determine that four significant digits are appropriate, you would round 95.673 to 95.67 (since the digit dropped, 3, is less than 5). Similarly, if you determine that five significant digits are appropriate, you would round 0.0124457 to 0.012446 (since the digit dropped, 7, is greater than 5).

How do you determine the appropriate number of significant digits in a calculation? Two rules will suffice here:

1. When multiplying or dividing numbers, report the result to the number of *significant digits* of the value with the smallest number of significant digits.
2. When adding or subtracting numbers, report the result to the number of *decimal places* of the value with the smallest number of decimal places.

It is important to note the difference between how numbers are reported in different calculations. In multiplication and division, the reported value is based on the smallest number of *significant digits* in the calculation. This rule implies that the product or division of numbers cannot be more precise than the least precise number. For example, your calculator may report:

$$56.122/2.31 = 24.2952381 \ (\textit{Warning: Too many digits reported})$$

Key idea: The reported value is based on the smallest number of *significant digits* in the calculation for multiplication and division and on the smallest number of *decimal places* in the calculation for addition and subtraction. Exact numbers do not affect the number of digits reported.

PONDER THIS

How would you round the results of the calculation of 56.122/2.31 = 24.2952381?

You round the result to 24.3, because the smallest number of significant digits in the numbers on the left side of the equation is three ("2.31" has three significant digits).

In addition and subtraction, the second rule says that the reported value is based on the smallest number of *decimal places* (numbers to the right of the decimal place) in the calculation. As an example, your calculator may report

$$23.52 + 4.215 + 6.1 = 33.835 \qquad (\textit{Warning: Too many digits reported})$$

PONDER THIS

How would you round the results of the calculation of 23.52 + 4.215 + 6.1 = 33.835?

You round the sum to 33.8, because the number "6.1" has only one digit to the right of the decimal point. Note that the sum is reported to three significant digits, even though one of the numbers on the left side (the number "6.1") has only two significant digits.

What about exact numbers in calculations? Exact numbers play no role in determining the number of digits reported.

PONDER THIS

Why should exact numbers not affect the number of reported digits in multiplication and division?

Recall from Section 3.3 that *exact numbers are treated as having an infinite number of significant digits*. Thus, exact numbers do not affect the number of reported digits in multiplication and division. Why? Exact numbers can *never* have the smallest number of significant digits and can never control the number of digits reported.

In addition and subtraction, it also makes sense that exact numbers should not play a role in determining the number of digits reported. For example, suppose you are trying to convert a temperature reading from Kelvin to Celsius. A temperature of zero Kelvin (0 K) is defined to be exactly $-273.16°C$. Thus, 298.103 K is equal to $-273.16 + 298.103 = 24.943$ K. You report this temperature to three decimal places because the number "-273.16" is exact and does not affect the number of decimal places reported.

Finally, rounding is best performed on the final answer, not on intermediate calculations. If you round intermediate calculations, rounding errors may accumulate.

4   MEASURES OF CENTRAL TENDENCY

4.1   Introduction

Engineers usually take a more quantitative approach to the ideas of accuracy and precision than that presented in Section 2. To determine accuracy, you may wish to use one measure as representative of a set of data. This is called a measure of the *central tendency* of the data or the *average* (from the Arabic *'awariyah* meaning damaged merchandise, because the word "average" was originally applied to the process of proportionally distributing expenses for damaged goods during sea transport).

4.2   Arithmetic Mean

arithmetic mean: the sum of all values divided by the number of

values $= \dfrac{1}{N}\sum\limits_{i=1}^{N}x_i$

There are many ways to take the average of a set of data. The most common measure is the **arithmetic mean** (often just called the *mean*). The arithmetic mean is calculated by summing all the values and dividing by the number of data points. For example, if the fuel efficiency of an innovative automotive engine was measured to be 56.2, 61.4, 55.2, and 60.9 miles per gallon (mpg), then the arithmetic mean would be

$$(56.2 + 61.4 + 55.2 + 60.9 \text{ mpg})/4 = (233.7 \text{ mpg})/4 = 58.4 \text{ mpg}$$

(Why was the answer reported to one decimal place? Each number to be summed was reported to one decimal place, so the sum should be reported to one decimal place. The number 4 is exact and does not affect how the result is reported.) If each data point is designated x_i and there are N data points $(x_1, x_2, x_3, \ldots, x_N)$, then the arithmetic mean is

$$\text{arithmetic mean} = \frac{x_1 + x_2 + x_3 + \cdots + x_N}{N} = \sum_{i=1}^{N}x_i$$

The uppercase sigma (see Appendix B) is read, "the sum from i equals 1 to i equals N of ...."

At first glance, it appears that the arithmetic mean is the *only* reasonable way to determine an average. However, the arithmetic mean can be misleading and is not always appropriate. Can you think of a situation where the arithmetic mean is **not** the best measure of central tendency?

THOUGHTFUL PAUSE

> **Take a guess at the mean wealth of eyeglass-wearing men in Washington state with the initials WHG who were born in 1951.**

Now guess the mean wealth of this group if *one* member, Microsoft President Bill Gates, is excluded. The exclusion of Bill Gates would probably decrease the arithmetic mean of the wealth significantly.

Key idea: The arithmetic mean is sensitive to extreme values in the data set.

Similarly, note what happens to the arithmetic mean if you change *one* data point in the fuel efficiency data. If the fuel efficiencies were 56.2, 61.4, 55.2, and *20.9* mpg (rather than 56.2, 61.4, 55.2, and *60.9* mpg), then the arithmetic mean changes from 58.4 mpg to 48.4 mpg. These exercises demonstrate that the *arithmetic mean is sensitive to extreme values*. In other words, the largest and smallest values in the data set strongly affect the arithmetic mean.

4.3   Median

median: the middle data point when the values are listed in numerical order

To avoid the influence of extreme values, the median sometimes is used as a measure of central tendency. The **median** of a data set is the middle data point when the values are listed in numerical order. (For an odd number of data points, the median is the middle value when ordered. For an even number of data points, the median is the arithmetic mean of the two middle values when ordered.)

Say the engineering library has ten very old personal computers with hard-drive storage capacities of 1.2, 4.5, 6.4, 5.2, 6.4, 5.0, 2.3, 3.4, 6.3, and 8.2 gigabytes (1 gigabyte = 1 GB = 10^9 bytes). To determine the median storage capacity, order the values (8.2, 6.4, 6.4, 6.3, 5.2, 5.0, 4.5, 3.4, 2.3, and 1.2 GB). Since there is an even number of values, take the arithmetic mean of the middle two values (5.2 and 5.0 GB). The median amount of storage capacity is then 5.1 GB. (You may wish to confirm that the arithmetic mean amount of storage capacity is 4.9 GB. This is similar to the median, since there are no really extreme values here.) As another example, find the median value of 5.62, 4.1, and 6.2:

Values: 5.62, 4.1, 6.2

Ordered values:

4.1	5.62	6.2
smallest		largest

Median: 5.62

(use the middle value, since the number of values is odd)

4.4   Geometric Mean

geometric mean: the product of the values raised to the 1/N power = $(x_1 x_2 x_3 \ldots x_N)^{1/N} =$ $\left(\prod\limits_{i=1}^{N} x_i \right)^{1/N}$

There are several other types of less commonly used averages. The **geometric mean** is the product of the values raised to the 1/N power $(x_1 x_2 x_3 \ldots x_N)^{1/N}$, or, equivalently, the Nth root of the product of the values:

$$\text{geometric mean} = (x_1 x_2 x_3 \ldots x_N)^{1/N} = \sqrt[N]{x_1 x_2 x_3 \ldots x_N}$$

You can use uppercase pi (Π) to read "the product of . . ." (just as Σ means "the sum of . . .").

Thus,

$$\text{geometric mean} = \left(\prod_{i=1}^{N} x_i \right)^{1/N}$$

You can show that the logarithm of the geometric mean of a set of positive numbers is equal to the arithmetic mean of the logarithms of the numbers (see also Problem 10).

The geometric mean sometimes is used as a measure of central tendency with values that change over several orders of magnitude. For example, in environmental engineering, treated wastewater can contain no more than a specified number of a certain kind of microorganism. Since microorganism concentrations can vary greatly, the geometric mean is regulated. If the data for one week are 400, 100, 250, 100, 15, 20, and 15,000 organisms per 100 milliliters, then the seven-day geometric mean is as follows:

$$(400 \times 100 \times 250 \times 100 \times 15 \times 20 \times 15{,}000)^{1/7}$$

or 240 organisms per 100 milliliters.

4.5   Harmonic Mean

harmonic mean: the reciprocal of the arithmetic mean of the reciprocals of the values =

$$\frac{N}{\displaystyle\sum_{i=1}^{N}\frac{1}{x_i}}$$

The **harmonic mean** is the reciprocal of the arithmetic mean of the reciprocals of the values:

$$\text{harmonic mean} = \frac{1}{\dfrac{1}{N}\displaystyle\sum_{i=1}^{N}\dfrac{1}{x_i}} = \frac{N}{\displaystyle\sum_{i=1}^{N}\dfrac{1}{x_i}}$$

The harmonic mean is used when the *reciprocals* of the data are important. For example, computer speeds often are assessed by benchmark tests, where the computation speeds (expressed in millions of instructions per second or MIPS) for several tasks are recorded. The computation *time* is more important than the computation *speed* for most computer users. The computation time is inversely proportional to the computation speed (speed = number of operations/time, so time = number of operations/speed). Thus, the appropriate measure of central tendency for computational speed is the harmonic mean.

As an example, suppose that five benchmark programs execute at 30, 700, 15, and 13,000 MIPS. The harmonic mean is

$$\frac{4}{\dfrac{1}{30\text{ MIPS}} + \dfrac{1}{700\text{ MIPS}} + \dfrac{1}{15\text{ MIPS}} + \dfrac{1}{13{,}000\text{ MIPS}}} = 39\text{ MIPS}$$

The harmonic mean is influenced most strongly by the *smallest* values. For example, if the *largest* computation speed was doubled from 13,000 to 26,000 MIPS, the harmonic mean remains unchanged at 39 MIPS. However, if the *smallest* computational speed was doubled from 15 to 30 MIPS, the harmonic mean increases from 39 MIPS to 59 MIPS.

4.6   Quadratic Mean

quadratic mean (root mean square, RMS): the square root of the arithmetic mean of the squares of the values =

$$\sqrt{\frac{1}{N}\sum_{i=1}^{N}x_i^2}$$

The **quadratic mean** (commonly called the **root mean square, RMS**) is the square root of the arithmetic mean of the squares of the values:

$$\text{quadratic mean} = \text{RMS} = \sqrt{\frac{1}{N}\sum_{i=1}^{N}x_i^2}$$

The quadratic mean is used when an important property is proportional to the *square* of a measured value. For example, suppose a mechanical engineer bombards a surface with high-energy particles to learn more about the surface properties of the material. The information to be gathered depends on the energy of the particles. The engineer may be more interested in the quadratic mean velocity (RMS velocity) of the particles, rather than the arithmetic mean, because the energy of the particles is proportional to the velocity squared. (Recall that the kinetic energy = $\frac{1}{2}mv^2$, where m = mass and v = velocity.)

4.7   Mode

mode: the most frequently occurring value in a data set

Finally, the **mode** of a data set is the most frequently occurring value in a data set. In the hard-drive storage capacity example (Section 4.3), the mode is 6.4 GB, since that value is present at a higher frequency (2 out of 10 values) than any other (all others present at one out of ten values). An example of how to select the most appropriate measure of central tendency is given in Example 3.

EXAMPLE 3
MEASURES OF
CENTRAL
TENDENCY

Select and calculate the most appropriate measure of central tendency for the diameters of catalyst particles used in ammonia synthesis. A particle size analysis of 400 catalyst particles revealed 100 particles with diameter 5.4 μm, 100 particles with diameter 10.6 μm, 100 particles with diameter 7.5 μm, and 100 particles with diameter 8.4 μm. You are interested in the particle diameter, surface area, and surface-to-volume ratio (S/V).

SOLUTION

For the particle diameter, either the mean or median is appropriate, since the distribution is narrow. The mean of the particle diameters is $[(100)(5.4\ \mu\text{m}) + (100)(10.6\ \mu\text{m}) + (100)(7.5\ \mu\text{m}) + (100)(8.4\ \mu\text{m})]/400$ or **8.0 μm**. The median of the particle diameters is the arithmetic mean of 7.5 μm and 8.4 μm or **8.0 μm**. (Note the number of significant figures through this problem.)

Surface area is proportional to the diameter squared, so the quadratic mean of the particle diameters is the appropriate type of mean. The quadratic mean of the particle diameters is $\{[(100)(5.4\ \mu\text{m})^2 + (100)(10.6\ \mu\text{m})^2 + (100)(7.5\ \mu\text{m})^2 + (100)(8.4\ \mu\text{m})^2]/400\}^{1/2}$ or **8.2 μm**.

S/V is proportional to the reciprocal of the diameter, so the harmonic mean of the particle diameters is the appropriate type of mean. The harmonic mean of the particle diameters is $400/[(100)/(5.4\ \mu\text{m}) + (100)/(10.6\ \mu\text{m}) + (100)/(7.5\ \mu\text{m}) + (100)/(8.4\ \mu\text{m})]$ or **7.5 μm**.

(*Note:* The surface area and S/V also can be calculated directly and the arithmetic mean of their values calculated.)

---

5   MEASURES OF VARIABILITY

5.1   Introduction

Precision is a qualitative indicator of the variability of the data. There are three common *quantitative* measures of data variability: variance, standard deviation, and relative standard deviation.

Before developing the formulas for these measures, it is important to review two important types of data sets. If you examine all possible members of some group, then the measures of central tendency and variability are called **population** measures. For example, if you measured propulsion characteristics of all Space Shuttle engines, you could calculate the population mean of the propulsion characteristics.

population: all possible members of a group

In many cases in engineering, you can examine only a few members of the population. If so, label your measures **sample** measures. For example, you may determine the failure rate of a handful of circuit boards from a production line and calculate the sample mean of the failure rate. (Why test only a handful? If you tested *all* the boards to failure, there wouldn't be any left to sell.) If you have n members of the sample and N members of the population (where $n \leq N$), then you can define

sample: selected members of a group

$$\text{sample (arithmetic) mean} = \bar{x} = \frac{1}{n}\sum_{i=1}^{n} x_i, \text{ and}$$

$$\text{population (arithmetic) mean} = \mu = \frac{1}{N}\sum_{i=1}^{N} x_i$$

Note that different symbols are used for the sample and population means.

5.2   Variance

The formulas for the population mean and sample mean look similar. However, the differences between the sample and population measures of *variability* are more pronounced. The **variance** is one measure of data variability. The variance is proportional to the sum of the squares of the differences between each data point and the mean. The *sample variance* is given by

variance: a measure of data variability proportional to the sum of the squares of the differences between each data point and the mean

$$s^2 = \frac{1}{n-1}\sum_{i=1}^{n}(x_i - \bar{x})^2$$

The *population variance* is given by

$$\sigma^2 = \frac{1}{N}\sum_{i=1}^{N}(x_i - \mu)^2$$

(Note that the sample variance is calculated by dividing by $n - 1$, while the population variance is calculated by dividing by N.) Why square the difference between the data and the mean? Squaring makes all the terms in the summation positive. Thus, contributions to the variance from data points *less* than the mean do not cancel out contributions from data points *greater* than the sample mean.

The variance has one big disadvantage as a measure of variability. To illustrate the problem, calculate the sample mean of the fuel efficiencies discussed in Section 4.2. The sample mean was 58.4 mpg. The sample variance is

$$s^2 = [(56.2 \text{ mpg} - 58.4 \text{ mpg})^2 + (61.4 \text{ mpg} - 58.4 \text{ mpg})^2 +$$
$$(55.2 \text{ mpg} - 58.4 \text{ mpg})^2 + (60.9 \text{ mpg} - 58.4 \text{ mpg})^2]/3$$
$$= 10.1 \text{ (mpg)}^2$$

Is 10.1 $(\text{mpg})^2$ big or small? It is hard to tell, because of the strange units of the variance. The units of the variance are the squares of the units of the observations.

5.3   Standard Deviation

standard deviation: a measure of data variability with the same units as each data point and equal to the square root of the variance

A more easily interpreted measure of data variability is the **standard deviation**. The standard deviation is the square root of the variance. Thus, the sample standard deviation is $s = (s^2)^{1/2}$ and the population standard deviation is $\sigma = (\sigma^2)^{1/2}$. For example, the sample standard deviation for the fuel efficiency example is

$$s = [10.1 \text{ miles}^2/\text{gallon}^2]^{1/2} = 3.2 \text{ mpg}$$

The standard deviation makes it clear that the variability is fairly low: the sample standard deviation is small compared with the sample mean.

5.4   Relative Standard Deviation

relative standard deviation (RSD or standard error): a dimensionless measure of data variability and equal to the standard deviation divided by the mean

The mean and standard deviation can be compared even more directly in the final common measure of variability: **relative standard deviation (RSD**, also called the **standard error**). The relative standard deviation is the standard deviation divided by the mean. It is usually expressed as a percentage. For the fuel efficiency data, the RSD is

$$(3.2 \text{ mpg})/(58.4 \text{ mpg}) = 0.055 \text{ or } 5.5\%$$

This reaffirms the observation that the variability in the data is fairly low. Another example of calculating the measures of variability is given in Example 4.

EXAMPLE 4
MEASURES OF
VARIABILITY

Calculate the relative standard deviations for the volumes of the Great Lakes and the lengths of all the pencils in the Western Hemisphere.

The volumes of the Great Lakes are as follows: Superior ($11,800 \text{ km}^3$), Michigan ($4,800 \text{ km}^3$), Huron ($3,500 \text{ km}^3$), Erie (500 km^3), and Ontario ($1,600 \text{ km}^3$). Using the pencils in my desk as examples, the lengths are 18.3 cm, 17.0 cm, 13.2 cm, 16.5 cm, and 18.5 cm.

SOLUTION

Since the data for all the Great Lakes are known, use population statistics. Thus, $\mu = 4,400 \text{ km}^3$, $\sigma = 3,969 \text{ km}^3$, and RSD = $\boldsymbol{\sigma/\mu = 0.89}$ **or 89%**. (Remember to divide by $N = 5$ for σ^2.)

Since the data for the pencils are samples, use sample statistics: $\bar{x} = 16.7$ cm and $s = 2.1$ cm, so RSD = $\boldsymbol{s/\bar{x} = 0.13, \text{ or } 13\%}$. (Remember to divide by $n - 1 = 4$ for s^2.)

5.5   Variability and Data Collection in Engineering

In engineering, variability leads to uncertainty. For example, increased variability in a parameter such as Young's modulus means more uncertainty about the stability of a structure. More uncertainty leads to more conservative designs. More conservative designs are more expensive. For example, if you are uncertain about the properties of a capacitor, then you may specify an overly large capacitor to account for the uncertainty. As a result, variability leads to higher costs.

Key idea: Variability increases uncertainty, leading to higher costs. Engineers collect data to reduce uncertainty.

How do engineers reduce uncertainty? Simply put, *engineers collect data to reduce uncertainty*. Two examples will demonstrate the relationship between data collection and uncertainty reduction. Suppose your firm is hired to design a waterproof cover for a baseball infield. You might design the cover with the assumption that the bases are spaced 90 feet apart. Are the bases exactly 90 feet apart? No, it is possible that they might be off by a tiny distance. However, the uncertainty regarding the base path distance is very small. In addition, the cost of overdesign (i.e., the cost of making the cover a little too big) is also very small. Therefore, the cost of actually measuring the base path distances probably is not outweighed by the reduction in uncertainty that the measurements would bring.

Now imagine you are designing the steel columns in a high-rise building. The columns transmit the force generated by the structure's mass to the foundation. Is it worthwhile to test the mechanical properties of the steel columns? The answer might very well be *yes*. While the cost of collecting the data is high, the potential payoff is very high. If you have to design for uncertain structural properties, then you might have to specify many additional columns. In addition, the cost of failure (in this case, the cost of collapse) is extremely high. Another example of how engineers pay to reduce uncertainty is shown in the *Focus on Variability: Paying to Reduce Uncertainty*.

safety factor: a multiplier of a design parameter used to account in part for uncertainty

Uncertainty in design sometimes is expressed by a *safety factor*. Design parameters sometimes are multiplied by safety factors to account for uncertainty. For example, steel buildings are designed with a safety factor of 2, while wooden buildings are designed with a safety factor of 6. Why the difference? The structural properties of wood are more variable than the structural properties of steel.°

°As the examples in the text show, safety factors are determined in part by the uncertainty in materials properties and the cost of overdesign. Safety factors also are influenced by the variability in loads and by the cost of failure. For example, the cables in high-speed elevators (which experience variable loads and for which the cost of failure is high) are designed with a safety factor of 11.9.

FOCUS ON VARIABILITY: PAYING TO REDUCE UNCERTAINTY

This chapter was devoted to how to *use* data. Perhaps a more fundamental question should be asked: why do engineers gather data in the first place? After all, data collection—whether a phone call or an hour on the Internet or two year's worth of laboratory research—costs money. The simple answer from the text is that engineers collect data to reduce uncertainty. When engineers pay for data collection, they are really paying to reduce uncertainty. So when should you collect data? *You collect data only when the benefits of reducing uncertainty outweigh the cost of data collection.*

You sometimes can quantify both the cost of collecting data and the degree of uncertainty reduction. Consider the case of simple random sampling. In many cases, it is common to collect a small number of samples relative to the total possible number of samples (using the symbols in Section 5.1: $n \ll N$). From the samples collected, it is possible to estimate the standard deviation of the sample mean. For example, if you collected five samples on ten occasions, you could calculate ten different sample means. Using those ten values, you could calculate the variance of the sample mean.

One result from statistics is that the variance of the sample mean [$\text{var}(\bar{x})$] is equal to the population variance divided by the number of samples (σ^2/n):

$$\text{var}(\bar{x}) = \sigma^2/n$$

Rearranging terms yields

$$n = \sigma^2/\text{var}(\bar{x})$$

This equation tells you that you need to collect twice as many samples in a given population to reduce the variance in the sample mean by half. In other words, decreasing $\text{var}(\bar{x})$ by a factor of two means increasing n by a factor of two. In addition, the equation tells you that

an inherently more variable population (i.e., larger σ^2) will require more samples to maintain the same variance in the sample mean.

Suppose you are working on a new aircraft design and need to test the tensile strength of an aluminum alloy. How many alloy samples should you test? Say, from previous work, you know that $\sigma = 0.3$ ksi (tensile strength is measured in thousands of pounds per square inch, or ksi). Each test costs $25. By reducing the uncertainty in $\bar{x}$, you increase the benefits. Suppose that the relationship between benefits and variability is given by

$$\text{benefits (in \$)} = 2{,}000[0.3 - \text{sd}(\bar{x})]$$

where $\text{sd}(\bar{x})$ is the standard deviation of the sample mean in ksi. You know that

$$\text{sd}(\bar{x}) = [\text{var}(\bar{x})]^{1/2} = (\sigma^2/n)^{1/2} = \sigma/n^{1/2}$$

The cost of testing n samples (in $) is $25n$, since the tests cost $25 each. Thus,

$$\begin{aligned} \text{net benefits} &= \text{benefits} - \text{costs} \\ &= 2{,}000[0.3 - \text{sd}(\bar{x})] - 25n \\ &= 2{,}000[0.3 - \sigma/n^{1/2}] - 25n. \end{aligned}$$

The net benefits are plotted as a function of n in the accompanying figure. Note that collecting a *small* number of samples is undesirable: the sample cost, although small, is not outweighed by the very small reduction in uncertainty. (A negative value for net benefits means that the costs are larger than the benefits.) Similarly, collecting a *large* number of samples is undesirable: the large sample cost is not offset by the corresponding reduction in uncertainty. Net benefits are maximized by collecting five samples in this case.

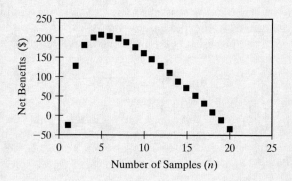

6   SUMMARY

Engineers generate and use data. Data may have errors, described qualitatively by the concepts of precision and accuracy. Calculated values should be presented with an appropriate number of significant digits (usually **not** the number given by your calculator or spreadsheet). Use measures of central tendency and variability to summarize your data and quantify data variability.

SUMMARY OF KEY IDEAS

- Do not blindly report the numbers given to you by a calculator or spreadsheet—determine the proper number of digits to report.
- Avoid writing numbers without decimal points, because such numbers have an indeterminate number of significant digits.
- Report one more significant digit than the number of digits you are certain about. The last significant digit is understood to include some uncertainty.
- The reported value is based on the smallest number of *significant digits* in the calculation for multiplication and division and on the smallest number of *decimal places* in the calculation for addition and subtraction. Exact numbers do not affect the number of digits reported.
- The arithmetic mean is sensitive to extreme values in the data set.
- Variability increases uncertainty, leading to higher costs. Engineers collect data to reduce uncertainty.

Problems

1. Describe whether the following measures are more related to accuracy or precision:
    a. The range of scores on the midterm exam
    b. Free-throw shooting percentages
    c. Tolerance values on spark-plug gaps
    d. Length of a cold medication capsule
    e. Reproducibility of the lengths of cold medication capsules

2. The subtraction of two values can result in a loss in the number of significant digits. Give an example of this phenomenon.

3. Find three numbers in this text outside of this chapter. Determine the number of significant digits in each number and explain your reasoning.

4. Consider two resistors having resistance R_1 and R_2. If the resistors are in series (i.e., connected end-to-end), the overall resistance R is given by $R = R_1 + R_2$. If the resistors are in parallel (i.e., the current is split between the resistors), then $1/R = 1/R_1 + 1/R_2$.

    a. What kind of mean of R_1 and R_2 would you use to calculate the overall resistance of resistors in series?

    b. What kind of mean of R_1 and R_2 would you use to calculate the overall resistance of resistors in parallel?

5. Using the *Help* functions in your favorite spreadsheet software, find and report the spreadsheet functions used to calculate the arithmetic mean, geometric

mean, harmonic mean, median, mode, sample standard deviation, and population standard deviation.

6. Using the data in Section 4.2, how does *median* change when one fuel efficiency value is changed? Does this make sense?

7. Measure the heights of ten students as samples of the larger student population. Calculate the variance in their heights.

8. For each of the following situations, state the most appropriate type of mean:

    a. The mean of the interest rates for three years (i_1, i_2, and i_3), if you are interested in the interest rate i over the entire three-year period. [*Hint*: You want the most appropriate type of mean of i_1, i_2, and i_3 to describe i, where $(1 + i)^3 = (1 + i_1)(1 + i_2)(1 + i_3)$.]

    b. The mean speed of four legs of an automobile trip, if you are interested in the mean speed of the entire trip.

    c. The mean frequencies of the three A notes nearest to middle C on a piano. (*Hint*: The frequencies of the A notes nearest middle C are 220, 440, and 880 Hz, where 1 Hz = 1 hertz = 1 cycle/s.)

9. Can the geometric mean ever be greater than the arithmetic mean?

10. The geometric, harmonic, and quadratic means are related to the arithmetic mean in a way that helps in calculating their values. It is possible to find three functions so that

$$f(\text{geometric mean}) = \text{arithmetic mean of } f(x_i)$$
$$g(\text{harmonic mean}) = \text{arithmetic mean of } g(x_i)$$
$$h(\text{quadratic mean}) = \text{arithmetic mean of } h(x_i)$$

where f, g, and h are the functions and the x_i are the data. Another way to write this is

$$\text{geometric mean} = f^{-1}(\text{arithmetic mean of } f(x_i))$$
$$\text{harmonic mean} = g^{-1}(\text{arithmetic mean of } g(x_i))$$
$$\text{quadratic mean} = h^{-1}(\text{arithmetic mean of } h(x_i))$$

where f^{-1}, g^{-1}, and h^{-1} are the inverses of f, g, and h, respectively. The inverse of a function means that $f^{-1}(f(x)) = x$, $g^{-1}(g(x)) = x$, and $h^{-1}(h(x)) = x$. For example, if $f(x) = e^x$, then $f^{-1}(x) = \ln(x)$ because $\ln(e^x) = x$.

    a. Find a function f so that geometric mean = $f^{-1}(\text{arithmetic mean of } f(x_i))$.
    b. Find a function g so that harmonic mean = $g^{-1}(\text{arithmetic mean of } g(x_i))$.
    c. Find a function h so that quadratic mean = $h^{-1}(\text{arithmetic mean of } h(x_i))$.

11

Engineering Models

1   INTRODUCTION

To facilitate analysis and design, engineers often rely on models. There are several different types of engineering **models**.

To some people, the phrase "engineering model" conjures up an image of a hastily drawn sketch of a Rube Goldberg machine on a napkin (see Figure 1). This is an example of a *conceptual model*. Conceptual models will be discussed in more detail in Section 3.2.

To others, the term "engineering model" evokes images of clay cars on pedestals or small airplanes in wind tunnels or miniature supertankers suspended in wave tanks. These are examples of *physical models* and will be discussed further in Section 3.3.

Finally, "engineering model" may bring to mind page after page of densely written mathematical formulas. This is an example of a *mathematical model*. More details on mathematical models may be found in Section 3.4. Each type of model will be illustrated with the following problem: predict the time required to reach the engineering building from your apartment.

2   WHY USE MODELS?

Why will you use models as an engineer? Models serve a number of roles in engineering. First, models aid in organizing ideas about engineered systems. In particular, conceptual models are a useful way to enumerate the important elements of a system.

Second, models can be used to simulate expensive or critical systems prior to construction. Physical models often are used prior to assembly. It is now possible to design even large engineered systems by computer.

OBJECTIVES

After reading this chapter, you will be able to:

- explain why engineers use models;
- list the types of models used by engineers;
- solve engineering problems using models and data;
- explain how models and data interact.

model: a conceptual, mathematical, or physical representation of an engineering system

Key idea: Types of engineering models include conceptual, physical, and mathematical models.

"what if" scenario: a question (usually probed by models) regarding how a system will respond to a set of conditions

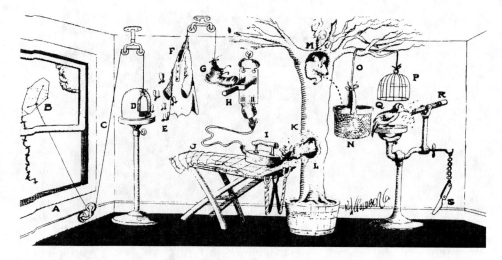

Figure 1. A Rube Goldberg Pencil Sharpener. Reuben (Rube) Lucius Goldberg (1883–1970) was a Pulitzer prize–winning cartoonist. He is known for his drawings of incredibly complicated machines designed to perform very simple jobs. The term "Rube Goldberg" refers to a complex solution to a simple problem. (Image courtesy of Rube Goldberg Inc.)

PONDER THIS

Key idea: Engineers use models to organize ideas, simulate expensive or critical systems prior to construction, and probe the response of a system to a large number of conditions.

What does the phrase "engineering model" mean to you?

Third, models aid in probing the response of a system to a large number of conditions. This use of models is sometimes referred to as a **"what if" scenario**. Examples of "what if" scenarios include "What if the primary braking system fails on the Maglev (magnetically levitated) train?" and "What if a voltage spike occurs in a DVD player?" By way of another illustration, suppose you have a mathematical model for the steps involved in the construction of a high-rise apartment building. You could use the model to determine the effects of delays on the project completion time. (Delays may result from adverse weather, delivery delays, or labor strikes.) In this way, models can be used for prediction of future conditions.

3   TYPES OF MODELS

conceptual (descriptive) model: a model showing the main elements and how they interact, including *boundaries* (which define the system in space and time), *variables* (elements that may change), *parameters* (or constants: elements that do not change), and *forcing functions* (external processes that affect the system)

boundaries: the part of the model that defines the system in space and time

variables: elements of the system that may change

3.1   Introduction

As stated in Section 1, engineers use three types of models: conceptual, physical, and mathematical models. Each model type will be explored in more detail in this section.

3.2   Conceptual Models

A **conceptual model** (also called a **descriptive model**) contains the main elements of the model and how they interact. Almost all modeling efforts begin with a conceptual model of the system. Conceptual models are often summarized in a sketch or diagram. A conceptual model should include the following elements of the system to be modeled: boundaries, variables, parameters, and forcing functions.

Boundaries define the system. The system must be defined in both space and time. For example, the boundaries of a model for the movement of a pollutant through groundwater would include the area under investigation (spatial boundaries) and time period being modeled (temporal boundaries). The space and time domain described by the model boundaries is sometimes called the *control volume*.

Variables are elements of the system that may change. For example, in modeling life support systems for the International Space Station (ISS), variables would include

Artist's rendering of the International Space Station. The solar panel wings are 11.9 m × 34.2 m (39 ft × 112 ft) each. (Image courtesy of NASA/JPL.)

the size of the crew and the water usage rate. The crew size and water usage rates are expected to change over time.

Variables can be divided into two types. *Independent variables* serve as inputs to the model. In the ISS example, the crew size is an independent variable. *Dependent variables* are calculated by the model. For the ISS example, dependent variables include the size of the air cleaning system (called the atmosphere revitalization subsystem) and the capacity of the water treatment system (called the water recovery and management subsystem).

As the names imply, dependent variables *depend* on independent variables. For example, the sizes of the ISS subsystems depend on the crew size.

parameters: elements of the system that do not change

Parameters (also called *constants*) are system elements that do not change. If you were modeling the velocity of a water droplet in a decorative fountain, parameters would include gravitational acceleration, water density, and water viscosity (if density and viscosity are constant over the spatial and temporal domain of interest). In some types of mathematical models, the values of some parameters are changed to best fit the data (see Section 4). These parameters are called *adjustable parameters*: they are not functions of the variables, but are changed in the mathematical modeling process.

Conceptual models also should include external processes that affect the system. These processes are called ***forcing functions*** (or *inputs*). Forcing functions are external to the model at hand and not modeled explicitly. If you were modeling the water level in a reservoir behind a hydroelectric dam, then the forcing functions might include rainfall and evaporation.

forcing functions: external processes that affect the system but are not modeled explicitly

The boundaries, variables, parameters, and forcing functions combine to form the conceptual model. A conceptual model of the time-to-school problem is shown in Figure 2. In this case, a model is developed for commuting by bicycle.

The system boundaries are listed in the sketch title and include the spatial path (e.g., Main Street to University Avenue to Engineering Lane) and the time (year-round). The model is designed to calculate the speed at any time during the commute (also called the *instantaneous speed* and shown in the thickly outlined box in Figure 2). The total commuting time, the model output, will be calculated from the instantaneous speed. Thus, time is the independent variable and instantaneous speed and total commuting time are the dependent variables. Note that the dependent variable is expected to change over the course of the system boundaries and should be modeled.

Parameters include information about the route (i.e., the number of stop signs and the hill slope). Forcing functions include the bike condition, traffic, weather, and initial fatigue (i.e., fatigue at the beginning of your commute). The conceptual model shows

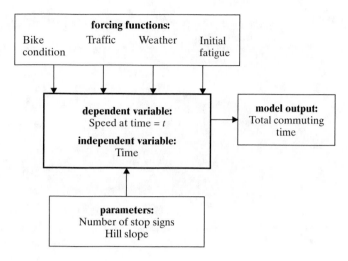

Figure 2. Conceptual Model for the Time-to-School Problem

that the forcing functions will influence the instantaneous speed. This, in turn, will affect the time required to complete the trip. Another example of a conceptual model is presented in Example 1.

physical model:
a (usually) smaller version of the full-scale system

mock-up: a full-size physical model

3.3   Physical Models

Physical models are often used for evaluating proposed solutions to engineering problems. A **physical model** usually is a smaller version of the full-scale system. (A full-size physical model is called a **mock-up**.) Physical models are typically used with large engineering projects, from the Great Pyramids to automobiles to the Space Shuttle.

**EXAMPLE 1
CONCEPTUAL
MODELS**

Develop a conceptual model for the design of a wooden pedestrian bridge over a river.

SOLUTION

A conceptual model for a wooden pedestrian bridge over a river would include the following items:

1. Boundaries:
   spatial boundaries (e.g., a river crossing a location), temporal boundaries (e.g., design life)
2. Independent variables:
   number of pedestrians crossing the bridge over time, properties of wood that change over time
3. Dependent variables:
   design elements (e.g., deck, trusses, railings, piers)
4. Parameters:
   wood properties that do not change over time, gravitational acceleration
5. Forcing functions:
   weather, cost constraints

A wind tunnel is an example of a physical engineering model. Conditions of an aircraft in flight can be simulated by placing a physical model of the aircraft in a wind tunnel and moving the air past it. Knowledge of fluid mechanics is used to correct for the size of the model and wind tunnel conditions to provide a good prediction of how the full-size aircraft will perform in flight. Other examples of physical models include rotating hydrodynamic laboratories (to study the effect of the Earth's rotation on the movement of water in large water bodies), laboratory robotic systems (to study interferences in automated materials-handling systems), and rapid mixing devices (to simulate chemical reactions and separations in the synthesis of plastics).

To develop a physical model for the commuting example, consider transportation to school by skateboard. You could build bench-scale physical models of the terrain and skateboard. This would allow you to perform experiments to estimate the travel time. The success of the model (i.e., its ability to predict the actual commuting time) would depend on how well the physical model mimicked friction, air resistance, and other elements of the system.

mathematical model:
a representation of the logical and quantitative relationships (usually mathematical expressions) between model components

deterministic model:
a mathematical model which provides a single answer for a given set of inputs

3.4   Mathematical Models

Mathematical models commonly are used in engineering evaluations. **Mathematical models** are built on the logical and quantitative relationships between model components. If the model is valid, then the real system can be probed by altering the independent variables and observing the model output.

Mathematical models may be further subdivided into deterministic and stochastic models. In a **deterministic model**, the input *determines* the output. Typically, a deterministic model provides a *single answer for a given set of inputs*. For example, the equation $t = d/v$ is a simple model describing the time t required for an object to travel a distance d at a constant velocity v. The model is deterministic: any combination of d and v determines a single value of t. The model $t = d/v$ is an accurate representation of the motion of a satellite in space.

PONDER THIS

Would a simple mathematical model (such as $t = d/v$) accurately predict the time required to commute to school by bus?

This simple mathematical model would fail in many instances because it assumes a constant velocity. It does not take into account acceleration, deceleration, time spent at traffic lights or stop signs, or time spent at bus stops. A deterministic model sophisticated enough to include all factors may be so complex that it has little value.

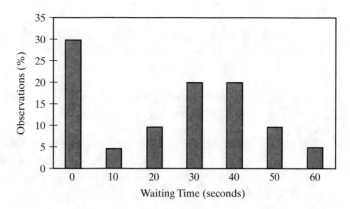

Figure 3. Hypothetical Distribution of Stoplight Waiting Times for a Time-to-School Stochastic Model

stochastic (or probabilistic) model: a mathematical model which provides a distribution of outputs for a given set of inputs

Stochastic models (from the Greek *stochos*, meaning target, aim, or guess) have different outputs, each with their own probability, for each set of inputs. Stochastic models have variables or parameters with probability distributions. For example, imagine that your commute to school passes through only one intersection and the intersection is controlled by a traffic light. You carry a stopwatch with you for a year and record your waiting time at the traffic light. Since you reach the traffic light at a random time in its cycle, your waiting time is expected to show a *distribution* of values, say between zero (if you hit a green light) and one minute (if you hit the light as it turns yellow). An example of a distribution of waiting times is shown in Figure 3. You could incorporate the distribution of waiting times into a stochastic model.

The stochastic model output would also be a distribution of commuting times, each with its own probability of occurrence. In other words, the output of the stochastic model could state, "There is a 50% probability that the commuting time will be greater than 20 minutes." Compare this statement with the output of a deterministic model, which might read, "The expected commuting time is 23 minutes." Other examples of mathematical models are given in Examples 2 and 3.

In engineering applications, mathematical models usually have a basis in theory. For example, suppose you are designing a new way to airlift food supplies to flood victims. You want to know how far the food crates will fall in a given time. Starting with basic definitions, you can derive the following common kinematic expression:

$$d = \tfrac{1}{2}gt^2$$

where d = distance fallen, g = gravitational acceleration, and t = time.

empirical model: a mathematical model based on observations, not theory

The equation $d = \tfrac{1}{2}gt^2$ is derived by theory. Suppose you had sought the relationship between the distance fallen and the time by a series of experiments. By analyzing the experimental data, you might come up with the following relationship: d is proportional to t^2, or $d = kt^2$, where k is a constant. The model $d = kt^2$ is an **empirical model**.

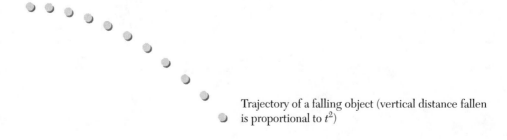

Trajectory of a falling object (vertical distance fallen is proportional to t^2)

Empirical models are based on observations, not theory. Most engineers are more comfortable using models with theoretical underpinnings. However, empirical models also are useful and may lead to research designed to provide the theory to support the observations.

EXAMPLE 2 DETERMINISTIC MATHEMATICAL MODEL

You are developing new polychromatic lenses for sunglasses. Polychromatic sunglasses darken when exposed to ultraviolet light. The glass in the lenses contains silver chloride (AgCl). You find from experiments that the degree of darkening of the lenses is proportional to both the thickness of the lens (d) and the concentration of AgCl in the layer (C). Further experiments show that when d and C are both doubled, the degree of darkening increases by fourfold. Develop a mathematical model for the degree of darkening of the lenses.

SOLUTION

The degree of darkening is proportional to the lens thickness d and AgCl concentration C. There are two possible models to describe this behavior:

$$\text{Model \#1: darkening} = ad + bC$$
$$\text{Model \#2: darkening} = edC$$

where a, b, and e are constants.

Both models describe the observation that the degree of darkening of the lenses is proportional to both d and C. However, recall that other experiments showed that the degree of darkening increased fourfold when d and C both were doubled. Model #1 predicts that the degree of darkening will only double when d and C both are doubled. Model #2 correctly predicts the behavior of the system when both d and C are doubled. Thus, **Model #2 correctly predicts the observations**.

Note: Model 2 is analogous to the Beer–Lambert Law of absorbance.

EXAMPLE 3 STOCHASTIC MATHEMATICAL MODEL

A nonprofit organization has asked you to help them evaluate the ticket price for a carnival ride at a charity event. For safety reasons, the riders must be at least 54 inches tall. You anticipate that 20% of the fair customers will be unable to ride the roller coaster because of the height constraint. The tickets for the ride cost \$1 and the ride costs \$7 per hour to operate. During a particular one-hour time period, 10 customers visited the charity event. What is the probability that the revenues collected during the hour will equal or exceed the operational costs?

SOLUTION

Systems of this sort follow a binomial distribution. If the proportion of eligible riders to the total population is p, then the probability (P) that n out of N people are eligible to ride is

$$P = \binom{N}{n} p^n (1 - p)^{N-n}$$

Here,

$$\binom{N}{n} = \frac{N!}{n!(N - n)!},$$

where $N! = N(N - 1)(N - 2) \cdots (2)(1)$. ($N!$ is read "N factorial," with $0! = 1$.)

In this example, $p = 1 - 0.20 = 0.80$ and $N = 10$. The number of eligible riders is n ($n = 0, 1, 2, \ldots, 10$). The revenue is

$$\text{revenue} = (\text{ticket price})(\text{number of eligible riders}) = (\$1)(n) = n \text{ (in dollars)}$$

The probability that there will be exactly n eligible riders (and therefore, exactly n dollars taken in during the hour) is

$$P = \binom{10}{n} 0.8^n \, 0.2^{10-n}$$

The revenue and probabilities of occurrence for each value of n are listed in the following table:

Number of Eligible Riders per Hour (n)	Revenue (dollars per hour)	Probability that Exactly n Riders Will Be Eligible
0	0	1.02×10^{-7}
1	1	4.10×10^{-6}
2	2	7.37×10^{-5}
3	3	0.000786
4	4	0.00551
5	5	0.0264
6	6	0.0881
7	7	0.201
8	8	0.302
9	9	0.268
10	10	0.107

Revenues will equal or exceed \$7 per hour only when 7, 8, 9, or 10 riders are present each hour (i.e., only when n = 7, 8, 9, or 10). The P values for n = 7, 8, 9, and 10 are 0.201, 0.302, 0.268, and 0.107, respectively. The probability that n = 7 or 8 or 9 or 10 is the sum of the probabilities with n = 7, 8, 9, and 10. Summing these values, **the probability that the revenue will equal or exceed the operational costs of \$7 per hour is 0.879 or about 88%.**

Note: If there are only eight visitors per hour (N = 8), then the probability that the revenue will equal or exceed the operational costs decreases to about 50%. Of course, if only six or fewer people enter the charity event every hour, then the probability of generating \$7 per hour drops to zero.

3.5   Other Kinds of Models

As computing power increases, the line between mathematical and physical models is being blurred. Computer-controlled milling machines now make it possible to quickly turn mathematical models into physical models. One name for this approach is "3-D printing." As the name implies, engineers may soon be able to "print" prototypes at their desktops as easily as they print reports.

In some cases, mathematical models coupled with computer-controlled milling machines allow engineers to bypass physical models completely. For example, the Boeing 777, first flown in June 1994, was the first aircraft to be designed without physical models. For more information, see *Focus on Models: Mathematical or Physical Model?*

FOCUS ON MODELS: MATHEMATICAL OR PHYSICAL MODEL?

BACKGROUND

Physical models often give engineers a sense of comfort. A model of a bridge or skyscraper sitting on a table can reduce the anxiety over whether the parts really can come together to make a whole. On the other hand, a large-scale physical model (especially a full-scale mock-up) can be very expensive. Engineers must decide whether a physical model is economically feasible; that is, whether the value of the information produced by the physical model exceeds its cost. For many years, engineers have sought other modeling tools that could provide the "comfort level" of a physical model at less expense.

Rapid changes in computing power have created opportunities for replacing some large-scale physical models with mathematical models. A good example is the design of the Boeing 777 series of jetliners. With a wingspan of 60 m and a length of about 64 m, the Boeing 777-200 is the world's largest twinjet airliner. Clearly, the design and assembly of such a large, sophisticated aircraft was a formidable challenge.

(Image courtesy of Boeing Commercial Airplane Group.)

COMPUTER-AIDED MANUFACTURING

Prior to the 777, aircraft parts were manufactured and assembled in large assembly buildings. If parts did not fit, change orders were issued to redesign and remanufacture the part. The Boeing 777 was preassembled digitally using solid, three-dimensional parts generated by computer. The computing power necessary for this effort was extremely high. Over 1,700 workstations were linked to a mainframe cluster of four IBM mainframe computers; this was the largest mainframe installation of its kind in the world at the time.

The innovative design approach had a number of advantages over traditional design/assembly methods.

The approach allowed engineers to identify parts-fitting problems without the extensive use of physical models. In addition, design and manufacturing operations could occur concurrently. In fact, a number of parts for the

A Boeing engineer designing a portion of the 777 (Image courtesy of Boeing Commercial Airplane Group.)

craft were made by metalworking machines controlled directly from the design software. This approach, called *computer-aided design/computer-aided manufacturing* (CAD/CAM), greatly sped up the time from design to construction of the first aircraft.

DIGITAL CLAY

The replacement of computer models for physical models is not limited to aircraft. Some automobile manufacturers have adopted "digital clay": computer representations of prototypes instead of clay models. The use of computer models allows designers all over the world to work on the same new car around the clock. The result is a cheaper, faster design. Volvo used digital clay to design a new station-wagon concept car. The company saved $100 million and cut the design time in half.

Returning to the CAD/CAM process, did Boeing use physical models or mathematical models for the 777? The answer is not readily apparent. Without a solid mock-up, you might say that the design used a very sophisticated mathematical model. However, when solid parts are generated digitally and allowed to interact, it is easy to argue that the design tool was as close to a physical model as you can get without the use of a milling machine. The design of the 777 represents the latest step in the blurring of the differences between mathematical and physical models. You can imagine a day where all physical models are holograms and the term "mathematical model" is no longer in use.

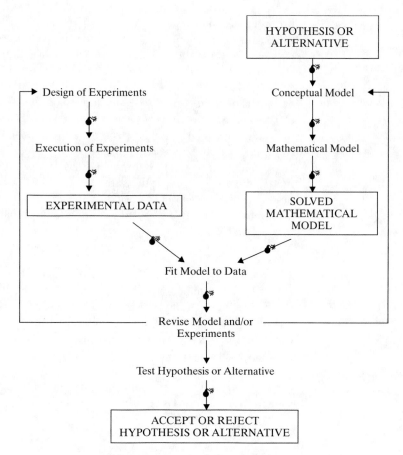

Figure 4. Interplay of Models and Data

4   USING MODELS AND DATA TO ANSWER ENGINEERING QUESTIONS

4.1   Interplay of Models and Data

Data collection is an important part of hypothesis testing and alternatives evaluation. The interplay of models and data is illustrated in Figure 4.

There are several steps to using models and data to answer questions. First, develop a conceptual model (see the upper right corner of Figure 4). An example conceptual model for the commuting problem was shown in Figure 2.

Second, translate the conceptual model into a mathematical model. A reasonable mathematical model might contain both deterministic elements (e.g., $t = d/v$) and stochastic elements (e.g., waiting time at traffic lights).

Third, solve the mathematical model. Note that experimental data may be needed to solve the mathematical equations. Why? Experiments may provide parameters needed for the model. As you may know from past experience, errors may occur during the solution of mathematical equations.

On a parallel path with model development, you may gather data. Data may be used to determine model parameters (discussed in Section 4.3) or to compare model output with measured values. For example, you might measure the time required to reach school under a number of conditions and compare the measured values with the times predicted by the model. Note that *the model influences the design of experiments.*

Key idea: Data are used to determine model parameters, and models influence the design of data collection activities.

For example, your model may include parameters such as hill slope and the number of stop signs. Thus, procedures must be developed to measure these parameters.

The interplay between modeling and data gathering is the engineer's friend. Data can point out errors in the model. A carefully constructed model may lead to the remeasurement of key parameters. The process shown in Figure 4 may have to be iterated several times until the model gives satisfactory results. The iteration process is the way that engineers refine their view of engineering problems and solutions.

If the model fit is not satisfactory (see Section 4.4), then revise the model. In some cases, the experiments may require revision as well. If the model is revised incorrectly, errors can occur on the next iteration. For example, imagine that the output of the commuting model does not fit the data. After some thought, you conclude that wind resistance must be included in the model to account for the discrepancies. If the real culprit is an incorrect formulation of the waiting time probabilities, then the model revisions may not help.

4.2   Potential Errors

Key idea: Models are limited by their scope (i.e., the elements included or excluded) and the input data.

GIGO (garbage in, garbage out): the idea that model output will be meaningless if the model input data are poor

The bombs in Figure 4 indicate where errors could occur. The first chance for error comes in the formulation of the conceptual model. If the conceptual model is incomplete (i.e., if important variables, parameters, or forcing functions are left out), then the model will be a poorer representation of reality. In general, *models are limited in their usefulness by their scope and input data*. If the commuting time is influenced significantly by road construction and road construction is *not* included in the model, then the model will likely not predict the commuting time accurately. Similarly, if you make an error in measuring the hill slope, then the model output may be useless. In other words, we apply the term **GIGO** (garbage in, garbage out).

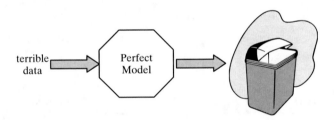

Errors also can creep in if the selected mathematical model is incompatible with the conceptual model. For example, if the conceptual model included the elements of acceleration and deceleration, then a constant-velocity model (such as $t = d/v$) would be inappropriate.

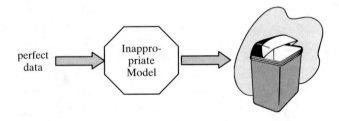

Errors can arise in experiments as well (see the bombs in Figure 4). Experiments can be improperly designed. For example, suppose you chose to determine the length of a road up a hill by measuring the hill height and hill length and by using basic trigonometry. This design is inappropriate if the hill is undulating.

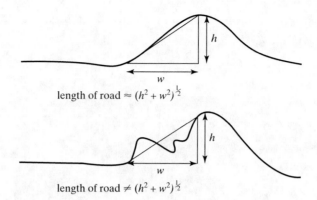

length of road $\approx (h^2 + w^2)^{\frac{1}{2}}$

length of road $\neq (h^2 + w^2)^{\frac{1}{2}}$

The next step is to execute the experiments to gather the data. Again, errors can occur through improper execution. In the bicycling-to-school example, the stopwatch may be slow or the surveying equipment may be incorrectly calibrated.

4.3   Model Fits

Key idea: Fit the model to the data; **never** fit the data to the model.

Assuming the model and experimental errors are small, you now can compare the model output with the measured values. It is critical at this stage to *fit the model to the data rather than the data to the model*. **Never** exclude data because they do not fit your pre-conceived notions of what the data should look like. In other words, do not reject data just because the data does not match the model.°

What is meant by "fitting the model to the data"? Fitting a model means finding the values of the adjustable parameters so that the model output matches the experimental data as closely as possible. This process is called *model calibration*.

model calibration: the process of finding the values of the adjustable parameters so that the model output matches the experimental data as closely as possible

There are a number of fitting tools used by engineers to calibrate models. In this text, a numerical approach will be introduced. Before discussing the fitting method, it is necessary to think about how you will know when the model output matches the data satisfactorily. A common approach is to formulate a function that describes the error in the model prediction and then pick adjustable parameter values to minimize the function. The objective then becomes to minimize the error. (The error function becomes the *objective function*.) Say, for example, that the deterministic model has one independent variable x, one dependent variable y, and one parameter m. From experiments, you have n pairs of x and y values. The x values are denoted $x_1, x_2, \ldots, x_n$ and the y values are denoted $y_1, y_2, \ldots, y_n$. Since the model is deterministic, each value of x (i.e., each x_i) will give one predicted value of y (usually denoted $\hat{y}_i$ and pronounced "why eye hat").

objective function: a mathematical statement of the success of the project

One possibility for an objective function is the sum of the differences between the model predictions and the data. This is called the *sum of the errors* (or SE). For the n data points (i.e., n pairs of x_i and y_i), SE is given by

$$\mathrm{SE} = \sum_{i=1}^{n} (y_i - \hat{y}_i)$$

An example of computing SE is given in Figure 5. For the data in Figure 5:

$$\sum_{i=1}^{3} (y_i - \hat{y}_i) = -3 + 2 + 0 = -1.$$

°While you should not *reject* data that do not fit the preconceived model, sometimes it is appropriate to *question* data that do not fit the model. Models can be used to identify data that do not fit preconceived notions. If repeated measurements show that the original data are in error, then the original data are rejected. If the original data are *not* in error, then the model must be revised.

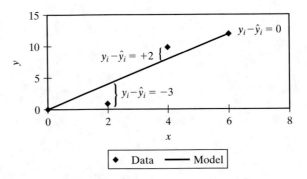

Figure 5. Example of Computing SE

Is SE a good measure of the differences between the model predictions and the experimental data?

SE is **not** a good measure of how well the model fits the data. Why? In SE, the "negative" errors (i.e., $y_i - \hat{y}_i$ less than zero) will cancel out "positive" errors (i.e., $y_i - \hat{y}_i$ greater than zero). For example, consider the data and model output in Figure 6. The model is $y_i = mx_i$. Model output is shown for $m = 2$. For this value of m, SE = 0 because the negative errors and positive errors cancel out. Even though SE = 0, it is clear from Figure 6 that the model $y_i = 2x_i$ is not a "perfect" model for the data.

There are many possible objective functions where the positive and negative errors do not cancel out (see Problem 2). A commonly used objective function is the *sum of the squares of the errors,* **SSE**:

SSE: sum of the squares of the errors (square of the differences between the model output and data)

$$\text{SSE} = \sum_{i=1}^{n} (y_i - \hat{y}_i)^2 \qquad (1)$$

To fit a model to data, the mathematical problem becomes "Find the set of adjustable parameter values that minimize the SSE."

To illustrate the use of SSE, consider an exciting new field of engineering: the use of *fractal geometry* to describe the dimensions of irregular objects. In common objects, the area (A) increases proportionally to the square of a characteristic length (l). Examples

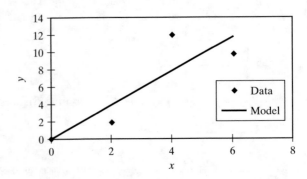

Figure 6. Example Model and Data to Illustrate Model Fit

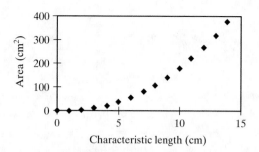

Figure 7. Data for Fractal Example

include circles (where $A = \pi r^2$; r = radius), spheres (where the surface area = $4\pi r^2$), squares (where $A = s^2$; s = side), cubes (where the surface area = $6s^2$), and equilateral triangles (where $A = \dfrac{\sqrt{3}}{4}s$). With fractal objects, A increases proportionally to l raised to the power n, where n is not necessarily equal to 2. Suppose you measure the area of a family of fractal objects and plot the area against the characteristic length (see Figure 7).

PONDER THIS   **What is your model for the relationship between l and A?**

The model is $A = $ (proportionality constant)l^n. Suppose you know from other data that the proportionality constant is equal to 1. Thus, $A = l^n$. How would you find n? One approach would be to vary n and calculate the SSE. You can do this easily with a spreadsheet. Values of SSE are plotted against n in Figure 8. Note that the units of SSE are the units of the dependent variable squared.

PONDER THIS   **What is your estimate of n from Figure 8?**

Key idea: Select the values of the adjustable parameters to minimize the objective function (i.e., minimize SSE).

From Figure 8, SSE is minimized at $n = 2.2$–2.3. As shown in this example, the *values of the adjustable parameters should be selected so that SSE is minimized*.

The graphical approach of determining the values of the adjustable parameters that minimize SSE works well when your model has one adjustable parameter. The approach becomes more cumbersome with two adjustable parameters and virtually impossible to visualize with more than two adjustable parameters. A common approach to calibrating models containing more than one adjustable parameter is called *regression analysis*.

4.4   Using Calibrated Models

During model calibration, the values of the adjustable parameters are determined. In this process, the values of the dependent variables are calculated where data exist. For example, in the crate-drop example of Section 3.4, the values of the distance that the crate fell would be calculated for each time at which data were collected. These data are sometimes called the *calibration data set*. The model outputs for the calibration data set are called **model fits**. You *expect* the model fits to be close to the data, because you are using the data to fit the adjustable parameters.

model fits: comparison of model output to the calibration data set

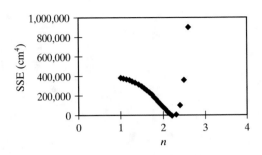

Figure 8. Variation of SSE with n in the Fractal Problem

If you compare the calibrated model output to other data (i.e., data outside the calibration data set), the model outputs are called **model predictions**. Be sure to differentiate between model fits and model predictions in your engineering work. We want our models to be *predictive*; that is, they should predict data outside the calibration data set (but they have some limitations, as shown in Section 4.6).

4.5   Determining Model Fit

Another important issue in using models is determining how well the model fits the data. In fact, you already know one way to look at model fits: SSE. Unfortunately, SSE has a problem. It has units of $(\text{units of } y)^2$, so the magnitude of SSE depends on the units of y. Say you have a model relating the current in a photocircuit with light intensity. The photodiode produces a current in amps equal to a constant times the light intensity in watts. You calibrate the model twice with the same data set: once with current in amps and once with current in milliamps. The values of the SSE will be different even though the model is the same, as illustrated below:

Photodiode example: Data in watts and amps
model: current (A) = a (light intensity in watts)

Light Intensity (W)	Measured Current (A)	Predicted Current (in A, a = 0.3)	Error = measured − (A) predicted	Square of Error (A²)
0	0	0	0	0
1	0.2	0.3	−0.1	0.01
2	0.6	0.6	0	0
5	1.7	1.5	+0.2	0.04

$$\text{SSE} = 0.05 \text{ A}^2$$

Photodiode example: Data in mW and mA
model: current (mA) = a (light intensity in mW)

Light Intensity (mW)	Measured Current (mA)	Predicted Current (in mA; a = 0.3)	Error = measured − predicted (mA)	Square of Error (mA²)
0	0	0	0	0
1,000	200	300	−100	10,000
2,000	600	600	0	0
5,000	1,700	1,500	+200	40,000

$$\text{SSE} = 50,000 \text{ mA}^2$$

As this example shows, SSE would be more useful if it is dimensionless. One way to make SSE dimensionless is to compare your model with the simplest model for your dependent data.

What is the simplest possible model for *any* data?

The simplest model for a dependent variable y is $y =$ constant. A reasonable value of the constant is the arithmetic mean of the y values. Thus, the simplest model is

$$y = \overline{y}$$

A more useful measure of model fit would be

(SSE for your model)/(SSE for the simplest model), or

(SSE for your model)/(SSE for the model $y =$ mean y)

In mathematical terms, this new measure is

$$\frac{\sum_{i=1}^{n}(y_i - \hat{y}_i)^2}{\sum_{i=1}^{n}(y_i - \overline{y})^2}$$

correlation coefficient (r^2): a dimensionless measure of the degree of fit of a model to data ($r^2 > 0.9$ is good)

This new measure is equal to zero when the model is perfect ($SSE = 0$) and is equal to one when the model is no better than the simplest model ($y =$ mean y). This is okay, but it would be nice to have a measure that is equal to one when the model is perfect and is equal to zero when the model is no better than the simplest model. This is accomplished by defining the ***correlation coefficient*** r^2:

$$r^2 = 1 - \frac{\sum_{i=1}^{n}(y_i - \hat{y}_i)^2}{\sum_{i=1}^{n}(y_i - \overline{y})^2} \qquad (2)$$

The correlation coefficient is a very valuable measure of the degree of fit of *any* model. It is dimensionless and near one if the model fits the data well. You can verify for the data in Figure 6 that r^2 is equal to 0.98, indicating a good fit ($r^2 > 0.9$ generally represents a good fit of the model to the data).

4.6   Are Engineering Models Real?

It is easy to become overly enamored with models and model output. Sometimes engineers come to believe that the calibrated model represents the truth and that data and model interpretation just get in the way.

Key idea: When using models, remember that (1) the final model is only as good as the underlying conceptual model and resulting mathematical model, (2) models should not be used outside their calibration range, (3) engineers should not be misled by a good model fit, and (4) model output must be interpreted.

You should remember four points about using engineering models. First, the final model is only as good as the underlying conceptual model and resulting mathematical model. As discussed in Section 4.2, models cannot predict behavior missing from the conceptual model.

Second, take great care not to use models outside the range of the independent variable for which the model has been calibrated. As an example, consider the prediction of the trajectory of a projectile (Figure 9). At short times, the height appears to be proportional with time. An extrapolation of the data at short time (≤ 6 seconds) is

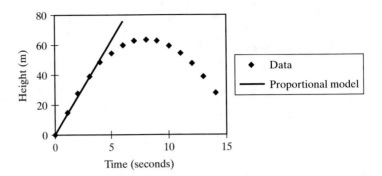

Figure 9. Example of an Extrapolated Model

shown by the line in Figure 9. The proportional model fits the data used to calibrate the model well. However, extrapolation of the model output *beyond* six seconds gives the wrong picture of the flight of the projectile. Predictions made by the proportional model outside the range of calibration could be disastrously wrong.

Third, do not be misled by good model fit. It is incorrect to assume that the model is "good" just because it fits the data. The classic example of an incorrect but good-fitting model is the Ptolemaic model of the galaxy. Claudius Ptolemy (ca. 100–ca. 170) proposed in the second century that the Earth was the center of the universe. The motion of the planets was described by circular orbits called *epicycles* as the planets orbited the Earth. More and more layers of epicycles were added to explain the observations as measurement techniques improved. In its final form, the Ptolemaic model was a mishmash of epicycles based on a flawed premise (i.e., an Earth-centered universe), but it fit the observed data remarkably well. In fact, the Copernican Sun-centered model (after Nicholas Copernicus, 1473–1543), although correct, did not fit the observations as well as the Ptolemaic model! The bottom line: do not assume that good-fitting models are "real."

Fourth, model output must be interpreted. Models are only part of the analysis or design process. It is important to realize that you must use the results of models *in conjunction with other information* to make conclusions about alternatives. The "other information" may be other types of feasibility.

5   SUMMARY

Engineers often rely on models to conduct analysis or to evaluate alternatives. Models are used to organize ideas, simulate expensive or critical systems prior to construction, and probe the response of a system to a large number of conditions ("what if" scenarios).

Three types of models are used in engineering. First, *conceptual models* contain the main elements of the model (boundaries, variables, parameters, and forcing functions) and how they interact. Second, a *physical model* is usually a smaller version of the full-scale system. Finally, *mathematical models* represent systems in terms of logical and quantitative relationships and are of two types. *Deterministic models* provide one output for each set of inputs. *Stochastic models* contain variables or parameters with probability distributions and therefore predict a probability of a certain outcome with a given set of inputs.

Models and data interact. As mentioned earlier, model parameters may be measured through experiments. In addition, models may identify key variables and parameters, thereby influencing the design of experiments. If the model predictions do not match the measured values satisfactorily, then both the model and experiments may need to be revised. Although numerous opportunities for errors exist, the interplay of models and data aids in developing models that adequately describe natural and engineered systems.

When using models, remember that the final model is only as good as the underlying conceptual model and resulting mathematical model. In addition, take great care in using models outside the range of the independent variable for which the model has been calibrated. Finally, do not be misled by good model fit in interpreting model results.

SUMMARY OF KEY IDEAS

- Types of engineering models include conceptual, physical, and mathematical models.

- Engineers use models to organize ideas, simulate expensive or critical systems prior to construction, and probe the response of a system to a large number of conditions.

- Data are used to determine model parameters, and models influence the design of data collection activities.

- Models are limited by their scope (i.e., the elements included or excluded) and the input data.

- Fit the model to the data; **never** fit the data to the model.

- Select the values of the adjustable parameters to minimize the objective function (i.e., minimize SSE).

- When using models, remember that (1) the final model is only as good as the underlying conceptual model and resulting mathematical model, (2) models should not be used outside their calibration range, (3) engineers should not be misled by a good model fit, and (4) model output must be interpreted.

Problems

1. Develop a conceptual model for a device to screen airline passengers for concealed weapons. Include the boundaries, variables, parameters, and forcing functions.

2. List two objective functions other than SSE where the positive and negative errors do not cancel out. Discuss the advantages and disadvantages of your objective functions compared with SE and SSE.

3. Use the Internet to find a picture and description of a bridge of interest to you. Build a physical model of the bridge using everyday materials (e.g., Popsicle sticks). What characteristics of the actual bridge does your bridge model well? What characteristics of the actual bridge does your bridge model poorly?

4. Develop a mathematical model to calculate how deeply a ship will sit in the water. (*Hint*: Perform a force balance, where the buoyancy force is proportional to the mass of water displaced by the ship. Develop your model for a specific geometry of the ship.)

5. Collect data of the height and weight of 10 friends. Develop an empirical model relating their height and weight.

6. For the data below, find the slope and intercept relating two hardness scales for steel, the Brinell number and the Vickers number. Calculate the correlation coefficient and comment on the applicability of the linear model for the data given.

Brinell Number	Vickers Number
780	1,150
712	960
653	820
601	717
555	633

7. Thermistors are semiconductors used for measuring temperature. The electrical resistance of a thermistor changes with temperature. One model for the effect of temperature on a specific thermistor is $R = 2{,}252e^{4000\left(\frac{1}{T} - \frac{1}{298.16}\right)}$, where R is the resistance in ohms and T is the temperature in K. You can verify that this thermistor has a resistance of $2{,}252\ \Omega$ at $25°C = 298.16$ K. For the data below, calculate the correlation coefficient for the model and decide whether the model fits the data well or not.

Temperature (°C)	Resistance (Ω)
0	7,850
10	4,400
20	2,900
30	1,500
40	1,000

8. The number of transistors on processor chips has doubled every 18 months or so for at least the last 30 years. This doubling sometimes is called *Moore's Law* (after Intel founder Gordon Moore). For the data on Intel processors below, determine the doubling time that minimizes the SSE. Decide whether the model (with your fitted doubling time) fits the data well or not.

Processor	Year of Introduction	Number of Transistors
4004	1971	2,250
8008	1972	2,500
8080	1974	5,000
8086	1978	29,000
286	1982	120,000
386	1985	275,000
486 DX	1989	1,180,000
Pentium	1993	3,100,000
Pentium II	1997	7,500,000
Pentium III	1999	24,000,000
Pentium 4	2000	42,000,000

9. One example of 3-D printing (Section 3.5) is printable prescription lenses. Printable lenses, developed by Saul Griffith (winner of the 2004 Lemelson–MIT Student Prize), may be used to provide low-cost eyeglasses for less-developed regions. Write a short report about printable prescription lenses.

10. What is the difference between stochastic and deterministic models? Give an example of each in the engineering field of your choice.

12

Mechanics

1   INTRODUCTION

Mechanics is one of the most important fields of study in engineering. Mechanics was the first analytical science, and its historical roots can be traced to such great mathematicians and scientists as Archimedes (287–212 B.C.), Galileo Galilei (1564–1642), and Isaac Newton (1642–1727). **Mechanics** is the *study of the state of rest or motion of bodies that are subjected to forces*. As a discipline, mechanics is divided into three general areas: *rigid-body mechanics, deformable-body mechanics*, and *fluid mechanics*. As the term implies, rigid-body mechanics deals with the mechanical characteristics of bodies that are rigid (i.e., bodies that do not deform under the influence of forces). Rigid-body mechanics is subdivided into two main areas: *statics* and *dynamics*. Statics deals with rigid bodies in equilibrium. Equilibrium is a state in which a body is at rest with respect to its surroundings. When a body is in equilibrium, the forces that act on it are balanced, resulting in no motion. A state of equilibrium also exists when a body moves with a constant velocity, but this type of equilibrium is a dynamic equilibrium, not a static equilibrium. Dynamics deals with rigid bodies that are in motion with respect to its surroundings or to other rigid bodies. The body may have a constant velocity, in which case the acceleration is zero; but, generally, the body undergoes an acceleration due to the application of an unbalanced force. Deformable-body mechanics, often referred to as *mechanics of materials* or *strength of materials*, deals with solid bodies that deform under the application of external forces. In this branch of mechanics, the relationships between externally applied forces and the resulting internal forces and deformations are studied. Deformable-body mechanics is often subdivided into two specific areas: *elasticity* and *plasticity*. Elasticity deals with the behavior of solid materials that return to their original size and shape after a force is removed, whereas plasticity deals

OBJECTIVES

After reading this chapter, you will have learned

- The importance of mechanics in engineering
- The difference between a scalar and a vector
- How to perform basic vector operations
- How to add forces vectorially
- How to construct free-body diagrams
- How to use equilibrium principles to find unknown forces on a particle
- How to calculate normal stress, strain and deformation
- How to apply a factor of safety to stress

with the behavior of solid materials that experience a permanent deformation after a force is removed. Fluid mechanics deals with the behavior of liquids and gases at rest and in motion. The study of fluids at rest is called *fluid statics*; the study of fluids in motion is called *fluid dynamics*. Even though fluids are, strictly speaking, deformable materials, deformable-body mechanics is set apart from fluid mechanics because deformable-body mechanics deals exclusively with *solid* materials that have the ability, unlike fluids, to sustain shear forces. The topical structure of engineering mechanics is shown schematically in Figure 1.

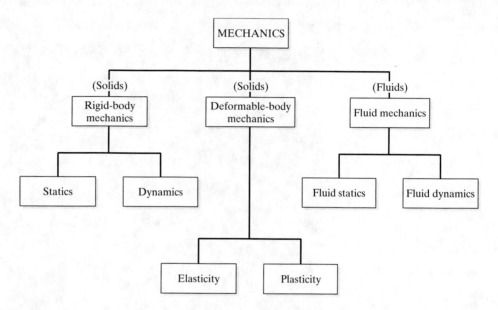

Figure 1. Topical structure of engineering mechanics.

In most colleges and universities, the branches of mechanics just outlined are generally taught as separate and distinct engineering courses. Hence, a typical engineering program consists of individual courses in statics, dynamics, mechanics of materials, and fluid mechanics. Other analytically oriented courses such as electrical circuits and thermodynamics are also offered. Mechanics is so essential to engineering education that students majoring in "nonmechanical" fields such as electrical engineering, environmental engineering, and chemical engineering gain a deeper understanding of energy, power, potential, equilibrium, and stability by first studying these principles in their mechanical contexts. However, depending on the specific curricular policies of your school or department, students in all engineering majors may or may not be required to take all of the aforementioned mechanics courses. In any case, the main purpose of this chapter is to introduce the beginning engineering student to the most fundamental principles of mechanics and to show how the general analysis procedure is applied to mechanics problems. In order to focus on the basics and to assist the student in the transition to more advanced material, our treatment of mechanics in this chapter is limited to a few fundamental principles of statics and mechanics of materials.

Engineers use principles of mechanics to analyze and design a wide variety of devices and systems. Look around you. Are you reading this chapter in a building? The structural members in the floor, roof, and walls were designed by structural or civil engineers to withstand forces exerted on them by the contents of the building, winds, earthquakes, snow, and other structural members. Bridges, dams, canals, underground pipelines, and other large, earthbound structures are designed with the use of mechanics. Do you see any mechanical devices nearby? The design of simple mechanisms such as staple removers, paper punches, door locks, and pencil sharpeners involves principles of mechanics. The automobile is an excellent example of a single engineering system that embodies virtually every branch of engineering mechanics, as well as other engineering disciplines. The chassis, bumpers, suspension system, power train, brakes, steering system, engine, air bag, doors, trunk, and even the windshield wipers were designed with the use of mechanics. Principles of mechanics are used to analyze and design virtually every type of engineering system that can be devised. Figures 2, 3, and 4 show some familiar engineering systems that involved the use of engineering mechanics in their design.

Figure 2. Engineers use principles of engineering mechanics to design spacecraft, such as the Hubble Space Telescope. (Photo courtesy of NASA).

2   SCALARS AND VECTORS

Every physical quantity used in mechanics, and in all of engineering and science, is classified as either a **scalar** or a **vector**. A scalar is a *quantity having magnitude, but no direction*. Having magnitude only, a scalar may be positive or negative, but has no directional characteristics. Common scalar quantities are length, mass, temperature, energy, volume, and density. A vector is a *quantity having both magnitude and direction*. A vector may be positive or negative and has a specified direction in space. Common vector quantities are displacement, force, velocity, acceleration, stress, and momentum. A scalar quantity can be fully defined by a single parameter, its magnitude, whereas a vector requires that both its magnitude and direction be specified. For example, speed is a scalar, but velocity is a vector. A typical speedometer of an automobile indicates how fast the

Figure 3. Principles of engineering mechanics are used to design heavy construction equipment.

Figure 4. Engineers used principles of engineering mechanics to design the Normandie Bridge in LeHavre, France. Completed in 1995, this bridge has one of the longest spans (856 m) of any cable-stayed bridge in the world.

vehicle is traveling, but does not reveal the direction of travel. The temperature of water boiling in an open container at sea level can be completely defined by a single number, 100°C. The force exerted on a beam used as a floor joist, however, must be defined by specifying a magnitude, 2 kN, for example, and a direction, down. The effect of the force on the beam (i.e., the stress and deformation) cannot be determined unless the direction of the force is specified. A force directed along the axis of the beam, for example, would produce a completely different stress and deformation than a normal downward force. Table 1 is a summary of some scalar and vector quantities.

TABLE 1   Scalar and Vector Quantities.

Scalar	Vector
Length	Force
Mass	Pressure
Time	Stress
Temperature	Moment of force
Speed	Velocity
Density	Acceleration
Volume	Momentum
Energy	Impulse
Work	Electric field
Resistance	Magnetic field

When writing scalars and vectors, standard nomenclature should be followed. Scalars are often written as a standard letter in italic font such as m for mass, T for temperature, ρ for density, etc. To differentiate vectors from scalars, vectors are written in a special way. For handwritten work, a vector in usually written as a letter with a bar ($^-$), arrow ($\vec{\ }$), or caret ($^\wedge$) over it such as $\bar{A}$, $\vec{A}$, and $\hat{A}$. In books and other printed matter, vectors are typically written in boldface type. For example, **A** is used to denote a vector "A." The magnitude of a vector, which is always a positive quantity, is normally written by hand, using "absolute value" notation. Thus, the magnitude of **A** is written as $|A|$. In books and other printed matter, the magnitude of **A** is usually written in italic type as A.

As shown in Figure 5, a vector is represented graphically by a straight arrow with a specified *magnitude, direction*, and *sense*. The magnitude is the length of the arrow, the

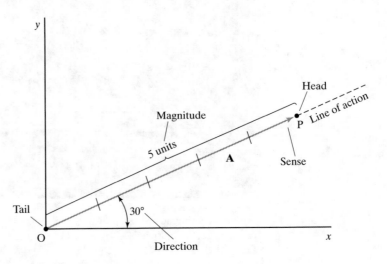

Figure 5.   A vector has magnitude, direction and sense.

direction is defined by the angle between the arrow and a reference axis, and the sense is defined by the orientation of the arrowhead. The *line of action* of the vector is a line that is collinear with the vector. The vector **A** in Figure 5 has a magnitude of 5 units, a direction of 30° with respect to the *x*-axis, and a sense that is upward and to the right. Point O is called the *tail* of the vector, and point P is called the *head* of the vector. The units of the vector depend on what physical quantity the vector represents. For example, if the vector is a force, the units would be N or lb$_f$. The 30° angle indicates that the force acts in a direction defined by a line of action coincident with the arrow. The orientation of the arrowhead indicates that the force acts upward and to the right, rather than downward and to the left.

2.1   Vector Operations

In order to utilize principles of mechanics to carry out an analysis, engineers must be able to mathematically manipulate vector quantities. Due to the directional character of vectors, the rules for performing algebraic operations with vectors are different from those of scalars. The product of a scalar k and a vector **A**, denoted by k**A**, has the effect of changing the length of the vector **A**, but its line of action is unaffected. For example, the product 3**A** increases the magnitude of the vector **A** by a factor of three, but the direction and sense of **A** is the same. The product −2**A** increases the magnitude of **A** by a factor of two, but reverses the direction of **A**, because the scalar is negative. Graphical examples of the product of scalars and a vector are illustrated in Figure 6. Two vectors, **A** and **B**, are *equal* if they have the same magnitude, direction, and sense regardless of the location of their tails and heads. As shown in Figure 6, **A** = **B**.

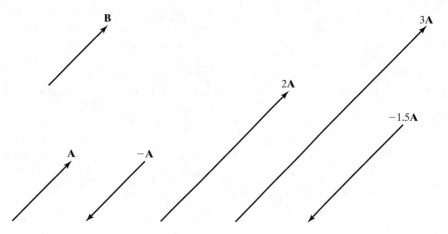

Figure 6.   Scalar multiplication and vector equality, **A** = **B**.

The addition of two scalars results in a simple algebraic sum, such as c = a + b. The addition of two vectors, however, cannot be obtained by simply adding the magnitudes of each vector. Vectors must be added such that their directions as well as their magnitudes are accounted for. Consider the vectors **A** and **B** in Figure 7(a). Vectors **A** and **B** may be added by using the *parallelogram law*. To form this sum, **A** and **B** are joined at their tails. Parallel lines are drawn from the head of each vector, intersecting at a common point, forming adjacent sides of a parallelogram. The vector sum of **A** and **B**, referred to as the *resultant vector* or simply **resultant**, is the diagonal of the parallelogram that extends from the vector tails to the intersection point, as illustrated in Figure 7(b). Hence, we may write the vector sum as **R** = **A** + **B**, where **R** is the resultant. The vector sum may also be obtained by constructing a triangle, which is actually half of a parallelogram. In this technique, the tail of **B** is connected to the head of **A**. The resultant **R** = **A** + **B** extends from the tail of **A** to the head of **B**, as shown in Figure 7(c).

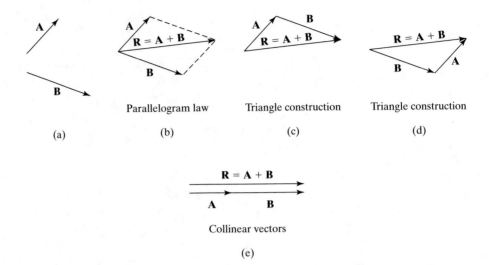

Figure 7. Vector addition.

Alternatively, the triangle may be constructed such that the tail of **A** is connected to the head of **B**, in which case we have **R** = **B** + **A**, as shown in Figure 7(d). In both triangles, the same resultant is obtained, so we conclude that vector addition is *commutative* (i.e., the vectors can be added in either order). Hence, **R** = **A** + **B** = **B** + **A**. A special case of the parallelogram law is when the two vectors are collinear (i.e., they have the same line of action). In that case, the parallelogram is degenerate, and the vector sum reduces to a scalar sum $R = A + B$, as indicated in Figure 7(e).

2.2   Vector Components

A powerful method for finding the resultant of two vectors is to first find the *rectangular components* of each vector and then add the corresponding components to obtain the resultant. To see how this method works, we draw the two vectors, **A** and **B**, in Figure 7 on a set of (x, y) coordinate axes, shown in Figure 8. For convenience, both vectors are drawn with their tails at the origin, and the directions of **A** and **B** with respect to the positive x-axis are defined by the angles α and β, respectively. For the moment, let's consider each vector separately. Using a modified form of the parallelogram law, we draw lines

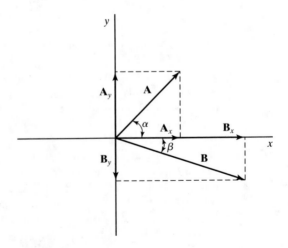

Figure 8. Vector components.

parallel to the x- and y-axes such that the vector **A** becomes the diagonal of a rectangle, which is a special type of parallelogram. The sides of the rectangle that lie along the x and y-axes are called the rectangular components of vector **A**, and are denoted $\mathbf{A}_x$ and $\mathbf{A}_y$ respectively. Because vector **A** is the diagonal of the rectangle, **A** becomes the resultant of vectors $\mathbf{A}_x$ and $\mathbf{A}_y$. Thus, we may write the vector as $\mathbf{A} = \mathbf{A}_x + \mathbf{A}_y$. Similarly, lines parallel to the x- and y-axes are drawn such that the vector **B** becomes the diagonal of a rectangle. The sides of the rectangle that lie along the x- and y-axes are the rectangular components of vector **B** and are denoted $\mathbf{B}_x$ and $\mathbf{B}_y$, respectively. Hence, we may write the vector as $\mathbf{B} = \mathbf{B}_x + \mathbf{B}_y$. The resultant of **A** and **B** may now be written as

$$\mathbf{R} = \mathbf{A} + \mathbf{B} = (\mathbf{A}_x + \mathbf{B}_x) + (\mathbf{A}_y + \mathbf{B}_y) \tag{1}$$

The magnitude of the components of **A** and **B** may be written in terms of the angles that define the vectors' directions. From the definitions of the trigonometric functions for cosine and sine, the x and y components of **A** are

$$A_x = A \cos \alpha \tag{2}$$

and

$$A_y = A \sin \alpha \tag{3}$$

where A is the magnitude of **A**. Similarly, the x and y components of **B** are

$$B_x = B \cos \beta \tag{4}$$

and

$$B_y = B \sin \beta \tag{5}$$

where B is the magnitude of **B**. Alternatively, we can also see from trigonometry that

$$A_y = A_x \tan \alpha \tag{6}$$

and

$$B_y = B_x \tan \beta \tag{7}$$

The magnitudes of **A** and **B** form the hypotenuse of their respective right triangles, so from the theorem of Pythagoras, we may write

$$A = \sqrt{A_x^2 + A_y^2} \tag{8}$$

and

$$B = \sqrt{B_x^2 + B_y^2} \tag{9}$$

2.3   Unit Vectors

The justification for grouping the x components of each vector and the y components of each vector in Equation (1) is based on the concept of *unit vectors*. A unit vector is a *dimensionless vector of unit length used to specify a given direction*. Unit vectors have no other physical meaning. The most common unit vectors are the *rectangular* or **Cartesian unit vectors**, denoted **i**, **j**, and **k**. The unit vectors **i**, **j**, and **k** coincide with the positive x-, y-, and z-axes, respectively, as shown in Figure 9. The rectangular unit vectors form a set of mutually perpendicular vectors and are used to specify the direction of a vector in three-dimensional space.

If the quantity of interest can be described by a two-dimensional vector, only the **i** and **j** unit vectors are required. The vectors **A** and **B**, shown in Figure 8, lie in the x–y plane, so they can be represented by the **i** and **j** unit vectors. The x component of **A** has a magnitude of A_x, and the y component of **A** has a magnitude of A_y. Note that the quantities A_x and A_y are not vectors, but scalars, because they represent magnitudes only.

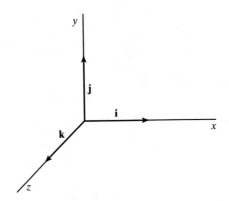

Figure 9.   Rectangular unit vectors.

The vector components, $\mathbf{A}_x$ and $\mathbf{A}_y$, can be written as products of a scalar and a unit vector as $\mathbf{A}_x = A_x\,\mathbf{i}$ and $\mathbf{A}_y = A_y\,\mathbf{j}$. Thus, vector $\mathbf{A}$ is expressed as

$$\mathbf{A} = A_x\mathbf{i} + A_y\mathbf{j} \tag{10}$$

and vector $\mathbf{B}$ is expressed as

$$\mathbf{B} = B_x\mathbf{i} + B_y\mathbf{j} \tag{11}$$

Rewriting Equation (1) in terms of the x and y component groups, the resultant of $\mathbf{A}$ and $\mathbf{B}$ is

$$\mathbf{R} = \mathbf{A} + \mathbf{B} = (A_x + B_x)\mathbf{i} + (A_y + B_y)\mathbf{j} \tag{12}$$

The rectangular components of the resultant vector $\mathbf{R}$ are given by

$$R_x = A_x + B_x \tag{13}$$

and

$$R_y = A_y + B_y \tag{14}$$

Hence, Equation (12) can be written

$$\mathbf{R} = R_x\mathbf{i} + R_y\mathbf{j} \tag{15}$$

where R_x and R_y are the x and y components of $\mathbf{R}$, as shown in Figure 10. By trigonometry, we may write

$$R_x = R\cos\theta \tag{16}$$

$$R_y = R\sin\theta \tag{17}$$

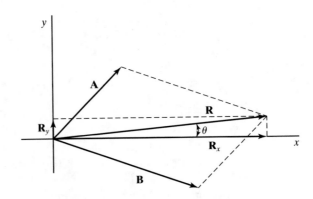

Figure 10.   Resultant vector.

and

$$R_y = R_x \tan \theta \qquad (18)$$

The magnitude of **R** forms the hypotenuse of a right triangle, hence, from the theorem of Pythagoras, we have

$$R = \sqrt{R_x^2 + R_y^2} \qquad (19)$$

EXAMPLE 1

Two vectors have magnitudes of $A = 8$ and $B = 6$ and directions as shown in Figure 11(a). Find the resultant vector, using (a) the parallelogram law and (b) by resolving the vectors into their x and y components.

SOLUTION

(a) Parallelogram law

The parallelogram for vectors **A** and **B** is shown in Figure 11(b). In order to find the magnitude and direction of the resultant vector **R**, some angles must be determined. By subtraction, the acute angle between the vectors is 45°. The sum of the interior angles of a quadrilateral is 360°, so the adjacent angle is found to be 135°. The magnitude of **R** may be found by using the law of cosines:

$$R = \sqrt{6^2 + 8^2 - 2(6)(8)\cos 135°}$$
$$R = \sqrt{36 + 64 - 96(-0.7071)}$$
$$= 13.0$$

The direction of **R** is found by calculating the angle θ. Using the law of sines, we have

$$\frac{\sin \theta}{6} = \frac{\sin 135°}{12.96}$$
$$\sin \theta = 0.3274$$
$$\theta = \sin^{-1}(0.3274) = 19.1°$$

Thus, the angle of **R** with respect to the positive x-axis is

$$\phi = 19.1° + 15° = 34.1°$$

The resultant vector **R** has now been completely defined, because both its direction and magnitude have been determined.

(b) Vector components

In Figure 11(c), vectors **A** and **B** are resolved into their x and y components. The magnitudes of these components are

$$A_x = A \cos 15° = 8 \cos 15° = 7.7274$$
$$A_y = A \sin 15° = 8 \sin 15° = 2.0706$$
$$B_x = B \cos 60° = 6 \cos 60° = 3$$
$$B_y = B \sin 60° = 6 \sin 60° = 5.1962$$

Vectors **A** and **B** may now be written in terms of the unit vectors **i** and **j**:

$$\mathbf{A} = A_x\mathbf{i} + A_y\mathbf{j} = 7.7274\mathbf{i} + 2.0706\mathbf{j}$$
$$\mathbf{B} = B_x\mathbf{i} + B_y\mathbf{j} = 3\mathbf{i} + 5.1962\mathbf{j}$$

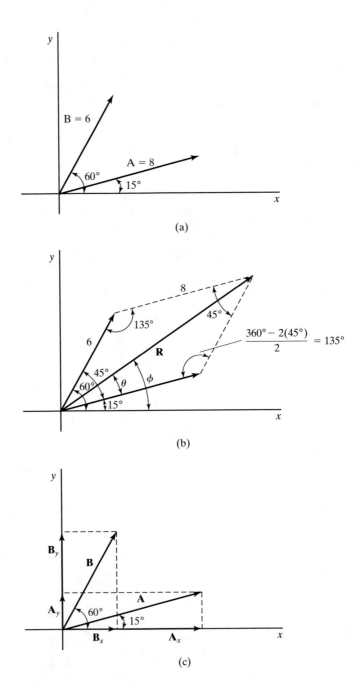

Figure 11. Example 1.

The resultant vector **R** is

$$\mathbf{R} = \mathbf{A} + \mathbf{B} = R_x\mathbf{i} + R_y\mathbf{j} = (7.7274 + 3)\mathbf{i} + (2.0706 + 5.1962)\mathbf{j}$$
$$= 10.7274\mathbf{i} + 7.2668\mathbf{j}$$

This is the answer, but to compare it with the answer obtained by the parallelogram law, we must find the magnitude of **R** and its direction with respect to the positive x-axis. Using the theorem of Pythagoras, we find that the magnitude of **R** is

$$R = \sqrt{10.7274^2 + 7.2668^2} = 13.0$$

The direction is given by

$$R_y = R_x \tan \phi$$

Solving for the angle ϕ, we get

$$\phi = \tan^{-1}(R_y/R_x) = \tan^{-1}(7.2668/10.7274) = 34.1°$$

We have obtained the same result with two different methods of vector addition. The second method may appear to involve more work. However, many mechanics problems involve more than two vectors, and the problem may be three dimensional. In these cases, resolving the vectors into their rectangular components is the preferred approach, since the parallelogram law is too cumbersome. In the example, to ensure that both methods yielded the same answers to three significant figures, four decimal places were used.

EXAMPLE 2

For the vectors $\mathbf{A} = 3\mathbf{i} - 6\mathbf{j} + \mathbf{k}, \mathbf{B} = 5\mathbf{i} + \mathbf{j} - 2\mathbf{k}$, and $\mathbf{C} = -2\mathbf{i} + 4\mathbf{j} + 3\mathbf{k},$ find the resultant vector and its magnitude.

SOLUTION

These vectors, unlike those in the previous example, are three-dimensional. They are already expressed in terms of the Cartesian unit vectors $\mathbf{i}, \mathbf{j}$, and $\mathbf{k}$, so it is a straightforward matter to add them vectorially. Recall that the $\mathbf{i}, \mathbf{j}$, and $\mathbf{k}$ unit vectors correspond to the positive x, y, and z directions, respectively. To find the resultant, we simply add the x components, the y components, and the z components of each vector. To help us avoid errors as we perform the addition, it is useful to write the vectors with their components aligned in columns:

$$\mathbf{A} = 3\mathbf{i} - 6\mathbf{j} + 1\mathbf{k}$$
$$\mathbf{B} = 5\mathbf{i} + 1\mathbf{j} - 2\mathbf{k}$$
$$\mathbf{C} = -2\mathbf{i} + 4\mathbf{j} + 3\mathbf{k}$$

Performing the additions, the resultant vector is

$$\mathbf{R} = (3 + 5 - 2)\mathbf{i} + (-6 + 1 + 4)\mathbf{j} + (1 - 2 + 3)\mathbf{k}$$
$$= 6\mathbf{i} - \mathbf{j} + 2\mathbf{k}$$

The magnitude of the resultant vector is found by extending the theorem of Pythagoras to three dimensions:

$$R = \sqrt{R_x^2 + R_y^2 + R_z^2}$$
$$= \sqrt{6^2 + (-1)^2 + 2^2} = 6.40$$

3   FORCES

From our early childhood experiences, we all have a basic understanding of the concept of force. We commonly use terms such as *push, pull*, and *lift* to describe forces that we encounter in our daily lives. *Mechanics* is the study of the state of rest or motion of bodies that are subjected to forces. To the engineer, **force** is defined as *an influence that causes a body to deform or accelerate*. For example, when you push or pull on a lump of clay, the clay deforms into a different shape. When you pull on a rubber band, the rubber band increases in length. The forces required to deform clay and rubber bands are much smaller than those required to deform engineering structures such as buildings, bridges, dams, and machines, but these objects deform nevertheless. What happens when you push on the wall with your hand? Unless you are exceptionally strong, the wall does not move and neither does your hand. In accordance with Newton's third law, as you push on the wall, the wall pushes back on your hand with the same force. When you push on a book in an attempt to slide it across the table, the book will not move unless the frictional force between the table and book is exceeded by the horizontal pushing force. These types of situations are encountered in virtually all engineering systems that are in static equilibrium. Forces are present, but motion does not occur because the forces cause the body to be in a state of balance. When the forces acting on a body are unbalanced, the body undergoes an acceleration. For example, the propulsive force delivered to the wheels of an automobile can exceed the frictional forces that tend to retard the automobile's motion, so the automobile accelerates. Similarly, the thrust and lift forces acting on an aircraft can exceed the weight and drag forces, thereby allowing the aircraft to accelerate vertically and horizontally.

Forces commonly encountered in the majority of engineering systems may be generally categorized as a *contact force, gravitational force, cable force, pressure force*, or *fluid dynamic force*. These five types of forces are depicted in Figure 12. A contact force is a force produced by two or more bodies in direct contact. The force produced by pushing on a wall is a contact force because the hand is in direct contact with the wall. When two billiard balls collide, a contact force is produced at the region where the balls touch each other. Friction is a type of contact force. A gravitational force, referred to as *weight*, is exerted on an object on or near the earth's surface. Gravitational forces are directed downward, toward the center of the earth, and act through a point in the body called the *center of gravity*. For a body that is uniform in density, the center of gravity lies at the geometric center of the body. This point is referred to as the *centroid*. The force in a cable is actually a special type of contact force, since the cable is in contact with a body, but it occurs so frequently that it deserves a separate definition. Cables, ropes, and cords are used in pulley systems, suspension bridges, and other engineering structures. A cable, due to its limp and flexible nature,

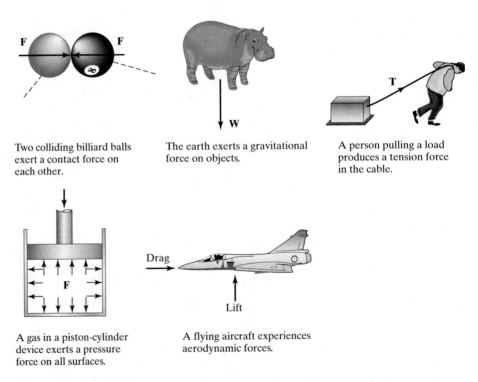

Two colliding billiard balls exert a contact force on each other.

The earth exerts a gravitational force on objects.

A person pulling a load produces a tension force in the cable.

A gas in a piston-cylinder device exerts a pressure force on all surfaces.

A flying aircraft experiences aerodynamic forces.

Figure 12. Types of forces commonly encountered in engineering applications.

can support tension forces only. Forces in cables are always directed along the axis of the cable, regardless of whether the cable is straight or not. Pressure forces are normally associated with static fluids. A gas in a cylinder exerts a pressure force on all surfaces of the cylinder. A static liquid, such as the water behind a dam, exerts a pressure force on the dam. Pressure forces always act in a direction normal to the surface. A fluid dynamic force is produced when a fluid flows around a body or through a pipe or conduit. When a fluid flows around a body (or when a body moves through a fluid) aerodynamic forces act on the body. There are basically two types of aerodynamic forces: pressure forces and viscous forces. Pressure forces are caused by pressure distributions around the body and are produced by certain fluid-related mechanisms and body geometry. Viscous forces, sometimes called friction or shear forces, are caused by fluid viscosity. Any object (for example, airplane, missile, ship, submarine, automobile, baseball, etc.) that moves through a fluid experiences aerodynamic forces. When a fluid flows through a pipe, a friction force is produced between the fluid and the inside surface of the pipe. This friction force, which is caused by fluid viscosity, has the effect of retarding the flow. The five types of forces just mentioned are the most common, but there are other kinds of forces that engineers sometimes encounter. These include electric, magnetic, nuclear, and surface tension forces.

Forces are vectors, so all the mathematical operations and expressions that apply to vectors apply to forces. Because a force is a vector, a force has magnitude, direction, and sense. For example, the weight of a 170-pound person is a vector with a magnitude of 170 lb$_f$, a direction of 90° with respect to the horizontal, and a downward sense. A situation in which more than one force acts on a body is referred to as a **force system**. A system of forces is *coplanar* or *two dimensional* if the lines of action of the forces lie in the same plane. Otherwise, the system of forces is *three dimensional*. Forces are *concurrent* if their lines of action pass through the same point and *parallel* if their lines of action are parallel. *Collinear* forces have their lines of action along the same line. These force concepts are illustrated in Figure 13.

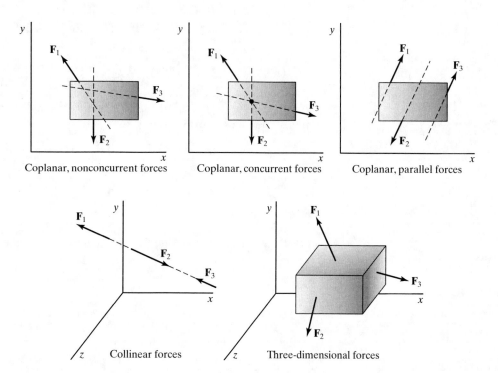

Figure 13.   Force systems.

EXAMPLE 3

Three coplanar forces act as shown in Figure 14. Find the resultant force, its magnitude, and its direction with respect to the positive x-axis.

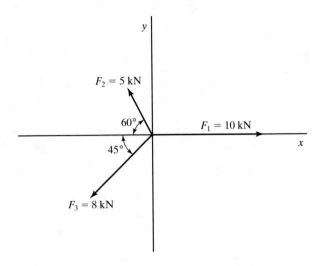

Figure 14. Concurrent forces for Example 3.

SOLUTION

We have three coplanar forces that act concurrently at the origin. Note that force, $\mathbf{F}_1$, lies along the x-axis. First, we resolve the forces into their x and y components:

$$F_{1x} = F_1 \cos 0° = 10 \cos 0° = 10 \text{ kN}$$
$$F_{1y} = F_1 \sin 0° = 10 \sin 0° = 0 \text{ kN}$$
$$F_{2x} = F_2 \cos 60° = -5 \cos 60° = -2.5 \text{ kN}$$
$$F_{2y} = F_2 \sin 60° = 5 \sin 60° = 4.330 \text{ kN}$$
$$F_{3x} = -F_3 \cos 45° = -8 \cos 45° = -5.657 \text{ kN}$$
$$F_{3y} = -F_3 \sin 45° = -8 \cos 45° = -5.657 \text{ kN}$$

Notice that F_{2x}, F_{3x}, and F_{3y} are *negative* quantities to reflect the proper directions of the vectors with respect to the positive x- and y-axes. The forces may now be written in terms of the unit vectors $\mathbf{i}$ and $\mathbf{j}$:

$$F_1 = F_{1x}\mathbf{i} + F_{1y}\mathbf{j} = 10\mathbf{i} + 0\mathbf{j} = 10\mathbf{i} \text{ kN}$$
$$F_2 = F_{2x}\mathbf{i} + F_{2y}\mathbf{j} = -2.5\mathbf{i} + 4.330\mathbf{j} \text{ kN}$$
$$F_3 = F_{3x}\mathbf{i} + F_{3y}\mathbf{j} = -5.657\mathbf{i} - 5.657\mathbf{j} \text{ kN}$$

Earlier in this chapter we learned that a resultant is the sum of two or more vectors. Here we define a **resultant force** as the sum of two or more forces. Therefore, the resultant force $\mathbf{F}_R$ is the vector sum of the three forces. Adding corresponding components, we obtain

$$\mathbf{F}_R = (10 - 2.5 - 5.657)\mathbf{i} + (0 + 4.330 - 5.657)\mathbf{j}$$
$$= 1.843\mathbf{i} - 1.327\mathbf{j} \text{ kN}$$

The signs on the x and y components of $\mathbf{F}_R$ are significant. A positive sign on the x component and a negative sign on the y component means that the resultant force lies in the fourth quadrant. The magnitude of $\mathbf{F}_R$ is

$$F_R = \sqrt{1.843^2 + (-1.327)^2}$$
$$= 2.271 \text{ kN}$$

The direction of $\mathbf{F}_R$ with respect to the positive x-axis is

$$\phi = \tan^{-1}(-1.327/1.843) = -35.8°$$

where the minus sign on the angle is consistent with the fact that $\mathbf{F}_R$ lies in the fourth quadrant, as shown in Figure 15.

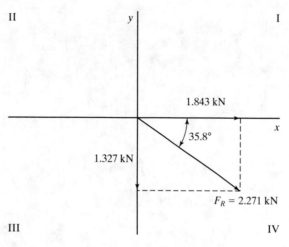

Figure 15. Resultant force for Example 4.

PRACTICE!

1. Find the resultant force for the forces shown by (a) using the parallelogram law and (b) by resolving the forces into their x and y components.
    Answer: 178 N, $-15.1°$

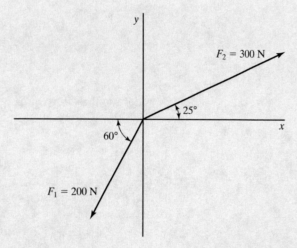

2. Find the resultant force for the forces shown by (a) using the parallelogram law and (b) by resolving the forces into their x and y components.
    Answer: 166 N, 5.5°

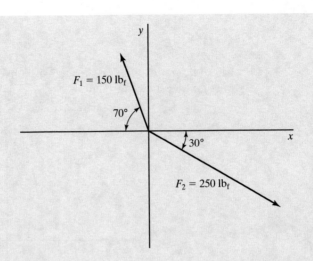

3. Find the resultant force for the forces shown by (a) using the parallelogram law and (b) by resolving the forces into their x and y components.
    Answer: 26.0 N, 75.0°

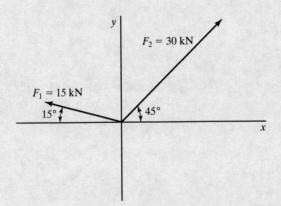

4. Consider the three forces, $\mathbf{F}_1 = 5\mathbf{i} + 2\mathbf{j}$ kN, $\mathbf{F}_2 = -2\mathbf{i} - 5\mathbf{j}$ kN, and $\mathbf{F}_3 = \mathbf{i} - \mathbf{j}$ kN. Find the resultant force, its magnitude, and direction with respect to the positive x-axis.
    Answer: $4\mathbf{i} - 4\mathbf{j}$ kN, 5.66 kN, −45.0°

5. Consider the three forces, $\mathbf{F}_1 = 2\mathbf{i} - 7\mathbf{j}$ lb$_f$, $\mathbf{F}_2 = 5\mathbf{i} + 8\mathbf{j}$ lb$_f$, and $\mathbf{F}_3 = 3\mathbf{i} + 4\mathbf{j}$ lb$_f$. Find the resultant force, its magnitude and direction with respect to the positive x-axis.
    Answer: $10\mathbf{i} + 5\mathbf{j}$ lb$_f$, 11.2 lb$_f$, 26.6°

6. Consider three forces, $\mathbf{F}_1 = 3\mathbf{i} + 5\mathbf{j} - 2\mathbf{k}$ N, $\mathbf{F}_2 = -\mathbf{i} - 4\mathbf{j} + 3\mathbf{k}$ N, and $\mathbf{F}_3 = 2\mathbf{i} - 2\mathbf{j} + 6\mathbf{k}$ N. Find the resultant force and its magnitude.
    Answer: $4\mathbf{i} - \mathbf{j} + 7\mathbf{k}$ N, 8.12 N

APPLICATION: STABILIZING A COMMUNICATIONS TOWER WITH CABLES

Tall slender structure often incorporate cables to stabilize them. The cables, which are connected at various points around the structure and along its length, are connected to concrete anchors buried deep in the ground. Shown in Figure 16(a) is a typical communications tower that is stabilized with several cables. On this particular tower each ground anchor facilitates two cables that are connected at a common point, as shown in Figure 16(b). The upper and lower cables exert forces of 15 kN and 25 kN, respectively, and their directions are

(a)

(b)

15 kN

25 kN

45°   32°

(c)

Figure 16. A communications tower stabilized with cables.

45° and 32°, respectively, as measured from the ground [Figure 16(c)]. What is the resultant force exerted by the cables on the ground anchor?

Any two forces in three-dimensional space lie in a single plane, so we may arbitrarily locate our two cable forces in the x–y plane. Thus, we have two coplanar forces that act concurrently at the origin. We let $F_1 = 15$ kN and $F_2 = 25$ kN. We resolve the forces into their x and y components:

$$F_{1x} = F_1 \cos 45° = 15 \cos 45° = 10.607 \text{ kN}$$

$$F_{1y} = F_1 \sin 45° = 15 \sin 45° = 10.607 \text{ kN}$$

$$F_{2x} = F_2 \cos 32° = 25 \cos 32° = 21.201 \text{ kN}$$

$$F_{2y} = F_2 \sin 32° = 25 \sin 32° = 13.248 \text{ kN}$$

The forces may now be written in terms of the unit vectors $\mathbf{i}$ and $\mathbf{j}$:

$$\mathbf{F}_1 = F_{1x}\mathbf{i} + F_{1y}\mathbf{j} = 10.607\mathbf{i} + 10.607\mathbf{j} \text{ kN}$$

$$\mathbf{F}_2 = F_{2x}\mathbf{i} + F_{2y}\mathbf{j} = 21.201\mathbf{i} + 13.248\mathbf{j} \text{ kN}$$

The resultant force $\mathbf{F}_R$, is the vector sum of the two forces. Adding corresponding components, we obtain

$$\mathbf{F}_R = (10.607 + 21.201)\mathbf{i} + (10.607 + 13.248)\mathbf{j}$$

$$= 31.808\mathbf{i} + 23.855\mathbf{j} \text{ kN}$$

The magnitude of $\mathbf{F}_R$ is

$$F_R = \sqrt{R_x^2 + R_y^2}$$

$$= \sqrt{31.808^2 + 23.855^2}$$

$$= 39.76 \text{ kN}$$

and the direction of $\mathbf{F}_R$ with respect to the ground is

$$\phi = \tan^{-1}(23.855/31.808)$$

$$= 36.9°$$

What does our answer mean, and how would it be used? The resultant force would be used by an engineer (probably a civil engineer) to design the concrete anchor. A force of nearly 40 kN directed at an angle of about 37° with respect to the ground would have a tendency to pull the anchor out of the ground. If not designed properly, the anchor could become loose or break under the load, thereby causing an unbalanced force on the tower. Look carefully at Figure 16(b). Notice that the two cables connect via turnbuckles at a ring assembly connected to a single rod that goes into the concrete anchor, which is not shown. The resultant force would also be used to ascertain the structural integrity of the ring assembly and rod.

4   FREE-BODY DIAGRAMS

One of the most important steps in the general analysis procedure is to construct a diagram of the system being analyzed. In engineering mechanics, this diagram is referred to as a free-body diagram. A **free-body diagram** is a *diagram that shows all external forces acting on the body*. As the term implies, a free-body diagram shows only the body in question, being isolated or "free" from all other bodies. The body is conceptually removed from all supports, connections, and regions of contact with other bodies. All forces produced by these external influences are schematically represented on the free-body diagram. In a free-body diagram, only the *external* forces acting on the body in question are considered in the analysis. There may be **internal forces** (i.e., forces originating from inside the body that act on other parts of the body), but it can be shown that these forces cancel one another and therefore do not contribute to the overall mechanical state of the body. The free-body diagram is one of the most critical parts of a mechanical analysis. It focuses the engineer's attention on the body being analyzed and helps to identify all the external forces acting on the body. The free-body diagram also helps the engineer to write the correct governing equations.

Free-body diagrams are used in statics, dynamics, and strength of materials, but their application to statics and strength of materials will be emphasized here. **Statics** is the branch of engineering mechanics that deals with bodies in static equilibrium. If a body is in static equilibrium, the external forces cause the body to be in a state of balance. Even though the body does not move, it experiences stresses and deformations that must be determined if its performance as a structural member is to be evaluated. In order to determine the forces that act on the body, a free-body diagram must be properly constructed.

Procedure for Constructing Free-Body Diagrams

The following procedure should be followed when constructing free-body diagrams:

1. *Identify* the body you wish to isolate and make a *simple drawing* of it.
2. Draw the appropriate *force vectors* at all locations of supports, connections and contacts with other bodies.
3. Draw a force vector for the *weight* of the body, unless the gravitational force is to be neglected in the analysis.
4. *Label* all forces that are known with a numerical value and those that are unknown with a letter.
5. Draw a *coordinate system* on, or near, the free-body to establish directions of the forces.
6. Add *geometric data* such as lengths, angles, etc., as required.

Free-body diagrams for some of the most common force configurations are illustrated in Figure 17.

PROFESSIONAL SUCCESS: DON'T BEGIN IN THE MIDDLE OF A PROBLEM

It's human nature to want to finish a job in the least amount of time. Sometimes, we take shortcuts without taking enough time to assure that the job is done thoroughly. Like everyone else, engineers are only human and may sometimes take shortcuts in the solution of a problem. Engineers may take shortcuts for a variety of reasons. Perhaps the engineer is simply overloaded with work, and the only way to meet deadlines is to spend less time on each problem. Perhaps the engineers manager has unrealistic expectations and does not budget enough time for each project. Time and budget-related reasons, while serious enough to warrant corrective action, are not usually the reasons that engineers take shortcuts in their analytical work. They take shortcuts because they either have become lax in their problem-solving practices or have forgotten how to perform a thorough analysis of a problem. Perhaps they have forgotten some of the steps in the general analysis procedure, or even worse, never learned them at all.

Regardless of the underlying reasons, the practice of taking problem-solving shortcuts may provoke an engineer to begin an analysis "in the middle of the problem." How does this happen? In an attempt to solve the problem more efficiently, the engineer may want to get right to the equations and calculations. By going directly to the *governing equations* and *calculations* steps of the analysis procedure, three crucial steps are omitted: problem statement, diagram, and assumptions. How can an engineer solve a problem if he or she does not even state what the problem is? The engineer may defensively exclaim. "But I know what the problem statement is. It's in my head." A problem statement not written is a not a problem statement! Others who will review the analysis cannot read minds. A good engineer documents everything in writing, including problem statements. The engineer further retorts, "Everyone knows exactly what the component looks like, and the forces acting on it are straightforward. A free-body diagram is unnecessary." Everyone may be intimately familiar with the component's configuration and loading today, but 18 months from now, when the analysis is reevaluated because the component failed in its first year of service, everyone, including the engineer who did the analysis, may not remember all the details. Once again, written documentation is essential. The formulation of good assumptions is as much an art as it is a science. A hurried engineer may declare, "The assumptions are obvious. It's no big deal," The assumptions may or may not be obvious, but they are critical to the outcome of the problem. Assumptions must be explicitly stated, and the governing equations and calculations must be consistent with those assumptions. If the component failed in its first year of service, it is perhaps because the engineer *thought* the assumptions were obvious, and they were not, resulting in a flawed analysis and a failed component.

While you are in school, develop the habit of conscientiously applying the general analysis procedure to all your analytical problem-solving work. Then, as you make the transition from student to engineering professional, you will not experience the pitfalls of beginning "in the middle of a problem."

Configuration	Free-body diagram	Comments
Gravitational force 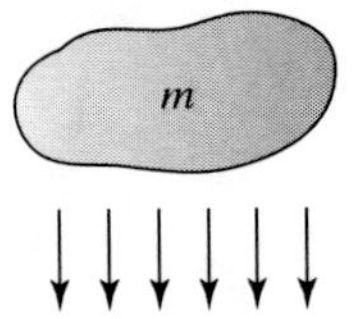 	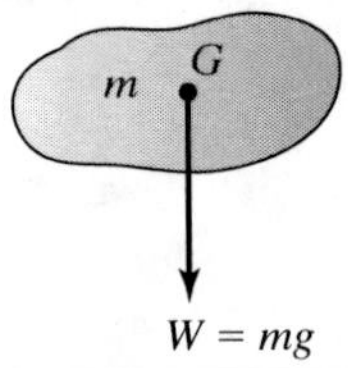 $W = mg$	The gravitational force acts through the center of gravity, G.
Cable force 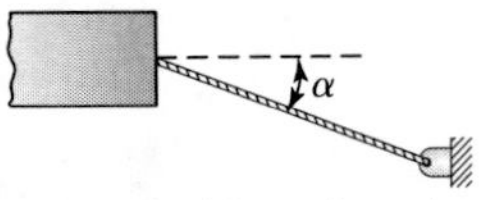 Weight of cable neglected 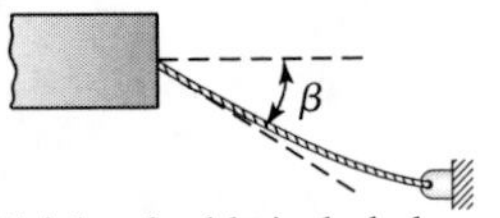 Weight of cable included	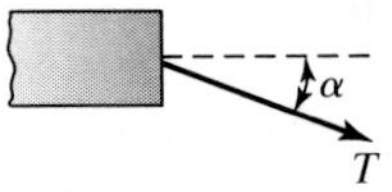 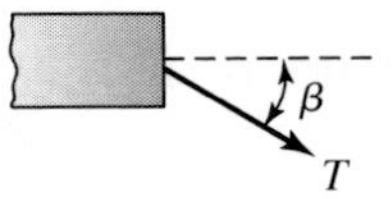 T T	The tension force T in a cable is always directed along the axis of the cable.
Contact force 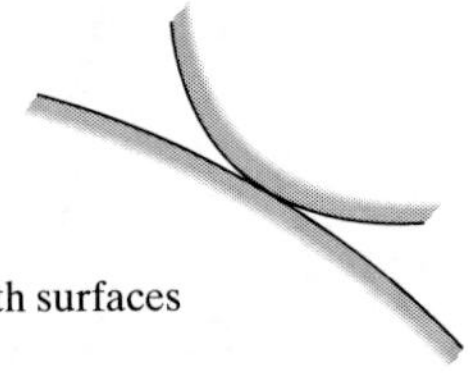 Smooth surfaces 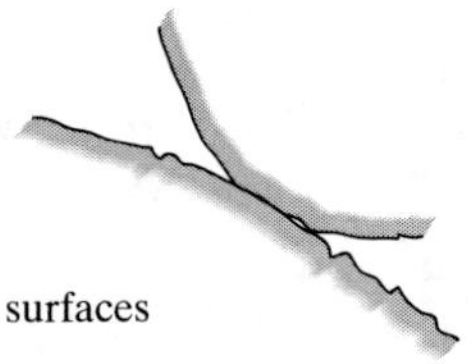 Rough surfaces	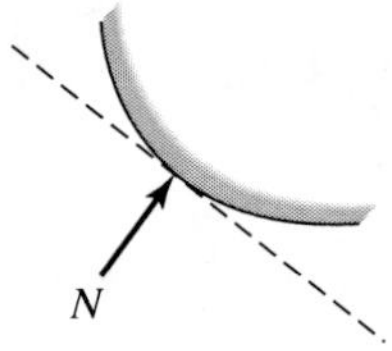 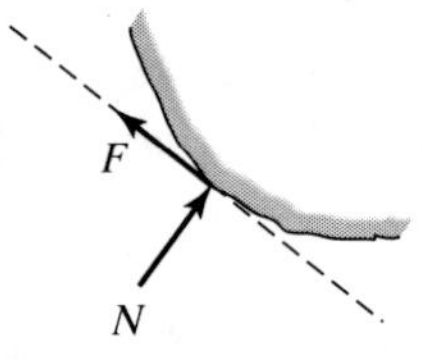 N F N	For smooth surfaces, the contact force N is toward the body, normal to the tangent drawn through the point of contact. For rough surfaces, there are two forces, a normal force N and a friction force, F. These two forces are perpendicular to each other. The friction force F acts in the direction opposite of the impeding motion.
Roller support 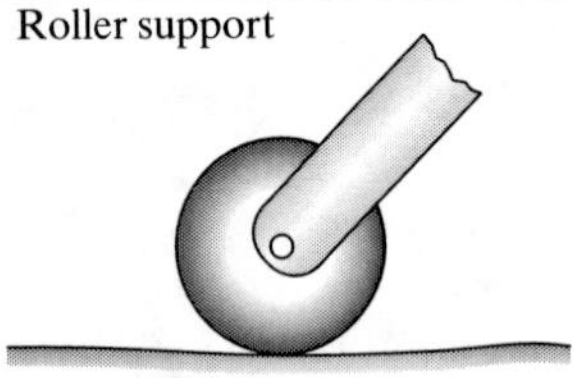 	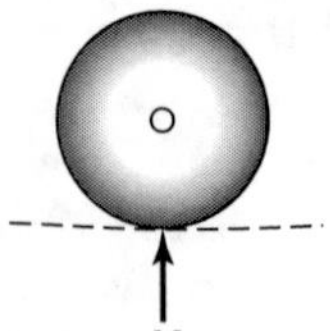 N	A roller supports a normal force but no friction force because a friction force would cause the roller to rotate.
Pin connection 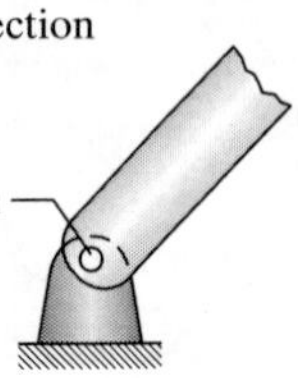 Pin 	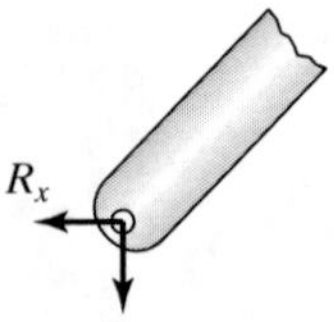 R_x R_y	A pin connection can support a reaction force in any direction in the plane normal to the pin's axis. This force may be resolved into its x and y components, R_x and R_y.

Figure 17. Free-body diagrams for some common force configurations.

PRACTICE!

1. A crate hangs by a rope as shown. Construct a free-body diagram of the crate.

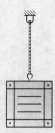

2. Two crates hang by ropes from a ceiling as shown. Construct a free-body diagram of (a) crate *A* and (b) crate *B*.

3. A wooden block rests on a rough inclined plane as shown. Construct a free-body diagram of the block.

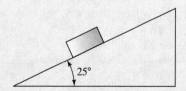

4. An obliquely loaded I-beam is supported by a roller at *A* and a pin at *B* as shown. Construct a free-body diagram of the beam. Include the weight of the beam.

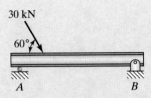

5. Two pipes rest in a long V-shaped channel as shown. Construct a free-body diagram of each pipe.

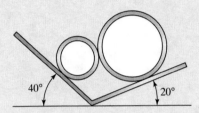

6. A box is held in position on the bed of a truck by a cable as shown. The surface of the truck bed is rough. Construct a free-body diagram of the box.

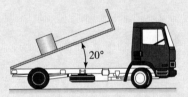

5   EQUILIBRIUM

Equilibrium is a state of balance between or among opposing forces, and it is one of the most important concepts in engineering mechanics. There are two types of equilibrium in engineering mechanics: static and dynamic. If a body is in static equilibrium, the body does not move, whereas if a body is in dynamic equilibrium, the body moves with a constant velocity. In this book, we will restrict our discussion to static equilibrium. Furthermore, we will confine our treatment of static equilibrium to *concurrent* force systems. In a concurrent force system, the lines of action of all forces pass through a single point, so the forces do not have a tendency to rotate the body. Therefore, there are no *moments of force* to deal with, only the forces themselves. Because the forces act concurrently, the body effectively becomes a *particle* (i.e., a dimensionless point in space through which the forces act). The actual body may or not be a particle, but is modeled as such for purposes of the analysis. This concept will be demonstrated in some examples later.

A body is in static equilibrium if the vector sum of all external forces is zero. Consistent with this definition, the condition of static equilibrium may be stated mathematically as

$$\Sigma \mathbf{F} = \mathbf{0} \qquad (20)$$

where the summation symbol Σ denotes a sum of all external forces. Note that the zero is written as a vector to preserve the vector character of the equation across the equal sign. Equation (20) is a necessary and sufficient condition for equilibrium according to Newton's second law, which can be written as $\Sigma \mathbf{F} = m\mathbf{a}$. If the sum of the forces is zero, then $m\mathbf{a} = \mathbf{0}$. The quantity m is a scalar that can be divided out, leaving $\mathbf{a} = \mathbf{0}$. Thus, the acceleration is zero, so the body either moves with a constant velocity or remains at rest. Equation (20) is a vector equation that may be broken into its scalar components. Writing the equation in terms of the unit vectors $\mathbf{i}$, $\mathbf{j}$, and $\mathbf{k}$, we obtain

$$\Sigma F_x \mathbf{i} + \Sigma F_y \mathbf{j} + \Sigma F_z \mathbf{k} = \mathbf{0} \tag{21}$$

where the three terms on the left side are the total *scalar* forces in the x, y, and z directions, respectively. Equation (21) can only be satisfied if the sum of the scalar forces in each coordinate direction is zero. Hence, we have three scalar equations

$$\Sigma F_x = 0, \ \Sigma F_y = 0, \ \Sigma F_z = 0 \tag{22}$$

These relations are referred to as the *equations of equilibrium for a particle*. Each of these three scalar equations must be satisfied for the particle to be in equilibrium. If *any one* of these scalar equations is not satisfied, the particle is not in equilibrium. For example, if $\Sigma F_x = 0$ and $\Sigma F_y = 0$, but $\Sigma F_z \neq 0$, the particle will be in equilibrium in the x and y directions, but will accelerate in the z direction. Similarly, if $\Sigma F_x = 0$, but $\Sigma F_y \neq 0$ and $\Sigma F_z \neq 0$, the particle will be in equilibrium in the x direction, but will have components of acceleration in the y and z directions.

Equations (22) are the governing equations for a particle in static equilibrium. Using those equations and a free-body diagram of the particle, the unknown external forces can be determined. Consider the particle in Figure 18(a). A force of 2 kN acts

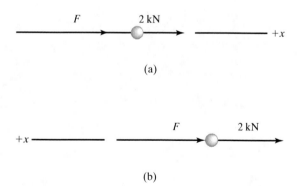

(a)

(b)

Figure 18. A force of $F = -2$ kN required to maintain equilibrium, regardless of the orientation of the coordinate system.

on the particle in the positive x direction. An unknown force F, whose direction is *assumed* to act in the positive x direction, also acts on the particle. Applying the first equation of equilibrium, we have

$$\Sigma F_x = 0 = +F + 2$$

Both forces are positive because they act in the positive x direction. Solving for the unknown force F, we obtain

$$F = -2 \text{ kN}$$

Thus, in order for the particle to be in equilibrium, a 2-kN force acting to the *left* must be applied. The negative sign on the answer is consistent with the direction of the positive x-axis. In mechanics, the orientation of the coordinate system is arbitrary (i.e., does not affect the solution), as long as it is used consistently. Let's rework the example by reversing the direction of the x-axis. As shown in Figure 18(b), the positive x-axis is now directed to the *left*, but the forces remain unchanged. Writing the equation of equilibrium, we have

$$\Sigma F_x = 0 = -F - 2$$

Solving yields

$$F = -2 \text{ kN}$$

and we obtain the same answer as before. The direction of the x-axis has no influence on the answer. In both cases, the negative sign indicates that the direction of F required to maintain the particle in equilibrium is *opposite* to the assumed direction.

The examples that follow demonstrate how to find forces acting on a particle. Each example is worked in detail, in accordance with the general analysis procedure of (1) problem statement, (2) diagram, (3) assumptions, (4) governing equations, (5) calculations, (6) solution check, and (7) discussion. For the sake of simplicity, the examples are limited to coplanar force systems.

EXAMPLE 4

Problem statement

Two blocks hang from cords as shown in Figure 19. Find the tension in each cord.

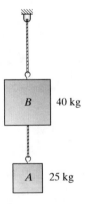

Figure 19.   Suspended blocks for Example 4.

Diagram

In order to find the tension in each cord, a separate free-body diagram is constructed for each block. The most critical part of a free-body diagram is the inclusion of every external force acting on the body in question. Two forces act on block A, its weight and the tension force in the lower cord. Three forces act on block B, its weight, the tension force in the lower cord, and the tension force in the upper cord. All forces are concurrent, so we treat the boxes as particles. The free-body diagrams for the blocks are shown in Figure 20(a).

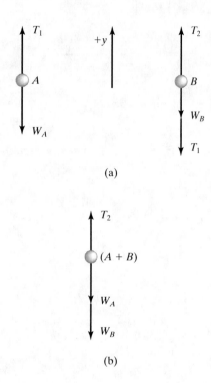

(a)

(b)

Figure 20. Free-body diagrams for Example 4.

Assumptions

1. All forces are concurrent.
2. The weights of the cords are negligible.
3. The cords are sufficiently flexible to hang straight down.

Governing equations

Because forces act in one direction only, there is only one governing equation: the equation of equilibrium for the vertical direction. Thus, for both blocks, we have

$$\sum F_y = 0$$

Calculations

To solve the problem, the equation of equilibrium must be written for both blocks. Noting the direction of the positive y-axis and using the free-body diagrams in Figure 20(a), we have

Block A:

$$\sum F_y = 0 = T_1 - W_A$$

$$= T_1 - (25 \text{ kg})(9.81 \text{ m/s}^2)$$

Block B:

$$\sum F_y = 0 = T_2 - T_1 - W_B$$

$$= T_2 - T_1 - (40 \text{ kg})(9.81 \text{ m/s}^2)$$

Solving the first equation for T_1, we obtain

$$T_1 = 245.25 \text{ N}$$

Substituting this value of T_1 into the second equation and solving for T_2, we obtain

$$T_2 = 637.65 \text{ N}$$

We commonly express engineering answers in three significant figures, so our answers are reported as

$$T_1 = \underline{\underline{245 \text{ N}}}, T_2 = \underline{\underline{638 \text{ N}}}$$

Solution Check

No mathematical or calculation-related errors are detected. Do the answers seem reasonable? The lower cord supports block A only, so tension, T_1, is simply the weight of block A. Because the upper cord supports both blocks, the tension T_2 should be the sum of the weights:

$$W_A + W_B = (m_A + m_B)g$$
$$= (25 \text{ kg} + 40 \text{ kg})(9.81 \text{ m/s}^2)$$
$$= 637.65 \text{ N}$$

Our solution checks out.

Discussion

An alternative method for finding the tension in the upper cord T_2 is to construct a free-body diagram of both blocks as a *single* particle. The interesting thing about this approach is that the tension forces produced by the lower cord on both blocks are ignored because they are *internal* forces, not external forces. The internal forces exerted on each block by the lower cord are equal in magnitude, but opposite in direction; hence, they cancel, thereby having no overall mechanical effect on the system. There are three external forces acting on the combined blocks, the weights of each block, and the tension T_2. Using the free-body diagram in Figure 20(b), we have

$$\Sigma F_y = 0 = T_2 - W_A - W_B$$
$$= T_2 - (25 \text{ kg} + 40 \text{ kg})(9.81 \text{ m/s}^2)$$

which yields

$$T_2 = 637.65 \text{ N}$$

EXAMPLE 5

Problem statement

A 200-kg engine block hangs from a system of cables as shown in Figure 21. Find the tension in cables AB and AC.

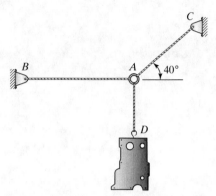

Figure 21.   Suspended engine block for Example 5.

Diagram

We have a coplanar force system in which the force in each cable acts concurrently at A, so we construct a free-body diagram for a "particle" at A. (See Figure 22). The tension force in cable AB acts to the left along the x-axis, and the tension force in cable AC acts along a line 40° with respect to the x-axis. The tension force in cable AD, which is equivalent to the engine block's weight, acts straight down.

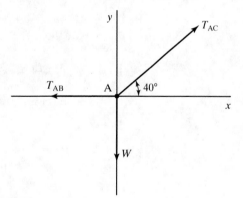

Figure 22.   Free-body diagram for Example 5.

Assumptions

1.   All forces are concurrent at A.
2.   The weights of the cables are negligible.
3.   All cables are taut.

Governing equations

The governing equations are the equations of equilibrium in the x and y directions:

$$\Sigma F_x = 0$$
$$\Sigma F_y = 0$$

Calculations

Using the free-body diagram in Figure 22, the equations of equilibrium become

$$\sum F_x = 0 = -T_{AB} + T_{AC} \cos 40°$$

$$\sum F_y = 0 = T_{AC} \sin 40° - W$$

where $W = mg = (200 \text{ kg})(9.81 \text{ m/s}^2) = 1962 \text{ N}$. The second equation can be immediately solved for T_{AC},

$$T_{AC} = \underline{3052 \text{ N}}$$

Substituting this value of T_{AC} into the first equation and solving for T_{AB}, we get

$$T_{AB} = \underline{2338 \text{ N}}$$

Solution check

To verify that our answers are correct, we substitute them back into the equilibrium equations. If they satisfy the equations, they are correct.

$$\Sigma F_x = -2338 \text{ N} + (3052 \text{ N}) \cos 40° = -0.032 \approx 0$$

$$\Sigma F_y = (3052 \text{ N}) \sin 40° - (200 \text{ kg})(9.81 \text{ m/s}^2) = -0.212 \approx 0$$

Within the numerical precision of the calculations, the sum of the forces in the x and y directions is zero. Our answers are therefore correct.

Discussion

Now that we know the tension forces in the cables, what do we do with them? Knowing the forces per se do not really tell us how the cables perform structurally. The next step in the analysis would be to determine the stress in each cable. If the calculated stresses are less than an allowable or design stress, the cables will support the engine block without experiencing failure. In this situation, failure most likely means cable breakage, but may also mean permanent cable strain. Stress and strain would have to be calculated in order to make a full structural assessment of the cables.

PRACTICE!

For the following practice problems, use the general analysis procedure of (1) problem statement, (2) diagram, (3) assumptions, (4) governing equations, (5) calculations, (6) solution check, and (7) discussion.

1. A 30-cm diameter solid steel sphere hangs from cables as shown. Find the tension in cables AB and AC. For the density of steel, use $\rho = 7270$ kg/m^3.

    Answer: $T_{AB} = T_{AC} = 712.9$ N

    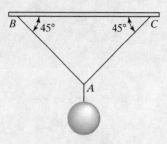

2. A 250-kg cylinder rests in a long channel as shown. Find the forces acting on the cylinder by the sides of the channel.

    Answer: 1999 N, 893 N

    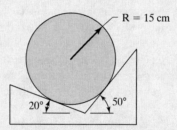

3. Three coplanar forces are applied to a box in an attempt to slide it across the floor, as shown. If the box remains at rest, what is the friction force between the box and the floor?

    Answer: 116.5 N

    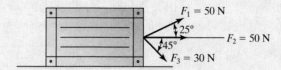

4. A 15-kg flowerpot hangs from wires as shown. Find the tension in wires AB and AC.

    Answer: $T_{AB} = 88.3$ N, $T_{AC} = 117.7$ N

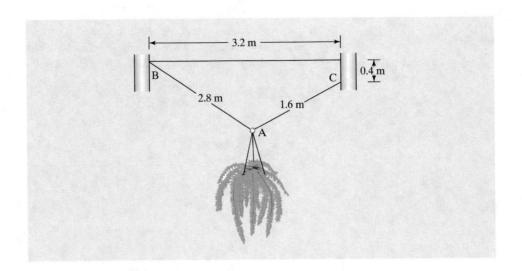

6   STRESS AND STRAIN

If the vector sum of the external forces acting on a body is zero, the body is in a state of static equilibrium. There are also internal forces acting on the body. Internal forces are *caused* by external forces, but internal forces do not affect the equilibrium of the body. So, if internal forces do not affect equilibrium, how are they important? To illustrate the importance of internal forces, let's use a familiar example from the sport of weight lifting. (See Figure 23.) As a weight lifter holds a heavy set of weights, his body and the weights are momentarily in a state of static equilibrium. The gravitational force of the weights is balanced by the force exerted on the bar by the weight lifter's hands or shoulders, and the gravitational forces of the weights plus his body are balanced by the force exerted by the floor on his feet. Are there internal forces acting on the weight lifter? Most definitely, yes. If the weight he is holding is great, he is painfully aware of those internal forces. The external forces of the weights and the reaction at the floor cause internal forces in his arms, torso, and legs. The magnitude of these internal forces usually limits the time the weight lifter can sustain his position to only a few seconds. Like the weight lifter, engineering structures such as buildings, bridges, and machines experience internal forces when external forces are applied to them. Engineering structures, however, must usually sustain internal forces for long periods of time, perhaps years. Principles of statics alone, which yield the external forces acting on a body, are insufficient to define the mechanical state of the body. In order for an engineer to make a complete assessment of the structural integrity of any body, internal forces must be considered. From the internal forces and the deformations resulting from them, stress and strain are determined.

6.1   Stress

The concept of stress is of prime importance in mechanics of materials. **Stress** is the primary physical quantity that engineers use to ascertain whether a structure can withstand the external forces applied to it. By finding stresses, engineers have a standard method of comparing the abilities of given materials to withstand external forces. There are two types of stress: *normal stress* and *shear stress*. In this book, we will confine our attention to normal stress. Normal stress is the *stress that acts normal (perpendicular)*

Figure 23.   A weight lifter is in equilibrium, but his body is in a state of stress. (Art by Kathryn Hagen).

to a selected plane or axis within a body. Normal stress is often associated with the stress in the axial direction in long slender members such as rods, beams, and columns. Consider the slender bar shown in Figure 24. An axial force F acts on each end of the bar, maintaining the bar in equilibrium, as indicated in Figure 24(a). Now, suppose that we pass an imaginary plane through the bar perpendicular to its axis, as shown in Figure 24(b). Conceptually, we then remove the bottom portion of the bar that was "cut away" by the imaginary plane. In removing the bottom portion of the bar, we also removed the force applied at the bottom end of the bar that balanced the force applied at the top end. To restore equilibrium, we must apply an equivalent force P at the "cut" end. This force, unlike the external force applied at the top of the bar, is an *internal* force because it acts *within* the bar. The internal force P acts perpendicular to the cross-sectional area created by passing the imaginary plane through the bar, as indicated in Figure 24(c). The normal stress σ in the bar is defined as the internal force P divided by the cross-sectional area A:

$$\sigma = \frac{P}{A} \tag{23}$$

This mathematical definition of normal stress is actually an *average* normal stress, because there may be a variation of stress across the cross section of the bar. Stress variations are normally present only near points where the external forces are applied,

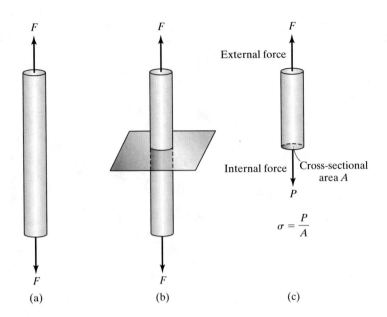

Figure 24. Normal stress in a rod.

however, so Equation (23) may be used in the majority of stress calculations without regard to stress variations. The cross section of the bar in Figure 24 is circular, but the quantity A represents the cross-sectional area of a member of any shape (i.e., circular, rectangular, triangular, etc.). Note that the definition of stress is very similar to that of pressure. Both quantities are defined as a force divided by an area. Accordingly, stress has the same units as pressure. Typical units for stress are kPa or MPa in the SI system and psi or ksi in the English system.

In Figure 24, the force vectors are directed away from each other, indicating that the bar is stretched. The normal stress associated with this force configuration is referred to as *tensile stress* because the forces place the body in tension. Conversely, if the force vectors are directed toward each other, the bar is compressed. The normal stress associated with this force configuration is referred to as *compressive stress* because the forces place the body in compression. These two force configurations are illustrated in Figure 25. One may think that the type of normal stress, tensile or compressive, does not matter, since Equation (23) says nothing about direction. However, some materials can withstand one type of stress more readily than the other. For example, concrete is stronger in compression than in tension. Consequently, concrete

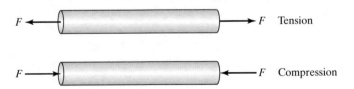

Figure 25. External forces for tension and compression.

is typically used in applications where the stresses are compressive, such as columns that support bridge decks and highway overpasses. When concrete members are designed for applications that involve tensile stresses, reinforcing bars are used.

6.2   Strain

External forces are responsible for producing stress, and they are also responsible for producing deformation. Deformation may also be caused by temperature changes. **Deformation** is defined as a *change in the size or shape of a body*. No material is perfectly rigid; hence, when external forces are applied to a body, the body changes its size or shape according to the magnitude and direction of the external forces applied to it. We have all stretched a rubber band and noticed that its length changes appreciably under a small tensile force. All materials—steel, concrete, wood, and other structural materials—deform to some extent under applied forces, but the deformations are usually too small to detect visually, so special measuring instruments are employed. Consider the bar shown in Figure 26. Prior to applying an external force, the bar has a length L. Now, the bar is placed in tension, applying an external force F at each end. The tensile force causes the bar to increase in length by an amount δ. The quantity δ is called the *normal deformation* or *axial deformation*, since the change in length is normal to the di-

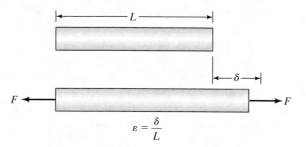

Figure 26.   Normal strain in a rod.

rection of the force, which is along the axis of the rod. Depending on the bar's material and the magnitude of the applied force, the normal deformation may be small, perhaps only a few thousandths of an inch. In order to normalize the change in size or shape of a body with respect to the body's original geometry, engineers use a quantity called **strain**. There are two types of strain, *normal strain* and *shear strain*. In this book, we confine our attention to normal strain. Normal strain ε is defined as the *normal deformation δ divided by the original length L*:

$$\varepsilon = \frac{\delta}{L} \tag{24}$$

Because strain is a ratio of two lengths, it is a dimensionless quantity. It is customary, however, to express strain as a ratio of two length units. In the SI unit system, strain is usually expressed in units of μm/m because, as mentioned before, deformations are typically small. In the English unit system, strain is usually expressed in units of in/in. Since strain is a dimensionless quantity, it is sometimes expressed as a percentage. The normal strain illustrated in Figure 26 is for a body in tension, but the definition given by Equation (24) also applies to bodies in compression.

6.3   Hooke's Law

About three centuries ago, the English mathematician Robert Hooke (1635–1703) discovered that the force required to stretch or compress a spring is proportional to the displacement of a point on the spring. The law describing this phenomena, known as Hooke's law, is expressed mathematically as

$$F = kx \tag{25}$$

where F is force, x is displacement, and k is a constant of proportionality called the spring constant. Equation (25) applies only if the spring is not deformed beyond its ability to resume its original length after the force is removed. A more useful form of Hooke's law for engineering materials has the same mathematical form as Equation (25), but is expressed in terms of stress and strain:

$$\sigma = E\varepsilon \tag{26}$$

Hooke's law, given by Equation (26), states that the stress σ in a material is proportional to the strain ε. The constant of proportionality E is called the **modulus of elasticity** or *Young's modulus*, after the English mathematician Thomas Young (1773–1829). Like the spring equation, the engineering version of Hooke's law applies only if the material is not deformed beyond its ability to resume its original size after the force is removed. A material that obeys Hooke's law is said to be *elastic* because it returns to its original size after the removal of the force. As strain ε is a dimensionless quantity, the modulus of elasticity E has the same units as stress. Equation (26) describes a straight line with E as the slope. The modulus of elasticity is an experimentally derived quantity. A sample of the material in question is subjected to tensile stresses in a special apparatus that facilitates a sequence of stress and strain measurements in the elastic range of the material. The **elastic range** is the distance or extent a material can be deformed and still be capable of returning to its original shape. Stress-strain data points are plotted on a linear scale, and a best fit straight line is drawn through the points. The slope of this line is the modulus of elasticity E.

A useful relationship may be obtained by combining Equations (23), (24), and (26). The axial deformation δ may be expressed directly in terms of the internal force P and the geometrical and material properties of the member. This is done by substituting the definition of strain ε given by Equation (24) into Equation (26), Hooke's law, and noting that normal stress is the internal force divided by the cross-sectional area given in Equation (23). Thus, the resulting expression is

$$\delta = \frac{PL}{AE} \tag{27}$$

Equation (27) is useful because the strain does not have to be calculated first to find the deformation of the member. However, this equation is valid only over the linear region of the stress-strain curve.

6.4   Stress-Strain Diagram

A **stress-strain diagram** *is a graph of stress as a function of strain in a given material.* The shape of this graph varies somewhat with material, but stress-strain diagrams have some common features. A typical stress-strain diagram is illustrated in Figure 27. The upper stress limit of the linear relationship described by Hooke's law is called the *proportional limit*, labeled point A. At any stress between point A and the *elastic limit*, labeled point B, stress is not proportional to strain, but the material will still return to its original size after the force is removed. For many materials, the proportional and elastic limits are very close

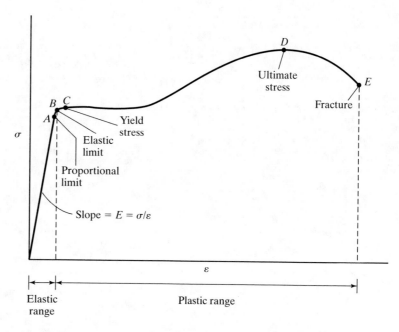

Figure 27. A typical stress-strain diagram.

together. Point C is called the **yield stress** or *yield strength*. Any stress above the yield stress will result in *plastic* deformation of the material (i.e., the material will not return to its original size, but will deform permanently). As the stress increases beyond the yield stress, the material experiences a large increase in strain for a small increase in stress. At about point D, called the **ultimate stress** or *ultimate strength*, the cross-sectional area of the material begins to decrease rapidly until the material experiences *fracture* at point E.

In the next example, we use the general analysis procedure of (1) problem statement, (2) diagram, (3) assumptions, (4) governing equations, (5) calculations, (6) solution check, and (7) discussion.

EXAMPLE 6

Problem statement

A 200-kg engine block hangs from a system of cables as shown in Figure 28. Find the normal stress and axial deformation in cables AB and AC. The cables are 0.7 m long and have a diameter of 4 mm. The cables are steel with a modulus of elasticity of $E = 200$ GPa.

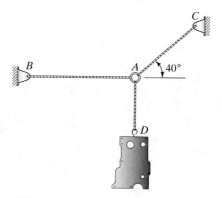

Figure 28. Suspended engine block for Example 6.

Diagram

We will presume that the statics portion of the problem has been solved, so a free-body diagram of the entire system is unnecessary. Diagrams showing a cross section of the cables and the corresponding internal forces are sufficient. (See Figure 29.)

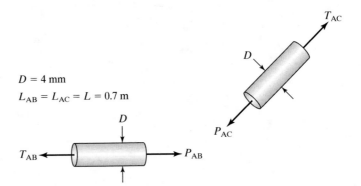

$D = 4$ mm

$L_{AB} = L_{AC} = L = 0.7$ m

Figure 29. Cables for Example 6.

Assumptions

1. Cables are circular in cross section.
2. Cables have the same modulus of elasticity.
3. Stress is uniform in the cables.

Governing equations

Cross-sectional area:

$$A = \frac{\pi D^2}{4}$$

Normal stress:

$$\sigma = \frac{P}{A}$$

Axial deformation:

$$\delta = \frac{PL}{AE}$$

Calculations

The cross-sectional area of the cables is

$$A = \frac{\pi D^2}{4}$$

$$= \frac{\pi (0.004 \text{ m})^2}{4} = 1.2566 \times 10^{-5} \text{ m}^2$$

From a prior statics analysis, the tensions in cables AB and AC are 2338 N and 3052 N, respectively. Hence, the normal stress in each cable is

$$\sigma_{AB} = \frac{P_{AB}}{A}$$

$$= \frac{2338 \text{ N}}{1.2566 \times 10^{-5} \text{ m}^2} = 186.1 \times 10^6 \text{ N/m}^2 = \underline{186.1 \text{ MPa}}$$

$$\sigma_{AC} = \frac{P_{AC}}{A}$$

$$= \frac{3052 \text{ N}}{1.2566 \times 10^{-5} \text{ m}^2} = 242.9 \times 10^6 \text{ N/m}^2 = \underline{242.9 \text{ MPa}}$$

The deformation in each cable is

$$\delta_{AB} = \frac{P_{AB}L}{AE}$$

$$= \frac{(2338 \text{ N})(0.7 \text{ m})}{(1.2566 \times 10^{-5} \text{ m}^2)(200 \times 10^9 \text{ N/m}^2)} = 6.51 \times 10^{-4} \text{ m} = \underline{0.651 \text{ mm}}$$

$$\delta_{AC} = \frac{P_{AC}L}{AE}$$

$$= \frac{(3052 \text{ N})(0.7 \text{ m})}{(1.2566 \times 10^{-5} \text{ m}^2)(200 \times 10^9 \text{ N/m}^2)} = 8.50 \times 10^{-4} \text{ m} = \underline{0.850 \text{ mm}}$$

Solution check

One way to check the validity of the results is to compare the relative magnitudes of the stress and deformation in each cable. The internal force in cable *AC* is greater than the normal stress in cable *AB*. Consequently, the normal stress and axial deformation in cable *AC* must also be greater because the cables are geometrically and materially identical. Our calculations show that this is indeed the case.

Discussion

The deformations are small, less than a millimeter in both cables. These deformations would probably not be significant in an engine hoist application and would not be perceptible by the naked eye. Are the stresses excessive? Will they plastically deform the cables? To answer these questions, we must know something about the yield stress of the cable material and the stresses for which the cables were designed.

PRACTICE!

In the following practice problems, use the general analysis procedure of (1) problem statement, (2) diagram, (3) assumptions, (4) governing equations, (5) calculations, (6) solution check, and (7) discussion.

1. A solid rod of stainless steel ($E = 190$ GPa) is 50 cm in length and has a 4 mm $\times$ 4 mm cross section. The rod is subjected to an axial tensile force of 8 kN. Find the normal stress, strain, and axial deformation.

   Answer: 500 MPa, 1.32 mm, 0.00263

2. A 25-cm-long 10-gauge wire of yellow brass ($E = 105$ GPa) is subjected to an axial tensile force of 1.75 kN. Find the normal stress and deformation in the wire. A 10-gauge wire has a diameter of 2.588 mm.

    Answer: 333 MPa, 0.792 mm

3. An 8-m-high granite column sustains an axial compressive load of 500 kN. If the column shortens 0.12 mm under the load, what is the diameter of the column? For granite, $E = 70$ GPa.

    Answer: 0.779 m

4. A solid rod with a length and diameter of 1 m and 5 mm, respectively, is subjected to an axial tensile force of 20 kN. If the axial deformation is measured as $\delta = 1$ cm, what is the modulus of elasticity of the material?

    Answer: 1018 GPa

5. A plastic ($E = 3$ GPa) tube with an outside and inside diameter of 6 cm and 5.4 cm, respectively, is subjected to an axial compressive force of 12 kN. If the tube is 25 cm long, how much does the tube shorten under the load?

    Answer: 1.86 mm

7   DESIGN STRESS

Most engineering structures are not designed to deform permanently or fracture. Every member in a structure must maintain a certain degree of dimensional control to assure that it does not plastically deform, thereby losing its size or shape, interfering with surrounding structures or other members in the same structure. Obviously, the members must not fracture either, because this would lead to a catastrophic failure that would result in material and financial loss and perhaps the loss of human life. Therefore, members in most structures are designed to sustain a maximum stress that is *below* the yield stress on the stress-strain diagram for the particular material used to construct that member. This maximum stress is called the *design stress* or **allowable stress**. When a properly designed member is subjected to a load, the stress in the member will not exceed the design stress. Because the design stress is within the elastic range of the material, the member will return to its original dimensions after the load is removed. A bridge, for example, sustains stresses in its members while traffic passes over it. When there is no traffic, the members in the bridge return to their original size. Similarly, while a boiler is operating, the pressure vessel sustains stresses that deform it, but when the pressure is reduced to atmospheric pressure, the vessel returns to its original dimensions.

If a structural member is designed to carry stresses below the yield stress, how does an engineer choose what the allowable stress should be? And why choose a stress below the yield stress in the first place? Why not design the member by using the yield stress itself, since that would allow the member to carry the maximum possible load? Engineering design is not an exact science. If it was, structures could be designed with ultimate precision by using the yield stress, or any other stress for that matter, as the design stress, and the design stress would never be exceeded while the structure was in service. Because design is not an exact science, engineers incorporate an allowance in their designs that takes into account the following uncertainties:

1. *Loadings* The design engineer may not anticipate every type of loading or the number of loadings that may occur. Vibration, impact, or accidental loadings may occur that were not accounted for in the design of the structure.

2. *Failure modes* Materials can fail by one or more of several different mechanisms. The design engineer may not have anticipated every failure mode by which the structure can possibly fail.

3. *Material properties* Physical properties of materials are subject to variations during manufacture, and there are experimental uncertainties in their numerical values. Properties may also be altered by heating or by deformation during manufacture, handling, and storage.

4. *Deterioration* Exposure to the elements, poor maintenance, or unexpected natural phenomena may cause a material to deteriorate, thereby compromising its structural integrity. Various types of corrosion are the most common forms of material deterioration.

5. *Analysis* Engineering analysis is a critical part of design, and analysis involves making simplifying assumptions. Thus, analytical results are not precise, but are approximations.

To account for the uncertainties listed, engineers use a design or allowable stress based on a parameter called the **factor of safety**. The factor of safety (*F.S.*) is defined as the *ratio of the failure stress to the allowable stress*:

$$F.S. = \frac{\sigma_{\text{fail}}}{\sigma_{\text{allow}}} \qquad (28)$$

Because the yield stress is the stress above which a material plastically deforms, the yield stress σ_y is commonly used as the failure stress σ_{fail}. The ultimate stress σ_{u} may also be used. The failure stress is always greater than the allowable stress, so $F.S. > 1$. The value chosen for the factor of safety depends on the type of engineering structure, the relative importance of the member compared with other members in the structure, the risk to property and life, and the severity of the design uncertainties previously listed. For example, to minimize weight, the factor of safety for aircraft and spacecraft structures is typically close to 1. However, the factor of safety for ground-based structures such as dams, bridges and buildings may be higher, perhaps 1.5 or 2. High-risk structures that pose a safety hazard to people in the event of failure, such as certain nuclear power plant components, may have a factor of safety as high as 3. Factors of safety for structural members in specific engineering systems have been standardized through many years of testing and industrial evaluation. Factors of safety are often defined by building codes or engineering standards established by city, state, or federal agencies and professional engineering societies.

APPLICATION: DESIGNING A TURNBUCKLE

Turnbuckles are special mechanical fasteners that facilitate connections between cables, chains, or cords. A basic turnbuckle consists of a slender, cylindrical shaped body threaded on each end to accept an eyebolt, a hook, or other type of tying component. The tension in the cables that are tied to a turnbuckle is adjusted by rotating the body of the turnbuckle. Turnbuckles are designed such that tightening or loosening may be accomplished without twisting the cables. Like the cables that are connected to them, turnbuckles must sustain the tensile stresses to which

they are subjected. Consider a turnbuckle used to adjust the tension in a cable that stabilizes a communications tower. From a prior analysis, the tension in the cable is determined to be 25kN. The loaded turnbuckle is shown in Figure 30(a). Let us suppose that, as a new engineer, your first job is to select a turnbuckle for this application. Turnbuckles are available in a variety of sizes and materials from several suppliers. Hardware suppliers specify the maximum recommended load that a particular turnbuckle can sustain without failing. It is, therefore, a simple matter for you, the end user, to

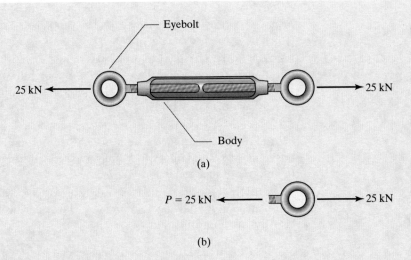

Figure 30. A loaded turnbuckle.

select a turnbuckle with a recommended maximum load that is somewhat greater than the actual load of 25kN. But how did the engineers who designed the turnbuckle obtain this load value? The example that follows shows how fundamental concepts of stress and factor of safety may be used to design the eyebolt portion of a turnbuckle. The general analysis procedure of (1) problem statement, (2) diagram, (3) assumptions, (4) governing equations, (5) calculations, (6) solution check, and (7) discussion, is used.

Problem statement

Determine the minimum-diameter eyebolt in a turnbuckle used to stabilize a communications tower. The tensile force in the cable is 25kN. The eyebolt is to be made of AISI 4130 steel, a high-strength forging steel. (AISI is an abbreviation for American Iron and Steel Institute.) To account for potential high wind loads and other uncertainties, use a factor of safety of 2.0.

Diagram

The internal and external forces acting on the eyebolt are shown in Figure 30(b).

Assumptions

1. Stress is uniform in the eyebolt.
2. Stress in the eyebolt is purely axial.
3. Consider stress in the main body of the eyebolt only, not the threads.

Governing equations

The governing equations for this, problem are the cross-sectional area for a circular bolt, the definition of normal stress, and the factor of safety.

$$A = \frac{\pi D^2}{4} \tag{a}$$

$$\sigma_{\text{allow}} = \frac{P}{A} \tag{b}$$

$$F.S. = \frac{\sigma_{\text{fail}}}{\sigma_{\text{allow}}} = \frac{\sigma_y}{\sigma_{\text{allow}}} \tag{c}$$

Calculations

In the third governing equation, we have used the yield stress σ_y as the failure stress. The yield stress of AISI 4130 steel is 760 MPa. The objective of the analysis is to find the diameter D of the eyebolt required to sustain the applied load. There are three unknown quantities: σ_{allow}, A, and D. Because the three governing equations are not dependent, we may combine them algebraically to obtain the diameter, D. Upon substituting Equation (a) into Equation (b) and then Equation (b) into Equation (c) we obtain

$$D = \left(\frac{4 \, P.F.S.}{\pi \sigma_y} \right)^{1/2}$$

$$= \left(\frac{4(25 \times 10^3 \, \text{N})(2.0)}{\pi (760 \times 10^6 \, \text{Pa})} \right)^{1/2}$$

$$= 9.15 \times 10^{-3} \, \text{m} = \underline{9.15 \, \text{mm}}$$

Solution check

No errors were found.

Discussion

The minimum eyebolt diameter that will sustain the applied load with a factor of safety of 2.0 is 9.15 mm. In English units, this diameter is

$$D = 9.15 \text{ mm} \times \frac{1 \text{ in}}{25.4 \text{ mm}} = 0.360 \text{ in}$$

Bolts come in standard diameters, and 0.360 in is not a standard size. Bolts are typically available in standard sizes of $\frac{1}{4}$-in, $\frac{5}{16}$-in, $\frac{3}{8}$-in etc. A $\frac{5}{16}$-in (0.3125 in) bolt is too small, so the $\frac{3}{8}$-in (0.375 in) should be chosen, even though it is slightly larger than required. It should be emphasized that this analysis reflects only a part of the analysis that would be required in the total design of a turnbuckle. Stresses in the threads of the eyebolt and the turnbuckle body, as well as the main body of the turnbuckle itself, would also have to be calculated.

PRACTICE!

In the practice problems, use the general analysis procedure of (1) problem statement, (2) diagram, (3) assumptions, (4) governing equations, (5) calculations, (6) solution check, and (7) discussion.

1. A rod of aluminum 6061-T6 has a square cross section measuring 0.25 in $\times$ 0.25 *in*. Using the yield stress as the failure stress, find the maximum tensile load that the rod can sustain for a factor of safety of 1.5. The yield stress of aluminum 6061-T6 is 240 MPa.

   Answer: 6.45 kN

2. A concrete column with a diameter of 60 cm supports a portion of a highway overpass. Using the ultimate stress as the failure stress, what is the maximum compressive load that the column can carry for a factor of safety of 1.25? For the ultimate stress of concrete, use $\sigma_u = 40$ MPa.

   Answer: 9.05 MN

3. A column of rectangular cross section constructed from fir timber is subjected to a compressive load of 6 MN. If the width of the column is 12 cm, find the depth required to sustain the load with a factor of safety of 1.6. The ultimate stress of fir is $\sigma_u = 50$ MPa.

   Answer: 1.60 m

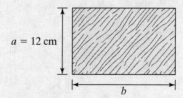

a = 12 cm

b

KEY TERMS

allowable stress	free-body diagram	strain
Cartesian unit vector	internal force	stress
deformation	mechanics	stress-strain diagram
elastic range	modulus of elasticity	ultimate stress
equilibrium	resultant	vector
factor of safety	resultant force	yield stress
force	scalar	
force system	statics	

REFERENCES   Bedford, A. and W. Fowler, *Engineering Mechanics: Statics*, 3d ed., Upper Saddle River, NJ: Prentice Hall, 2002.

Beer, F.P., E.R. Johnston, E.R. Eisenberg, and G.H. Staab, *Vector Mechanics for Engineers: Statics*, 7th ed. NY: McGraw-Hill, 2003.

Johnston, E.R. and J.T. DeWolf, *Mechanics of Materials*, 3d ed., NY: McGraw-Hill, 2002.

Hibbeler, R.C., *Engineering Mechanics: Statics*, 10th ed., Upper Saddle River, NJ: Prentice Hall, 2004.

Hibbeler, R.C., *Mechanics of Materials*, 5th Edition, Upper Saddle River, NJ: Prentice Hall, 2003.

Problems

1.   Find the resultant force for the forces shown in Figure P1 (a) by using the parallelogram law and (b) by resolving the forces into their x and y components.

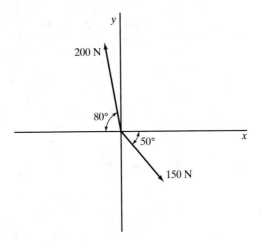

Figure P1.

2.   Find the resultant force for the forces shown in Figure P2 (a) by using the parallelogram law and (b) by resolving the forces into their x and y components.

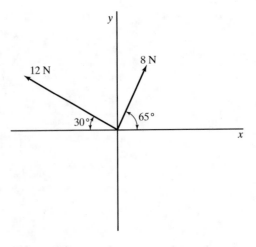

Figure P2.

3.   For the three forces shown in Figure P3, find the resultant force, its magnitude, and direction with respect to the x-axis.

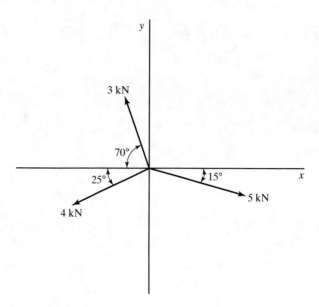

Figure P3.

4.   For the three forces shown in Figure P4, find the resultant force, its magnitude, and direction with respect to the x-axis.

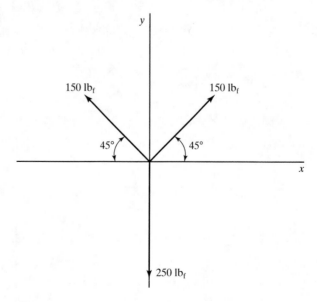

Figure P4.

5.   Consider the three forces $\mathbf{F}_1 = 3\mathbf{i} + 2\mathbf{j} - 5\mathbf{k}$ N, $\mathbf{F}_2 = -4\mathbf{i} - 7\mathbf{j} + 2\mathbf{k}$ N, and $\mathbf{F}_3 = \mathbf{i} - \mathbf{j} - \mathbf{k}$ N. Find the resultant force and its magnitude.

6.   A particle is subjected to three forces: $\mathbf{F}_1 = 3\mathbf{i} + 5\mathbf{j} - 8\mathbf{k}$ kN, $\mathbf{F}_2 = -2\mathbf{i} - 3\mathbf{j} + 4\mathbf{k}$ kN, and $\mathbf{F}_3 = -\mathbf{i} - 2\mathbf{j} + 5\mathbf{k}$ kN. Is this particle in equilibrium? Explain.

7.   A particle is subjected to three forces: $\mathbf{F}_1 = 6\mathbf{i} - a\mathbf{j} - 7\mathbf{k}$ N, $\mathbf{F}_2 = -4\mathbf{i} - 5\mathbf{j} + b\mathbf{k}$ N, and $\mathbf{F}_3 = c\mathbf{i} - 2\mathbf{j} + 4\mathbf{k}$ N. Find the values of the scalars a, b, and c such that the particle is in equilibrium.

8.   Find the magnitudes of forces $\mathbf{F}_1$ and $\mathbf{F}_2$ so that the particle P is in equilibrium. (See Figure P8.)

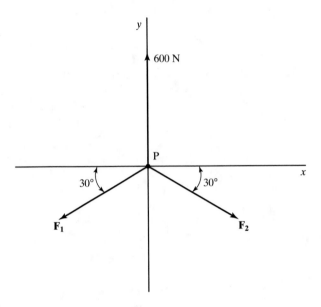

Figure P8.

9.   Find the magnitude of the force $\mathbf{F}$ and its direction θ so that the particle P is in equilibrium. (See Figure P9.)

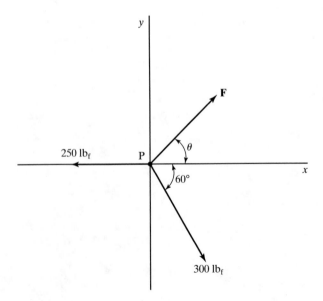

Figure P9.

10.   A gusset plate is subjected to the forces shown in Figure P10. Find the magnitude and direction θ of the force in member B so that the plate is in equilibrium.

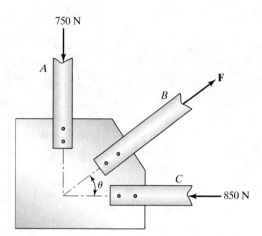

Figure P10.

For problems 11 through 27, use the general analysis procedure of (1) problem statement, (2) diagram, (3) assumptions, (4) governing equations, (5) calculations, (6) solution check, and (7) discussion.

11.   A 400-kg crate hangs from ropes as shown in Figure P11. Find the tension in ropes AB and AC.

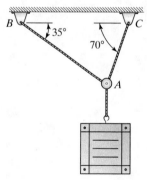

Figure P11.

12.   A 250-lb$_m$ box is held in place by a cord with a spring scale on an inclined plane as shown in Figure P12. If all surfaces are smooth, what is the force reading on the scale?

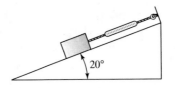

Figure P12.

13.   A concrete pipe with an inside and outside diameter of 60 cm and 70 cm, respectively, hangs from cables as shown in Figure P13. The pipe is supported at two locations, and a spreader bar maintains cable segments AB and AC at 45°. Each support carries half the total weight of the pipe. If the density of concrete is $\rho = 2320 \ \text{kg} / \text{m}^3$, find the tension in cable segments AB and AC.

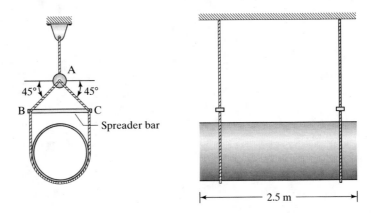

Figure P13.

14.   A construction worker holds a 600-lb$_f$ crate in the position shown in Figure P14. What force must the worker exert on the cable?

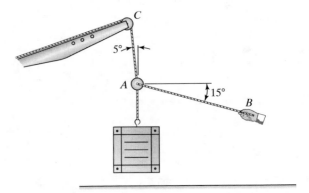

Figure P14.

15.   A 10-slug cylinder is suspended by a cord and frictionless pulley system as shown in Figure P15. A person standing on the floor pulls on the free end of the cord to hold the cylinder in a stationary position. What is the person's minimum weight for this to be possible?

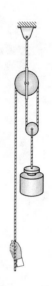

Figure P15.

16.   A 150-N traffic signal is suspended from a symmetrical system of cables as shown in Figure P16. Find the tension in all cables. Cable BC is horizontal.

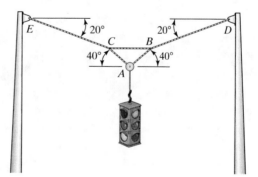

Figure P16.

17.   A 1.4-m-diameter wrecking ball hangs motionless from a 1.75-cm diameter cable. The wrecking ball is solid and is constructed of steel ($\rho = 7800$ kg / m^3). If the cable is 18 m long, how much does the cable stretch? For the cable, use $E = 175$ GPa.

18.   A 4-m-high wooden column with a rectangular cross section is subjected to a 210 kN axial compressive force. The modulus of elasticity of the wood is 13

GPa. If one side of the column is 25 cm across, find the minimum dimension of the other side to keep the columns deformation under 1.3 mm.

19.   The column is subjected to a 15-kN force as shown in Figure P19. Find the average normal stress in the column.

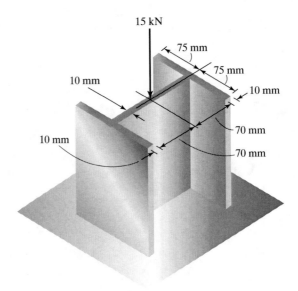

Figure P19.

20.   A solid composite shaft is subjected to a 2-MN force as shown in Figure P20. Section AB is red brass ($E = 120$ GPa), and section BC is AISI 1010 steel

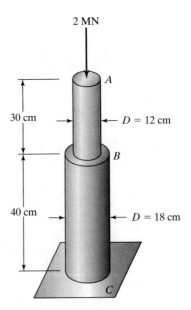

Figure P20.

($E = 200$ GPa). Find the normal stress in each section and the total axial deformation of the shaft.

21. A tapered column of concrete ($E = 30$ GPa) is subjected to a 200-kN force as shown in Figure P21. Find the axial deformation of the column. *Hint*: Express the cross-sectional area A as a function of x and perform the integration:

$$\delta = \int_0^L \frac{P\,dx}{A(x)E}$$

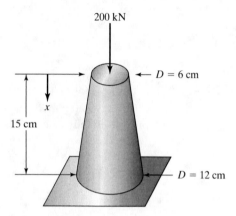

Figure P21.

22. A 12-cm × 12-cm square plate of AISI 1010 steel ($E = 200$ GPa) is subjected to normal tensile forces of 15 kN and 20 kN on the top and right edges as shown in Figure P22. The thickness of the plate is 5 mm, and the left and bottom edges of the plate are fixed. Find the normal strain and deformation of the plate in the horizontal and vertical directions.

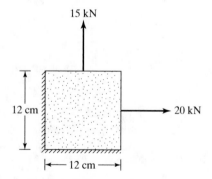

Figure P22.

23.   A tensile test is conducted on a steel specimen with a diameter of 8.0 mm and a test length of 6.0 cm. The data is shown in the table. Plot the stress-strain diagram, and find the approximate value of the modulus of elasticity for the steel.

Load (kN)	Deformation (mm)
2.0	0.0119
5.0	0.0303
10.0	0.0585
15.0	0.0895
20.0	0.122
25.0	0.145

24.   A 1-cm-diameter, 0.4-m-long steel rod is to be used in an application where it will be subjected to an axial tensile force of 15 kN. The factor of safety based on yield stress must be at least 1.5, and the axial deformation must not exceed 2 cm. Is the steel whose stress-strain diagram is shown in Figure P24 suitable for this application? Explain.

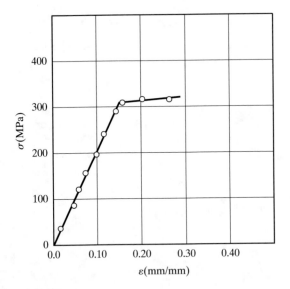

Figure P24.

25.   A 4-cm-diameter rod of AISI 302 stainless steel is to subjected to an axial tensile force such that the factor of safety based on the yield stress is 1.75. Find the maximum allowable tensile force. The yield stress of AISI 302 stainless steel is $\sigma_y = 520$ MPa.

26.   A 18-in-diameter sandstone column is subjected to an axial compressive force of 2×10^6 lb$_f$. Find the factor of safety based on the ultimate compressive stress. For the ultimate compressive stress of sandstone, use $\sigma_u = 85$ MPa.

27.   A slender cylindrical member in a child's toy made of polystyrene plastic is to be subjected to an axial tensile force of 400N. Find the minimum diameter of this member for a factor of safety of 1.5 based on yield stress. The yield stress for polystyrene is $\sigma_y = 55$ MPa.

13

Electrical Circuits

1   INTRODUCTION

Electrical engineering is one of the most diverse and well-established branches of engineering. Electrical engineers design systems and devices that harness the power of electricity to perform a variety of tasks. Electricity is one of the most useful forms of energy, and it impacts our everyday lives in fundamental ways. Without electricity, commonplace, but important devices such as automobiles, aircraft, computers, household appliances, telephones, television, radio, and electric lights would not exist. The historical roots of electricity can be traced to such notable scientists, engineers and technologists as Alessandro Volta (1745–1827), Andre Ampere (1775–1836), Georg Ohm (1787–1854), Michael Faraday (1791–1867), James Joule (1818–1889), Heinrich Hertz (1857–1894), and Thomas Edison (1847–1931). These individuals, among others, established the fundamental theoretical and practical foundations of electrical phenomena. This chapter deals with a category of electrical engineering referred to as *electrical circuits*. In nearly every electrical engineering curriculum, *electrical circuit analysis* is one of the first courses taken by the engineering student. The principles covered in basic electrical circuit theory are so important that even nonelectrical engineering majors are often required to take at least one course in the subject. Nearly all branches of electrical engineering are fundamentally based on circuit theory. The only subject in electrical engineering that is more fundamental than circuit theory is electromagnetic field theory, which deals with the physics of electromagnetic fields and waves.

As an electrical engineering subject, electrical circuits may be broken down into two general areas: *power* and *signal*. Power may be subdivided further into three categories, *power generation*, *heating and lighting*, and *motors and generators*. Similarly, signal may be divided into three

OBJECTIVES

After reading this chapter, you will have learned

- The relationship between charge and current
- The concept of voltage
- The concept of resistance
- How to combine resistances in series and parallel
- How to use Ohm's law
- How to analyze simple DC circuits
- How to use Kirchhoff's laws of circuit analysis

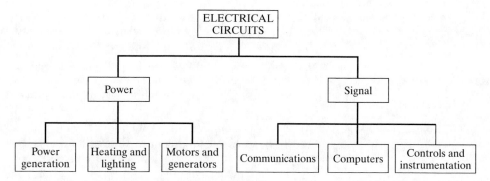

Figure 1. Topical structure of electrical circuits.

subcategories: *communications, computers,* and *controls and instrumentation.* This structure is schematically illustrated in Figure 1. Power deals with systems designed to provide electrical energy to various mechanical and electrical devices. Power generation refers to the production and transmission of electrical power by power plants. The energy source from which these power stations derive electrical power is typically fossil fuels, nuclear materials, or moving water. To a lesser degree, solar or wind power is also used. Electrical energy is required to run heating and cooling equipment such as furnaces, electric heaters, boilers, and air conditioners. The illumination provided by incandescent and fluorescent lights requires electrical power. Motors are found in numerous systems, including refrigerators, furnaces, fans, CD players, kitchen appliances, and printers. In motors, electrical energy is converted to mechanical energy via a rotating shaft. Unlike a motor, a generator is used to convert mechanical energy to electrical energy. Generators are used in power plants, automobiles, and other power systems. The signal area of electrical circuits deals with systems that transmit and process information. The power transmitted is not a primary consideration in signal applications. Communications refers to the transmission of information via electrical signals. Telephone, television, radio, and computers are types of communication systems. The heart of a computer is its digital circuits, circuits that utilize logic operations for the rapid processing of information. Computers are such a dominant area of engineering that electrical engineering programs in the United States are referred to as electrical and computer engineering to give students the option of focusing on the hardware (electrical) or the software, firmware, and operating systems (computer) aspects of the field. Controls are special circuits that activate or adjust other electrical or mechanical devices. A thermostat that turns a furnace or air conditioner on and off is a simple example. Instrumentation circuits are used to process electrical signals generated by various types of sensors that control a device. For example, an automobile has a circuit that processes an electrical signal generated by a temperature sensor in the cooling system. If the temperature exceeds a certain value, the circuit activates a visual display that warns the driver of an overheating condition.

Now that the basic topical structure of electrical circuits has been defined, what is an electrical circuit? An **electrical circuit** may be defined as *two or more electrical devices interconnected by conductors.* In electrical circuits, there are numerous types of electrical devices such as resistors, capacitors, inductors, diodes, transistors, transformers, batteries, lamps, fuses, switches, and motors. The "conductors" that interconnect these devices is usually a wire or a metal pathway integrated on a printed circuit board. Electrical circuits can be very simple, such as the circuit in a flashlight containing two batteries, a lightbulb, and a switch. Most electrical circuits, however, are much more complex than a flashlight. A standard television contains, among other things, power supplies, amplifiers, speakers, and a cathode ray tube. The microprocessor in a computer may contain the equivalent of millions of transistors interconnected in a single chip that is smaller than a business card. Electrical engineers use principles of electrical circuit theory to analyze and design a wide variety of systems. Look around you. How many devices do you see nearby that utilize electricity for their operation? You are probably not reading this chapter by the illumination of candles, but by incandescent or fluorescent lights. The room most likely has many electrical outlets on the walls that facilitate the operation of various electrical devices such as computers, vacuum cleaners, clocks, toasters, microwave ovens, etc. Electrical devices are so pervasive that we take them for granted, but our world would be vastly different without them. To anyone born in an industrialized nation during the latter half of the 20th century, a world without television, stereo, cellular phones, and CD players would seem foreign and strange. Electrical devices change rapidly, being driven by the ever increasing need for higher speed, smaller size, and lower cost. This period of time saw gargantuan mainframe computers with thousands of heat-generating vacuum tubes evolve into desktop computers with cracker-sized microprocessors. The second half of the 20th century also witnessed sweeping improvements in telecommunications, automotive, electronics, and automation.

All electrical devices have circuits of one kind or another, and the electrical engineer must know how to design these circuits to perform specific electrical functions. Some familiar examples of devices that have electrical circuits are shown in Figures 2 and 3. Students must learn the fundamental principles of electrical circuits before proceeding with more advanced study in circuit analysis and other electrical engineering courses.

Figure 2. A computer contains electrical circuits that perform a variety of functions.

Figure 3. In future space missions, a nano rover for planetary surface exploration will rely on miniature electrical circuits for its operation. (Image courtesy of NASA).

PROFESSIONAL SUCCESS: RETAIN YOUR COURSE MATERIALS

Engineering students may sometimes wonder, "How much of my engineering course materials should I keep after completing a course or after graduation? Should I sell my textbooks back to the bookstore? Should I discard my lecture notes, exams, and laboratory reports? Will I need these materials after I graduate?" The engineering curriculum is a challenging academic road to travel. By the time you graduate, you will have devoted much time and energy and spent a lot of money in the pursuit of your engineering degree. Do not trivialize this great commitment by squandering your textbooks for a few dollars. As you complete each engineering course, keep your books and other course materials for reference in future engineering courses. Engineering courses build on one another, so you will most likely need these resources to help you learn new material. Never sell an engineering text back to the bookstore just because you are a little short of cash. Your engineering texts are a wellspring of information, the backbone of your engineering course work. Will you need your books even after graduation when you have secured employment as an engineer? Depending on the nature of your engineering position and the company you work for, your college textbooks could be a valuable resource, particularly in engineering design and analysis. Because you do not know exactly what kinds of engineering activities you will be involved in after graduation, keep your textbooks.

At the end of each course, organize your lecture notes, lab reports, homework problems, exams, and other materials into a three-ring binder. Label the binder with the course name and number. Divide the binder into sections with dividers and labeled tabs. You will probably need a section for lecture notes, homework problems, exams, quizzes, and laboratory reports. Depending on the nature of the course, other sections may be required. In addition to your engineering courses, you should probably keep materials from technical support courses such as physics, chemistry, and mathematics. Retaining course materials will help you as a student and as a practicing engineer.

2   ELECTRIC CHARGE AND CURRENT

We are familiar with forces caused by bodies in contact with other bodies and gravity. Forces exerted on bodies by other bodies are commonly encountered in a variety of everyday situations and engineering structures. The gravitational force is an attractive force that tends to move objects toward one another, the most common example being the earth's gravitational force that attracts objects toward the center of the earth, thereby maintaining those objects on its surface. Gravitational forces govern the motions of planets, stars, galaxies, and other celestial objects in the universe, and yet it is the weakest of all the natural forces. A type of force that is much stronger than gravity is electrical in nature. Electrical forces are produced by **electric charges**. An electrical force is established between two charged particles when they are in proximity. The force between the particles is attractive if the charges are unlike (i.e., if one charge is positive and the other is negative). The force is repulsive if the charges are alike, that is, if both charges are either positive or negative. (See Figure 4.) Charges are created by producing an imbalance in the number of charged particles in the atom. Atoms consist of a nucleus composed of neutrons (neutral particles) and protons (positively charged particles) surrounded by a cloud of electrons (negatively charged particles). An atom with the same number of protons and electrons is electrically neutral (has no charge), because the positive charge of the protons precisely balances the negative charge of the electrons. The atom may become positively charged by losing electrons or negatively charged by gaining electrons from other atoms. For example, rubbing a silk cloth over a glass rod strips some electrons from the surface atoms of the glass, adding them to the atoms of the cloth, thereby creating a negatively charged rod. A negative charge may also be produced on a balloon by rubbing it against our hair. This force is referred to as an *electrostatic* force because the charges are static or stationary. The branch of electrical studies that deals with static charges is called *electrostatics*.

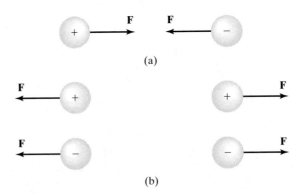

Figure 4.   (a) Unlike charges attract and (b) like charges repel.

Electric charges are quantified by means of a physical parameter called the *coulomb* (C). The coulomb, named in honor of the French physicist Charles Coulomb is defined as the *charge possessed by approximately* 6.242×10^{18} *electrons*. Another way to define the coulomb is to state that a single electron has a charge of approximately 1.602×10^{-19} C, the inverse of 6.242×10^{18}. The charge on a single electron is said to be quantized, because it is the smallest amount of charge that can

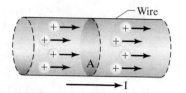

Figure 5. Current is the passage of electric charges through a cross-sectional area in a conductor.

exist. Symbols typically used for electric charge are Q or q. The symbol Q usually denotes a constant charge, such as $Q = 2C$, whereas the symbol q usually denotes a charge that is changing with time. In the latter case, charge is sometimes written in the functional form $q(t)$.

When electric charges of the same sign move, an **electric current** is said to exist. To define electric current more precisely, consider the charges moving in a wire perpendicular to a cross-sectional area, A. (See Figure 5.) Electric current I is defined as the *rate at which charge flows through the area*. The *average* current that flows through the area may be written in terms of the amount of charge Δq that passes through the area in a given time interval Δt, as

$$I_{av} = \frac{\Delta q}{\Delta t} \qquad (1)$$

If the current changes with time, the rate at which charge flows through the area A also changes with time, and the current is an *instantaneous* current expressed as a derivative

$$I = \frac{dq}{dt} \qquad (2)$$

The SI unit for electric current is the ampere (A). From its definition, given by Equations (1) and (2), 1 A of current is equivalent to 1 C of charge passing through the area in 1 s. Hence, 1 A = 1 C/s. Because the ampere is one of the seven base dimensions, electric charge may be alternatively defined as the charge transferred in 1 s by a current of 1 A. To give you a physical feel for current, 1 A is approximately the current that flows through the filament of a 115-V, 100-watt lightbulb. Some electrical devices, such as CD players and radios, may utilize very small currents, on the order of mA or even μA. For example, a typical flashlight utilizes about 300 mA. A toaster may utilize around 8 A, and an electric kitchen range or electric dryer may utilize 15 A or more. The total current supplied to a typical home is around 200 A. Large machines used in heavy industries may utilize hundreds or even thousands of amperes.

In electric circuit theory, current is generally considered to be the movement of *positive* charges. This convention is based on the work of Benjamin Franklin (1706–1790), who conjectured that electricity flowed from positive to negative. Today, we know that electric current in wires and other conductors is due to the drift of free electrons (negatively charged particles) in the atoms of the conductor. When dealing with electric current, we need to distinguish between *conventional current* (the movement of positive charges) and *electron current* (the movement of free electrons). In a real sense, however, it does not matter whether we use conventional current or electron current, because positive charges moving to the right is equivalent to negative charges moving to the left. The only thing that matters is that we use the same sign convention consistently. By adoption, conventional current is generally used in electrical circuit analysis.

There are several types of current in use in various electrical devices, but we will study the two major types. **Direct current (DC)** is a flow of charge in which the direction of flow is always the same. **Alternating current (AC)** is a flow of charge in which the charge flows back and forth, alternating in direction, usually following a sinusoidal pattern. If the current always flows in the same direction, but the magnitude varies somewhat in a periodic fashion, the current is said to be *pulsating* direct current. Power supplies that are poorly filtered generate pulsating direct current. Another type of current is a current that flows in the same direction while increasing or decreasing *exponentially*. Exponentially changing currents are sometimes very short lived, such as when electrical devices are turned on or off. Still another type of current is one that flows in the same direction, while its magnitude varies according to a so-called *sawtooth* function. Sawtooth currents are useful in equipment such as oscilloscopes, which are measurement instruments that display electrical characteristics on a screen. These current types are illustrated in Figure 6. It should be noted that the symbol I is usually reserved for DC, whereas the symbol i is generally used for AC or other types of currents that change with time.

Electric current is measured by means of an instrument called an *ammeter*. There are basically two types of ammeters: analog and digital. An analog ammeter

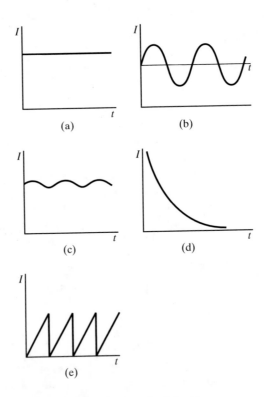

Figure 6. Common types of electric currents: (a) direct current (DC), (b) alternating current (AC), (c) pulsating direct current, (d) exponential current, and (e) sawtooth current.

provides a current reading by means of a needle or pointer that moves across a calibrated scale. Digital ammeters provide a current reading by displaying numbers in a window. Each type of ammeter has two terminals. In order to use an ammeter, the circuit must be *broken* at the location where the current measurement is desired and the ammeter must be inserted directly into the current path. Most ammeters have function switches that enable both direct and alternating current measurements. Most also have manual or automatic range selector functions that facilitate current readings in units of A, mA, or μA.

EXAMPLE 1

As an electrical circuit is powered off, the current in a device changes exponentially with time according to the function

$$i(t) = 5\,e^{-kt}\;\text{A}$$

where k is a constant. If $k = 2\;\text{s}^{-1}$, how many coulombs pass through the device during the first second after the power is turned off? What is the current in the device at the instant just prior to turning off the power?

SOLUTION

The current decreases exponentially according to the relation

$$i(t) = 5\,e^{-2t}\;\text{A}$$

The number of coulombs that pass through the device during the first second after the power is turned off may be found by using Equation (2),

$$i = \frac{dq}{dt}$$

Multiplying both sides of this equation by dt and integrating, we obtain

$$\int_{q_1}^{q_2} dq = \int_0^1 i(t)\,dt = 5\int_0^1 e^{-2t}\,dt$$

Hence,

$$q_2 - q_1 = \left.\frac{5e^{-2t}}{-2}\right|_0^1 = \frac{5(e^{-2} - e^0)}{-2}$$
$$= 2.16\;\text{C}$$

Thus, 2.16 C pass through the device during the first second after the power is turned off. The current immediately before the power is turned off is the current at $t = 0$ s. Therefore, we have

$$i(0) = 5\,e^{-2(0)} = 5\,e^0$$
$$= 5\;\text{A}$$

APPLICATION: TRANSIENT CURRENT AND THE TIME CONSTANT

Upon turning them on or off, some electrical circuits exhibit exponential variations of current with time. In many cases, these variations are very short in duration, perhaps only a few milliseconds. Such a current variation is referred to as *transient*, because it is very short-lived. A typical transient current has the mathematical form

$$i(t) = C(1 - e^{-t/\tau})$$

where C is a constant, t is time, and τ is the *time constant*. The value of the time constant depends on the specific electrical characteristics of the circuit. For a simple circuit consisting of a resistor in series with an inductor, the time constant is $\tau = L/R$, where L is inductance and R is resistance. By inspection of the equation, the current is zero at $t = 0$, the instant the circuit is turned on. The current then increases exponentially with time until, after a long period of time, the current attains a steady value of C.

The time constant τ is defined as the time it takes for the current to change by 36.8 percent. To see how this works, let's examine the equation more closely. After one time constant ($t = \tau$), the exponential term is e^{-1}, or 0.368, and the current has increased to 0.632 times its steady value of C. After two time constants ($t = 2\tau$), the exponential term is e^{-2}, or 0.135, and the current has increased to 0.865 times its steady value. Extending the analysis to five time constants ($t = 5\tau$), the exponential term is e^{-5}, or 0.00674, and the current has increased to approximately 0.993 times its steady value. (See Table 1 and Figure 7). Theoretically, the current never reaches a steady value; it asymptotically approaches a steady value. For practical purposes, however, we may say that the current attains a steady value after five time constants because, as shown in Table 1, the current comes to within one percent of the steady value. Thus, the "rule of thumb" for transient currents is that it takes five time constants for a steady condition to be achieved.

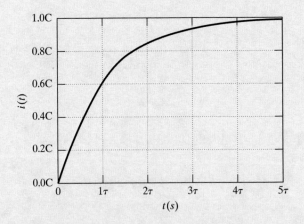

Figure 7.   After five time constants, the current has practically reached a steady value.

TABLE 1

$t(s)$	$e^{-t/\tau}$	$i(t)$(A)
0	1	0
τ	0.368	0.632 C
2τ	0.135	0.865 C
3τ	0.050	0.950 C
4τ	0.0183	0.9817 C
5τ	0.00674	0.99326 C
∞	0	C

PRACTICE!

1. How many electrons are represented by a charge of 1 μC? 50 pC?
   Answer: 6.242×10^{12}, 3.121×10^8

2. The rate at which charge moves through a conductor is given by the relation
   $$q(t) = C \ln(t + 1) + 2t^2 \, \text{C}$$
   where C is a constant. Find the current at $t = 0$ s and $t = 2$ s.
   Answer: $(C/3 + 8)$ A

3. The current in a device varies with time according to the function
   $$i(t) = (1 + 2 \, e^{-5t}) \, \text{A}$$
   How many coulombs pass through the device during the time interval $1 < t < 3$ s? What is the current for large values of time?
   Answer: 2.0027 C, 1 A

4. The current in a device varies sinusoidally with time, according to the function
   $$i(t) = 5 \sin(\pi + 2\pi t) \, \text{A}$$
   How many coulombs pass through the device during the time interval $0 < t < 0.5$ s?
   Answer: 1.59 C

3 VOLTAGE

In the absence of a controlling force, electric charges in a conductor have a tendency to move about in a random manner. If we want the charges to unitedly move in a single direction so as to constitute an electric current, we must apply an external force to the charges called an *electromotive force* (emf). This force, since it causes a movement of charges through the conductor, does work on the charges. The electromotive force is typically called voltage. We therefore define **voltage** as the *work done in moving a charge of one coulomb*. The unit of voltage is the volt (V), named after the Italian physicist Alessandro Volta, who invented the voltaic battery. Because voltage is defined as the work done in moving a unit charge, one volt is defined as 1 V = 1 J/C. *Instantaneous voltage v* is expressed as a derivative,

$$v = \frac{dw}{dq} \tag{3}$$

where w is the work measured in joules (J). The symbol V may also be used for voltage. Do not confuse the roman V, which stands for the unit called volts, with italic V, which denotes the variable voltage or potential difference. Voltage is sometimes referred to as *potential difference*. In its technical context, the word *potential* refers to a source of stored energy that is available for doing work. For example, a compressed spring has potential energy, and it performs work when it is allowed to return to its original, undeformed state. A stone that is nudged from the brink of a cliff converts its potential energy to work as it falls to the ground. Voltage is the electrical equivalent of mechanical potential energy. A battery, for example, has potential energy to do electrical work (that is, to drive a current), but does not do so until a closed circuit is connected across the battery. The word *difference* denotes that voltage is always taken *between two points*. To speak of voltage "at a point" is meaningless, unless a second point (reference point) is implied. A voltage exists across the positive and negative terminals of a battery. If we were to place the probes of a voltmeter across the terminals of a standard dry cell, we would measure a voltage of about 1.5 volts. In many circuits, a reference voltage referred to as *ground* is established. Ground may be the actual ground of the earth, referred to as *earth* ground or an arbitrary reference voltage on the chassis or case of the system, referred to as *chassis* ground. In either case, voltage is always taken between two points in the circuit.

We are all familiar with several electrical devices that supply a specified voltage. Batteries supply a voltage by converting chemical energy to electrical energy. Flashlights, lanterns, and electronic devices such as radios, CD players, cameras, and children's toys use batteries as a source of electrical energy. A few of the common types of batteries are illustrated in Figure 8. Of all the battery types, the 1.5-volt dry cell [Figure 8(a)] is probably the most popular. The 1.5-volt dry cell comes in a variety of sizes, designated by letters such as D, C, A, AA, AAA, etc. Some electronic devices such as radios and digital clocks use 9-volt dry cells [See Figure 8(b)]. Automobiles, trucks, and recreational vehicles use large 12-volt or 6-volt batteries for starting and other electrical functions [See Figure 8(c).] By connecting a closed circuit across the positive and negative terminals of a battery, DC flows through the circuit. What about the voltage supplied by the electrical outlets in our homes? In the United States, local power utilities supply residential and commercial customers with standard voltages of 110 V and 220 V [See Figure 8(d).] Unlike the current supplied by batteries, the current supplied by utility companies is AC that has a frequency of 60 Hz; that is, the current changes direction 60 times per second. Virtually all household appliances and electronic devices—washing machines, ranges, clothes dryers, microwave ovens, toasters, televisions, VCRs, etc.—operate on 110 VAC or 220 VAC. The abbreviation, VAC, means "volts AC," and the abbreviation VDC means "volts DC."

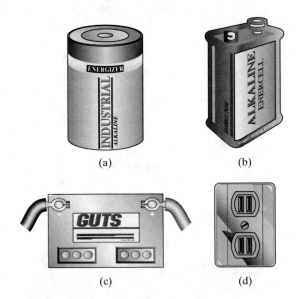

(a)   (b)

(c)   (d)

Figure 8. Typical voltage sources: (a) 1.5-V dry cell, (b) 9-V dry cell, (c) 6-V or 12-V automotive battery, and (d) standard 110-VAC wall outlet.

Now that voltage has been defined, let's consider the electrical energy that is supplied to, or by, a circuit element. **Circuit element** is a generic term that refers to an *electrical device or component*, such as a resistor, capacitor, inductor, etc. As shown in Figure 9, a steady electric current *I* flows through a circuit element. In order to ascertain whether energy is being supplied *to* the element, or *by*, the element to the rest of the circuit, we must know the direction of current flow and the *polarity* of the voltage across the element. The direction of current flow in Figure 9 is from positive to negative, which is consistent with the conventional current standard. Because the current enters the positive terminal of the element, an external electromotive force must be

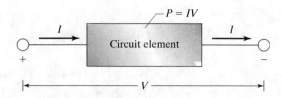

Figure 9. A circuit element with the relationship between current I, voltage V, and power P.

driving the current into the element, thereby supplying energy *to* the element. Thus, we say that the circuit element *absorbs* electrical energy. If, on the other hand, the current enters the negative terminal, the element supplies energy to the rest of the circuit. It is important to know the *rate* at which the energy is supplied to, or by, the circuit element. Rearranging Equation (3), and denoting voltage by V, we obtain

$$dw = V\,dq \tag{4}$$

Dividing both sides of Equation (4) by a time interval dt we obtain

$$\frac{dw}{dt} = V\frac{dq}{dt} \tag{5}$$

The quantity on the left side of Equation (5) is the rate at which work is done to move charge through the circuit element. By definition, the *rate at which work is performed* is **power** P. The quantity dq/dt is defined as electric current I. Hence, the power supplied to or by the circuit element is given by the relation

$$P = VI \tag{6}$$

The dimensional consistency of Equation (6) can be checked by noting that the units of VI are (J/C)(C/s) or J/s, which is defined as the watt (W), the SI unit for power.

Voltage is measured by means of an instrument called a *voltmeter*. Like ammeters that measure current, there are basically two types of voltmeters: analog and digital. An analog voltmeter provides a voltage reading by means of a needle or pointer that moves across a calibrated scale. Digital voltmeters provide a voltage reading by displaying numbers in a window. Each type of voltmeter has two terminals. Unlike a current measurement, a voltage measurement does not require that the circuit be broken at the location where the measurement is desired. In order to use a voltmeter, the terminals of the meter are connected *across* the device for which the potential difference is to be measured. Most voltmeters have function switches that enable both DC and AC voltage measurements. Most voltmeters also have manual or automatic range-selector functions that facilitate voltage readings in units of V, mV, or μV.

As a final comment on voltage, it may be instructive to invoke a physical analogy to voltage and its relationship to current. Voltage has been defined as the work required to move charge. We also stated that voltage is often referred to as a potential difference. To understand how voltage relates to current, it may be helpful to think of voltage as an electrical "pressure" or, more precisely, a pressure difference. Voltage is the "pressure difference" that drives electric current through a circuit element. In a pipe that carries water or some other fluid, a pressure difference between one end of the pipe and the other is the "potential" that drives the fluid through the pipe. Thus, we may consider voltage across a circuit element to be analogous to the pressure difference across a length of pipe and the flow of charge (current) through the circuit element to be analogous to the flow of fluid in the pipe. In a pipe, if there is no pressure difference, there is no fluid flow. In a circuit element, if there is no potential difference (voltage), there is no current flow.

PRACTICE!

1. A circuit element absorbs 2 W of power due to the passage of a steady current of 250 mA. What is the voltage across the element?
   Answer: 8 V

2. Resistors are devices that absorb electrical energy. If a steady current of 500 mA passes through a resistor with a voltage of 6 V across it, how much power must the resistor be able to absorb? What happens to this absorbed energy? What physical change does the resistor exhibit as it absorbs this energy?
   Answer: 3 W, The energy is transformed to heat, which causes the temperature of the resistor to increase.

3. A 12-V automobile lamp is rated at 40 W. What is the total charge that flows through the filament of the lamp in 1 minute? How many electrons does this represent?
   Answer: 200 C, 1.248×10^{21}

4. A battery-operated radio requires a current of 200 mA at 12 V. Find the power required to run the radio and the energy consumed in 2 hours of operation.
   Answer 2.4 W, 17.3 kJ

5. Borrow a voltmeter from your instructor or the electrical engineering department at your school. Measure the voltage across a 1.5-V and a 9-V dry cell. What are your voltage readings?

4   RESISTANCE

In addition to current and voltage, resistance is a very important electrical quantity. Electrical **resistance** may be defined as an *impedance to current flow through a circuit element*. All circuit elements, including even the **conductors** (wires) that connect them, impede the flow of current to some extent. When current flows in a conductor, free electrons collide with the lattices of the atoms inside the conductor. These collisions tend to retard or impede the organized motion of electrons through the conductor. Resistance in the wires connecting circuit elements is generally undesirable, but there are numerous situations where resistance is needed in electrical circuits to control other electrical quantities. The circuit element specifically designed for providing resistance in circuits is the **resistor**. Of all the circuit elements used in electrical circuits, the resistor is the most common. When electrical engineers design circuits, the circuit elements and their connections are drawn as a schematic diagram. The schematic symbol for a resistor is a zig-zag line, as shown in Figure 10(a). A very popular type of resistor uses carbon as the resistive material. A *carbon-composition* resistor consists of carbon particles mixed

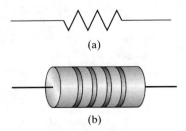

(a)

(b)

Figure 10. Resistance. (a) Schematic symbol and (b) actual resistor.

with a binder and molded into a cylindrical shape. A *carbon-film* resistor consists of carbon powder that is deposited on an insulating substrate. The wires connected to the body of the resistor, or any type of circuit element for that matter, are called *leads*. A typical carbon composition resistor is illustrated in Figure 10(b).

There are other types of resistors in addition to the carbon devices. Some resistors employ a wire wrapped around a central core of ceramic or other insulating material. These resistors are referred to as wire-wound resistors. Wire-wound resistors are generally larger than carbon resistors and can handle more power. Other resistors use a combination of ceramic and metal for their resistive material. These resistors are referred to as CERMETS. The resistive material in some resistors is a metal or metal oxide. Resistors are manufactured in a variety of package styles, sizes, and power capabilities. An assortment of resistors used in various electrical circuit applications is shown in Figure 11.

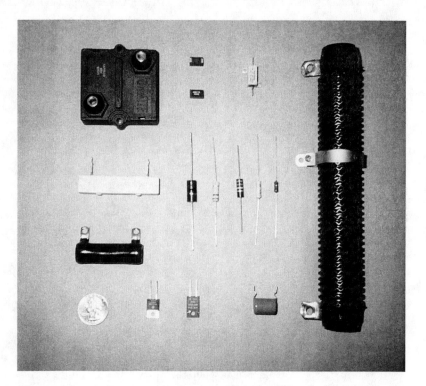

Figure 11. Assortment of resistors for various applications. (Resistors for photograph provided courtesy of Ohmite Manufacturing Co., Skokie, IL.)

The unit for electrical resistance is the *ohm* (Ω), in honor of Georg Ohm, who is credited with formulating the relationship between current, voltage, and resistance, based on experiments performed in 1826. A resistor with a very small resistance has a low ohm value, whereas a resistor with a very high resistance has a high ohm value. Because resistances of various magnitudes are needed in specific circuit applications, resistors are manufactured in a wide range of ohm values. For example, some manufacturers supply carbon-composition resistors in the range 2.2 Ω to 1 MΩ. Some precision resistors are available in very small resistances, such as 0.008 Ω. It is interesting to note that 0.008 Ω is about the same resistance as a 1.5-m length of 12-gauge copper wire, the size of wire typically used in the electrical systems of homes. The resistance of most resistors is fixed, but some resistors are adjustable by means of a sliding or rotating electrical contact. This type of adjustable resistor is known as a potentiometer, or rheostat.

In circuit analysis, it is often necessary to determine the *total* or *equivalent* resistance of two or more resistors connected together. There are two ways in which circuit elements can be connected to each other. If the circuit elements are connected *end to end*, the elements are said to be connected in **series**. If the circuit elements are connected *across* each other, the elements are said to be connected in **parallel**. Figure 12 shows, in schematic form, three resistors connected in series and three resistors connected in parallel. The total resistance R_t for resistors connected in series is simply the arithmetic sum of the resistances for each resistor. Thus,

$$R_t = R_1 + R_2 + R_3 + \cdots + R_N \text{ (series)} \tag{7}$$

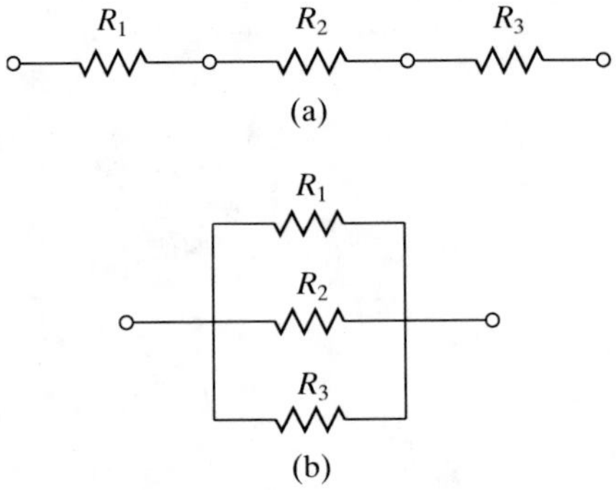

(a)

(b)

Figure 12.   Resistors connected in (a) series and (b) parallel.

where N is the total number of resistors connected in series. The total resistance for resistors connected in parallel is given by the relation

$$\frac{1}{R_t} = \frac{1}{R_1} + \frac{1}{R_2} + \frac{1}{R_3} + \cdots + \frac{1}{R_N} \text{(parallel)} \tag{8}$$

where, as before, N is the total number of resistors. To obtain the total resistance, R_t, we simply find the reciprocal of the total resistance by using Equation (8) and then invert it.

Resistance is measured by means of an instrument called an *ohmmeter*. Like ammeters and voltmeters that measure current and voltage, there are basically two types of ohmmeters: analog and digital. An analog ohmmeter provides a resistance reading by means of a needle or pointer that moves across a calibrated scale. Digital ohmmeters provide a resistance reading by displaying numbers in a window. Each type of ohmmeter has two terminals. The terminals are connected across the resistor for which the measurement is desired. Ohmmeters supply a current to the resistor, so the current in the circuit itself must be turned off while the measurement is being made. Ohmmeters have manual or automatic range selector functions that facilitate resistance readings in units of Ω, kΩ, or MΩ.

EXAMPLE 2

Find the total resistance for the resistor circuit shown in Figure 13.

SOLUTION

The resistor configuration in Figure 13 is a series–parallel combination. The 1-kΩ, 500-Ω, and 20-kΩ resistors are connected in parallel, and the 200-Ω resistor is connected in series with the set of parallel resistors. To find the total resistance, we must first find the equivalent resistance for the three resistors that are connected in parallel by using Equation (8). We then add that equivalent resistance to the   200-Ω resistor by using Equation (7). We assign the resistors the variable names

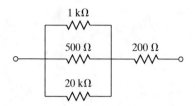

Figure P13.   Resistor circuit
for Example 2.

$$R_1 = 1\text{ k}\Omega, R_2 = 500\ \Omega, R_3 = 20\text{ k}\Omega, \text{and } R_4 = 200\ \Omega$$

The equivalent resistance R_P of the three resistors in parallel is given by

$$\frac{1}{R_p} = \frac{1}{R_1} + \frac{1}{R_2} + \frac{1}{R_3}$$

$$= \frac{1}{1000\ \Omega} + \frac{1}{500\ \Omega} + \frac{1}{20{,}000\ \Omega} = 3.050 \times 10^{-3}\ \Omega^{-1}$$

Thus,

$$R_p = \frac{1}{3.050 \times 10^{-3}\ \Omega^{-1}} = 328\ \Omega$$

We now add R_p to R_4 in series to obtain the total resistance, R_t:

$$R_t = R_p + R_4$$
$$= 328\ \Omega + 200\ \Omega = 528\ \Omega$$

Hence, the series–parallel combination of resistors has a total resistance of 528 Ω. This means that the resistor configuration is equivalent to a *single* resistor with a resistance of 528 Ω.

PRACTICE!

1. What is the total resistance of five resistors, each with a resistance of $R\ \Omega$, if the resistors are connected in series? In parallel?

    Answer: series: $5R\ \Omega$, parallel: $R/5\ \Omega$

2. Consider two resistors connected in parallel. The resistance R_1 of the first resistor is very large, and the resistance R_2 of the second resistor is very small. What is the approximate total resistance?

    Answer: R_2

3. Find the total resistance for the resistor circuit shown in the accompanying figure.

    Answer: 59.5 Ω

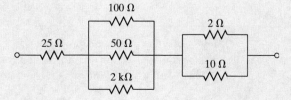

4. Find the total resistance for the resistor circuit shown in the accompanying figure.

    Answer: 13.3 kΩ

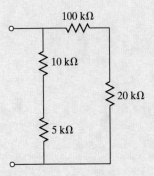

5. Find the total resistance for the resistor circuit shown in the accompanying figure.

    Answer: 1.998 Ω

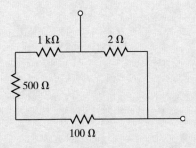

6. For the resistor circuit shown in the accompanying figure, what resistance must R_1 have to give a total resistance of 250 Ω?

    Answer: 525 Ω

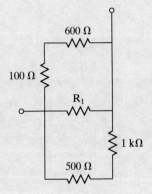

5   OHM'S LAW

In a series of experiments performed in 1826, the German physicist Georg Ohm discovered a relationship between the voltage across a conductor and the current flow through it. This relationship, known as **Ohm's law**, states that *the potential difference across a* *conductor is directly proportional to the current.* Stated mathematically, Ohm's law is

$$V \propto I \qquad (9)$$

where V is potential difference (voltage) and I is current. Equation (9) may be written as an equality by introducing a constant of proportionality R, denoting resistance:

$$V = RI \qquad (10)$$

Ohm's law, given by Equation (10), is one of the simplest, but most important laws in electrical circuit theory. Because the unit of voltage is volt (V) and the unit of current is ampere (A), a resistance of one ohm (Ω) is defined as $1 \ \Omega = 1 \ \text{V/A}$. Hence, a resistor with a resistance of $1 \ \Omega$ carrying a current of 1 A will have a voltage across it of 1 V. Unlike the law of universal gravitation or Newton's laws of motion, Ohm's law is not a fundamental law of nature. Ohm's law is an empirical (experimental) relationship that is valid only for certain materials. The electrical properties of *most* materials is such that the ratio of voltage to current is a constant and, according to Ohm's law, that constant is the resistance of the material. Ohm's law applies to wires and other metal conductors and, of course, resistors. A resistor, showing the relationship between voltage V, current I, and resistance R, is depicted in Figure 14.

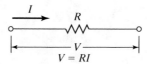

Figure 14. Ohm's law.

A resistance absorbs electrical energy. As current flows through a resistor, the absorbed electrical energy is transformed into thermal energy (heat), which is transferred to the surroundings. The rate at which the absorbed electrical energy is transformed into heat is referred to as *power dissipation*. All resistive circuit elements dissipate energy in the form of heat. We can calculate the power dissipation by combining Ohm's law given by Equation (10) with the relationship between power P, voltage V, and current I:

$$P = VI \qquad (11)$$

Upon substituting Ohm's law, $V = RI$, into Equation (11), we obtain

$$P = I^2 R \qquad (12)$$

A second relationship for power dissipation may be obtained by substituting Ohm's law in the form $I = V/R$ into Equation (11), yielding

$$P = \frac{V^2}{R} \qquad (13)$$

Equations (12) and (13) are useful for finding the power dissipation from a resistive circuit element when the resistance and either the current or the voltage is known.

APPLICATION: SIZING A RESISTOR FOR A POWER-SUPPLY CIRCUIT

Resistors are available in a variety of ohm values and power ratings. The power rating of a resistor is the maximum number of watts of absorbed electrical power that the resistor is capable of dissipating as heat. If a resistor is used in a circuit where the actual power exceeds the power rating specified by the resistor supplier, the resistor may overheat. Resistance is a function of temperature, so if a resistor overheats, its resistance may vary significantly, thereby altering the electrical characteristics of the circuit. In extreme cases, an overheated resistor may even cause a complete failure of the device and perhaps a fire. The physical size of a resistor is usually an indication of its power rating. Large resistors have a lot of surface area and are therefore able to transfer more heat to the surroundings. Some resistors have ridges or fins to increase their surface area, whereas others, in order to minimize the resistor's temperature, have built-in heat sinks or provisions for mounting to heat sinks. Large resistors designed for high-power applications are called *power resistors*. A typical chassis-mounted power resistor is illustrated in Figure 5.

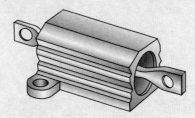

Figure 5. A power resistor.

Suppose that we are designing a power-supply circuit. Our circuit design calls for a resistor that carries a direct current of 800 mA and has a voltage drop of 24 V. What is the resistance of the resistor? What power rating must the resistor have? The resistance may be calculated by using Ohm's law,

$$R = \frac{V}{I}$$
$$= \frac{24\ V}{0.800\ A} = 30\ \Omega$$

The power absorbed by the resistor may be found by using Equations (12) or (13). Let's calculate the power by using both equations to verify that we obtain the same result. Using Equation (12), we have

$$P = I^2 R$$
$$= (0.800\ A)^2 (30\ \Omega) = 19.2\ W$$

Using Equation (13), we have

$$R = \frac{V^2}{R}$$
$$= \frac{(24\ V)^2}{30\ \Omega} = 19.2\ W$$

Hence, we need a power resistor with a resistance of 30 Ω and the resistor must be capable of dissipating 19.2 W of power. It turns out that 30 Ω is a common resistance value for power resistors supplied by many manufacturers, but can we buy a resistor with a 19.2-W power rating? Resistors are available only in certain sizes and therefore only in certain power ratings. One supplier has power resistors in power ratings of 5, 10, 15, and 25 W. A power rating of 15 W is too low, so we choose a 25-W resistor even though it will handle more power than the design value. The additional 5.8 W may be considered a "factor of safety" for the resistor.

PRACTICE!

1. A 100-Ω carbon-composition resistor has a voltage of 12 V across it. What is the current? How much power does the resistor dissipate?

   Answer: 120 mA, 1.44 W

2. A circuit design calls for a resistor that will produce a voltage drop of 15 V where the current is 200 mA. How much power does the resistor dissipate? What resistance is required?

    Answer: 3.0 W, 75 Ω

3. A portable, 1320-W forced-air heater runs on standard 110-V residential voltage. The heating element is a nichrome ribbon that crosses in front of a polished metal plate. What is the current drawn by the heater? What is the resistance of the nichrome heating element?

    Answer: 12.0 A, 9.17 Ω

4. Two 75-Ω resistors connected in parallel dissipate 2.5 W each. What is the voltage across the resistors? What is the current in each resistor?

    Answer: 13.7 V, 183 mA

6   SIMPLE DC CIRCUITS

With any subject, we learn by studying the basic principles first and then progress toward more complex concepts. The study of electrical circuits works the same way. Beginning engineering students must first acquire a solid grasp of the fundamentals before proceeding to more advanced material. Hence, this section deals with some basic circuit concepts. Because the current changes direction in AC circuits, the analysis of AC circuits can be quite complex. We therefore focus our attention on DC circuits. A simple electrical circuit consists of two or more electrical devices interconnected by conductors. In many electrical circuits, there are numerous types of electrical devices such as resistors, capacitors, inductors, diodes, transistors, transformers, batteries, lamps, fuses, switches, and motors. Because the resistor is the most common circuit device and the analysis of resistors is the most straightforward, our coverage is limited to resistive circuits (i.e., circuits that have resistors as the only circuit element other than a source of constant voltage, such as a battery).

Consider the electrical circuit for a common household flashlight. As shown in Figure 16(a), a basic flashlight contains two 1.5-V dry cells, a lamp, and a switch. The conductor that interconnects these devices is normally a metal strip that helps hold the batteries in place and serves as a spring member in the switch mechanism. When the switch is closed, a direct current flows in a closed loop through the dry cells, switch, and lamp filament. Because the dry cells are connected in series, the voltages of each dry cell add, providing a total voltage of 3 V. Based on an arbitrarily selected standard, the direction for conventional current flow is *from* the positive terminal of the voltage source to the external circuit. The electrical schematic diagram that represents the flashlight circuit is shown in Figure 16(b). A **schematic diagram** is a *symbolic representation of the devices and interconnections in the circuit*. The schematic diagram may be loosely considered as the electrical equivalent of the free-body diagram used in engineering mechanics. A free-body diagram schematically shows a mechanical system with all the external forces acting on it as well as the other physical features of the system. To the mechanical and civil engineer, the free-body diagram is an indispensable analytical tool. Likewise, the schematic diagram is an indispensable tool to the electrical engineer. A schematic diagram shows how all the electrical devices are interconnected and also shows their numerical values. For example, a schematic diagram consisting of a voltage source, a resistor, a capacitor, and an inductor would show how these circuit elements are interconnected and would indicate the potential difference of

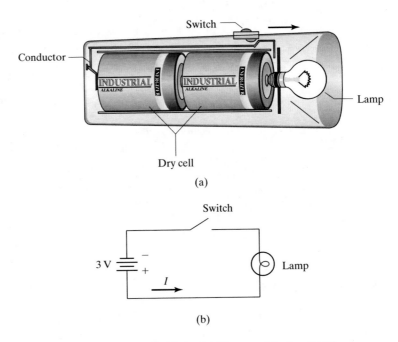

Figure 16. A common flashlight. (a) The actual device. (b) The schematic diagram.

the voltage source in volts (V), the resistance of the resistor in ohms (Ω), the capacitance of the capacitor in farads (F), and the inductance of the inductor in henrys (H). The schematic diagram contains all the pertinent information an engineer needs to evaluate the electrical functions of the circuit.

Every electrical device (circuit element) has a unique schematic symbol. Illustrated in Figure 17 are the schematic symbols for a few common circuit elements. By examining the schematic symbols in the figure, we note that the schematic symbol resembles the electrical or mechanical characteristics of the actual electrical device. The schematic symbol for a battery, for example, is a series of short parallel lines of alternating lengths. Batteries consist of at least two elements or terminals, a positive and a negative, separated by a substance that participates in a chemical reaction. The schematic symbol for a resistor is a zig-zag line. Resistors retard the flow of current through them, so a zig-zag line, indicative of an impeded electrical path, is used. A switch is an electrical "gate" that is either open or closed, allowing the current to flow or not. Capacitors consist of two plates separated by a dielectric (nonconducting) material. Inductors are coils of wire wrapped around a core. The major element in lamps is a filament in which a portion of the absorbed electrical energy is converted into visible light. Obviously, there are many more electrical devices used in electrical circuits than those shown in Figure 17. During the course of the electrical engineering program, the engineering student will become familiar with numerous electrical devices and their corresponding schematic symbols.

Circuit elements are broadly classified into two categories: *active* elements and *passive* elements. An active circuit element is a device that *supplies* energy to an external circuit. Common examples of active elements are batteries and generators. A passive circuit element, therefore, is any device that is not active. Resistors, capacitors, and inductors are common examples of passive elements. The two most important types of active circuit elements are referred to as the **independent voltage source** and the **independent current source**. An independent voltage source is a two-terminal circuit

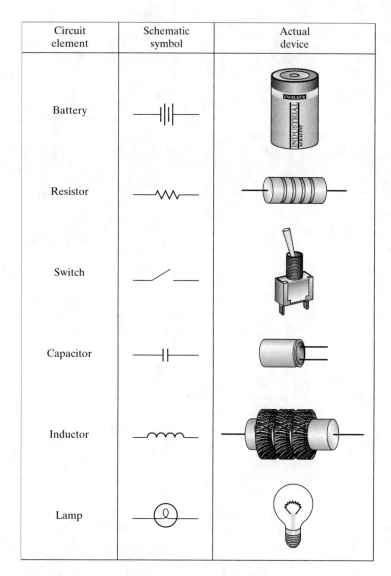

Circuit element	Schematic symbol	Actual device
Battery		
Resistor		
Switch		
Capacitor		
Inductor		
Lamp		

Figure 17. Common circuit elements and their schematic symbols.

element, such as a battery or generator, that maintains a specified voltage between its terminals. The voltage is independent of the current through the element. Because the voltage is independent of current, the *internal* resistance of the independent voltage source is zero. Actual voltage sources such as batteries do not have a zero internal resistance, but the internal resistance can be neglected if the resistance of the external circuit is large. Thus, the independent voltage source is an idealization that simplifies circuit analysis. The schematic symbol for the independent voltage source is illustrated in Figure 18(a). An independent current source is a two-terminal circuit element through which a specified current flows. The current is independent of the voltage across the element. Hence, like the independent voltage source, the independent current source is an idealization. The schematic symbol for the independent current source is shown in Figure 18(b).

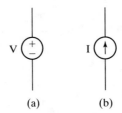

(a)   (b)

Figure 18.   Schematic symbols for (a) independent voltage source and (b) independent current source.

In the next two examples, we demonstrate how to analyze simple DC circuits by using Ohm's law and other fundamental electrical relationships. Each example is worked in detail, following the general analysis procedure of (1) problem statement, (2) diagram, (3) assumptions, (4) governing equations, (5) calculations, (6) solution check, and (7) discussion.

EXAMPLE 3

Problem statement

The DC circuit shown in Figure 19 consists of a 10-V independent voltage source connected to two resistors in series. Find (a) the current, (b) the voltage across each resistor, and (c) the power dissipated by each resistor.

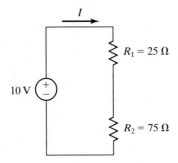

Figure 19.   DC circuit for Example 3.

Diagram

The diagram for this problem is the schematic diagram shown in Figure 19.

Assumptions

1.   The voltage source is ideal.
2.   The resistance of the connecting wires is negligible.
3.   The resistances of the resistors are constant.

Governing equations

Three equations are needed to solve this problem. There are two resistors in the circuit, so we need a formula for the total resistance. We also need Ohm's law and a relation for the power dissipation. The three equations are

$$R_t = R_1 + R_2$$
$$V = IR$$
$$P = I^2R$$

Calculations

(a) All the elements, voltage source, and resistors in this simple DC circuit are connected in series, so the current through each element is the same. The total resistance is found by adding the values of each resistor and then by using Ohm's law to calculate the current. The total resistance is

$$R_t = R_1 + R_2$$
$$= 25\ \Omega + 75\ \Omega = 100\ \Omega$$

We have effectively combined two resistors into one resistor with an equivalent resistance. The voltage across this equivalent resistor is 10 V. The current is found by using Ohm's law:

$$I = \frac{V}{R_t}$$
$$= \frac{(10\ \text{V})}{100\ \Omega} = 0.1\ \text{A} = \underline{100\ \text{mA}}$$

(b) Now that the current is known, the voltage across each resistor can be calculated. Once again, we use Ohm's law:

$$V_1 = IR_1$$
$$= (0.1\ \text{A})(25\ \Omega) = \underline{2.5\ \text{V}}$$
$$V_2 = IR_2$$
$$= (0.1\ \text{A})(75\ \Omega) = \underline{7.5\ \text{V}}$$

(c) The power dissipated as heat by each resistor is

$$P_1 = I^2 R_1$$
$$= (0.1\ \text{A})^2 (25\ \Omega) = \underline{0.25\ \text{W}}$$
$$P_2 = I^2 R_2$$
$$= (0.1\ \text{A})^2 (75\ \Omega) = \underline{0.75\ \text{W}}$$

Solution check

After a careful review of our solution, no errors are found.

Discussion

Note that resistors R_1 and R_2 dissipate the same fractions of the total power as their fractions of the total resistance: 25 percent and 75 percent, respectively. Note also that the sum of the voltages across the resistors equals the voltage of the independent voltage source and that the voltage across each resistor is proportional to the resistance of that resistor. This type of resistor circuit is known as a *voltage divider*, because it divides the total voltage into two or more specified voltages.

EXAMPLE 4

Problem statement

The DC circuit shown in Figure 20 consists of a 200-mA independent current source connected to two resistors in parallel. Find the voltage across the resistors and the current in each resistor.

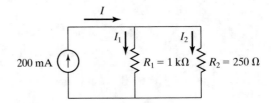

Figure 20. DC circuit for Example 4.

Diagram

The diagram for this problem is the schematic diagram shown in Figure 20.

Assumptions

1. The current source is ideal.
2. The resistance of the connecting wires is negligible.
3. The resistances of the resistors are constant.

Governing equations

Two equations are needed to solve this problem. There are two resistors in the circuit, so we need a formula for the total resistance. We also need Ohm's law. These equations are

$$\frac{1}{R_t} = \frac{1}{R_1} + \frac{1}{R_2}$$

$$V = IR$$

Calculations

All the elements, current source, and resistors in this simple DC circuit are connected in parallel, so the voltage across each element is the same. We can calculate the voltage across the resistors by finding the total resistance. Two resistors connected in parallel add according to the formula

$$\frac{1}{R_t} = \frac{1}{R_1} + \frac{1}{R_2}$$

$$= \frac{1}{1000\ \Omega} + \frac{1}{250\ \Omega} = 0.005\ \Omega^{-1}$$

Inverting to obtain the total resistance R_t, we have

$$R_t = \frac{1}{0.005\ \Omega^{-1}} = 200\ \Omega$$

Using Ohm's law, we find that the voltage across the resistors is

$$V = IR_t$$

$$= (0.2\ \text{A})(200\ \Omega) = \underline{40\ \text{V}}$$

Examine the circuit closely. When the 200-mA current reaches the junction of the first resistor R_1, part of the current flows into R_1 and the remainder flows into R_2. Hence, the total current, I is "split" in some fashion between the two resistors. The current in each resistor can be calculated by applying Ohm's law for each resistor. Thus,

$$I_1 = \frac{V}{R_1}$$

$$= \frac{40 \text{ V}}{1000 \text{ }\Omega} = 0.040 \text{ A} = \underline{40 \text{ mA}}$$

$$I_2 = \frac{V}{R_2}$$

$$= \frac{40 \text{ V}}{250 \text{ }\Omega} = 0.160 \text{ A} = \underline{160 \text{ mA}}$$

Solution check

After a careful review of our solution, no errors are found.

Discussion

The total current 200 mA equals the sum of the currents in resistors R_1 and R_2: 40 mA and 160 mA, respectively. It is important to note that the currents in R_1 and R_2 are inversely related to the resistance values. Resistor R_1 is larger than R_2, so it carries a smaller current. Most of the current is in resistor R_2, because the current "prefers" to take the path of least resistance. The resistance of R_2 is one-fourth the resistance of R_1, so the current in resistor R_1 is one-fourth the current in resistor R_2. This type of resistor circuit is known as a *current divider*, because it divides the total current into two or more specified currents.

PRACTICE!

1. For the resistor circuit shown, find (a) the current, (b) the voltage across each resistor, and (c) the power dissipated by each resistor.
   Answer: (a) 250 mA (b) 25 V, 5.0 V, 20 V (c) 6.25 W, 1.25 W, 5.0 W

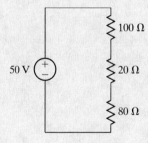

2. For the resistor circuit shown, find the current in each resistor and the voltage across each resistor.
   Answer: 20 mA, 80 mA; 15.0 V, 4.0 V, 1.0 V, 18.0 V, 2.0 V

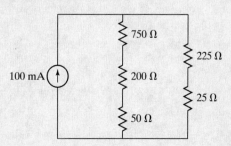

7   KIRCHHOFF'S LAWS

Ohm's law $V = IR$ is a fundamental and powerful principle for calculating current, voltage and power associated with a single resistor or a simple combination of resistors. However, Ohm's law alone cannot be used to analyze the majority of simple DC circuits. In addition to Ohm's law, two additional laws, stated by the German physicist Gustav Kirchhoff (1824–1887), are required. These two laws are known as **Kirchhoff's current law (KCL)** and **Kirchhoff's voltage law (KVL)**. Let us first consider Kirchhoff's current law, for which we will hereafter use the abbreviation KCL.

7.1   Kirchhoff's Current Law

Kirchhoff's current law states that the *algebraic sum of the currents entering a node is zero*. To understand the physical meaning of KCL, we must first understand what a *node* is. An electrical circuit consists of circuit elements (i.e., resistors, capacitors, inductors, etc.) interconnected by conductors. A node is defined as a *point of connection of two or more circuit elements*. The actual node may or may not be a physical "point" where the conductors from two or more circuit elements come together, but rather a general region in which all points on the conductor are electrically the same. Consider the circuit shown in Figure 21(a).

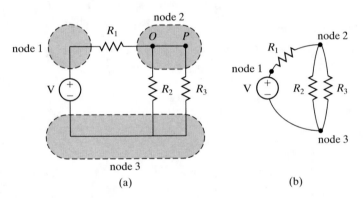

Figure 21.   A circuit with three nodes. (a) Standard schematic. (b) Schematic redrawn to emphasize that there are only three nodes.

Node 1 is not a single point, but a collection of points, indicated by the shaded region, anywhere along the conductor that connects the independent voltage source to resistor R_1. One may be tempted to define two separate nodes, one node at point O and another node at point P, but points O and P are electrically identical, since they are separated only by pure conductors, not circuit elements. Hence, the entire shaded region surrounding points O and P is node 2. Similarly, node 3 is the entire shaded region shown, because all points on the conductors in this region are electrically identical. The understanding of the node concept may be facilitated by redrawing the schematic in a different form, as shown in Figure 21(b). The conductors' lengths have been "shrunk" and the ends of the circuit elements brought together into common points, which are the nodes of the circuit.

Having provided a verbal definition of KCL and defined the term node, we are now ready to give a mathematical definition of KCL. The mathematical expression for KCL is

$$\Sigma I_{\text{in}} = 0 \qquad (14)$$

where I_{in} is a single current, entering or leaving, a specified node. If the current enters the node, I_{in} is positive, whereas if the current leaves the node, I_{in} is negative. Consider

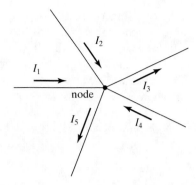

Figure 22. A node with five currents, three entering and two leaving.

the node shown in Figure 22. Five currents are entering or leaving the node. Kirchhoff's current law for this configuration is written as

$$\Sigma I_{in} = 0$$
$$= I_1 + I_2 - I_3 + I_4 - I_5$$

where minus signs are used for currents I_3 and I_5 because these currents are leaving the node. Conservation of charge in a perfect conductor is the physical principle on which KCL is based. Suppose that the right side of Equation (14) were replaced by a nonzero constant Δ. A positive value of Δ would imply that the node accumulates charges, and a negative value of Δ would imply that the node is a source of charges. A node consists of perfect conductors and therefore cannot accumulate or generate charges. Another way of saying this is that whatever current enters the node must exit the node.

7.2 Kirchhoff's Voltage Law

Kirchhoff's voltage law, hereafter abbreviated as KVL, states that the *algebraic sum of the voltages around a loop is zero*. The mathematical form of KVL law is

$$\Sigma V = 0 \qquad\qquad (15)$$

A loop is defined as a *closed path in a circuit*. Kirchhoff's voltage law applies for any closed loop, regardless of the number of circuit elements contained in the loop. Consider the simple series circuit shown in Figure 23. A 10-V ideal voltage source is connected in series with two resistors, forming a closed loop. Kirchhoff's voltage law for this circuit is written as

$$\Sigma V = 0$$
$$= +10 - V_1 - V_2$$

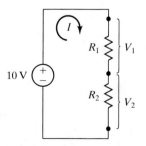

Figure 23. For this circuit, Kirchhoff's voltage law states that $\Sigma V = 0 = 10 - V_1 - V_2$.

where V_1 and V_2 are the voltages across resistors R_1 and R_2, respectively. The negative signs on the voltages mean that the voltage *drops* as we proceed around the loop in a clockwise sense, following the direction for conventional current. The voltage across the ideal voltage source is 10 V. A portion of this voltage is dropped by resistor R_1, and the remaining voltage is dropped by resistor R_2, bringing the total voltage drop to 10 V. Stated another way, the voltage rises equal the voltage drops, so KVL may also be written as $V_1 + V_2 = 10$. Alternatively, we may proceed around the loop in a counterclockwise direction, in which case the signs of all the voltages change, and KVL is expressed as

$$\Sigma V = 0$$
$$= -10 + V_1 + V_2$$

Regardless of which direction is used, the same result is obtained; that is, the sum of the voltages across the resistors equals the voltage of the independent voltage source. Conservation of energy is the physical principle on which KCL is based. Kirchhoff's voltage law states that there is no gain or loss of electrical potential energy for the charges that are traveling around a closed loop. Suppose that the right side of Equation (15) were replaced by a nonzero constant Δ. A nonzero value of Δ would imply that electrical energy is either being created or destroyed in the loop. This is contrary to the first law of thermodynamics, which states that energy is conserved.

In the next example, using KCL and KVL, we demonstrate how to analyze a simple DC circuit. The example is worked in detail, with the general analysis procedure of (1) problem statement, (2) diagram, (3) assumptions, (4) governing equations, (5) calculations, (6) solution check, and (7) discussion.

EXAMPLE 5

Problem statement

For the DC circuit shown in Figure 24, find the voltage across each resistor and the current in each resistor.

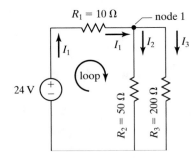

Figure 24.   Circuit for Example 5.

Diagram

The diagram for this problem is the schematic diagram shown in Figure 24.

Assumptions

1. The voltage source is ideal.
2. The resistance of the connecting wires is negligible.
3. The resistances of the resistors are constant.

Governing equations

Three governing equations are needed to solve this problem:

$$\Sigma I_{in} = 0 \, (\text{KCL})$$
$$\Sigma V = 0 \, (\text{KVL})$$
$$V = IR \, (\text{Ohm's law})$$

Calculations

We designate the current through the ideal voltage source and resistor R_1 as I_1. At node 1, the current splits into two currents that flow through resistors R_2 and R_3. Applying KCL to node 1, we have

$$\Sigma I_{in} = 0$$
$$= I_1 - I_2 - I_3$$

Invoking Ohm's law, we can rewrite the relation as

$$\frac{V_1}{R_1} = \frac{V_2}{R_2} + \frac{V_3}{R_3}$$

Resistors R_2 and R_3 are connected in parallel, so the voltage across them is the same. Because $V_2 = V_3$, we can simplify the KCL relation further as

$$\frac{V_1}{R_1} = V_2 \left(\frac{1}{R_2} + \frac{1}{R_3} \right) \tag{a}$$

Kirchhoff's voltage law, written for the loop containing the voltage source as well as R_1 and R_2 is

$$\Sigma V = 0$$
$$= 24 - V_1 - V_2 \tag{b}$$

Solving Equation (b) for V_1 and substituting the result into Equation (a), we obtain a relation in terms of V_2 only. Thus, we have

$$\frac{24 - V_2}{R_1} = V_2 \left(\frac{1}{R_2} + \frac{1}{R_3} \right) \tag{c}$$

After a little algebra, we solve Equation (c) for V_2 and obtain

$$V_2 = V_3 = \underline{19.2 \, \text{V}}$$

To find the voltage across resistor R_1, we substitute the calculated value of V_2 into Equation (c), which yields

$$V_1 = 24 - V_2$$
$$= 24 \, \text{V} - 19.2 \, \text{V} = \underline{4.8 \, \text{V}}$$

Now that all voltages have been calculated, it is a straightforward matter to calculate the current in each resistor, using Ohm's law:

$$I_1 = \frac{V_1}{R_1} = \frac{4.8 \, \text{V}}{10 \, \Omega} = 0.48 \, \text{A} = \underline{480 \, \text{mA}}$$

$$I_2 = \frac{V_2}{R_2} = \frac{19.2 \, \text{V}}{50 \, \Omega} = 0.384 \, \text{A} = \underline{384 \, \text{mA}}$$

$$I_3 = \frac{V_3}{R_3} = \frac{19.2 \, \text{V}}{200 \, \Omega} = 0.096 \, \text{A} = \underline{96 \, \text{mA}}$$

Solution check

After a careful review of our solution, no errors are found.

Discussion

The total current I_1 that flows through the ideal voltage source and resistor R_1 can be found by first calculating the total resistance and then using Ohm's law. Resistors R_2 and R_3 add in parallel and that resistance adds in series to R_1. Thus, the total resistance is

$$R_t = \cfrac{1}{\cfrac{1}{R_2} + \cfrac{1}{R_3}} + R_1$$

$$= \cfrac{1}{\cfrac{1}{50\ \Omega} + \cfrac{1}{200\ \Omega}} + 10\ \Omega = 50\ \Omega$$

The total current I_1 is

$$I_1 = \frac{V}{R_t}$$

$$= \frac{24\ \text{V}}{50\ \Omega} = 0.48\ \text{A}$$

which is in agreement with our previous result.

PRACTICE!

1. For the node shown in the accompanying figure, find the current I_4. Does current I_4 enter or leave the node?
   Answer: 13 A, leave

   $I_2 = 5\ \text{A}$

   $I_3 = 10\ \text{A}$

   $I_1 = 2\ \text{A}$

   I_4

2. For the DC circuit shown in the accompanying figure, find the voltage across each resistor and the current through each resistor.
   Answer: 8.077 V, 1.923 V, 1.923 V; 0.269 A, 0.0769 A, 0.1923 A

   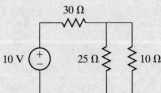

3. For the DC circuit shown in the accompanying figure, find the voltage across each resistor and the current through each resistor.

Answer: 100 V, 7.69 V, 3.85 V, 11.55 V; 100 mA, 76.9 mA, 23.1 mA

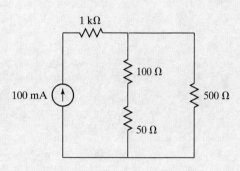

KEY TERMS

alternating current (AC)
circuit element
conductor
direct current (DC)
electric charge
electrical circuit
electric current

independent current source
independent voltage source
Kirchhoff's current law (KCL)
Kirchhoff's voltage law (KVL)
Ohm's law
parallel
power

resistance
resistor
schematic diagram
series
voltage

REFERENCES

Bird, J.O., *Electrical Circuit Theory and Technology*, 2d ed., Boston, MA: Butterworth-Heinemann, 2003.

Johnson, D.E., J.L. Hilburn, and J.R. Johnson, *Basic Electric Circuit Analysis*, 5th ed., Upper Saddle River, NJ: Prentice Hall, 2000.

Nilsson, J.W. and S.A. Riedel, *Electric Circuits*, 6th ed., Reading, MA: Addison-Wesley, 2000.

Roadstrum, W.H. and D.H. Wolaver, *Electrical Engineering for All Engineers*, 2d ed., NY: John Wiley & Sons, 1993.

Smith, R.J. and R.C. Dorf, *Circuits, Devices and Systems*, 5th ed., NY: John Wiley & Sons, 1992.

Problems

1. The flow of charge in a conductor varies with time according to the function

$$q(t) = (1 - 4e^{-kt}) \, C$$

If $k = 0.2 \, s^{-1}$, find the current at $t = 5$ s. What is the current for very large values of time?

2. For a period of 1 s immediately after the power is turned on, the current in an electrical device varies with time according to the function

$$i(t) = 3t^{\frac{1}{2}} \, A$$

How many coulombs have passed through the device during the first 0.25 s? 0.75 s? What is the current at the instant the power is turned on?

3. After the power is turned off, the current in an electrical device varies with time according to the function

$$i(t) = 4e^{-kt} \, A$$

If $k = 0.1 \text{ s}^{-1}$, how many coulombs have passed through the device during the first 2 s? 5 s? What is the current at the instant the power is turned off? What is the current a long time after the power is turned off?

4.   The current in a device varies with time according to the function

$$i(t) = 3e^{-t/\tau} \text{ A}$$

where τ is the time constant. How many time constants are required for the current to drop to 250 mA? 10 mA?

5.   A miniature incandescent lamp is connected to a 6-V lantern battery. If the current flow through the filament of the lamp is 85 mA, how much power does the lamp absorb?

6.   A standard power value for a household incandescent lightbulb is 60 W. What is the current through the filament of such a lightbulb if the voltage is 110 V? Is the entire 60 W of electrical power converted into visible light?

7.   A standard voltage for homes in the United States is 110 V. Each circuit in the home is protected by a circuit breaker, a safety device designed to break the flow of current in the event of an electrical overload. A particular circuit must provide power to a baseboard electric heater, lights, and two televisions. If the total power required for these devices is 1.8 kW, what is the minimum required amperage of the circuit breaker?

8.   Using an order-of-magnitude analysis, estimate the amount of electrical energy (J) used per person in the United States each year. What is the corresponding power (W)?

9.   A common resistance of carbon resistors is 33 Ω. How many 33-Ω resistors, connected in parallel, are needed to give a total resistance of 5.5 Ω?

10.   Consider two resistors, R_1 and R_2. The resistance of R_1 is lower than the resistance of R_2. If these two resistors are connected in parallel, which of the following statements about the total resistance is true?

    A.   The total resistance is higher than the resistance of R_2.
    B.   The total resistance is between the resistances of R_1 and R_2.
    C.   The total resistance is lower than the resistance of R_1.

11.   Without doing the calculation, what is the approximate total resistance of a 10-Ω resistor and a 1-M Ω resistor connected in parallel?

12.   Find the total resistance for the resistor circuit shown in Figure P12.

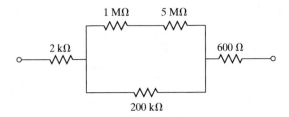

Figure P12.

13.   Find the total resistance for the resistor circuit shown in Figure P13

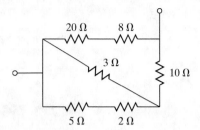

Figure P13.

14.   Find the total resistance for the resistor circuit shown in Figure P14

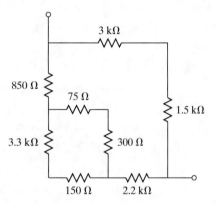

Figure P14.

15.   Find the total resistance for the resistor circuit shown in Figure P15

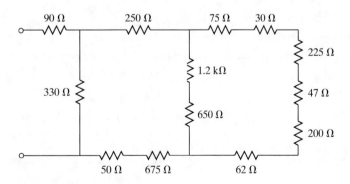

Figure P15.

16.   For the resistor circuit shown in Figure P16, what resistance must resistor R_1 have to give a total resistance of 20 Ω?

17.   For the resistor circuit shown in Figure P17, what resistance must resistor R_3 have to give a total resistance of 500 Ω?

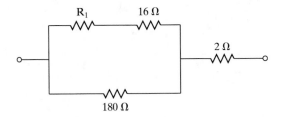

Figure P16.

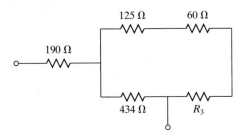

Figure P17.

18.   Precision resistors are resistors whose resistance is known to within a tolerance of ±1 percent or less. These resistors are typically used in *current-sensing* applications. In this application, a precision resistor with a very low resistance is connected in a circuit where a measurement of current is desired. Because the resistance is low, the resistor does not significantly affect the electrical attributes of the circuit. Current is measured, not by using an ammeter, but by placing a voltmeter across the resistor. By knowing the resistance of the resistor, the current can be readily calculated by using Ohm's law. Furthermore, by a judicious selection of the resistance of the resistor, the voltmeter can be made to read the current directly. If the voltmeter is to read current directly, what should the resistance of the precision resistor be?

19.   A 47-Ω power resistor carries a current of 300 mA. What is the voltage across the resistor? What is the power dissipation? If power resistors are available in power ratings of 1, 2, 5, and 10 W, which power rating should probably be selected?

20.   Borrow an ohmmeter from your instructor or the electrical engineering department at your school. Measure the resistance of a 40-W incandescent lightbulb. What is the resistance? If this type of lightbulb operates on 110 V, what is the current through the filament? Is the resistance of the lightbulb the same as your measured value when the filament is hot?

For problems 21 through 30, use the general analysis procedure of (1) problem statement, (2) diagram, (3) assumptions, (4) governing equations, (5) calculations, (6) solution check, and (7) discussion.

21.   A simple DC circuit consists of a 12-V independent voltage source and three resistors as shown in Figure P21. Find (a) the current, (b) the voltage across each resistor, and (c) the power dissipated by each resistor.

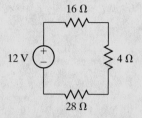

Figure P21.

22.   A 50-V independent voltage source supplies power to three resistors in the DC circuit shown in Figure P22. For each resistor, find the voltage drop and current.

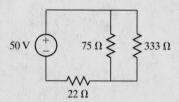

Figure P22.

23.   Four resistors are connected in parallel across a 200-mA independent current source as shown in Figure P23. What is the voltage across the resistors and the current in each resistor?

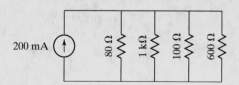

Figure P23.

24.   Two power resistors, a 130-Ω fixed-carbon resistor and a variable wire-wound resistor, are connected in series with a 100-V independent voltage source as shown in Figure P24. One terminal of the variable resistor is a slider that contacts the wire windings as it moves along the resistor. The maximum resistance of the variable resistor is 1.5 kΩ. If 30 percent of the resistor's windings carry current, find (a) the current, (b) the voltage across the variable resistor, and (c) the power dissipated by both resistors.

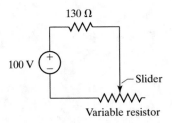

Figure P24.

25.   For the DC circuit shown in Figure P25, find the voltage across each resistor and the current in each resistor.

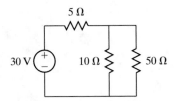

Figure P25.

26.   For the DC circuit shown in Figure P26, find the voltage across each resistor and the current in each resistor. Find the power dissipations in the 20-Ω and 100-Ω resistors.

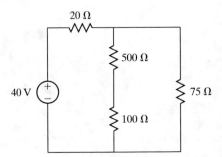

Figure P26.

27.   For the DC circuit shown in Figure P27, find the voltage across each resistor and the current in each resistor.

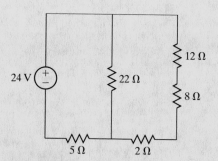

Figure P27.

28. For the DC circuit shown in Figure P28, find the voltage across each resistor and the current in each resistor.

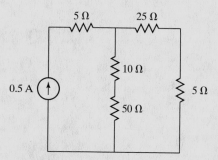

Figure P28.

29. For the DC circuit shown in Figure P29, find the voltage across each resistor and the current in each resistor. Find the power dissipations in the 2-Ω, 6-Ω and 22-Ω resistors.

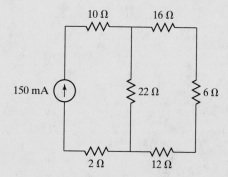

Figure P29.

30.   For the DC circuit shown in Figure P30, find the voltage across each resistor and the current in each resistor.

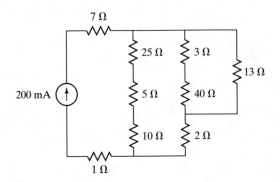

Figure P30.

14

Thermodynamics

1 INTRODUCTION

One of the most important subjects in the study of engineering is thermodynamics. Because the principles of thermodynamics find applications in virtually every engineering system, many colleges and universities require all engineering majors to take at least one course in the subject. As a specific engineering discipline, thermodynamics typically falls within the domain of mechanical and chemical engineering, because mechanical and chemical engineers have primary responsibility for designing and analyzing energy-based systems. Consistent with this observation, **thermodynamics** may be defined as *the science of energy transformation and utilization*. This is a very broad definition, so it is no wonder that thermodynamics spans all engineering disciplines.

The word *thermodynamics* originates from the Greek words *therm* (heat) and *dynamics* (power). These root words are appropriate, because thermodynamics often deals with systems that convert heat to power. Thermodynamics is the science that describes how energy is converted from one form into another. One of the most important physical laws is the **first law of thermodynamics**, which states that energy can be converted from one form to another, but the total energy remains constant. A popular statement of the first law of thermodynamics is that energy cannot be created or destroyed. For example, a boulder poised on the brink of a cliff has potential energy by virtue of its height above the ground. As the boulder falls toward the ground, its speed increases, thereby converting its potential energy to kinetic energy, but the total energy at any point is constant. Thermodynamics is also the science that reveals whether a given energy conversion is physically possible. This concept is revealed by the **second law of thermodynamics**, which states that energy conversions occur in the direction of decreasing quality of energy. For example, a

OBJECTIVES

After reading this chapter, you will have learned

- The importance of thermodynamics in engineering
- The relationships between the various types of pressures
- The thermodynamic meaning of temperature
- The various forms of energy
- How to determine various forms of work
- The difference between heat and temperature
- How to use the first law of thermodynamics to analyze basic energy systems
- What a heat engine is
- How to analyze a basic heat engine using the first and second laws of thermodynamics

hot beverage on a table eventually cools by itself to the temperature of the surroundings, thereby degrading the energy of the high temperature beverage into a less useful form.

Interestingly, working steam engines were developed prior to the emergence of thermodynamics as a science. Two Englishmen, Thomas Savery and Thomas Newcomen, constructed crude steam engines in 1697 and 1712, respectively. Practical improvements in these first steam engines were made in the ensuing years, but the fundamental thermodynamic principles on which they operated were not fully understood until much later. The first and second laws of thermodynamics were not pronounced until the 1850s. The laws of thermodynamics and other thermodynamics concepts were pioneered by scientists and mathematicians such as Gabriel Fahrenheit (1686–1736), Sadi Carnot (1796–1832), Rudolph Clausius (1822–1888), William Rankine (1820–1872), and Lord Kelvin (1824–1907). These individuals, and many others, laid the theoretical foundations for modern thermodynamics.

Because thermodynamics is the science of energy, it would be difficult to find any engineering system that does not embody thermodynamic principles in some way. Principles of thermodynamics are at work all around us. The illumination by which you are reading this page is produced by converting electrical energy to visible light. Our homes are maintained at comfortable living temperatures by furnaces, heat pumps, and air conditioners. These devices utilize the energy contained in fossil fuels or electrical energy to heat and cool our homes. Common household appliances such as dishwashers, microwave ovens, refrigerators, humidifiers, clothes dryers, toasters, water heaters, irons, and pressure cookers rely on principles of thermodynamics for their operation. Industrial systems that utilize thermodynamics include internal combustion and diesel engines, turbines, pumps and compressors, heat exchangers, cooling towers, and solar panels, to name a few. Shown in Figures 1, 2, and 3 are some engineering systems that utilize thermodynamic processes.

Figure 1. Household refrigerators utilize basic principles of thermodynamics for removing thermal energy from food items. (Courtesy of KitchenAid, Benton Harbor, MI.)

Figure 2.   Wind turbines convert wind energy to electrical energy. The wind power plant shown here is owned and operated by the Sacramento Municipal Utility District. (Courtesy of the U.S. Department of Energy/National Renewable Energy Laboratory.)

Figure 3.   The Vogtle Electric Generating Plant, located in eastern Georgia, converts nuclear energy to electrical energy. The plant is capable of producing over 2000 MW of power. (Courtesy of Southern Nuclear, Birmingham, AL.)

2   PRESSURE AND TEMPERATURE

Systems that use thermodynamic processes for their operation can be described by certain physical characteristics. Any such characteristic of a system is called a *property*. In its broadest engineering context, a property can refer to any physical aspect of a system, such as length, density, velocity, modulus of elasticity, viscosity, etc. In thermodynamics, a property usually refers to a characteristic that relates directly to the energy of the system. Two of the most important properties in thermodynamics are *pressure* and *temperature*.

2.1   Pressure

When a fluid (liquid or gas) is confined by a solid boundary, the fluid exerts a force on the boundary. The direction of the force is normal (perpendicular) to the boundary. From a microscopic point of view, the force is the result of a change in momentum experienced by the fluid molecules as they collide with the solid surface. Molecules collide with the surface in many directions, but the overall effect of the collisions is a net force that is normal to the surface. **Pressure** is defined as the *normal force exerted by a fluid per unit area*. Thus, the formula for pressure is

$$P = \frac{F}{A} \tag{1}$$

where P is pressure (N/m^2), F is the normal force (N), and A is area (m^2). For a liquid at rest, pressure increases with depth as a consequence of the weight of the liquid. For example, the pressure exerted by sea water on the hull of a submarine at a depth of 200 m is greater than the pressure exerted by seawater on a scuba diver at a depth of 10 m. The pressure in a tank containing a gas is essentially constant, however, because the weight of the gas is usually negligible compared with the force required to compress the gas. For example, consider a gas enclosed in a piston-cylinder device, as illustrated in Figure 4. A force F is applied to the piston, compressing the gas in the

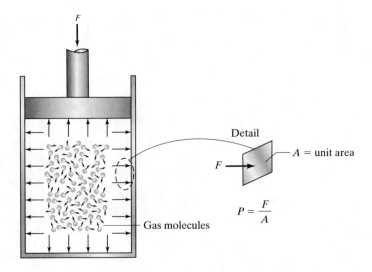

Figure 4.   An enclosed gas exerts a pressure on the walls of its container.

cylinder. A constant pressure, whose magnitude is given by Equation (1), acts on *all* interior surfaces of the enclosure. If the force F increases, the pressure P increases accordingly.

The unit of pressure in the SI system is N/m^2, which is defined as the pascal (Pa). Hence, $1 \text{ Pa} = 1 \text{ N/m}^2$. The pascal is a very small unit of pressure, so it is customary to use the standard SI multiples kPa (kilopascal) and MPa (megapascal), which stand for 10^3 Pa and 10^6 Pa, respectively. Pressure is sometimes expressed in terms of the bar ($1 \text{ bar} = 10^5$ Pa). The most commonly used unit of pressure in the English system is pound-force per square inch (lb_f/in^2), typically written in shorthand notation as psi.

When doing calculations involving pressure, care must be taken to specify the reference on which the pressure is based. Pressure referenced to a perfect vacuum is called *absolute pressure* (P_{abs}). *Atmospheric pressure* (P_{atm}) is the pressure exerted by the atmosphere at a specified location. At sea level, atmospheric pressure is $P_{atm} = 101{,}325$ Pa = 14.696 psi. At higher elevations, the atmospheric pressure is lower, due to decreasing air density. The pressure that uses atmospheric pressure as the reference is called *gauge pressure* (P_{gauge}). Gauge pressure is the difference between the absolute pressure and the local atmospheric pressure. Most pressure-measuring instruments, such as an automobile tire gauge, measure gauge pressure. A pressure below atmospheric pressure is called *vacuum pressure* (P_{vac}). Vacuum pressure is measured by vacuum gauges that indicate the difference between the local atmospheric pressure and absolute pressure. Gauge, absolute, and vacuum pressures are all positive quantities and are related to one another by the relations

$$P_{gauge} = P_{abs} - P_{atm} \text{ (for pressures above } P_{atm}) \tag{2}$$

$$P_{vac} = P_{atm} - P_{abs} \text{ (for pressures below } P_{atm}) \tag{3}$$

The majority of thermodynamic equations and data tables use absolute pressure. Sometimes, the letter "a" is used to specify absolute pressure and the letter "g" is used to specify gauge pressure. For example, absolute, and gauge pressures are sometimes written in English units as psia and psig, respectively.

2.2   Temperature

Our physiological sense of temperature tells us how hot or how cold something is, but does not provide a quantitative definition of temperature for engineering use. A scientific definition, based on microscopic considerations, is that temperature is a measure of atomic and molecular kinetic energy of a substance. Thus, at a temperature of absolute zero, all translational, rotational, and vibrational motions of atoms and molecules cease. A practical engineering definition is that **temperature**, or, more specifically, a temperature *difference*, is an *indicator of heat transfer*. As illustrated in Figure 5, heat flows from a region of high temperature to a region of low temperature. This engineering definition of temperature is consistent with our common experiences. For example, a hot beverage will gradually cool until it reaches the temperature of the surroundings. Conversely, a cold beverage will eventually warm until it reaches the temperature of the surroundings. In either case, when the beverage attains the temperature of the surroundings, heat transfer stops, and the beverage and surroundings are said to be in *thermal equilibrium*, because their temperatures are equal. We can therefore state that when any two bodies have the same temperature, the bodies are in thermal equilibrium.

The **zeroth law of thermodynamics** states that *if two bodies are in thermal equilibrium with a third body, they are also in thermal equilibrium with each other*. This law is analogous to the arithmetic axiom which states that if $A = C$ and $B = C$, then $A = B$. The

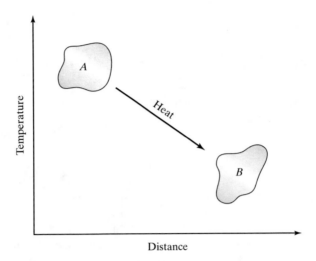

Figure 5. Heat is transferred from a high-temperature region to a low-temperature region.

zeroth law, as obvious as it sounds, cannot be derived from the first or second laws of thermodynamics. The zeroth law of thermodynamics is the underlying physical basis for a key element of thermodynamics: temperature measurement. By the zeroth law of thermodynamics, if body A and body B are in thermal equilibrium with body C, then body A and body B are in thermal equilibrium with each other. By letting body C be a thermometer, the zeroth law of thermodynamics infers that bodies A and B are in thermal equilibrium if their temperatures, as measured by the thermometer, are equal. The interesting aspect of the zeroth law is that bodies A and B do not even have to be in physical contact with each other. They only have to have the same temperature to be in thermal equilibrium.

Like length, mass, time, electrical current, luminous intensity, and amount of substance, temperature is a base dimension. As a base dimension, temperature is predicated on a measurable physical standard. Temperature *scales* enable engineers to make temperature measurements on a common basis. International temperature scales have been adopted that are based on fixed reproducible thermodynamic states of matter. The ice point and boiling point of water at 1 atmosphere pressure are defined as 0°C and 100°C, respectively, on the *Celsius* temperature scale. On the *Fahrenheit* temperature scale, these points have the values 32°F and 212°F, respectively. The *Kelvin* and *Rankine* temperature scales are absolute temperature scales that have 0 K and 0°R as their lowest possible temperature values. Thus, we say that *absolute zero* temperature refers to either 0 K or 0°R. By convention, the degree symbol "°" is used for the Celsius, Fahrenheit, and Rankine temperature scales, but not the Kelvin scale. A comparison of these four temperature scales is shown in Figure 6.

Because engineers use four different temperature scales in the analysis of thermodynamic systems, it is important to know how to convert from one temperature scale to another. The Kelvin scale is related to the Celsius scale by the formula

$$T(\text{K}) = T(°\text{C}) + 273.15 \qquad (4)$$

and the Rankine scale is related to the Fahrenheit scale by the formula

$$T(°\text{R}) = T(°\text{F}) + 459.67 \qquad (5)$$

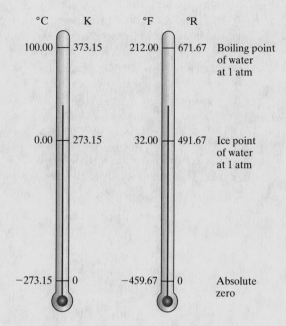

Figure 6. The Celsius, Kelvin, Fahrenheit, and Rankine temperature scales.

In the majority of practical applications, temperature precision beyond the decimal point is not required, so the constants in Equations (4) and (5) are typically rounded to 273 and 460, respectively. The Rankine and Kelvin scales are related by the formula

$$T(°R) = 1.8\, T(K) \tag{6}$$

and the Fahrenheit and Celsius scales are related by the formula

$$T(°F) = 1.8\, T(°C) + 32 \tag{7}$$

Equations (4) through (7) are used to convert one temperature value or measurement to another. Using Figure 6, we find that the validity of these relations can be readily checked by converting the boiling point and ice point of water from one temperature scale to the other three scales.

We mentioned earlier in this section that temperature difference is an indicator of heat transfer. When calculating a temperature *difference*, it is important to note that the size of the temperature divisions for the Kelvin and Celsius scales are equal and that the size of the temperature divisions for the Rankine and Fahrenheit scales are also equal. In other words, increasing the temperature of a substance by 1 K is the same as increasing the temperature by 1°C. Similarly, increasing the temperature of a substance by 1°R is the same as increasing the temperature by 1°F. Thus, we write the relations for temperature differences as

$$\Delta T(K) = \Delta T(°C) \tag{8}$$

and

$$\Delta T(°R) = \Delta T(°F) \tag{9}$$

where the Greek symbol Δ refers to a difference or change. When doing thermodynamics calculations involving temperature differences in the SI system, it does not matter whether K or °C is used. Similarly, when doing thermodynamics calculations involving temperature differences in the English system, it does not matter whether °R or °F is used. In analysis work, care must be taken to distinguish between a single temperature value T and a temperature difference ΔT. If the thermodynamic relation is of the form $x = y \Delta T$, it does not matter whether ΔT is expresses in K or °C. If the thermodynamic relation is of the form $x = yT$, however, the temperature T must be expressed in K. The same rules apply for the corresponding English temperature units °R and °F.

EXAMPLE 1

The atmospheric pressure in Denver, Colorado (elevation 1 mile) is approximately 83.4 kPa. If we were to inflate the tire of an automobile in Denver to a gauge pressure of 35 psi, what is the absolute pressure in units of kPa?

SOLUTION

In order to work in a consistent set of units, we convert the gauge pressure to units of kPa:

$$35 \; \text{psi} \times \frac{1 \; \text{kPa}}{0.14504 \; \text{psi}} = 241.3 \; \text{kPa}$$

Solving for absolute pressure from Equation (2), we have

$$
\begin{aligned}
P_{abs} &= P_{gauge} + P_{atm} \\
&= 241.3 \; \text{kPa} + 83.4 \; \text{kPa} \\
&= 325 \; \text{kPa}
\end{aligned}
$$

EXAMPLE 2

Steam in a boiler has a temperature of 300°C. What is this temperature in units of K, °R, and °F? If the temperature drops to 225 °C, what is the temperature change in units of K, °R, and °F?

SOLUTION

Using Equation (4), we find that the temperature in K is

$$
\begin{aligned}
T(\text{K}) &= T(°\text{C}) + 273 \\
&= 300°\text{C} + 273 \\
&= 573 \; \text{K}
\end{aligned}
$$

Now that the temperature in K is known, we use Equation (6) to find the temperature in °R:

$$
\begin{aligned}
T(°\text{R}) &= 1.8 \; T(\text{K}) \\
&= 1.8(573 \; \text{K}) \\
&= 1031°\text{R}
\end{aligned}
$$

Using Equation (7), we find that the temperature in °F is

$$
\begin{aligned}
T(°\text{F}) &= 1.8 \; T(°\text{C}) + 32 \\
&= 1.8(300°\text{C}) + 32 \\
&= 572°\text{F}
\end{aligned}
$$

The temperature change is

$$
\begin{aligned}
\Delta T &= 300°\text{C} - 225°\text{C} \\
&= 75°\text{C} = 75 \; \text{K}
\end{aligned}
$$

The Rankine and Kelvin temperature scales are related through Equation (6). Because these temperature scales are absolute scales, we can write Equation (6) in terms of temperature differences as

$$\Delta T(°R) = 1.8 \, \Delta T(K)$$

Hence,

$$\Delta T = 1.8(75 \text{ K})$$
$$= 135°R = 135°F$$

PRACTICE!

1. A pressure gauge on the discharge side of an air compressor reads 260 kPa. What is the absolute pressure at this point in units of psi if the local atmospheric pressure is 95 kPa?
    Answer: 51.5 psi

2. A force of 1.2 kN is applied to the piston of a cylinder, compressing the gas within the cylinder. The piston has a radius of 4 cm. If the local atmospheric pressure is 100 kPa, what is the pressure inside the cylinder?
    Answer: 339 kPa

3. A vacuum gauge connected to a tank reads 30 kPa. If the local atmospheric pressure is 13.5 psi, what is the absolute pressure in units of psi?
    Answer: 8.42 psi

4. A boiler at sea level contains superheated steam at 0.4 MPa absolute pressure and 300°C. Find the gauge pressure in the boiler and the steam temperature in units of K, °R, and °F.
    Answer: 298.7 kPa, 573 K, 1031°R, 572°F

5. A hard-boiled egg removed from a pot of boiling water at 96°C is placed in a 40°F refrigerator to cool. Find the temperature of the egg in units of K, °C, and °R after the egg has attained thermal equilibrium with the refrigerator. What is the temperature change of the egg in units of °F, °C, and K?
    Answer: 164.9°F, 91.6°C, 91.6 K

3   FORMS OF ENERGY

The concept of *energy* is central to the study of engineering in general and thermodynamics in particular. A concise definition of **energy** is the *capacity to do work*. If a system has the capacity to do work, it possesses at least one form of energy that is available for transformation to another form of energy. For example, a compressed spring possesses a type of energy referred to as potential energy. As the term implies, potential energy is a type of stored energy that has the potential for producing some useful external effect. Consider a mass attached to a compressed spring, as illustrated in Figure 7. When the compressed spring is released, the stored energy in the spring will begin to resume its original undeformed length, imparting a velocity to the mass. As the spring elongates, the potential energy in the spring is converted to kinetic energy. Actually, a small portion of the potential energy in the spring is converted to thermal energy (heat), because there is friction between the mass and the surface, as well as within the spring itself. The important thing to realize is that *all* the potential energy in the compressed spring is converted to other forms of energy (i.e., the total energy of the transformation is constant). In accordance with the first law of thermodynamics, no energy is produced or destroyed during the energy transformation.

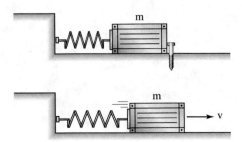

Figure 7. The potential energy in a compressed spring is converted to kinetic energy.

Energy can exist in many forms. For purposes of thermodynamic analysis, energy is classified into two broad categories, *macroscopic* energy and *microscopic* energy. Macroscopic forms of energy are those that a whole system possesses with respect to a fixed external reference. In thermodynamics, the macroscopic forms of energy are potential energy and kinetic energy. Potential and kinetic energy are based on external position and velocity references, respectively. Microscopic forms of energy are those that relate to the system on a molecular or atomic level. There are several types of microscopic energies, so we conveniently group them together into a single category referred to as internal energy. Internal energy is the sum of all the various forms of microscopic energies possessed by the molecules and atoms in the system. Potential, kinetic, and internal energy warrant further discussion.

3.1   Potential Energy

Potential energy is the stored energy of position possessed by an object. In thermodynamics, there are primarily two forms of potential energy, *elastic* potential energy and *gravitational* potential energy. **Elastic potential energy** is the *energy stored in a deformable body such as an elastic solid or a spring.* **Gravitational potential energy** is the *energy that a system possesses by virtue of its elevation with respect to a reference in a gravitational field.* Elastic potential energy is usually of minor importance in most thermodynamics work, so gravitational potential energy is emphasized here. Gravitational potential energy, abbreviated PE, is given by the relation

$$PE = mgz \qquad (10)$$

where m is the mass of the system (kg), g is gravitational acceleration (m/s^2), and z is the elevation (m) of the center of mass of the system with respect to a selected reference plane. The location of the reference plane is arbitrary, but is usually selected on the basis of mathematical convenience. For example, consider a boulder poised on the edge of a cliff, as illustrated in Figure 8. The center of mass of the boulder is 20 m above the ground. A reasonable reference plane is the ground because it is a convenient origin. If the boulder's mass is 1500 kg, the gravitational potential energy of the boulder is

$$\begin{aligned} PE &= mgz \\ &= (1500 \text{ kg})(9.81 \text{ m/s}^2)(20 \text{ m}) \\ &= 2.94 \times 10^5 \text{ N·m} = 2.94 \times 10^5 \text{ J} = 294 \text{ kJ} \end{aligned}$$

What happens to the boulder's potential energy as it falls from the cliff?

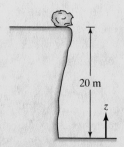

Figure 8. A boulder elevated above the ground has gravitational potential energy.

3.2   Kinetic Energy

Kinetic energy is the *energy that a system possess as a result of its motion with respect to a reference frame*. Kinetic energy, abbreviated KE, is given by the relation

$$KE = \tfrac{1}{2}\, mv^2 \tag{11}$$

where m is the mass of the system (kg) and v is the velocity of the system (m/s). When the boulder in Figure 8. is pushed off the cliff, it begins to fall toward the ground. As the boulder falls, its velocity increases, and its potential energy is converted to kinetic energy. If the velocity of the 1500-kg boulder is 10 m/s at a point between the cliff and ground, the boulder's kinetic energy at this point is

$$
\begin{aligned}
KE &= \tfrac{1}{2}\, mv^2 \\
&= \tfrac{1}{2}(1500 \text{ kg})(10 \text{ m/s})^2 \\
&= 7.50 \times 10^4 \text{ J} = 75.0 \text{ kJ}
\end{aligned}
$$

Immediately before the boulder impacts the ground, all the boulder's potential energy has been converted to kinetic energy. What happens to the boulder's kinetic energy during the impact with the ground?

3.3   Internal Energy

Internal energy is the *sum of all the microscopic forms of energy of a system*. Unlike potential energy and kinetic energy, which relate to the energy of a system with respect to external references, internal energy relates to the energy *within* the system itself. Internal energy, denoted by the symbol U, is a measure of the kinetic energies associated with the molecules, atoms, and subatomic particles of the system. Suppose the system under consideration is a polyatomic gas. [A polyatomic gas is a gas that consists of two or more atoms that form a molecule, such as carbon dioxide (CO_2). A monatomic gas consists of only one atom, such as helium (He) or argon (Ar).] Because gas molecules move about with certain velocities, the molecules possess kinetic energy. The movement of the molecules through space is called translation, so we refer to their kinetic energy as *translational* energy. As the gas molecules translate, they also rotate about their center of mass. The energy associated with this rotation is referred to as *rotational* energy. In addition to translating and rotating, the atoms of polyatomic gas molecules oscillate about their center of mass, giving rise to *vibrational* energy. On a subatomic scale, the electrons of atoms "orbit" the nucleus. Furthermore, electrons spin about their own axis, and the nucleus also possesses a spin. The sum of the translational, rotational, vibrational, and subatomic energies constitutes a *fraction* of the internal energy of the system called the *sensible* energy. Sensible energy is the *energy required to change the temperature of a system*. As an example of sensible energy, suppose that we wish to boil a pan of water on the stove. The water is initially at a temperature of about 20°C. The stove burner imparts energy to the water, increasing the kinetic energy of the water molecules. The increase in kinetic energy of the water molecules is manifested as an increase in temperature of the water. As the burner continues to supply energy to the water, the sensible energy of the water increases, thereby increasing the temperature, until the boiling point is reached.

If sensible energy is only a fraction of the internal energy, what kind of energy constitutes the other fraction? To answer this question, we must recognize the various forces that exist between molecules, between atoms, and between subatomic particles. From basic chemistry, we know that various *binding forces* exist between the molecules of a substance. When these binding forces are broken, the substance changes from one *phase* to another. The three phases of matter are solid, liquid, and gas. Binding forces are strongest in solids, weaker in liquids, and weakest in gases. If enough energy is supplied to a solid substance, ice for example, the binding forces are overcome and the substance changes to the liquid phase. Hence, if enough energy is supplied to ice (solid water), the ice changes to liquid water. If still more energy is supplied to the substance, the substance changes to the gas phase. The amount of energy required to produce a phase change is referred to as *latent* energy. In most thermodynamic processes, a phase change involves the breaking of molecular bonds only. Therefore, the atomic binding forces responsible for maintaining the chemical identity of a substance are not usually considered. Furthermore, the binding energy associated with the strong nuclear force—the force that binds the protons and neutrons in the nucleus—is relevant only in fission reactions.

3.4   Total Energy

The *total energy* of a system is the sum of the potential, kinetic, and internal energies. Thus, the total energy, E, is expressed as

$$E = \text{PE} + \text{KE} + U \tag{12}$$

As a matter of convenience, it is customary in thermodynamics work to express the energy of a system on a *per unit mass* basis. Dividing Equation (12) by mass m, and noting the definitions of potential and kinetic energies from Equations (10) and (11), we obtain

$$e = gz + \frac{v^2}{2} + u \tag{13}$$

where $e = E/m$ and $u = U/m$. The quantities e and u are called the *specific total energy* and *specific internal energy*, respectively.

In the analysis of many thermodynamic systems, the potential and kinetic energies are zero or are sufficiently small that they can be neglected. For example, a boiler containing high-temperature steam is stationary, so its kinetic energy is zero. The boiler has potential energy with respect to an external reference plane (such as the floor on which it rests), but the potential energy is irrelevant, since it has nothing to do with the operation of the boiler. If the potential and kinetic energies of a system are neglected, internal energy is the only form of energy present. Hence, the total energy equals the internal energy, and Equation (12) reduces to $E = U$.

The analysis of thermodynamic systems involves the determination of the *change* of the total energy of the system because this tells us how energy is converted from one form to another. It does not matter what the absolute value of the total energy is, as we are interested only in the change of the total energy. This is paramount to saying that it does not matter what the energy reference value is because the change of energy is the same regardless of what reference value we choose. The reference value is arbitrary. Returning to our falling boulder example, the change of potential energy of the boulder does not depend on the location of the reference plane. We could choose the ground as the reference plane or some other location, such as the top of the cliff or any other elevation for that matter. The change of potential energy of the boulder depends only on the elevation change. Hence, if potential and kinetic energies are neglected, the change of total energy of a system equals the change of internal energy, and Equation (12) is written as $\Delta E = \Delta U$.

PROFESSIONAL SUCCESS: DEALING WITH ENGINEERING PROFESSORS

As a new engineering student, you may believe that engineering professors are probably not that much different from professors in other disciplines on campus. Perhaps you think that they are not even that much different from people outside higher education who work in nonteaching occupations. However, after you have taken a few engineering courses, your opinion will probably change. Engineering professors are unique. It may even be said that they are somewhat odd. Some engineering professors are overly serious, while others may seem rather light minded. Some engineering professors dress very neatly, wearing a suit, tie, polished shoes, etc., while others come to school looking more like a student, wearing jeans, a sweatshirt, and sneakers. Regardless of their personalities and personal appearances, engineering professors are genuinely interested in their students and desire to see them succeed in their engineering studies. Engineering professors are very knowledgeable people in their disciplines, and they want to share that knowledge with students. They were students once, so they understand what you are going through. Professors are *teachers*, and quality instruction is what students expect from them. However, as a student, you should realize that most professors are involved in numerous activities outside the classroom that may or may not relate directly to teaching. Much of your professor's time is spent developing and improving the engineering curriculum. Depending on the availability of graduate teaching assistants, grading may also occupy a considerable fraction of the professor's time. Some colleges and universities, particularly the larger ones, are referred to as *research* institutions. At these schools, engineering professors are expected to conduct research and publish the results of their research. In addition to publishing research papers, some engineering professors write textbooks. Because most engineering professors specialize in a certain aspect of their discipline, some professors work part time as consultants to private or governmental agencies. Most colleges and universities expect their faculty to render service to the institution by serving on various campus committees. Some professors, in addition to their research, writing, and service activities, serve as department or program advisors to students. Professors may even be involved with student recruitment, fund raising, professional engineering societies, and a host of other activities.

What does all this mean to you, the engineering student? It means that there are right ways and wrong ways of dealing with your professors. Here are a few suggestions:

- Be an active member of your professor's class. Attend class, arrive on time, take notes, ask questions, and participate. Being actively engaged in the classroom not only helps you learn, but it also helps the professor teach!

- If you need to obtain help from your professor outside of class, schedule an appointment during an office hour, and *keep* the appointment. Unless your professor has an "open door" policy, scheduling appointments during regular office hours is preferred, because your professor is probably involved in research or other activities.

- Engineering professors appreciate students who give their best efforts in solving a problem *before* asking for help. Before you go to the professor's office, be prepared to tell your professor how you approached the problem and where the potential errors are. Many engineering professors become irritated when the first thing a student says is "Look at this problem, and tell me what I'm doing wrong" or "I just can't get the answer in the back of the book." Preparing to ask the right questions before the visit will enable your professor to help you more fully.

- Unless instructed to do otherwise, do not call professors at home. It you need assistance with homework, projects, etc., contact your professor at school during regular office hours if possible or by special

4   WORK AND HEAT

Work, like energy, is a word that is commonly used in our everyday language and a word that has many meanings. As a student, you know that studying engineering is a lot of "work." When we participate in sports or exercise at the gym, we get a "workout." A person who travels to a place of employment goes to "work," and when a mechanical device stops functioning, we say that it doesn't "work." While various day-to-day usages of this term are thrown about quite casually, engineering defines "work" precisely, with no ambiguity. **Work** is defined as a *form of energy that is transferred across the boundary of a system*. A *system* is a quantity of matter or a region in space chosen for study, and the *boundary* of a system is a real or imaginary surface that separates the system from the surroundings. For example, propane in a fuel tank is a thermodynamic system, and the boundary of the system is the inside surface of the tank wall. Besides work, there is a second form of energy that can be transferred across the boundary of a system. The second form of energy is heat. Heat is a special kind of energy transfer that is easily recognizable and differentiated from work. **Heat** is defined as the *form of energy that is transferred across the boundary of a system by virtue of a temperature difference*. A system with both work and heat crossing the boundary is illustrated in Figure 9. Depending on the nature of the interactions of the system with the surroundings, work and heat can be transferred across the boundary in either direction. The only requirement for heat transfer is a temperature difference between the system and the surroundings. If there is no temperature difference between the system and the surroundings, heat cannot be transferred, thus, the only form of energy transfer is work. Because work and heat are forms of energy, both quantities have the same units. Work and heat have units of J in the SI system and Btu in the English system. The most commonly used symbols for work and heat in thermodynamics are W and Q, respectively.

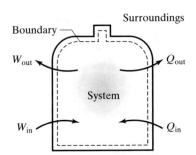

Figure 9. Energy in the form of work or heat can be transferred across the boundary of a system.

Now that work and heat have been defined in general terms, let us examine these forms of energy transfer more closely. In thermodynamics, work is usually categorized as *mechanical* work or *nonmechanical* work. The nonmechanical forms of work include electrical, magnetic, and electrical polarization work. Mechanical forms of work are generally the most important, so we will consider these in some detail.

4.1   Mechanical Work

There are several types of mechanical work. From basic physics, the work W done by a force F acting through a displacement s in the *same direction* of the force is given by the relation

$$W = Fs \qquad (14)$$

Equation (14) is valid only if the force is constant. If the force is not constant (i.e., if the force is a function of displacement), the work is obtained by integration. Thus, Equation (14) becomes

$$W = \int_1^2 F ds \qquad (15)$$

where the limits 1 and 2 denote the initial and final positions of the displacement, respectively. Equation (15) is a general mathematical definition from which equations for the various types of mechanical work are derived. Consider, for example, a vehicle that climbs a rough hill, as shown in Figure 10. As the vehicle climbs the hill, it encounters two forces that tend to oppose its motion. Gravity exerts a downward force on the vehicle that retards its upward motion, and friction between the wheels and the rough surface retards its motion along the surface. The vehicle does work against these two forces, and the magnitude of that work is found by integrating the total force from position s_1 to s_2, which is graphically interpreted as the area under the force-displacement curve. The various types of mechanical work are now considered.

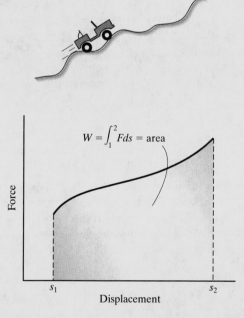

Figure 10. As a vehicle climbs a hill, gravitational and friction forces act on it.

Gravitational work

Gravitational work is defined as the *work done on an object by a gravitational force*. In a gravitational field, the force acting on a body is the *weight* of the body, and is given by

$$F = mg \tag{16}$$

where m is mass (kg) and g is the local gravitational acceleration (m/s^2). Consider a vehicle that climbs a hill from elevation z_1 to a higher elevation z_2, as shown in Figure 11. Substituting Equation (16) into Equation (15) and integrating, we obtain the gravitational work

$$W_g = \int_1^2 Fdz = mg \int_1^2 dz = mg(z_2 - z_1) \tag{17}$$

Note that the displacement in Equation (17) is in terms of elevation z, because work is defined as a force acting through a distance in the *same direction* of the force. Gravity acts in the *vertical* direction, so Equation (17) is written in terms of a vertical distance (elevation) and not a horizontal distance. The gravitational work for the vehicle in Figure 11 is *negative*, as the direction of the displacement (upward) is opposite to the direction of the gravitational force (downward). If the vehicle descends the hill, the gravitational work is positive, because the displacement is in the same direction as the force. Note also that gravitational work is equivalent to a change in potential energy, since $PE = mgz$.

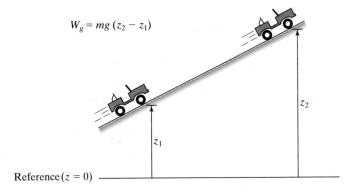

Figure 11.   Gravitational work is done on a body as it changes elevation.

Acceleration work

Acceleration work is the *work associated with a change in velocity of a system*. Newton's second law states that the force acting on a body equals the product of the body's mass and acceleration. But acceleration a is the time derivative of velocity v, so Newton's second law may be written as

$$F = ma = m\frac{dv}{dt} \tag{18}$$

Velocity is the time derivative of displacement,

$$v = \frac{ds}{dt} \tag{19}$$

so the differential displacement ds in Equation (15) is $ds = v\,dt$. Thus, acceleration work is

$$W_a = \int_1^2 Fds = \int_1^2 \left(m\frac{dv}{dt} \right)(vdt) = m\int_1^2 vdv = {}^1\!/_2\,m(v_2^2 - v_1^2) \qquad (20)$$

As shown in Figure 12, a vehicle traveling along a horizontal road increases its velocity from 10 mi/h to 65 mi/h. In doing so, the vehicle does acceleration work because its velocity changes. We note that the acceleration work is equivalent to a change in kinetic energy, since $\text{KE} = {}^1\!/_2\,mv^2$.

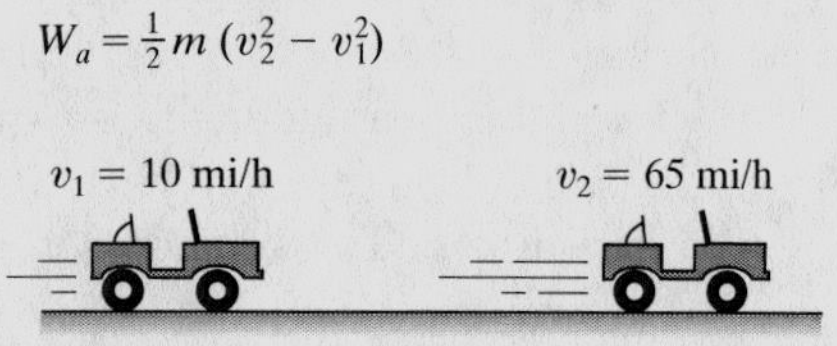

$$W_a = \tfrac{1}{2}m\,(v_2^2 - v_1^2)$$

$v_1 = 10$ mi/h $v_2 = 65$ mi/h

Figure 12. A body does acceleration work as its velocity changes.

Boundary work

Boundary work is the *work associated with the movement of a solid boundary*. The most common instance of boundary work is the compression or expansion of a gas within a piston-cylinder device, as illustrated in Figure 13. A force F is applied to the piston, compressing the gas within the cylinder. Because the cylinder is a closed vessel, the pressure increases as the gas volume decreases. As the gas volume decreases from V_1 to

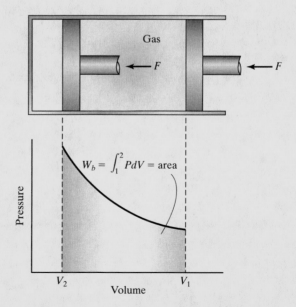

Figure 13. Boundary work is performed by a piston as it compresses a gas.

V_2, the pressure increases along a path that depends on certain physical characteristics of the compression process. Pressure is defined as a force divided by area, so the force causing the compression is given by the relation

$$F = PA \tag{21}$$

where A is the surface area of the face of the piston. A differential change in volume, dV is the product of the piston's differential displacement ds and the surface area of the piston A. Hence, $dV = Ads$ and the boundary work becomes

$$W_b = \int_1^2 Fds = \int_1^2 PA\frac{dV}{A} = \int_1^2 PdV \tag{22}$$

Because the product PdV appears in the definition, boundary work is sometimes referred to as "PdV" work. As indicated in Figure 13, the magnitude of the boundary work is the area under the pressure-volume curve. In order to evaluate the integral in Equation (22), we would have to know the functional relationship between pressure P and volume V. This relationship may be an analytical expression for P as a function of V or a graph that shows the variation of P with V.

Shaft work

Shaft work is *energy transfer by a rotating shaft*. Numerous engineering systems transfer energy by means of a rotating shaft. The drive shaft of an automobile, for example, transfers energy from the transmission to the axle. Energy is transferred from a boat motor to the propeller by a shaft. Even the mixing blades of a food blender perform shaft work on the food. As a shaft rotates, a constant torque is usually applied to the shaft that tends to retard its rotation. As illustrated in Figure 14, the torque τ is produced by a force F acting through a moment arm r according to the relation

$$\tau = Fr \tag{23}$$

The force acts through a distance s equal to the circumference times the number of revolutions of the shaft n. Thus,

$$s = (2\pi r)n \tag{24}$$

Upon substituting Equations (23) and (24) into Equation (14), the shaft work, becomes

$$W_{sh} = 2\pi n\tau \tag{25}$$

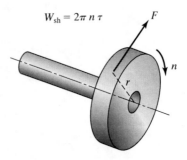

Figure 14. Work is produced by a rotating shaft.

Spring work

Spring work is the *work done in deforming a spring*. A force is required to compress or stretch a spring, so work is done. From elementary physics, we know that the force required to deform a linear elastic spring is proportional to the deformation. This principle is known as Hooke's law and is expressed as

$$F = kx \tag{26}$$

where F is force, x is displacement (change in spring length), and k is the spring constant. Substituting Equation (26) into Equation (15) and noting that $ds = dx$, the spring work becomes

$$W_{sp} = \int_1^2 F ds = \int_1^2 (kx)\, dx = \tfrac{1}{2} k (x_2^2 - x_1^2) \tag{27}$$

As indicated in Figure 15, the initial and final spring displacements are x_1 and x_2 respectively, as measured from the rest (undeformed) position of the spring.

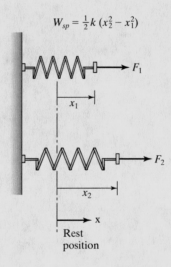

Figure 15. Work is done by stretching or compressing a spring.

4.2   Heat

As we defined it earlier in this chapter, you now know that *heat* is the transfer of energy across the boundary of a system by virtue of a temperature difference. In order for heat transfer to occur, there must be a temperature difference between the system and the surroundings. The transfer or flow of heat is not the flow of a material substance, as in the case of the flow of a fluid such as air or water. Rather, there is an exchange of internal energy across the system boundary by atomic or molecular motion or by electromagnetic waves. Heat transfer can occur by three distinct mechanisms: *conduction*, *convection*, and *radiation*. Conduction is the transfer of internal energy in solids and fluids at rest. The actual mechanism of conduction involves kinetic energy exchange between molecules in contact or, in the case of metals, movement of free electrons. Convection is the mechanism by which internal energy is transferred to or from a fluid near a solid surface. Convection is basically conduction at the solid surface with the added complexity of energy transfer by moving fluid molecules. Radiation is the mechanism by which energy is transferred by electromagnetic waves. Unlike conduction and convection, radiation does not require a medium. A familiar example of radiation is the thermal energy that we receive from the sun across the vacuum of space. Regardless of the heat transfer mechanism involved, the *direction* of heat transfer is always from a high-temperature region to a low-temperature region.

Heat transfer occurs all around us. As a familiar example, consider the hot beverage shown in Figure 16. Heat is transferred from the beverage to the surroundings by all three heat transfer mechanisms. A portion of the energy is transferred by convection from the liquid to the solid cup wall where the heat is subsequently conducted through the cup wall. That energy is then transferred to the surroundings by convection and radiation. The portion of the energy conducted into the bottom portion of the cup is transferred directly into the tabletop by conduction. The remaining energy is transferred from the surface of the liquid directly to the surroundings by convection and radiation.

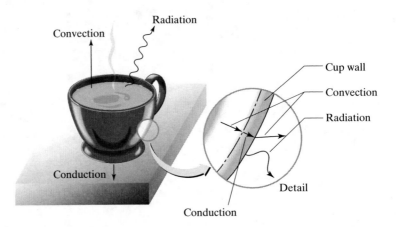

Figure 16. A hot beverage resting on a table transfers thermal energy to the surroundings by conduction, convection and radiation.

In the next example, we use the general analysis procedure of (1) problem statement, (2) diagram, (3) assumptions, (4) governing equations, (5) calculations, (6) solution check, and (7) discussion.

EXAMPLE 3

Problem statement

A 1200-kg automobile accelerates up a hill, increasing its speed from 5 mi/h to 45 mi/h, along a straight 100-m stretch of road. If the hill makes an angle of 6° with respect to the horizontal, find the total work.

Diagram

The diagram for this problem is shown in Figure 17.

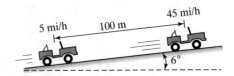

Figure 17. Example 3.

Assumptions

1. Neglect friction between wheels and road.
2. Neglect aerodynamic friction.
3. Mass of automobile is constant.

Governing equations

Two forms of work, gravitational and acceleration, are involved as the automobile ascends the hill, so we have two governing equations:

$$W_g = mg(z_2 - z_1)$$
$$W_a = \tfrac{1}{2} m(v_2^2 - v_1^2)$$

Calculations

The quantities in the problem statement are given in a mixed set of units, so we first convert the units of all quantities to SI units. Converting the velocities, we obtain

$$5\frac{mi}{h} \times \frac{5280 \text{ ft}}{1 \text{ mi}} \times \frac{1 \text{ m}}{3.2808 \text{ ft}} \times \frac{1 \text{ h}}{3600 \text{ s}} = 2.235 \text{ m/s}$$

and

$$45\frac{mi}{h} \times \frac{5280 \text{ ft}}{1 \text{ mi}} \times \frac{1 \text{ m}}{3.2808 \text{ ft}} \times \frac{1 \text{ h}}{3600 \text{ s}} = 20.12 \text{ m/s}$$

The vertical position, z_2, of the automobile when it attains a speed of 45 mi/h is

$$z_2 = (100 \text{ m}) \sin 6° = 10.45 \text{ m}$$

Assigning the position of the ground as $z_1 = 0$ m, the gravitational work is

$$W_g = -mg(z_2 - z_1)$$
$$= -(1200 \text{ kg})(9.81 \text{ m/s}^2)(10.45 \text{ m} - 0 \text{ m})$$
$$= -1.231 \times 10^5 \text{ J}$$

The acceleration work is

$$W_a = \tfrac{1}{2} m(v_2^2 - v_1^2)$$
$$= \tfrac{1}{2}(1200 \text{ kg})[(20.12 \text{ m/s})^2 - (2.235 \text{ m/s})^2]$$
$$= 2.399 \times 10^5 \text{ J}$$

The total work is the sum of the gravitational and acceleration work.

$$W_t = W_g + W_a$$
$$= -1.231 \times 10^5 \text{ J} + 2.399 \times 10^5 \text{ J} = 1.168 \times 10^5 \text{ J} = \underline{117 \text{ kJ}}$$

Solution check

No errors are found.

Discussion

Even though the gravitational work is negative, the total work is positive because the acceleration work is larger in magnitude. We must remember that gravitational work is the work done *by gravity* on the body and not the work done *by the body* in overcoming gravity. The work done by the automobile's engine in order to climb the hill is 123 kJ, but the gravitational work is −123 kJ.

APPLICATION: BOUNDARY WORK DURING A CONSTANT PRESSURE PROCESS

In some thermodynamic systems, boundary work is performed while the pressure remains constant. A common example is the heating of a gas contained in a piston-cylinder device, as illustrated in Figure 18(a). As heat is transferred to the gas within the cylinder, the internal energy of the gas increases, as exhibited by an increase in the gas temperature, and the piston moves up. If we assume that the piston-cylinder device is frictionless, the pressure of the gas remains constant, but, since the piston moves, boundary work is still done. Suppose that the frictionless piston-cylinder device shown in Figure 18(a) contains 2.5 L of nitrogen at 120 kPa. Heat is then transferred to the nitrogen until the volume is 4 L. Find the boundary work done by the nitrogen during this process.

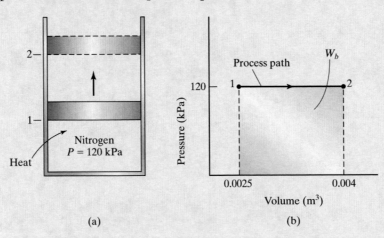

(a)   (b)

Figure 18. A constant pressure process.

Boundary work W_b is given by the relation

$$W_b = \int_1^2 PdV$$

where P is pressure and V is volume. Because the process occurs at constant pressure, P can be brought outside the integral, giving the relation

$$W_b = P \int_1^2 dV$$

The initial and final volumes of the nitrogen are

$$V_1 = 2.5 \text{ L} = 0.025 \text{ m}^3 \qquad V_2 = 4 \text{ L} = 0.004 \text{ m}^3$$

Thus, the boundary work is

$$W_b = P \int_1^2 dV = P(V_2 - V_1)$$

$$= (120 \times 10^3 \text{ Pa})(0.004 \text{ m}^3 - 0.025 \text{ m}^3)$$

$$= 180 \text{ J}$$

The boundary work calculated here is the work done *by* the nitrogen on the piston, not the work done *on* the nitrogen by the piston. Figure 18(b) shows the *process path* for the constant pressure process that occurs in the piston-cylinder device. The boundary work of 180 J is the shaded area under the process path.

PRACTICE!

1. As a 2500-kg truck climbs a hill, it changes speed from 20 mi/h to 50 mi/h along a straight 1600-ft section of road. If the hill is inclined at an angle of 8° with respect to the horizontal, find the total work.

   Answer: −1.14 MJ

2. A 95-slug automobile changes speed from 55 mi/h to 30 mi/h while climbing a 3° hill. If the change in speed occurs over a 1355-ft straight section of road, find the total work.

   Answer: −5605 Btu

3. A shaft rotating at 1200 rpm (revolutions per minute) experiences a constant torque of 60 N · m. How much work does the shaft perform in one hour?

   Answer: 27.1 MJ

4. The pressure inside a frictionless piston-cylinder device varies according to the function $P = a - bV$, where a and b are constants and V is volume. The initial and final volumes for the process are 1 m³ and 0.1 m³, respectively. If $a = 500$ Pa and $b = 2000$ Pa/m³, find the boundary work.

   Answer: 540 J

5. A linear elastic spring is compressed 3.5 cm from its at-rest position. The spring is then compressed an additional 7.5 cm. If the spring constant is 2600 N/cm, find the work done in compressing the spring.

   Answer: 1.57 kJ

6. A frictionless piston-cylinder device has a diameter of 10 cm. As the gas inside the cylinder is heated, the piston moves a distance of 16 cm. If the gas pressure is maintained at 120 kPa, how much work is done?

   Answer: 151 J

5   THE FIRST LAW OF THERMODYNAMICS

The first law of thermodynamics is one of the most important laws in science and engineering. The first law of thermodynamics, often referred to as the law of *conservation of energy*, enables engineers to analyze transformations that occur between the various forms of energy. Stated another way, the first law of thermodynamics allows engineers to study how one form of energy is converted to other forms. The most concise definition of the first law of thermodynamics is *energy is conserved*. Another way to state this law is *energy cannot be created or destroyed, but can only change forms*. The first law of thermodynamics, hereafter referred to as simply "the first law," cannot be proved mathematically. Like Newton's laws of motion, the first law is taken as an axiom, a sound physical principle based on countless measurements. No energy transformation, either natural or man made, is known to have violated the first law.

The first law is a very intuitive concept. Consider the system shown in Figure 19. The system may represent any substance or region in space chosen for thermodynamic analysis. The boundary of the system is the surface that separates the system from the surroundings. We may construct a mathematical representation of the first law by applying a simple physical argument. If an amount of energy E_{in} is supplied *to* the system, that energy can *leave* the system, *change* the energy of the system, or both. The energy that leaves the system is E_{out}, and the energy change of the system is ΔE. Thus, the energy that enters the system equals the energy that leaves the system plus the energy change

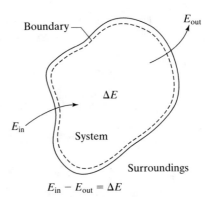

Boundary

E_{out}

ΔE

E_{in}

System

Surroundings

$$E_{in} - E_{out} = \Delta E$$

Figure 19. The first law of thermodynamics.

of the system. The first law may therefore be expressed mathematically as

$$E_{in} = E_{out} + \Delta E \qquad (28)$$

We see that the first law is nothing more than a simple accounting principle that maintains the system's "energy ledger" in balance. In fact, the first law is often referred to as an *energy balance* because that is precisely what it is. In most engineering thermodynamics texts, Equation (28) is typically written in the form

$$E_{in} - E_{out} = \Delta E \qquad (29)$$

As shown in Figure 19, E_{in} and E_{out} are energy quantities that are *transferred* across the system boundary, whereas ΔE is the *change* in energy of the system itself. Because E_{in} and E_{out} are transferred forms of energy, these terms can only represent energy in the forms of *heat, work,* and *mass flow.* Heat is the transport of energy across the boundary of a system by virtue of a temperature difference. For heat transfer to occur, there must be a temperature difference between the system and the surroundings. Work may be mechanical in nature, such as the movement of the system boundary or the turning of a shaft inside the system, or electrical in nature, such as the transfer of electrical energy by a wire that penetrates the system boundary. When mass crosses a system boundary, energy crosses the boundary as well, because mass carries energy with it. Thus, the left side of Equation (29) becomes

$$E_{in} - E_{out} = (Q_{in} - Q_{out}) + (W_{in} - W_{out}) + (E_{mass, in} - E_{mass, out}) \qquad (30)$$

where Q denotes heat, W denotes work, and E_{mass} denotes energy transfer by mass flow. The *in* and *out* subscripts refer to energy transferred *in* and *out* of the system, respectively. These energy quantities should always be clearly indicated on a diagram as arrows pointing into or out of the system. The energy change of the system ΔE is the sum of the potential, kinetic, and internal energy changes. Hence, the right side of Equation (29) is

$$\Delta E = \Delta PE + \Delta KE + \Delta U \qquad (31)$$

where PE, KE, and U represent the potential, kinetic, and internal energy, respectively. Most thermodynamic systems of practical interest are stationary with respect to external reference frames, so $\Delta \text{PE} = \Delta \text{KE} = 0$, leaving $\Delta E = \Delta U$. Furthermore, many thermodynamic systems are *closed*, which means that mass cannot enter or leave the system. For closed systems, the only forms of energy transfer possible are work and heat. The analysis of closed systems is considerably simpler than the analysis of systems that permit mass transfer. In this book, we consider closed systems only. Thus, the first law of thermodynamics for closed systems is

$$(Q_{\text{in}} - Q_{\text{out}}) + (W_{\text{in}} - W_{\text{out}}) = \Delta U \qquad (32)$$

The heat and work transferred across the system boundary causes a change in the internal energy of the system. This change alters the thermodynamic state or condition of the system. A change in the thermodynamic state of a system is called a *process*. The internal energy change ΔU is simply the difference between the internal energies at the end of the process and the beginning of the process. Thus, $\Delta U = U_2 - U_1$, where the subscripts 1 and 2 denote the beginning and end of the process, respectively.

The first law may be expressed in *rate form* by dividing each term in Equation (29) by a time interval Δt over which the process occurs. By dividing the energy terms by time, the quantities on the left side of the equation become quantities of *power*, and the quantity ΔE becomes a change in energy that occurs during the specified time interval. Equation (29) is then rewritten as

$$\dot{E}_{\text{in}} - \dot{E}_{\text{out}} = \Delta E / \Delta t \qquad (33)$$

where $\dot{E}_{\text{in}}$ and $\dot{E}_{\text{out}}$ denote the *rate* at which energy enters and leaves the system, respectively. The units for $\dot{E}_{\text{in}}$ and $\dot{E}_{\text{out}}$ are J/s, which is defined as the watt (W). If the problem is stated in terms of energy rates rather than absolute energy quantities, the use of the first law given by Equation (33) is preferred over Equation (29).

In the following examples, the first law is used to analyze some basic closed thermodynamic systems. We use the general analysis procedure of (1) problem statement, (2) diagram, (3) assumptions, (4) governing equations, (5) calculations, (6) solution check, and (7) discussion.

EXAMPLE 4

Problem statement

A closed tank contains a warm liquid whose initial internal energy is 1500 kJ. A paddle wheel connected to a rotating shaft imparts 250 kJ of work to the liquid, while 700 kJ of heat is lost from the liquid to the surroundings. What is the final internal energy of the liquid?

Diagram

A diagram representing the system is illustrated in Figure 20. The system is the liquid in the tank. Energy transferred across the system boundary as work and heat is shown.

Assumptions

1. The system is closed.
2. The tank is stationary, so $\Delta \text{PE} = \Delta \text{KE} = 0$.
3. Energy change in the paddle wheel is negligible.

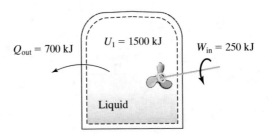

Figure 20.   System for Example 4.

Governing equations

The governing equation for this problem is the first law of thermodynamics for a closed system:

$$(Q_{in} - Q_{out}) + (W_{in} - W_{out}) = \Delta U = U_2 - U_1$$

Calculations

From the diagram, we see that

$$Q_{out} = 700 \text{ kJ}, \qquad W_{in} = 250 \text{ kJ}, \qquad U_1 = 1500 \text{ kJ}$$

but there is no heat input and no work output. Thus,

$$Q_{in} = 0, \qquad W_{out} = 0$$

Substituting known quantities into the first law, we have

$$(0 - 700)\text{kJ} + (250 - 0)\text{kJ} = U_2 - 1500 \text{ kJ}$$

Solving for U_2, the final energy of the liquid, we obtain

$$U_2 = \underline{1050 \text{ kJ}}$$

Solution check

No errors are found.

Discussion

The final internal energy of the liquid is 1050 kJ, a decrease of 450 kJ. The internal energy of the liquid must decrease because more energy (700 kJ) is removed from the system than is supplied (250 kJ) to the system.

EXAMPLE 5

Problem statement

The air in a small house is maintained at a constant temperature by an electric baseboard system that supplies 5.6 kW to the house. There are 10 light fixtures in the house and each dissipate 60 W and the major electrical appliances (dishwasher, range, clothes dryer, etc.) have a total dissipation of 2560 W. The house is occupied by four people who each dissipate 110 W. Find the total heat loss from the house to the surroundings.

Diagram

The diagram for this problem is shown in Figure 21. The air in the house is the system. Power supplied to the house by the baseboard system, shown as an electrical resistor, is represented on the diagram by electrical power input, $\dot{W}_{in}$. The rate of heat dissipation by lights, people, and appliances is shown on the diagram as $\dot{Q}_{in}$, and the heat loss from the house to the surroundings is shown as $\dot{Q}_{out}$. A careful reading of the problem statement indicates that the change in internal energy of the system is zero, since the baseboard system maintains the air in the house at a constant temperature.

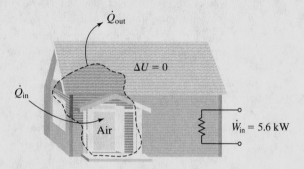

Figure 21.   System for Example 5.

Assumptions

1. The system is closed.
2. Energy change in the contents of the house is zero.
3. All energy transfer rates are constant.

Governing equations

The governing equation for this problem is the first law, in rate form, for a closed system. Because the house is maintained at a constant temperature, $\Delta U = 0$. Thus, we have

$$(\dot{Q}_{in} - \dot{Q}_{out}) + (\dot{W}_{in} - \dot{W}_{out}) = 0$$

Calculations

There are 10 lights that dissipate 60 W each, 4 people who dissipate 110 W each, and appliances that dissipate a total of 2560 W. The total rate of heat transfer into the house is

$$\dot{Q}_{in} = \dot{Q}_{lights} + \dot{Q}_{people} + \dot{Q}_{appliances}$$
$$= 10(60\ W) + 4(110\ W) + 2560\ W = 3600\ W$$

The electrical power supplied to the house by the baseboard system is

$$\dot{W}_{in} = 5600\ W$$

but there is no work output, so $\dot{W}_{out} = 0$. Substituting known quantities into the first law, we have

$$(3600 - \dot{Q}_{out})W + (5600 - 0)W = 0$$

Solving for the heat loss $\dot{Q}_{out}$, we obtain

$$\dot{Q}_{out} = \underline{9.2 \text{ kW}}$$

Solution check

No errors are found.

Discussion

The heat loss of 9.2 kW represents the rate of heat transfer from the house to the surroundings. Heat is lost from the house through the walls, roof, windows, doors, and any other building member that is part of the system boundary. Because the air in the house is maintained at a constant temperature, the rate of energy supplied to the house must equal the rate of energy lost by the house.

PRACTICE!

1. A 2500-kg boulder is pushed off a 75-m high cliff. What is the velocity of the boulder immediately before it strikes the ground? How does the boulder's mass affect the solution?
    Answer: 38.4 m/s, boulder's mass is irrelevant

2. Just before striking the ground, the boulder in practice problem 1 converts all its potential energy to kinetic energy (assuming negligible aerodynamic friction). After colliding with the ground, the boulder comes to rest, converting its kinetic energy into other energy forms. What are these forms?
    Answer: heat, sound, and deformation

3. The fluid in a closed-pressure vessel receives 500 kJ of heat, while a shaft does 250 kJ of work on the fluid. If the final internal energy of the fluid is 1100 kJ, what is the initial internal energy of the fluid?
    Answer: 350 kJ

4. The fluid in a closed tank loses 600 Btu of heat to the surroundings, while a shaft does 850 Btu of work on the fluid. If the initial internal energy of the fluid is 250 Btu, what is the final internal energy of the fluid?
    Answer: 500 Btu

5. A small house is to be air-conditioned. The house gains 18,000 Btu/h of heat from the surroundings, while lights, appliances, and occupants add 6000 Btu/h from within the house. If the house is to be maintained at a constant temperature, what is the required rating of the air conditioner?
    Answer: 24,000 Btu/h

6. A piston-cylinder device containing water is heated. During the heating process, 300 J of energy is supplied to the water, while 175 J of heat is lost through the walls of the cylinder to the surroundings. As a result of the heating, the piston moves, doing 140 J of boundary work. Find the change in the internal energy of the water for this process.
    Answer: −15 J

Engineering is the business of designing and producing devices and systems for the benefit of society. People who practice engineering for a living design and manufacture things—*practical* things that are useful in specific applications. Given the applied nature of engineering, one would assume that engineering education is likewise applied. After all, an engineering education is supposed to prepare students for engineering practice, right? While an engineering education does indeed prepare students for industrial practice, the nature of that preparation may not be what you expect. Generally speaking, engineering courses are very theoretical and mathematical in nature. If you have a few engineering courses under your belt already, you have no doubt discovered this. Engineering courses are usually deep in theory, but shallow in practical aspects. As a result, an electrical engineering student may know how to analyze a circuit with the use of a schematic diagram, but may not be able to recognize an actual electrical component such as a resistor, capacitor, inductor or integrated circuit. Similarly, a mechanical engineering student may be very comfortable with performing a first law analysis of a boiler, compressor, turbine, or heat exchanger, but would not recognize one of these devices if he or she saw one.

So, why is the emphasis placed on theory at the expense of the practical aspects? One of the main reasons is that many professors who are teaching you how to become a practicing engineer have never practiced engineering themselves. This may sound bizarre, but many engineering professors took a teaching position directly out of graduate school after receiving their Ph.D degree, have been teaching ever since, and therefore have little or no industrial experience. This situation is not likely to change significantly in the near future, so it is up to the engineering student to acquire some practical, hands-on experience. Here are some ways:

- Enroll in a vocational or technical course at the university, the local community college, or trade school. Technical programs usually offer a wide variety of very practical courses such as welding, machining, refrigeration repair, auto repair, pipe fitting, electrical wiring, small engine repair, and computer servicing. You should take these courses when they will not interfere with your engineering course work, such as during the summer.

- Take additional laboratory courses. Some engineering courses have laboratories associated with them. The engineering laboratory is a good place to acquire practical engineering skills.

- Read engineering and technical-related magazines and journals. These publications contain articles about real engineering systems that will help you bridge the gap between engineering theory and engineering practice.

- Participate in engineering projects and competitions sponsored by your school and professional engineering societies. The American Society of Mechanical Engineers (ASME), the Society of Automotive Engineers (SAE), the Institute for Electrical and Electronics Engineers (IEEE), the American Institute of Aeronautics and Astronautics (AIAA), and other professional societies sponsor various engineering competitions. Local participation in National Engineers Week, held annually in February, is an excellent opportunity for students to bolster their practical engineering skills.

- Tinker with various mechanical and electrical devices. Find an old electric hand drill and disassemble it. Figure out how it works. Do the same for a telephone, computer hard drive, and a small kitchen appliance. Disassembling, studying, and reassembling things will help you discover how actual devices work. You may even want to perform service on your own automobile, perhaps by replacing the brakes, doing a tune-up, or installing a sound system.

6   HEAT ENGINES

The first law of thermodynamics states that energy can be converted from one form to another, but cannot be created or destroyed. The first law is a conservation law, a simple accounting principle that tells us how a system's "energy ledger" is kept in balance. Although the first law tells us what forms of energy are involved in a particular energy conversion, it tells us nothing about whether the conversion is possible or in which direction the conversion process occurs. For example, consider the system in Figure 22. A closed tank containing a fluid has a shaft that facilitates the transfer of work to the fluid. When the shaft rotates, work is transferred to the fluid, increasing its internal energy and thereby transferring heat from the fluid to the surroundings, as shown in Figure 22(a). During this process, work is converted directly and completely to heat. But when heat is transferred to the fluid, as shown in Figure 22(b), the shaft does not rotate, and thus no work is performed. The first law of thermodynamics does not preclude the conversion of heat to work in this system, but we know from experience that such conversion does not occur. Based on this argument, we conclude that work can be converted to heat directly and completely, but heat cannot always be converted to work. The direct conversion from heat to work is impossible without the use of a special device called a heat engine.

A **heat engine** is a *device that converts heat to work*. Before describing how this conversion occurs, we must define an important thermodynamic term: *thermal energy*

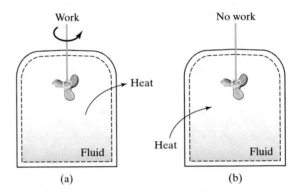

Figure 22. Work can always be converted to heat (a), but heat cannot always be converted to work (b).

reservoir. A thermal energy reservoir is a body with a very large thermal capacity. The distinctive characteristic of a thermal energy reservoir is that it can supply or receive large amounts of thermal energy without experiencing any change in temperature. In actual thermodynamic systems, because of their large masses and high heat capacities, expansive bodies of water such as oceans, lakes, or rivers are considered thermal energy reservoirs. The atmosphere is also considered a thermal energy reservoir. Any region or body whose thermal capacity is large compared with the amount of heat it supplies, or receives, may be considered a thermal energy reservoir. There are two types of thermal energy reservoirs: a thermal energy *source* and a thermal energy *sink*. A thermal energy source supplies heat to a system, whereas a thermal energy sink absorbs heat from a system. As illustrated in Figure 23, a heat engine receives an amount of heat (Q_{in}) from a high-temperature source and converts a portion of that heat to work (W_{out}). The heat engines rejects the remaining heat (Q_{out}) to a low-temperature sink. There are several thermodynamic systems that qualify as heat engines, but the system that best fits the definition of a heat engine is the steam-power plant. In a steam-power plant, Q_{in} is the heat supplied to a boiler from a combustion process or nuclear reaction. The heat Q_{out}, rejected to a low-temperature sink, is the heat transferred from a heat exchanger to a nearby lake, river, or the atmosphere. The work W_{out} produced by the power plant is the energy generated by a turbine. An electrical generator, which is connected to the turbine via a shaft, generates electrical energy.

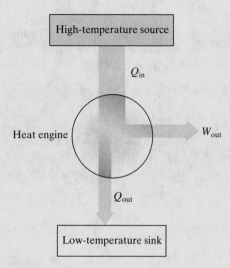

Figure 23. A heat engine converts a portion of the heat it receives from a high-temperature source to work and rejects the remaining heat to a low-temperature sink.

By inspection of Figure 23, the first law of thermodynamics for a heat engine is

$$Q_{in} = Q_{out} + W_{out} \tag{34}$$

The work W_{out} is the useful work produced by the heat engine. For a steam-power plant, W_{out} is actually a *net* work because some work has to be supplied to a pump in order to circulate the steam through the boiler and other power-plant components. The heat Q_{out}, rejected to a low-temperature sink, is wasted energy. So why don't we just eliminate Q_{out}, converting all Q_{in} to work? It turns out that, while this idea sounds very attractive, the elimination of Q_{out} violates the second law of thermodynamics. A nonzero amount of waste heat Q_{out} is necessary if the heat engine is to operate at all.

Efficiency is a useful engineering quantity that is used to measure the performance of numerous engineering systems. A general definition of efficiency is

$$\text{efficiency} = \frac{\text{desired output}}{\text{required input}} \tag{35}$$

For heat engines, the desired output is the work output, and the required input is the heat supplied by the high-temperature source. Hence, **thermal efficiency** of a heat engine, denoted η_{th}, is given by the relation:

$$\eta_{th} = \frac{W_{out}}{Q_{in}} \tag{36}$$

In accordance with the first law of thermodynamics, no heat engine (or any other device for that matter) can produce more energy than is supplied to it. Therefore, the thermal efficiency of a heat engine is always less than 1. This fact is apparent from Figure 23 because only a portion of the heat supplied to the heat engine is converted to work, the remaining heat being rejected to a low-temperature sink.

EXAMPLE 6

A heat engine produces 6 MW of power while absorbing 10 MW from a high-temperature source. What is the thermal efficiency of this heat engine? What is the rate of heat transfer to the low-temperature sink?

SOLUTION

The work output and heat input are given in terms of energy rates, not energy. The first law relation for a heat engine [Equation (34),] may be expressed in rate form by dividing each quantity by time. Similarly, the work and heat quantities in Equation (36) may be divided by time. Dividing the work and heat quantities by time yields power $\dot{W}_{out}$ and heat transfer rates, $\dot{Q}_{in}$ and $\dot{Q}_{out}$, where the "dot" denotes a rate quantity. Thus, the thermal efficiency of the heat engine is

$$\eta_{th} = \frac{\dot{W}_{out}}{\dot{Q}_{in}}$$

$$= \frac{(6 \text{ MW})}{10 \text{ MW}} = 0.6 \, (60\%)$$

The rate of heat transfer to the low-temperature sink is

$$\dot{Q}_{out} = \dot{Q}_{in} - \dot{W}_{out}$$

$$= 10 \text{ MW} - 6 \text{ MW} = 4 \text{ MW}$$

7   THE SECOND LAW OF THERMODYNAMICS

The first law of thermodynamics states that energy is conserved (i.e., energy can be converted from one form to another, but cannot be created or destroyed). The first law tells us what forms of energy are involved in a particular energy conversion, but it does not tell us anything about whether the conversion is possible or in which direction the conversion process occurs. Common experience tells us that a boulder naturally falls from a cliff to the ground, but never jumps from the ground to the top of the cliff by itself. The first law does not preclude the boulder from jumping from the ground to the top of the cliff, because energy (potential and kinetic) is still conserved in this process. We know by experience that a hot beverage naturally cools as heat is transferred from the beverage to the cool surroundings. The energy lost by the beverage equals the energy gained by the surroundings. The hot beverage will not get hotter, however, because heat flows from a high temperature to a low temperature. The first law does not preclude the beverage from getting hotter in a cool room as long as the energy lost by the room equals the energy gained by the beverage. Experience also tells us that if you drop a raw egg on the floor, it breaks and makes a big gooey mess. The reverse process will not occur (i.e., the shell fragments will not automatically reassemble around the egg white and yolk and then rebound from the floor into your hand). Once again, the first law does not preclude the reverse process from occurring; however, the overwhelming experimental evidence tells us that the reverse process does not take place. As a final example, consider the system in Figure 24. A closed tank containing a fluid has a shaft that facilitates the conversion between work and heat. Suppose that we wanted to use the apparatus as a heat engine, a device that converts heat to work. If we were to actually build this device and attempt to raise the weight by transferring heat to the fluid, we would discover that the weight would not be raised. As in the previous examples, the first law does not preclude

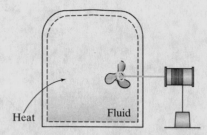

Figure 24.   Transferring heat to the fluid will not cause the shaft to rotate; therefore, no work will be done to raise the weight.

the conversion of heat to work in this system, but we know from experience that this conversion does not occur.

Based on direct observations of physical systems, it is clear that thermodynamic processes occur only in certain directions. While the first law places no restrictions on the direction in which a thermodynamic process occurs, it does not ensure that the process is *possible*. To answer that question, we need another thermodynamic principle or law that tells us something about the natural direction of thermodynamic processes. That principle is the second law of thermodynamics. In order for a process to occur, *both* the first and second laws of thermodynamics must be satisfied. There are various ways of stating the second law of thermodynamics. One of the most useful forms of the second law of thermodynamics, hereafter referred to as simply "the second law," is that *it is impossible for a heat engine to produce an amount of work equal to the amount of heat received from a thermal energy reservoir*. In other words, the second law states that it is impossible for a heat engine to convert all the heat it receives from a thermal energy reservoir to work. A heat engine that violates the second law is illustrated in Figure 25. In order to operate, a heat engine must reject some of the heat it receives from the high-temperature source to a low-temperature sink. A heat engine that violates the second law converts 100 percent of this heat to work. This is physically impossible.

The second law can also be stated as *no heat engine can have a thermal efficiency of 100 percent*. The thermal efficiency of a heat engine, denoted η_{th}, is defined as the ratio of the work output to the heat input:

$$\eta_{th} = \frac{W_{out}}{Q_{in}} \tag{37}$$

Clearly, if the thermal efficiency of a heat engine is 100 percent, then $Q_{in} = W_{out}$. If the second law precludes a heat engine from having a thermal efficiency of 100 percent, what is the maximum possible thermal efficiency of a heat engine? As illustrated in Figure 26, a heat engine is a device that converts a portion of the heat supplied to it from a high-temperature source into work. The remaining heat is rejected to a low-temperature sink. The thermal efficiency of a heat engine is given by Equation (37). Applying the first law to the heat engine, we obtain

$$Q_{in} = Q_{out} + W_{out} \tag{38}$$

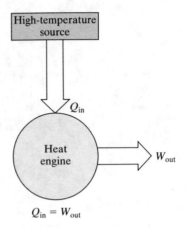

$$Q_{in} = W_{out}$$

Figure 25. This heat engine violates the second law of thermodynamics.

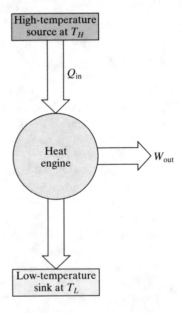

Figure 26. A heat engine, operating between thermal energy reservoirs at temperatures T_H and T_L, converts heat to work.

Solving for W_{out} from Equation (38) and substituting the result into Equation (37), we obtain

$$\eta_{th} = \frac{Q_{in} - Q_{out}}{Q_{in}} = 1 - \frac{Q_{out}}{Q_{in}} \tag{39}$$

It can be shown mathematically that, for an *ideal* heat engine operating between source and sink temperatures of T_H and T_L, respectively, the ratio of the heat supplied to the heat rejected equals the ratio of the absolute temperatures of the heat source and heat sink. Thus,

$$\frac{Q_{\text{out}}}{Q_{\text{in}}} = \frac{T_L}{T_H} \tag{40}$$

The details of the mathematical proof may be found in most thermodynamics texts. What does it mean for a heat engine to be ideal? The short answer is that a heat engine is considered ideal if the processes within the heat engine itself are reversible. A reversible process is a process that can be reversed in direction without leaving any trace on the surroundings. A simple example of a reversible process is a frictionless pendulum. A frictionless pendulum can swing in either direction without dissipating any heat to the surroundings. A more thorough discussion of this concept may be found in the references at the end of this chapter.

Substituting Equation (40) into Equation (39), we find that the thermal efficiency for an ideal heat engine becomes

$$\eta_{\text{th, ideal}} = 1 - \frac{T_L}{T_H} \tag{41}$$

where T_L and T_H denote the absolute temperatures of the low-temperature sink and high-temperature source, respectively. Because T_L and T_H are absolute temperatures, these quantities must be expressed in units of kelvin (K) or rankine (°R). The thermal efficiency given by Equation (41) is the maximum possible thermal efficiency a heat engine can have, and is often referred to as the **Carnot efficiency**, in honor of the French engineer Sadi Carnot. A heat engine whose thermal efficiency is given by Equation (41) is a theoretical heat engine only, an idealization that engineers use to compare with real heat engines. No real heat engine can have a thermal efficiency greater than the Carnot efficiency, because no real heat engine is reversible. Hence, the efficiencies of real heat engines, such as steam power plants, should not be compared to 100 percent. Instead, they should be compared to the Carnot efficiency for a heat engine operating between the same temperature limits. The Carnot efficiency is the theoretical upper limit for the thermal efficiency of a heat engine. If a heat engine is purported to have a thermal efficiency greater than the Carnot efficiency, the heat engine is in violation of the second law of thermodynamics.

The first and second laws of thermodynamics are the quintessential governing principles on which all energy processes are based. In summary: *The first law says you can't get something for nothing. The second law says you can't even come close.*

Earlier in this section, we mentioned that there are various ways of stating the second law of thermodynamics. The primary objective of science is to explain the universe in which we live. The second law of thermodynamics, while very useful for analyzing and designing engineering systems, is a scientific principle that has profound consequences. From a scientific standpoint, the second law is considered an "arrow of time," an immutable principle that assigns a natural direction to all physical processes. Stones fall from cliffs, but never the reverse. Heat flows from hot objects to cold objects, but never the reverse. Raw eggs dropped to the floor make a gooey mess, but do not reassemble. Cream mixes with coffee, but once mixed, the coffee and cream do not separate back out. Physical processes are ordered—they follow the arrow of time. Matter spreads and energy spreads, reducing the quality of things. According to the second law, things naturally move from order to disorder, from a higher quality to a lower quality, from a more useful

APPLICATION: EVALUATING A CLAIM FOR A NEW HEAT ENGINE

In a patent application for a new heat engine, an inventor claims that the device produces 1 kJ of work for every 1.8 kJ of heat supplied to it. In the application, the inventor states that the heat engine absorbs energy from a 350°C source and rejects energy to a 25°C sink. Evaluate this claim.

The feasibility of the new heat engine may be checked by ascertaining whether the heat engine violates either the first or second laws of thermodynamics. If the first law is violated, the heat engine would have to produce an amount of work greater than the amount of heat supplied to it. Because $W_{out} < Q_{in}$ (1 kJ < 1.8 kJ) for this heat engine, the first law is satisfied. If the second law is violated, the heat engine would have to have a thermal efficiency greater than the Carnot efficiency for a heat engine operating between the same temperature limits. The actual thermal efficiency of the heat engine is

$$\eta_{th,\ actual} = \frac{W_{out}}{Q_{in}} = \frac{1\ kJ}{1.8\ kJ} = 0.556(55.6\%)$$

Noting that the source and sink temperatures must be expressed in absolute units, the Carnot efficiency is

$$\eta_{th,\ Carnot} = 1 - \frac{T_L}{T_H}$$

$$= 1 - \frac{(25°C + 273)\ K}{(350°C + 273)\ K} = 0.522(52.2\%)$$

The actual thermal efficiency of the heat engine is greater than the Carnot efficiency (0.556 > 0.522), so the inventors's claim is invalid. It is physically impossible for this heat engine to produce 1 kJ of work for every 1.8 kJ of heat supplied to it, given the source and sink temperatures specified in the patent application.

state to a less useful state. In short, the second law says that, left to themselves, things get worse. As shown in Figure 27, the second law seems to apply to everything, not just energy systems.

Figure 27. The second law of thermodynamics has taken its toll on this structure.

PRACTICE!

1. A high-temperature source supplies a heat engine with 25 kJ of energy. The heat engine rejects 15 kJ of energy to a low-temperature sink. How much work does the heat engine produce?
   Answer: 10 kJ

2. A heat engine produces 5 MW of power while absorbing 8 MW of power from a high-temperature source. What is the thermal efficiency of this heat engine? What is the rate of heat transfer to the low-temperature sink?
   Answer: 0.625, 3 MW

3. A heat engine absorbs 20 MW from a 400°C furnace and rejects 12 MW to the atmosphere at 25°C. Find the actual and Carnot thermal efficiencies of this heat engine. How much power does the heat engine produce?
   Answer: 0.400, 0.557, 8 MW

4. Joe, a backyard tinkerer who fancies himself an engineer, tells his engineer neighbor, Jane, that he has developed a heat engine that receives heat from boiling water at 1 atm pressure and rejects heat to a freezer at −5°C. Joe claims that his heat engine produces 1 Btu of work for every 2.5 Btu of heat it receives from the boiling water. After a quick calculation, Jane informs Joe that if he intends to design heat engines, he needs to pursue an engineering education first. Is Jane justified in making this comment? Justify your answer by analysis.
   Answer: Yes, because $\eta_{actual} = 0.400$ and $\eta_{Carnot} = 0.282$, which is impossible.

KEY TERMS

Carnot efficiency
elastic potential energy
energy
first law of
   thermodynamics
gravitational potential
   energy
heat

heat engine
internal energy
kinetic energy
potential energy
pressure
second law of
   thermodynamics
temperature

thermal efficiency
thermodynamics
work
zeroth law of
   thermodynamics

REFERENCES

Cengel, Y.A. and M.A. Boles, *Thermodynamics: An Engineering Approach*, 4th ed., NY: McGraw-Hill, 2002.

Sonntag, R.E., C. Borgnakke, and G.J. Van Wylen, *Fundamentals of Thermodynamics*, 6th ed., NY: John Wiley & Sons, 2002.

Moran, M.J. and H.N. Shapiro, *Fundamentals of Engineering Thermodynamics*, 5th ed., NY: John Wiley & Sons, 2003.

Levenspiel, O., *Understanding Engineering Thermo*, Upper Saddle River, NJ: Prentice Hall, 1996.

Hagen, K.D., *Heat Transfer with Applications*, Upper Saddle River, NJ: Prentice Hall, 1999.

Incropera, F.P. and D.P. DeWitt, *Fundamentals of Heat and Mass Transfer*, 5th ed., NY: John Wiley & Sons, 2001.

Problems

1. What gauge pressure would you need to inflate an automobile tire in San Diego, California, to achieve an absolute pressure of 325 kPa?

2.   A pressure gauge connected to a tank reads 480 kPa at a location where the atmospheric pressure is 92 kPa. Find the absolute pressure in the tank.

3.   A vertical, frictionless piston-cylinder device contains a gas. The piston has a mass of 3 kg and a radius of 5 cm. A downward force of 75 N is applied to the piston. If the atmospheric pressure is 90 kPa, find the pressure inside the cylinder. (See Figure P3.)

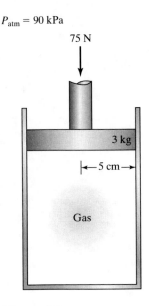

$P_{atm} = 90$ kPa

75 N

3 kg

5 cm

Gas

Figure P3.

4.   A vacuum gauge connected to a tank reads 7.6 psi at a location where the atmospheric pressure is 13.8 psi. Find the absolute pressure in the tank.

5.   A comfortable indoor air temperature is 70°F. What is this temperature in units of °R, °C, and K?

6.   The average body temperature of a healthy adult is approximately 98.6°F. What is this temperature in units of °R, °C, and K?

7.   Find the temperature at which the Fahrenheit and Celsius scales coincide.

8.   Heat exchangers are devices that facilitate the transfer of thermal energy from one fluid to another across a solid wall. In a particular heat exchanger, glycerine enters the unit at a temperature of 30°C and exits the unit at a temperature of 47°C. What is the temperature change of the glycerine in units of °F, °R, and K?

9.   As a 75-slug automobile travels along a horizontal, 1500-ft section of road, it changes speed from 5 mi/h to 60 mi/h. If the friction force acting on the automobile is 30 lb$_f$, what is the total work?

10.   The pressure in a frictionless piston-cylinder device varies according to the function $P = CV^{-n}$, where C and n are constants and V is volume. Derive a relationship for the boundary work in terms of the initial and final volumes V_1 and V_2 and the constants C and n. What is the restriction on the constant n?

11. A 180-lb$_m$ person climbs a stairway consisting of 150 stairs, each with a vertical rise of 8 in. How much work does this person do against gravity?

12. A shaft connected to a motor does 400 kJ of work in 3 minutes. If the shaft rotates at 1750 rpm, what is the torque on the shaft?

13. A crate is dragged across a rough floor by a force $F = 120$ N, as shown in Figure P13. A friction force of 40 N acts to retard the motion of the crate. If the crate is dragged 25 m across the floor, what is the work done by the 120-N force? By the friction force? What is the *net* work done?

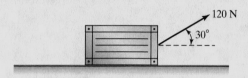

Figure P13.

For problems 14 through 39, use the general analysis procedure of (1) problem statement, (2) diagram, (3) assumptions, (4) governing equations, (5) calculations, (6) solution check, and (7) discussion.

14. A 3-kg block is dropped from rest onto a linear elastic spring as shown in Figure P14. The spring is initially undeformed and has a spring constant of 1130 N/m. What is the deformation of the spring when the block momentarily stops? (*Hint:* Remember that the block travels 2 m *plus* a distance equal to the deformation of the spring.)

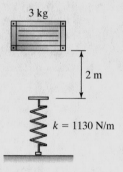

Figure P14.

15. A piston-cylinder device containing a gas receives 25 kJ of heat. During the heating process, the gas expands, moving the piston outward, performing 10 kJ of boundary work. Also, an electric heating element imparts 6 kJ to the gas. If the heat loss from the device is 8 kJ, what is the change in internal energy of the gas during the process?

16.   A machine shop is maintained at a constant temperature during the summer by small air-conditioning units with a rating of 8 kW. The rate of heat transfer from the surroundings to the machine shop is 24 kW. Five lathes and four mills dissipate a total of 4 kW, the lights in the shop dissipate 2.5 kW, and nine machinists dissipate a total of 3.5 kW. How many air-conditioning units are required?

17.   The piston-cylinder device shown in the Figure P17 contains a fluid that can be stirred by a rotating shaft. The outer surface of the device is covered with a thick layer of insulation. The shaft imparts 50 kJ to the fluid during a process in which the pressure is held constant at 130 kPa as the piston moves outward. If the internal energy of the fluid increases by 20 kJ during the process, what is the axial displacement of the piston?

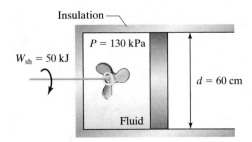

Figure P17.

18.   A closed tank containing hot air has an initial internal energy of 150 kJ. During the next 5 minutes, the tank loses heat to the surroundings at a rate of 1.2 kW, while an electrical element supplies 800 W to the air. Find the final internal energy of the air.

19.   A small research facility in a remote polar region is maintained at a comfortable temperature by heaters that burn propane. The propane storage capacity of the facility is 5000 kg. If the rate of heat loss from the facility is 40 kW and the heat of combustion of propane is 46 MJ/kg, how long can the facility be continuously heated before depleting the propane? Assume that only 80 percent of the heat of combustion is utilized as useful energy.

20.   A spherical hot-air balloon measuring 15 m in diameter flies at a constant altitude by periodically firing the burner system, maintaining the air within the canopy at a constant temperature. If the rate of heat loss per square meter through the canopy is 110 W/m^2, how much energy must the burner supply during a 1-hour period? If the burner system utilizes propane as fuel, how much propane is consumed during this time if the heat of combustion of propane is 46 MJ/kg? Assume that the entire heat of combustion is utilized to heat the air in the canopy.

21.   A standard incandescent lightbulb operates on a voltage and current of 110 V and 0.91 A, respectively. What is the wattage of this lightbulb? What is the electrical work input to the lightbulb during a time interval of 2 min? In which of the three forms of heat transfer does thermal energy leave the lightbulb?

22.   A cylindrical nuclear fuel rod with a length and diameter of 1.0 m and 2.0 cm, respectively, undergoes a fission process. During the fission process, the rod generates 3 GW/m^3 of energy uniformly within the rod. What is the total energy

generated by the rod during a time interval of 1 h? What is the rate of heat transfer from every square centimeter of rod surface, excluding the ends?

23.   The change in internal energy, ΔU, for a closed system undergoing a thermodynamic process may be approximated by the relation

$$\Delta U = mc(T_2 - T_1)$$

where m is the mass of the substance within the system (kg), c is the average specific heat of the substance (J/kg·°C), and T_1 and T_2 are the initial and final temperatures of the substance (°C), respectively, for the process. A rigid tank contains 10 kg of steam at 250°C. During the next 5 min, the rate of heat transfer from the tank is 3 kW. What is the final temperature of the steam? For steam, let $c = 1.411$ kJ/kg·°C.

24.   The change in internal energy, ΔU, for a closed system undergoing a thermodynamic process may be approximated by the relation

$$\Delta U = mc(T_2 - T_1)$$

where m is the mass of the substance within the system (kg), c is the average specific heat of the substance (J/kg·°C), and T_1 and T_2 are the initial and final temperatures of the substance (°C), respectively, for the process. A rigid tank contains 2 kg of air at 300°C. During the next 10 min, the rate of heat transfer from the tank is 1.3 kW, while during the same time, a rotating shaft does 500 kJ of work on the air. What is the final temperature of the air? For air, let $c = 0.718$ kJ/kg·°C.

25.   A high-temperature source supplies a heat engine with 20 kJ of energy. The heat engine rejects 12 kJ of energy to a low-temperature sink. How much work does the heat engine produce?

26.   During a time interval of 1h, a heat engine absorbs 360 MJ of energy from a high-temperature source while rejecting 40 kW to a low-temperature sink. How much power does the heat engine produce?

27.   A heat engine produces 2 MW of power while rejecting 750 kW to the environment. What is the rate of heat transfer from the high-temperature source to the heat engine?

28.   A heat engine produces 10 MW of power while absorbing 18 MW of power from a high-temperature source. What is the thermal efficiency of this heat engine? What is the rate of heat transfer to the low-temperature sink?

29.   A heat engine rejects 2×10^6 Btu/h to a lake while absorbing 5×10^6 Btu/h from a furnace. What is the thermal efficiency of this heat engine? What is the power output?

30.   The thermal efficiency of a heat engine is 70 percent. If the heat engine extracts 6 MJ of energy from a high-temperature source, how much energy is rejected to the low-temperature sink?

31.   A heat engine absorbs 25 MW from a 400°C combustion chamber and rejects 15 MW to the atmosphere at 30°C. Find the actual and Carnot thermal efficiencies of this heat engine. How much power does the heat engine produce?

32. A 2-GW steam power plant, which uses a nearby river as a low-temperature sink, has an actual thermal efficiency of 40 percent. The high-temperature source is a 400°C boiler, and the temperature of the river water is 10°C. Find the rate of heat transfer to the river and the ideal thermal efficiency of the power plant.

33. An engineer proposes to design a heat engine that uses the atmosphere as the high-temperature source and a deep cavern as the low-temperature sink. If the temperature of the atmosphere and cavern are 25°C and 8°C, respectively, what is the maximum thermal efficiency that this heat engine can achieve? What is the maximum possible power output if the heat engine absorbs 300 kW from the atmosphere?

34. A particular Carnot heat engine absorbs energy from a furnace and rejects energy to the atmosphere at 300 K. Graph the efficiency of this heat engine as a function of T_H, the temperature of the furnace. Use a range for T_H of 350 K to 2000 K. What can be concluded from this graph?

35. An inventor submits a patent application for a heat engine that produces 1 kJ for every 2.2 kJ supplied to it. In the application, the inventor states that his heat engine absorbs energy from a 250°C source and rejects energy to a 40°C sink. Evaluate this patent.

36. A 5-MW Carnot steam power plant operates between the temperature limits of 600°C and 20°C. Find the rates of heat transfer to and from the heat engine.

37. A heat engine utilizes solar energy as its energy source. The heat engine incorporates a solar panel that intercepts a solar radiation flux of 900 W/m^2 of panel surface. Assuming that the solar panel absorbs 85 percent of the incident solar radiation, find the exposed surface area of the solar panel required to yield a thermal efficiency of 20 percent and a power output of 3.6 kW for the heat engine.

38. What is the maximum possible power output of a heat engine operating between the temperature limits of 50°C and 800°C if 360 MJ of energy is supplied to the heat engine during a time period of 1 h? What is the actual power output if the heat engine rejects 216 MJ to the 50°C sink during the same time period?

39. A coal-fired steam power plant is to be designed for the purpose of generating electrical power for a city with a population of 60,000 residents. Based on an order-of-magnitude analysis, it is estimated that each resident of the city will consume an average energy of 55 MJ per day. The coal-fired boiler supplies 70 MW to the steam while thermal energy is rejected to a nearby lake whose average temperature is 15°C. What is the minimum required temperature of the boiler to meet the power demands of the city?

15

Fluid Mechanics

1 INTRODUCTION

An important field of study in engineering is *fluid mechanics*. Many of the basic principles of fluid mechanics were developed in parallel with those of solid mechanics, and its historical roots can be traced to such great scientists and mathematicians as Archimedes (287–212 B.C.), Leonardo da Vinci (1425–1519), Isaac Newton (1642–1727), Evangelista Torricelli (1608–1647), Blaise Pascal (1623–1662), Leonhard Euler (1707–1783), Osborne Reynolds (1842–1912), and Ernst Mach (1838–1916). **Fluid mechanics** is the *study of fluids at rest and in motion*. As a subdiscipline of engineering mechanics, fluid mechanics is broadly divided into two categories, fluid statics and fluid dynamics. As the term implies, **fluid statics** is the branch of fluid mechanics that deals with the behavior of fluids at rest. **Fluid dynamics** is the branch of fluid mechanics that deals with the behavior of fluids in motion. In fluid statics, the fluid is at rest with respect to a frame of reference. This means that the fluid does not move with respect to a body or surface with which the fluid is in physical contact. In fluid dynamics, the fluid moves with respect to a body or surface, common examples being the flow of a fluid within a pipe or channel or around an immersed object such as a submarine or aircraft.

There are two primary physical states of matter—solid and fluid, the fluid state being subdivided into the liquid and gas states. A fourth state, referred to as the plasma state, refers to atoms and molecules that are ionized (electrically charged). Plasmas are categorized as special types of fluids that respond to electromagnetic fields. The analysis of plasmas is complex and will not be considered in this book. A fundamental question to be answered is "What is the difference between a solid and a fluid?" Casual observations tell us that solids are "hard" whereas fluids are "soft." Solids have a distinct size and shape and retain their basic dimensions even when large forces are

OBJECTIVES

After reading this chapter, you will have learned

- The importance of fluid mechanics in engineering
- About density, specific weight, and specific gravity of fluids
- The concept of compressibility
- How viscosity affects shear forces in fluids
- To use the pressure-elevation relationship to find forces on submerged surfaces
- How to calculate volume flow rates and mass flow rates
- How to use the principle of continuity to analyze simple flow systems

applied to them. Fluids, however, do not really have a distinct size or shape unless they are confined in some manner by solid boundaries. When placed in a container, a fluid spreads throughout the container, taking on the shape of the container. Such phenomena occurs to one degree or another for liquids and gases. This behavior may be explained by examining the atomic and molecular structure of matter. In solids, the spacing of atoms or molecules is small, and there are large cohesive forces between these particles that enable solids to maintain their shape and size. In fluids, the atomic or molecular spacing is larger, and the cohesive forces are smaller, thereby permitting fluids more freedom of movement. At room temperature and atmospheric pressure, the average intermolecular spacing is approximately 10^{-10} m for liquids and 10^{-9} m for gases. The vast differences in cohesive forces in solids, liquids, and gases account for the rigidity of solids, the ability of liquids to fill containers from the bottom up, and the ability of gases to completely fill containers in which they are placed.

Although the differences between solids and fluids can be explained in terms of atomic or molecular structure, a more useful engineering explanation involves the response of solids and fluids to the application of external forces. Specifically, a **fluid** may be defined as *a substance that deforms continuously when acted upon by a shear stress of any magnitude*. Stress is a force that is applied over a specified area. A **shear stress** is produced when a force acts tangentially on a surface. When a solid material, such as metal, plastic, or wood, is subjected to a shear stress, the material deforms a small amount and maintains a deformed shape while the shear stress is applied. If the shear stress is not too great, the material even returns to its original shape when the force producing the stress is removed. When a fluid is subjected to a shear stress, however, the fluid continues to deform. Unlike a solid, a fluid cannot sustain a shear stress, so it continuously deforms (i.e., the fluid *flows* in response to the shear stress). Some substances, such as tar, toothpaste, putty, and other gunky and gooey materials, exhibit behavior that lies somewhere between solids and fluids. These types of substances will flow if the shear stress is high enough, but the analysis of these substances can be complex. We will therefore restrict our attention to common fluids such as water, oil, and air.

In most colleges and universities, one or more courses in fluid mechanics is required of mechanical, civil, and chemical engineering majors. Depending on the specific curricular policies of your school or department, other majors may also be required to take a course in fluid mechanics. Fluid mechanics is typically offered as part of a "thermofluid" sequence consisting of thermodynamics, fluid mechanics, and heat transfer, since these three disciplines are closely related to one another. Courses in statics, strength of materials, electrical circuits, and other analytically oriented courses round out the engineering science curriculum.

Engineers use principles of fluid mechanics to analyze and design a wide variety of devices and systems. Consider the plumbing fixtures in your home. The sink, bathtub or shower, toilet, dishwasher, and washing machine are supplied water by a system of pipes, pumps, and valves. When you turn on a faucet, the rate at which the water flows is determined by principles of fluid mechanics. The analysis and design of virtually every type of transportation system involves the use of fluid mechanics. Aircraft, surface ships, submarines, rockets, and automobiles require the application of fluid mechanics in their design. Mechanical engineers use fluid mechanics to design heating and air-conditioning systems, turbines, internal combustion engines, pumps, and air compressors. Aeronautical engineers use fluid mechanics to design aircraft, spacecraft, and missiles. Chemical engineers use fluid mechanics to design chemical processing equipment such as heat exchangers and cooling towers. Civil engineers use fluid mechanics to design water treatment plants, flood control systems, irrigation channels, and dams. Principles of fluid mechanics are even important in the design of ground-based structures. The collapse of the Tacoma Narrows Bridge in 1940 could have been prevented, had the designers paid attention to the possible effects of wind forces on suspension bridges. Principles of fluid mechanics are necessary for understanding winds and ocean currents. A proper understanding of fluid mechanics is also needed for studying blood flow in the human circulatory system. The list of fluid mechanics applications is long indeed. Figure 1, Figure 2, and Figure 3 show some engineering systems that involved the use of fluid mechanics in their design.

Figure 1. Aerial view of the Hoover Dam. Engineers used principles of fluid statics to determine the pressure forces acting on the structure.(Courtesy of the U.S. Department of the Interior Bureau of Reclamation, Lower Colorado Region.)

2   FLUID PROPERTIES

A *property* is a *physical characteristic or attribute of a substance*. Matter in either state, solid or fluid, may be characterized in terms of properties. For example, Young's modulus is a property of solids that relates stress to strain. Density is a property of solids and fluids that provides a measure of mass contained in a unit volume. In this section, we examine some of the more commonly used fluid properties. Specifically, we will discuss 1) density, specific weight, and specific gravity, 2) bulk modulus, and 3) viscosity.

Figure 2. Aerodynamics is a special discipline within fluid mechanics. Engineers used principles of aerodynamics to design the unique shape of the F-117 Nighthawk stealth fighter. (Courtesy of Lockheed Martin Corporation, Bethesda, MD.)

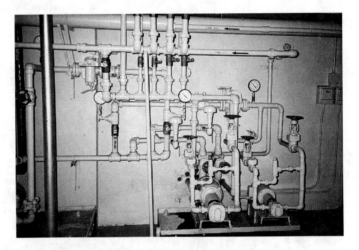

Figure 3. Principles of fluid dynamics are used to design and analyze complex piping systems.

2.1   Density, Specific Weight, and Specific Gravity

A fluid is a continuous medium; that is, a substance that is continuously distributed throughout a region in space. Because a fluid is a continuous medium, it would be rather awkward to analyze the fluid as a single entity with a total mass m, total weight W, or total volume V. It is more convenient to analyze the fluid in terms of the mass of fluid contained in a specified volume. **Density** is defined as *mass per unit volume*. Density is a property that applies to solids as well as fluids. The mathematical definition for density ρ is

$$\rho = \frac{m}{V} \tag{1}$$

The most commonly used units for density are kg/m^3 in the SI system and $slug/ft^3$ in the English system. Values for density can vary widely for different fluids. For example, the densities of water and air at 4°C and 1 atm pressure are about $1000 \ kg/m^3$ ($1.94 \ slug/ft^3$) and $1.27 \ kg/m^3$ ($0.00246 \ slug/ft^3$), respectively. Densities of liquids are higher than those of gases because the intermolecular spacing is smaller. Physical properties vary with temperature and pressure to some extent. For liquids, density does not vary significantly with changes in temperature and pressure, but the densities of gases are strongly influenced by changes in temperature and pressure.

A fluid property that is similar to density is specific weight. **Specific weight** is defined as *weight per unit volume*. The mathematical definition for specific weight γ is

$$\gamma = \frac{W}{V} \tag{2}$$

The most commonly used units for specific weight are N/m^3 in the SI system and lb_f/ft^3 in the English system. Note that the unit for specific weight in the English system is not lb_m/ft^3. The unit lb_m is a unit of mass, not a unit of weight. A quick inspection of Equation (1) and Equation (2) reveals that specific weight is essentially the same property as density with mass replaced by weight. A formula that relates density ρ and specific weight γ may be obtained by noting that the weight of a unit volume of fluid is $W = mg$, where g is the local gravitational acceleration. Substituting the relation for weight W into Equation (2) and combining the result with Equation (1), we obtain the relation

$$\gamma = \rho g \tag{3}$$

Using the standard value of gravitational acceleration, $g = 9.81 \ m/s^2$, water at 4°C has a specific weight of

$$\gamma = \rho g$$
$$= (1000 \ kg/m^3)(9.81 \ m/s^2) = 9810 \ N/m^3 = 9.81 \ kN/m^3$$

Doing the same calculation in English units, noting that the standard value of gravitational acceleration is $g = 32.2 \ ft/s^2$, water at 4°C (39.2°F) has a specific weight of

$$\gamma = \rho g$$
$$= (1.94 \ slug/ft^3)(32.2 \ ft/s^2) = 62.4 \ lb_f/ft^3$$

An alternative form of Equation (3) is

$$\gamma = \frac{\rho g}{g_c} \tag{3a}$$

where g_c is a constant whose magnitude and units depend on the choice of units used for γ. For example, the specific weight of water in SI units may be calculated as

$$\gamma = \frac{\rho g}{g_c}$$
$$= \frac{(1000 \ kg/m^3)(9.81 \ m/s^2)}{1\dfrac{kg \cdot m}{N \cdot s^2}} = 9810 \ N/m^3$$

Noting that 1 slug = 32.2 lb_m, the specific weight of water in English units may be calculated as

$$\gamma = \frac{\rho g}{g_c}$$

$$= \frac{(62.4 \ lb_m/ft^3)(32.2 \ ft/s^2)}{32.2 \dfrac{lb_m \cdot ft}{lb_f \cdot s^2}} = 62.4 \ lb_f/ft^3$$

The density and specific weight of water, or any other substance for that matter, are numerically equivalent as long as the standard value of g is used. The rationale for finding the density and specific weight of water at 4°C in the foregoing discussion is that 4°C is a reference temperature on which specific gravity is based. **Specific gravity** is defined as the *ratio of the density of a fluid to the density of water at a reference temperature*. Typically, the reference temperature is taken as 4°C because the density of water is maximum (about 1000 kg/m^3) at this temperature. The mathematical definition for specific gravity sg is

$$sg = \frac{\rho}{\rho_{H_2O} @ \ 4°C} \tag{4}$$

Because specific gravity is a ratio of two properties with the same units, it is a dimensionless quantity. Furthermore, the value of sg does not depend on the system of units used. For example, the density of mercury at 20°C is 13,550 kg/m^3 (26.29 $slug/ft^3$). Using SI units, the specific gravity of mercury is

$$sg = \frac{\rho}{\rho_{H_2O} @ \ 4°C}$$

$$= \frac{13,550 \ kg/m^3}{1000 \ kg/m^3} = 13.55$$

Using English units, we obtain the same value.

$$sg = \frac{\rho}{\rho_{H_2O} @ \ 4°C}$$

$$= \frac{26.29 \ slug/ft^3}{1.94 \ slug/ft^3} = 13.55$$

Specific gravity may also be defined as the *ratio of the specific weight of a fluid to the specific weight of water at a reference temperature*. This definition, which is derived by combining Equation (4) and Equation (3), is expressed as

$$sg = \frac{\gamma}{\gamma_{H_2O} @ \ 4°C} \tag{5}$$

It does not matter whether Equation (4) or Equation (5) is used to find sg because both relations yield the same value. The definitions given by Equation (4) and Equation (5) apply regardless of the temperature at which the specific gravity is being determined. In other words, the reference temperature for water is always 4°C, but the density and specific weight of the fluid being considered are based on the temperature specified in the problem. Table 1 summarizes the reference values used in the definitions of specific gravity.

TABLE 1   Density and Specific Weight of Water at 4°C.

	ρ	γ
SI	1000 kg/m^3	9810 N/m^3
English	1.94 slug/ft^3	62.4 lb$_f$/ft^3

2.2   Bulk Modulus

An important consideration in the analysis of fluids is the degree to which a given mass of fluid changes its volume (and therefore its density) when there is a change in pressure. Stated another way, how compressible is the fluid? **Compressibility** refers to the change in volume V of a fluid subjected to a change in pressure P. The property used to characterize compressibility is the **bulk modulus** K defined by the relation

$$K = \frac{-\Delta P}{\Delta V/V} \tag{6}$$

where ΔP is the change in pressure, ΔV is the change in volume, and V is the volume before the pressure change occurs. The negative sign is used in Equation (6) because an increase in pressure causes a decrease in volume, thereby assigning a negative sign to the quantity ΔV. The negative signs on ΔP and ΔV cancel, leaving a positive bulk modulus K, which is always a positive quantity. Because the ratio $\Delta V/V$ is dimensionless, the bulk modulus has units of pressure. Typical units used for K are MPa and psi in the SI and English systems, respectively. A large value of K means that the fluid is relatively incompressible (i.e., it takes a large change in pressure to produce a small change in volume). Equation (6) applies for liquids only. Compared with liquids, gases are considered compressible fluids, and the formula for bulk modulus depends on certain thermodynamic considerations. Only liquids will be considered here. Liquids are generally considered incompressible fluids because they compress very little when subjected to a large change in pressure. Hence, the value of K for liquids is typically large. For example, the bulk modulus for water at 20°C is $K = 2.24$ GPa. For mercury at 20°C, $K = 28.5$ GPa. A list of bulk modulus values for some common liquids is given in Table 2.

TABLE 2   Bulk Modulus for Common Liquids at 20°C.

LIQUID	K(GPa)	K(psi)
Benzene	1.48	2.15×10^5
Carbon tetrachloride	1.36	1.97×10^5
Castor oil	2.11	3.06×10^5
Glycerin	4.59	6.66×10^5
Heptane	0.886	1.29×10^5
Kerosene	1.43	2.07×10^5
Lubricating oil	1.44	2.09×10^5
Mercury	28.5	4.13×10^6
Octane	0.963	1.40×10^5
Seawater	2.42	3.51×10^5
Water	2.24	3.25×10^5

Compressibility is an important consideration in the analysis and design of hydraulic systems. Hydraulic systems are used to transmit and amplify forces by pressurizing a fluid in a cylinder. A tube or hose connects the fluid in the cylinder with a mechanical actuator. The hydraulic fluid completely fills the cylinder, connecting line, and actuator so that when a force is applied to the fluid in the cylinder, the fluid is pressurized with equal pressure everywhere in the system. A relatively low force applied to the fluid in the cylinder can produce a large actuator force because the cross-sectional area over which the pressure is applied is much larger in the actuator than in the cylinder. Thus, the force applied at the cylinder is amplified at the actuator. Hydraulic systems are used in a variety of applications, such as heavy construction equipment, manufacturing processes, and transportation systems. The brake system in your automobile is a hydraulic system. When you press the brake pedal, the brake fluid in the system is pressurized, causing the brake mechanism in the wheels to transmit friction forces to the wheels, thereby slowing the vehicle. Brake fluids must have high bulk modulus values for the brake system to function properly. If the value of the bulk modulus of the brake fluid is too low, a large change in pressure will produce a large change in volume that will cause the brake pedal to bottom out on the floor of the automobile, rather than activating the brake mechanism in the wheels. In principle, this is what happens when air becomes trapped inside the brake system. Brake fluid is incompressible, but air is compressible, so the brakes do not function. As an engineering student, you will understand the underlying engineering principles on which this hazardous situation is based. (See Figure 4)

Figure 4. An engineering student explains a brake system failure. (Art by Kathryn Hagen.)

2.3   Viscosity

The fluid properties of density, specific weight, and specific gravity are measures of the "heaviness" of a fluid, but these properties do not completely characterize a fluid. Two different fluids, water and oil, for example, have similar densities, but exhibit distinctly different flow behavior. Water flows readily when poured from a container, whereas oil, which is a "thicker" fluid, flows more slowly. Clearly, an additional fluid property is required to adequately describe the flow behavior of fluids. **Viscosity** may be qualitatively defined as the *property of a fluid that signifies the ease with which the fluid flows under specified conditions.*

To investigate viscosity further, consider the hypothetical experiment depicted in Figure 5. Two parallel plates, one stationary and the other moving with a constant

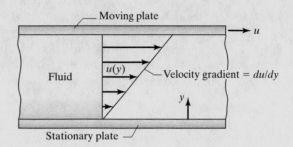

Figure 5.   A velocity gradient is established in a fluid between a stationary and a moving plate.

velocity u enclose a fluid. We observe in this experiment that the fluid in contact with both plates "sticks" to the plates. Hence, the fluid in contact with the bottom plate has a zero velocity, and the fluid in contact with the top plate has a velocity u. The velocity of the fluid changes linearly from zero at the bottom plate to u at the top plate, giving rise to a **velocity gradient** in the fluid. This velocity gradient is expressed as a derivative, du/dy, where y is the coordinate measured from the bottom plate. Because a velocity gradient exists in the fluid, adjacent parallel "layers" of fluid at slightly different y values have slightly different velocities, which means that adjacent layers of fluid slide over each other in the same direction as the velocity u. As adjacent layers of fluid slide across each other, they exert a shear stress τ in the fluid. Our experiment reveals that the shear stress τ is proportional to the velocity gradient du/dy, which is the slope of the function $u(y)$. Thus,

$$\tau \propto \frac{du}{dy} \tag{7}$$

The result indicates that for common fluids such as water, oil, and air, the proportionality in Equation (7) may be replaced by the equality

$$\tau = \mu \frac{du}{dy} \tag{8}$$

where the constant of proportionality μ is called the **dynamic viscosity**. Equation (8) is known as *Newton's law of viscosity*, and fluids that conform to this law are referred to as **Newtonian fluids**. Common liquids such as water, oil, glycerin, and gasoline are Newtonian fluids, as are common gases such as air, nitrogen, hydrogen, and argon. The value of the dynamic viscosity depends on the fluid. Liquids have higher viscosities than gases, and some liquids are more viscous than others. For example, oil, glycerin, and other gooey liquids have higher viscosities than water, gasoline, and alcohol. The viscosities of gases do not vary significantly from one gas to another, however.

Shear stress has the same units as pressure. In the SI system of units, shear stress is expressed in N/m^2, which is defined as a pascal (Pa). In the English system, shear stress is usually expressed in lb_f/ft^2 or lb_f/in^2 (psi). Velocity gradient has units of s^{-1}, so a quick inspection of Equation (8) shows that dynamic viscosity μ has units of $Pa \cdot s$ in the SI system. The units of $Pa \cdot s$ may be broken down into their base units of $kg/m \cdot s$. The units for μ are $lb_f \cdot s/ft^2$ or $slug/ft \cdot s$ in the English system.

Consider once again the configuration illustrated in Figure 5. As the fluid flows between the plates, shear forces caused by viscosity are resisted by inertia forces in the fluid. Inertia forces are forces that tend to maintain a state of rest or motion in all matter, as stated by Newton's first law. A second viscosity property that denotes the ratio of viscous forces to inertia forces in a fluid is kinematic viscosity. **Kinematic viscosity** ν is defined as *the ratio of dynamic viscosity to the density of the fluid*. Thus,

$$\nu = \frac{\mu}{\rho} \tag{9}$$

In the SI system of units, kinematic viscosity is expressed in m^2/s, and in the English system it is expressed in ft^2/s. Because the ratio of dynamic viscosity to density often appears in the analysis of fluid systems, kinematic viscosity may be the preferred viscosity property.

Viscosity, like all physical properties, is a function of temperature. For liquids, dynamic viscosity decreases dramatically with increasing temperature. For gases, however, dynamic viscosity increases, but only slightly, with increasing temperature. The kinematic viscosity of liquids behaves essentially the same as dynamic viscosity because liquid densities change little with temperature. However, because gas densities decrease sharply with increasing temperature, the kinematic viscosities of gases increase drastically with increasing temperature.

EXAMPLE 1

A graduated cylinder containing 100 mL of alcohol has a combined mass of 280 g. If the mass of the cylinder is 200 g, what is the density, specific weight, and specific gravity of the alcohol?

SOLUTION

The combined mass of the cylinder and alcohol is 280 g. By subtraction, the mass of the alcohol is

$$m = (0.280 - 0.200) \text{ kg} = 0.080 \text{ kg}$$

Converting 100 mL to m^3, we obtain

$$100 \text{ mL} \times \frac{1 \text{ L}}{1000 \text{ mL}} \times \frac{1 \text{ m}^3}{1000 \text{ L}} = 1 \times 10^{-4} \text{ m}^3$$

The density of the alcohol is

$$\rho = \frac{m}{V}$$
$$= \frac{0.080 \text{ kg}}{1 \times 10^{-4} \text{ m}^3}$$
$$= 800 \text{ kg/m}^3$$

The weight of the alcohol is

$$W = mg$$
$$= (0.080 \text{ kg})(9.81 \text{ m/s}^2)$$
$$= 0.7848 \text{ N}$$

so the specific weight is

$$\gamma = \frac{W}{V}$$
$$= \frac{(0.7848 \text{ N})}{1 \times 10^{-4} \text{ m}^3}$$
$$= 7848 \text{ N/m}^3$$

The specific gravity of the alcohol is

$$\text{sg} = \frac{\rho}{\rho_{\text{H}_2\text{O}}@ \, 4°C}$$
$$= \frac{800 \text{ kg/m}^3}{1000 \text{ kg/m}^3}$$
$$= 0.800$$

EXAMPLE 2

Find the change in pressure required to decrease the volume of water at 20 C by 1 percent.

SOLUTION

From Table 2, the bulk modulus of water at 20°C is $K = 2.24$ GPa. A 1 percent decrease in volume denotes that $\Delta V/V = -0.01$. Rearranging Equation (6) and solving for ΔP, we obtain

$$\Delta P = -K(\Delta V/V)$$
$$= -(2.24 \times 10^9 \text{ Pa})(-0.01)$$
$$= 22.4 \times 10^6 \text{ Pa} = 22.4 \text{ MPa}$$

EXAMPLE 3

Two parallel plates, spaced 3 mm apart, enclose a fluid. One plate is stationary, while the other plate moves parallel to the stationary plate with a constant velocity of 10 m/s. Both plates measure 60 cm × 80 cm. If a 12-N force is required to sustain the velocity of the moving plate, what is the dynamic viscosity of the fluid?

SOLUTION

The velocity varies from zero at the stationary plate to 10 m/s at the moving plate, and the spacing between the plates is 0.003 m. The velocity gradient in Newton's law of viscosity may be expressed in terms of differential quantities as

$$\Delta u/\Delta y = (10 \text{ m/s})/(0.003 \text{ m}) = 3333 \text{ s}^{-1}$$

The shear stress is found by dividing the force by the area of the plates. Thus,

$$\tau = \frac{F}{A}$$

$$= \frac{12 \text{ N}}{(0.6 \text{ m})(0.8 \text{ m})}$$

$$= 25 \text{ N/m}^2 = 25 \text{ Pa}$$

Rearranging Equation (8) and solving for dynamic viscosity μ we obtain

$$\mu = \frac{\tau}{\Delta u / \Delta y}$$

$$= \frac{25 \text{ Pa}}{3333 \text{ s}^{-1}}$$

$$= 7.50 \times 10^{-3} \text{ Pa} \cdot \text{s}$$

PRACTICE!

1. A cylindrical container with a height and diameter of 16 cm and 10 cm, respectively, contains 1.1 kg of liquid. If the liquid fills the container, find the density, specific weight, and specific gravity of the liquid.
   Answer: 875 kg/m³, 8585 N/m³, 0.875

2. A swimming pool measuring 30 ft × 18 ft × 8 ft is to be filled by using a water truck with a capacity of 5500 gallons. How many trips does the water truck have to make to fill the pool? If the density of the water is 1.93 slug/ft³, what is the mass and weight of the water in the pool after it has been filled?
   Answer: 6, 8381 slug, 2.70×10^5 lb$_f$

3. A cylinder containing benzene at 20°C has a piston that compresses the fluid from 0 to 37 MPa. Find the percent change in the volume of the benzene.
   Answer: −2.50%

4. Hydraulic fluid is compressed by a piston in a cylinder, producing a change in pressure of 40 MPa. Before the piston is activated, the hydraulic fluid fills a 20-cm length of the cylinder. If the axial displacement of the piston is 6.5 mm, what is the bulk modulus of the hydraulic fluid?
   Answer: 1.231 GPa

5. Glycerin at 20°C ($\rho = 1260$ kg/m³, $\mu = 1.48$ Pa·s) occupies a 1.6-mm space between two square parallel plates. One plate remains stationary while the other plate moves with a constant velocity of 8 m/s. If both plates measure 1 m on a side, what force must be exerted on the moving plate to sustain its motion? What is the kinematic viscosity of the glycerin?
   Answer: 7400 N, 1.175×10^{-3} m²/s

3   FLUID STATICS

Fluid mechanics is broadly divided into two categories: *fluid statics* and *fluid dynamics*. Fluid statics, the subject of this section, is the branch of fluid mechanics that deals with the behavior of fluids at rest. In fluid statics, the fluid is at rest with respect to a frame of reference. This means that the fluid does not move with respect to a body or surface with which the fluid is in physical contact. Because the fluid is at rest, the fluid is in a state of equilibrium where the vector sum of the external forces acting on the fluid is zero. As a subject, fluid statics encompasses several areas for study, including forces on submerged surfaces, pressure measurement and manometry, buoyancy, stability, and fluid masses subjected to acceleration. Our treatment of fluid statics will focus on the most fundamental of these subjects: forces on submerged surfaces.

3.1   Pressure Elevation Relationship

Common experience tells us that the pressure increases with depth in a fluid. For example, a scuba diver experiences higher pressures as he descends below the water's surface. If we are to know how to analyze the effect of forces exerted on submerged surfaces, we must first understand how pressure changes with elevation (vertical distance) in a static fluid. To obtain a relationship between pressure and elevation in a static fluid, refer to the configuration shown in Figure 6. In Figure 6, we consider a static body of fluid with

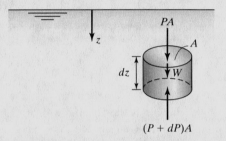

Figure 6. Differential fluid element used to derive the pressure elevation relation $\Delta P = \gamma h$.

density ρ. Because the entire body of fluid is in equilibrium, every particle of fluid must therefore be in equilibrium. Thus, we can isolate an infinitesimally small fluid element for analysis. We choose as our fluid element a cylinder of height dz whose top and bottom surface area is A. Treating the fluid element as a free body in equilibrium, we observe that there are three external forces acting on the element in the z direction. Two of the forces are pressure forces acting on the top and bottom surfaces of the element. The pressure force acting on the top surface is PA, the product of the pressure at a given z coordinate and the surface area. The pressure force acting on the bottom surface is $(P + dP)A$, the product of the pressure at $z + dz$ and the surface area. The pressure acting on the bottom surface is $(P + dP)$, because the pressure has increased a differential amount corresponding to an elevation change of dz. Note that both pressure forces are compressive forces. (There are also pressure forces acting around the perimeter of the cylinder on its curved surface, but these forces cancel one another and are not a function of elevation.) The third force acting on the fluid element is the weight of the fluid element W.

Writing a force balance on the fluid element in the z direction, we obtain

$$\Sigma F_z = 0 = PA - (P + dP)A - W \tag{10}$$

The weight of the fluid element is

$$W = mg = \rho Vg = \rho gAdz \tag{11}$$

where the volume of the element is $V = Adz$. Substituting Equation (11) into Equation (10) and simplifying, we obtain

$$dP = \rho gdz \tag{12}$$

Equation (12) can now be integrated. Pressure is integrated from P_1 to P_2, and elevation is integrated from z_1 to z_2. Thus,

$$\int_1^2 dP = \rho g \int_1^2 dz \tag{13}$$

which yields

$$P_2 - P_1 = \rho g (z_2 - z_1) \tag{14}$$

In many instances, P_1 is taken as the pressure at the origin, $z = z_1 = 0$. The pressure P_2 then becomes the pressure at a depth, z_2, below the free surface of the fluid. We are usually not concerned with the force exerted by atmospheric pressure, so the pressure P_1 at the free surface of the fluid is zero (i.e., the *gauge* pressure at the free surface is zero, and P_2 is the gauge pressure at z_2). Equation (14) may be expressed in a simplified form by letting $\Delta P = P_2 - P_1$ and $h = z_2 - z_1$. Noting that $\gamma = \rho g$, Equation (14) reduces to

$$\Delta P = \gamma h \tag{15}$$

where γ is the specific weight of the fluid and h is the elevation change as referenced from the free surface. As h increases, pressure increases in accordance with our experience. We may draw some general conclusions from the relationship between pressure and elevation given by Equation (15):

1. Equation (15) is valid only for a homogenous static *liquid*. It does not apply to gases, because γ is not constant for compressible fluids.
2. The change in pressure is directly proportional to the specific weight of the liquid.
3. Pressure varies linearly with depth, the specific weight of the liquid being the slope of the linear function.
4. Pressure increases with increasing depth and vice versa.
5. Points on the same horizontal plane have the same pressure.

Another important conclusion that may be drawn from Equation (15) is that, for a given liquid, the pressure change is a function of elevation change h only. Pressure is independent of any other geometrical parameter. The containers illustrated in Figure 7

Figure 7.   For the same liquid, the pressures in these containers at a given depth h are equal, being independent of the shape or size of the container.

are filled to a depth h with the same liquid, so the pressure at the bottom of these containers is the same. Each container has a different size and shape, and therefore contains different amounts of liquid, but the pressure is a function of depth only.

3.2   Forces on Submerged Surfaces

Now that the relationship between pressure and elevation in static liquids has been established, let us apply the relationship to the analysis of forces on submerged surfaces. We will examine two fundamental cases. The first case involves forces exerted by static liquids on horizontal submerged surfaces. The second case involves forces exerted by static liquids on partially submerged vertical surfaces. In both cases, we will restrict our analysis to plane surfaces.

In the first case, we find that the force exerted by a static liquid on a horizontal submerged surface is determined by a direct application of Equation (15). Consider a container with a plane horizontal surface filled with a liquid to a depth h, as shown in Figure 8. The pressure at the bottom of the container is given by $P = \gamma h$. Because the

Figure 8.   The pressure is uniform on a horizontal submerged surface.

bottom surface is horizontal, the pressure is uniform across the surface. The force exerted on the bottom surface is simply the product of the pressure and the surface area. Thus, the force exerted on a horizontal submerged surface is

$$F = PA \tag{16}$$

where $P = \gamma h$ and A is the surface area. Equation (16) is valid regardless of the shape of the horizontal surface. The force exerted on a horizontal submerged surface is equivalent to the weight W of the liquid above the surface. This fact is evident by writing Equation (16) as $F = \gamma(hA) = \gamma V = W$.

In the second case, we examine forces exerted on partially submerged vertical surfaces. One of the conclusions we gleaned from Equation (15) is that pressure varies linearly with depth in a static liquid. Consider the partially submerged vertical plane surface in Figure 9. The pressure (gauge pressure) is zero at the free surface of the liquid, and increases linearly with depth. At a depth h, below the free surface of the liquid, the gauge pressure is $P = \gamma h$. Because the pressure varies linearly from 0 to P over the range 0 to h, the average pressure, P_{avg}, is simply $P/2$. Thus

$$P_{\text{avg}} = \frac{P}{2} = \frac{\gamma h}{2} \tag{17}$$

The average pressure is a constant pressure that, when applied across the entire surface, is equivalent to the actual linearly varying pressure. Like pressure, the force exerted by

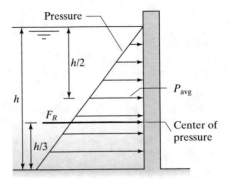

Figure 9. Pressure variation and resultant force on a partially submerged vertical surface.

the static liquid on the vertical surface increases linearly with depth. For purposes of structural design and analysis, we are generally interested in the *total force* or *resultant force* that acts on the vertical surface. The resultant force F_R is the product of the average pressure P_{avg} and the area A of the surface that is submerged. Hence,

$$F_R = P_{avg}A = \frac{\gamma h A}{2} \tag{18}$$

The resultant force is a concentrated force (a force applied at a point) that is equivalent to the linear force distribution on the vertical surface. In order to make use of the resultant force, the point of application of F_R must be known. From principles of statics, it can be shown that for a linearly varying force distribution, the point of application of the equivalent resultant force is two-thirds the distance from the end with the zero force. Consequently, as shown in Figure 9, the resultant force acts at a point $2h/3$ from the free surface of the liquid, or $h/3$ from the bottom of the vertical surface. The point at which the resultant force is applied is called the **center of pressure**. The resultant force, applied at the center of pressure, has the same structural effect on the surface as the actual linear force distribution. The reduction of a distributed force to a concentrated force simplifies the design and analysis of submerged surfaces such as dams, ship hulls, and storage tanks.

EXAMPLE 4

A small dam consists of a vertical plane wall with a height and width of 5 m and 30 m, respectively. The depth of the water ($\gamma = 9.81$ kN/m^3) is 4 m. Find the resultant force on the wall and the center of pressure.

SOLUTION

Using Equation (18) and noting that only 4 m of the dam wall is submerged, we find that the resultant force is

$$F_R = \frac{\gamma h A}{2}$$

$$= \frac{(9810 \text{ N/m}^3)(4 \text{ m})(4 \times 30) \text{ m}^2}{2}$$

$$= 2.35 \times 10^6 \text{ N} = 2.35 \text{ MN}$$

The center of pressure is located two-thirds from the free surface of the water. Thus, the center of pressure, which we denote by z_{cp}, is

$$z_{cp} = \frac{2h}{3}$$

$$= \frac{2(4 \text{ m})}{3} = 2.67 \text{ m (from the free surface)}$$

PRACTICE!

1. A barrel of motor oil ($\gamma = 8.61 \text{ kN/m}^3$) is filled to a depth of 1.15 m. Neglecting atmospheric pressure, what is the pressure on the bottom of the barrel? If the radius of the barrel's bottom is 20 cm, what is the force exerted by the motor oil on the bottom?

   Answer: 9.902 kPa, 78.8 kN

2. The bottom portion of the hull of a barge is submerged 12 ft in seawater ($\gamma = 64.2 \text{ lb}_f/\text{ft}^3$). The hull is horizontal and measures 30 ft $\times$ 70 ft. Find the total force exerted by the seawater on the hull.

   Answer: $1.618 \times 10^6 \text{ lb}_f$

3. The gauge pressure at the bottom of a tank containing ethyl alcohol ($\gamma = 7.87 \text{ kN/m}^3$) is 11 kPa. What is the depth of the alcohol?

   Answer: 1.398 m

4. A vertical gate in an irrigation canal holds back 2.2 m of water. Find the total force on the gate if its width is 3.6 m.

   Answer: 85.5 kN

5. A simple dam is constructed by erecting a vertical concrete wall whose base is secured firmly to the ground. The width of the wall is 16 m, and 5 m of the wall is submerged in water. Find the moment of force about the base of the wall. (*Hint*: The moment of force is the product of the resultant force and the perpendicular distance from the center of pressure to the base of the wall.)

   Answer: 3.27 MN $\cdot$ m

4   FLOW RATES

The concept of flow rate is fundamental to the understanding of elementary fluid dynamics. In general terms, flow rate refers to the time it takes a quantity of fluid to pass a specified location. Virtually all engineering systems that incorporate moving fluids for their operation involve the principle of flow rate. For example, the pipes in your home carry water at certain flow rates to various fixtures and appliances such as sinks, bathtubs, and washing machines. Heating and air-conditioning systems supply air at specified flow rates to the rooms in a building to achieve the desired heating or cooling effects. Minimum flow rates are required to produce the lifting forces that sustain the flight of aircraft. The design of turbines, pumps, compressors, heat exchangers, and other fluid-based devices involves the use of flow rates.

In fluid dynamics, there are primarily two types of flow rates: volume flow rate and mass flow rate. **Volume flow rate** is the *rate at which a volume of fluid passes a location per unit time*. **Mass flow rate** is the *rate at which a mass of fluid passes a location per unit time*. These are general definitions that apply to all fluid dynamic situations, but our application of these definitions will be limited to the flow of fluids in conduits such as pipes, ducts, and channels. Volume flow rate Q is calculated by using the relation

$$Q = AV \tag{19}$$

where A is the inside cross-sectional area of the conduit and V is the *average* velocity of the fluid. The word "average" is emphasized here because the velocity of the fluid in a conduit is not constant. Effects of viscosity produce a velocity gradient or profile in the fluid across the breadth of the conduit. (Be careful not to confuse fluid velocity with volume because the symbol V is used for both quantities. Similarly, do not confuse volume flow rate with heat, which both use the symbol Q.) Common units for volume flow rate are m^3/s in the SI system and ft^3/s in the English system. Other units frequently used for volume flow rate are L/min and gal/min or L/h and gal/h. Equation (19) applies to any conduit, regardless of its cross-sectional shape. For example, if the conduit is a circular pipe or tube, then $A = \pi R^2$, where R is the inside radius, whereas if the conduit is a duct with a square cross section, then $A = L^2$, where L is the inside dimension of the duct. Mass flow rate m is calculated by using the relation

$$\dot{m} = \rho Q \tag{20}$$

where ρ is the density of the fluid and Q is the volume flow rate given by Equation (19). The 'dot' over the m denotes a time derivative or a rate quantity. However, by convention, the dot is not used for Q. Common units for mass flow rate are kg/s in the SI system and slug/s or lb_m/s in the English system. Equations (19) and (20) apply to liquids and gases.

EXAMPLE 5

A pipe with an inside diameter of 5 cm carries water at an average velocity of 3 m/s. Find the volume flow rate and mass flow rate.

SOLUTION

The cross-sectional area of the pipe is

$$A = \frac{\pi D^2}{4}$$

$$= \frac{\pi (0.05 \text{ m})^2}{4} = 1.963 \times 10^{-3} \text{ m}^2$$

The volume flow rate is

$$Q = AV$$

$$= (1.936 \times 10^{-3} \text{ m}^2)(3 \text{ m/s})$$

$$= 5.89 \times 10^{-3} \text{ m}^3/s$$

Taking the density of water to be $\rho = 1000 \text{ kg/m}^3$, the mass flow rate is

$$\dot{m} = \rho Q$$

$$= (1000 \text{ kg/m}^3)(5.89 \times 10^{-3} \text{ m}^3/s)$$

$$= 5.89 \text{ kg/s}$$

PROFESSIONAL SUCCESS: THINGS TO CONSIDER AT THE "HUMP"

A traditional engineering bachelor's degree takes four years to complete. The times that mark the conclusion of the freshman, sophomore, junior, and senior years of a college career are sometimes facetiously referred to as the bump, hump, slump, and dump, respectively. (The fact that you are reading this book suggests that you have not bumped yet.) By the time you hump, you should begin thinking about what you want to do after graduation. Should you accept an engineering position immediately after graduation or go to graduate school? What about going to work as an engineer while working on a graduate degree part time? Should you work for a few years and then go back to school for a graduate degree? Should you obtain your professional engineering license? Should you pursue a nontechnical graduate degree to complement your engineering background? These are some of the questions that you should be asking yourself about midway through your undergraduate engineering program.

A bachelor's degree in engineering paves the road to a rewarding career with a very respectable salary, so many four-year engineering graduates do not pursue graduate studies. However, many engineering companies have a need for engineers with in-depth expertise in specific technical disciplines, so engineers with graduate degrees are in high demand. In general, engineers with graduate degrees have higher salaries than their coworkers with only a bachelor's degree and are frequently well positioned for supervisory and managerial roles. If a graduate degree is in the future for you, is it better to enter graduate school immediately after you graduate with your four-year degree, or should you accrue some engineering experience first and then pursue a graduate degree while you are working? That depends on your personal circumstances, the nature of the graduate school you wish to attend and the policies of your employer. Many people feel that their lives are busy enough with a full-time job, family, and other responsibilities without adding graduate school to the list. Some graduate programs may not look favorably upon part-time graduate students who, because of work commitments, cannot devote their whole body and soul to their graduate studies.

However, many schools are quite willing to work with (and even welcome) part-time graduate students in their engineering programs. Most engineering companies offer educational assistance to their engineers who wish to pursue graduate studies. This assistance most often comes in the form of tuition reimbursement and flexible working schedules so their employees can take graduate courses at a nearby university. As for pursuing a graduate degree in engineering or a nontechnical field such as business or management, you should examine your personal educational and career goals. Do you want to advance technically in a specific discipline, or do you want to climb the management ladder?

Should you become professionally licensed? Regardless of your answer to this question, you should seriously consider taking the Fundamentals of Engineering (FE) examination in the junior or senior year of your program. This test is a state-sponsored exam offered twice a year and administered at your own school or at a school in your area. The FE exam, or the EIT (Engineer in Training) exam, as it is sometimes called, is an 8-hour exam that covers the fundamental principles of engineering that are covered in a typical undergraduate engineering curriculum. Some engineering schools require their students to pass the FE exam to graduate. After you have passed the exam and have worked a few years as a practicing engineer, you can take the PE (Professional Engineer) exam that is specific to your discipline. If you pass that exam and if you have satisfied the other licensing requirements specified by your state, you can write the initials PE after your name on official letters, drawings, and other documents. A professional engineer is an engineer who is officially recognized by the state as having demonstrated proficiencies in a specific engineering discipline. Most engineering companies do not require their engineers to be professionally licensed, but some firms, particularly state and municipal governments, have strict rules about employing engineers who are professionally licensed. Thus, your decision to become professionally licensed or not may be largely based on the requirements or recommendations of your employer.

PRACTICE!

1. A steel tube carries gasoline ($\rho = 751 \text{ kg/m}^3$) at an average velocity of 0.85 m/s. If the inside diameter of the tube is 7 mm, find the volume flow rate and mass flow rate.

    Answer: 3.271×10^{-5} m^3/s, 0.0246 kg/s

2. Water flows through a plastic pipe at a volume flow rate of 160 gal/min. What is the inside radius of the pipe if the average velocity of the water is 8 ft/s? Express your answer in inches and centimeters.

   Answer: 1.43 in, 3.63 cm

3. A blower forces air ($\gamma = 11.7 \text{ N/m}^3$) through a rectangular duct with a 50 cm × 80 cm inside cross section. If the average velocity of the air is 7 m/s, find the volume flow rate and mass flow rate. Express the volume flow rate in m^3/s and ft^3/min (CFM) and the mass flow rate in kg/s and slug/h.

   Answer: 2.80 m^3/s, 5933 ft^3/min, 3.339 kg/s, 824 slug/h

4. A pump removes water from a 1200-gallon storage tank at a rate of 0.05 m^3/s. How long will it take the pump to empty the tank? If a pipe with an inside diameter of 6 cm connects the pump to the tank, what is the average velocity of the water in the pipe?

   Answer: 17.7 m/s

5. Air flows through a duct with a rectangular cross section at an average velocity of 20 ft/s and a volume flow rate of 3000 CFM. If the inside dimension of one side of the duct measures 18 in, what is the dimension of the other side?

   Answer: 1.667 ft

5   CONSERVATION OF MASS

Some of the most important fundamental principles used to analyze engineering systems are the conservation laws. A conservation law is an immutable law of nature declaring that certain physical quantities are conserved. Defined another way, a conservation law states that the total amount of a particular physical quantity is constant during a process. A familiar conservation law is the first law of thermodynamics, which states that energy is conserved. According to the first law of thermodynamics, energy may be converted from one form to another, but the total energy is constant. Another conservation law is Kirchhoff's current law, which states that the algebraic sum of the currents entering a circuit node is zero. Kirchhoff's current law is a statement of the law of conservation of electric charge. Other quantities that are conserved are linear and angular momentum.

In this section, we examine the principal conservation law used in fluid mechanics, the law of conservation of mass. Like the first law of thermodynamics, the law of conservation of mass is an intuitive concept. To introduce the conservation of mass principle, consider the system shown in Figure 10. The system may represent any region in space chosen for analysis. The boundary of the system is the surface that separates the system from the surroundings. We may construct a mathematical representation of the conservation of mass principle by applying a simple physical argument. If an amount of mass m_{in} is supplied *to* the system, that mass can either *leave* the system or *accumulate* within the system, or both. The mass that leaves the system is m_{out}, and the change in mass within the system is Δm. Thus, the mass that enters the system equals the mass that leaves the system plus the change in mass within the system. The conservation of mass principle may therefore be expressed mathematically as

$$m_{in} = m_{out} + \Delta m \qquad (21)$$

We see that the conservation of mass law is nothing more than a simple accounting principle that maintains the system's "mass ledger" in balance. In fact, this conservation law is often referred to as a *mass balance* because that is precisely what it is. Equation (21)

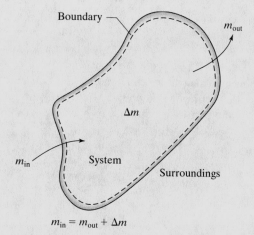

Figure 10. The law of conservation of mass.

is more useful when expressed as a rate equation. Dividing each term by a time interval Δt, we obtain

$$\dot{m}_{in} = \dot{m}_{out} + \Delta m / \Delta t \tag{22}$$

where $\dot{m}_{in}$ and $\dot{m}_{out}$ are the inlet and outlet mass flow rates, respectively, and $\Delta m / \Delta t$ is the rate at which mass accumulates within the system. The law of conservation of mass is called the **continuity principle**, and Equation (22), or a similar relation, is referred to as the *continuity equation*.

We now examine a special case of the configuration given in Figure 10. Consider the converging pipe shown in Figure 11. The dashed line outlines the boundary of

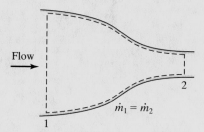

Figure 11. Continuity principle for a converging pipe.

the flow system defined by the region inside the pipe wall and between sections 1 and 2. A fluid flows at a constant rate from section 1 to section 2. Because fluid does not accumulate between sections 1 and 2, $\Delta m / \Delta t = 0$, and Equation (22) becomes

$$\dot{m}_1 = \dot{m}_2 \tag{23}$$

where the subscripts 1 and 2 denote the input and output, respectively. Thus, the mass of fluid flowing past section 1 per unit time is the same as the mass of fluid flowing past section 2 per unit time. Because $\dot{m} = \rho Q$, Equation (23) may also be expressed as

$$\rho_1 Q_1 = \rho_2 Q_2 \qquad (24)$$

where ρ and Q denote density and volume flow rate, respectively. Equation (23), and its alternative form, Equation (24), are valid for liquids and gases. Hence, these relations apply to compressible and incompressible fluids. If the fluid is incompressible, the fluid density is constant, so $\rho_1 = \rho_2 = \rho$. Dividing Equation (24) by density ρ, yields

$$Q_1 = Q_2 \qquad (25)$$

which may be written as

$$A_1 V_1 = A_2 V_2 \qquad (26)$$

where A and V refer to cross-sectional area and average velocity, respectively. Equations (25) and (26) apply strictly to liquids, but these relations may also be used for gases with little error if the velocities are below approximately 100 m/s.

The continuity principle can also be used to analyze more complex flow configurations, such as a flow branch. A flow branch is a junction where three or more conduits are connected. Consider the pipe branch shown in Figure 12. A fluid enters a junction from a supply pipe, where it splits into two pipe branches. The flow rates in the branching pipes depend on the size of the pipes and other characteristics of the system, but

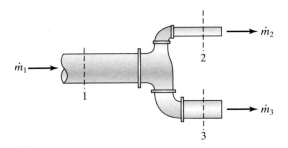

Figure 12.   A pipe branch.

from the continuity principle it is clear that the mass flow rate in the supply pipe must equal the sum of the mass flow rates in the two pipe branches. Thus, we have

$$\dot{m}_1 = \dot{m}_2 + \dot{m}_3 \qquad (27)$$

Junctions in flow branches are analogous to nodes in electrical circuits. Kirchhoff's current law, which is a statement of the law of conservation of electric charge, states that the algebraic sum of the currents entering a node is zero. For a flow branch, the continuity principle states that *the algebraic sum of the mass flow rates entering a junction is zero.* The mathematical expression for this principle is similar to Kirchhoff's current law and is written as

$$\Sigma \dot{m}_{in} = 0 \qquad (28)$$

The continuity relation given by Equation (27) for the specific case illustrated in Figure 12 is equivalent to the general form of the relation given by Equation (28). We have

$$\begin{aligned} \Sigma \dot{m}_{in} &= 0 \\ &= \dot{m}_1 - \dot{m}_2 - \dot{m}_3 \end{aligned} \qquad (29)$$

where minus signs are used for mass flow rates $\dot{m}_2$ and $\dot{m}_3$ because the fluid in each pipe branch is leaving the junction. The mass flow rate $\dot{m}_1$ is positive because the fluid in the supply pipe is entering the junction.

In the next example, we analyze a basic flow system by using the general analysis procedure of (1) problem statement, (2) diagram, (3) assumptions, (4) governing equations, (5) calculations, (6) solution check, and (7) discussion.

EXAMPLE 6

Problem statement

A converging duct carries oxygen ($\rho = 1.320 \text{ kg/m}^3$) at a mass flow rate of 110 kg/s. The duct converges from a cross-sectional area of 2 m^2 to a cross-sectional area of 1.25 m^2. Find the volume flow rate and the average velocities in both duct sections.

Diagram

The diagram for this problem is shown in Figure 13.

Assumptions

1. The flow is steady.
2. The fluid is incompressible.
3. There are no leaks in the duct.

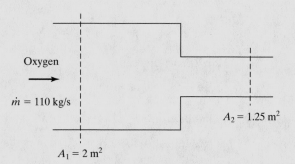

Oxygen

$\dot{m} = 110 \text{ kg/s}$

$A_2 = 1.25 \text{ m}^2$

$A_1 = 2 \text{ m}^2$

Figure 13. Converging duct for Example 6.

Governing equations

Two equations are needed to solve this problem—the relation for mass flow rate and the continuity relation:

$$\dot{m} = \rho Q$$

$$Q = A_1 V_1 = A_2 V_2$$

Calculations

By continuity, the volume flow rate and mass flow rate are equal at sections 1 and 2. The volume flow rate is

$$Q = \frac{\dot{m}}{\rho}$$

$$= \frac{110 \text{ kg/s}}{1.320 \text{ kg/m}^3}$$

$$= \underline{\underline{83.33 \text{ m}^3/\text{s}}}$$

The average velocity in the large section is

$$V_1 = \frac{Q}{A_1}$$

$$= \frac{83.33 \text{ m}^3/\text{s}}{2 \text{ m}^2}$$

$$= \underline{\underline{41.7 \text{ m/s}}}$$

and the average velocity in the small section is

$$V_2 = \frac{Q}{A_2}$$

$$= \frac{83.33 \text{ m}^3/\text{s}}{1.25 \text{ m}^2}$$

$$= \underline{\underline{66.7 \text{ m/s}}}$$

Solution check

After a careful review of our solution, no errors are found.

Discussion

Note that velocity and cross-sectional area are inversely related. The velocity is low in the large portion of the duct and high in the small portion of the duct. The maximum velocity in the duct is below 100 m/s, so the oxygen may be considered an incompressible fluid with little error. Our assumption that the fluid is incompressible is therefore valid.

APPLICATION: ANALYZING A PIPE BRANCH

Pipe branches are used frequently in piping systems to split a stream into two or more flows. Consider a pipe branch similar to the one shown in Figure 12. Water enters the pipe junction at a volume flow rate of 350 gal/min, and the flow splits into two branches. One pipe branch has an inside diameter of 7 cm, and the other pipe branch has an inside diameter of 4 cm. If the average velocity of the water in the 7-cm branch is 3 m/s, find the mass flow rate and volume flow rate in each branch and the average velocity in the 4-cm branch. A flow schematic with the pertinent information is shown in Figure 14. First, we convert the volume flow rate in the supply pipe to m^3/s.

$$Q_1 = 350 \frac{\text{gal}}{\text{min}} \times \frac{1 \text{ m}^3}{264.17 \text{ gal}} \times \frac{1 \text{ min}}{60 \text{ s}} = 0.02208 \text{ m}^3/\text{s}$$

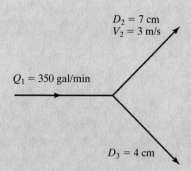

$D_2 = 7$ cm
$V_2 = 3$ m/s

$Q_1 = 350$ gal/min

$D_3 = 4$ cm

Figure 14. Flow schematic for a pipe branch.

The cross-sectional areas of the pipes branches are

$$A_2 = \frac{\pi D_2^2}{4}$$
$$= \frac{\pi (0.07 \text{ m})^2}{4} = 3.848 \times 10^{-3} \text{ m}^2$$

$$A_3 = \frac{\pi D_3^2}{4}$$
$$= \frac{\pi (0.04 \text{ m})^2}{4} = 1.257 \times 10^{-3} \text{ m}^2$$

The volume flow rate in the 7-cm pipe branch is

$$Q_2 = A_2 V_2$$
$$= (3.848 \times 10^{-3} \text{ m}^2)(3 \text{ m/s})$$
$$= 0.01154 \text{ m}^3/\text{s}$$

and the mass flow rate is

$$\dot{m}_2 = \rho Q_2$$
$$= (1000 \text{ kg/m}^3)(0.01154 \text{ m}^3/\text{s})$$
$$= 11.54 \text{ kg/s}$$

In order to find the flow rates in the other pipe branch, the continuity principle is required:

$$Q_1 = Q_2 + Q_3$$

Solving for Q_3, we obtain

$$Q_3 = Q_1 - Q_2$$
$$= (0.02208 - 0.01154) \text{ m}^3/\text{s}$$
$$= 0.01054 \text{ m}^3/\text{s}$$

and the corresponding mass flow rate is

$$\dot{m}_3 = \rho Q_3$$
$$= (1000 \text{ kg/m}^3)(0.01054 \text{ m}^3/\text{s})$$
$$= 10.54 \text{ kg/s}$$

Finally, the average velocity in the 4-cm branch is

$$V_3 = \frac{Q_3}{A_3}$$
$$= \frac{0.01054 \text{ m}^3/\text{s}}{1.257 \times 10^{-3} \text{ m}^2}$$
$$= 8.38 \text{ m/s}$$

As a way of checking for errors, we use the continuity principle to assure that our flow rates are correct. The volume flow rate into the junction must equal the sum of the volume flow rates out of the junction. Thus,

$$Q_1 = Q_2 + Q_3$$
$$0.02208 \text{ m}^3/\text{s} = 0.01154 \text{ m}^3/\text{s} + 0.01054 \text{ m}^3/\text{s}$$

The flow rates balance, so our answers are correct. Notice that the flow rates in the pipe branches are nearly equal (11.54 kg/s and 10.54 kg/s), but the velocities are quite different (3 m/s and 8.38 m/s). This is due to the difference in diameters of the pipes. The velocity is nearly three times higher in the 4-cm pipe than in the 7-cm pipe.

PRACTICE!

1. Water flows through a converging pipe at a mass flow rate of 25 kg/s. If the inside diameters of the pipes sections are 7 cm and 5 cm, find the volume flow rate and the average velocity in each pipe section.
    Answer: 0.025 m³/s, 6.50 m/s, 12.7 m/s

2. A fluid flows through a pipe whose diameter decreases by a factor of three from section 1 to section 2 in the direction of the flow. If the average velocity at section 1 is 10 ft/s, what is the average velocity at section 2?
    Answer: 90 ft/s

3. Air enters a junction in a duct at a volume flow rate of 2000 CFM. Two square duct branches, one measuring 12 in × 12 in and the other measuring 16 in × 16 in, carry the air from the junction. If the average velocity in the small branch is 20 ft/s, find the volume flow rates in each branch and the average velocity in the large branch.
   Answer: 20 ft³/s, 13.3 ft³/s, 9.98 ft/s

4. Two water streams, a cold stream and a hot stream, enter a mixing chamber where both streams combine and exit through a single tube. The mass flow rate of the hot stream is 5 kg/s, and the inside diameter of the tube carrying the cold stream is 3 cm. Find the mass flow rate of the cold stream required to produce an exit velocity of 8 m/s in a tube with an inside diameter of 4.5 cm.
   Answer: 7.72 kg/s

KEY TERMS

bulk modulus	fluid dynamics	specific gravity
center of pressure	fluid mechanics	specific weight
compressibility	fluid statics	velocity gradient
continuity principle	kinematic viscosity	viscosity
density	mass flow rate	volume flow rate
dynamic viscosity	Newtonian fluid	
fluid	shear stress	

REFERENCES

Fox, R.W., A.T. McDonald, and P.J. Pritchard, *Introduction to Fluid Mechanics*, 6th ed. NY: John Wiley & Sons, 2004.

Munson, B.R., D.F. Young, and T.H. Okiishi, *Fundamentals of Fluid Mechanics*, 4th ed., NY: John Wiley & Sons, 2002.

Douglas, D.F., J.M. Gasiorek, and J.A. Swaffield, *Fluid Mechanics*, 4th ed., Upper Saddle River, NJ: Prentice Hall, 2001.

Street, R.L., G.Z. Watters, and J.K. Vennard, *Elementary Fluid Mechanics*, 7th ed., NY: John Wiley & Sons, 1996.

White, W.M., *Fluid Mechanics*, 5th ed., NY: McGraw-Hill, 2002.

Problems

1. The specific gravity of a liquid is 0.920. Find the density and specific weight of the liquid in SI and English units.

2. A 12-cm diameter cylindrical can is filled to a depth of 10 cm with motor oil ($\rho = 878$ kg/m³). Find the mass and weight of the motor oil.

3. The fuel tank of a truck has a capacity of 0.12 m³. If the tank is full of gasoline (sg = 0.751), what is the mass and weight of the gasoline?

4. A 5-m diameter spherical balloon contains hydrogen. If the density of the hydrogen is $\rho = 0.0830$ kg/m³, what is the mass and weight of the hydrogen in the balloon?

5. Find the volume of mercury (sg = 13.55) that weighs the same as 0.04 m³ of ammonia (sg = 0.600).

6. Find the pressure change required to produce a 1.5 percent decrease in the volume of carbon tetrachloride at 20°C.

7. Hydraulic fluid is compressed by a piston in a cylinder producing a change in pressure of 120 MPa. Before the piston is activated, the hydraulic fluid fills a 16-cm length of the cylinder. If the axial displacement of the piston is 8 mm, what is the bulk modulus of the hydraulic fluid?

8. The pressure change in a hydraulic cylinder is 180 MPa for an axial displacement of 15 mm of the piston. If the bulk modulus of the hydraulic fluid is 4500 MPa, what is the minimum length of cylinder required?

9. What is the percent change in the volume of a liquid whose bulk modulus value is 100 times the change in pressure?

10. The velocity gradient $u(y)$ near the surface of a single plate over which a fluid flows is given by the function

$$u(y) = ay + by^2 + cy^3$$

where y is the distance from the plate's surface and a, b, and c are constants with the values $a = 10.0 \text{ s}^{-1}$, $b = 0.02 \text{ m}^{-1}\text{s}^{-1}$, and $c = 0.005 \text{ m}^{-2}\text{s}^{-1}$. If the fluid is water at 20°C ($\mu = 1.0 \times 10^{-3} \text{ Pa} \cdot \text{s}$), find the shear force at the surface of the plate (at $y = 0$).

For problems 11 through 31, use the general analysis procedure of (1) problem statement, (2) diagram, (3) assumptions, (4) governing equations, (5) calculations, (6) solution check, and (7) discussion.

11. Two square parallel plates enclose 20°C glycerin ($\mu = 1.48 \text{ Pa} \cdot \text{s}$) as illustrated in Figure P11. The bottom plate is fixed, and the top plate is attached to a hanging mass by a cord that passes over a frictionless pulley. What mass m is required to sustain a constant velocity of 1.5 m/s for the top plate?

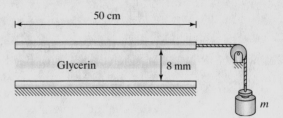

Figure P11.

12. The deepest known point in the oceans of the earth is the Mariana Trench, east of the Philippines, with a depth of approximately 10.9 km. Taking the specific gravity of seawater as sg = 1.030, what is the pressure at the bottom of the Mariana Trench? Express your answer in kPa and atmospheres.

13. The average depth of the world's oceans is 5000 m, and the oceans cover 71 percent of the earth's surface. What is the approximate total force exerted by the oceans on the earth's surface? The earth is nearly spherical with an average diameter of approximately 12.7×10^6 m, and the specific weight of seawater is $\gamma = 10.1 \text{ kN/m}^3$.

14.   A storage tank containing heavy fuel oil ($\rho = 906 \text{ kg/m}^3$) is filled to a depth of 7 m. Find the gauge pressure at the bottom of the tank.

15.   A container holds three immiscible liquids as shown in Figure P15. Find the gauge pressure at the bottom of the container.

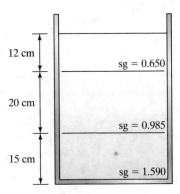

Figure P15.

16.   The side of a barge is submerged 6 m below the surface of the ocean ($\gamma = 10.1 \text{ kN/m}^3$). The length of the barge is 40 m. Treating the side of the barge as a plane vertical surface, what is the total force exerted by the ocean on the side of the barge?

17.   To what depth would a container of glycerin (sg = 1.26) have to be filled to yield the same pressure at the bottom of a container with 4.5 in of mercury (sg = 13.55)?

18.   Calculate the gauge pressure at the bottom of an open 2-liter container full of soft drink.

19.   Calculate the force required to remove a 5-cm diameter plug from a hot-tub drain when the hot tub is filled with water to a depth of 60 cm. Neglect friction.

20.   A cast iron pipe carries waste water at an average velocity of 5 m/s. If the inside diameter of the pipe is 10 cm, find the volume flow rate and the mass flow rate.

21.   An open canal with the cross section shown in Figure P21 carries irrigation water at an average velocity of 2 m/s. Find the volume flow rate and mass flow rate.

22.   An intravenous device for administering a sucrose solution to a hospital patient deposits a drop of solution into the mouth of a delivery tube every two seconds. The drops are spherical in shape with a diameter of 3.5 mm. If the inside diameter of the delivery tube is 2.0 mm, what is the mass flow rate and the average velocity of sucrose solution in the tube? If the plastic vessel containing the sucrose solution holds 500 mL, how long will it take to empty? The sucrose solution has a specific weight of $\gamma = 10.8 \text{ kN/m}^3$.

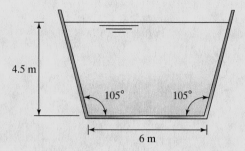

Figure P21.

23. A furnace requires 1500 lb_m/h of cold air for efficient combustion. If the air has a specific weight of 0.064 lb_f/ft^3, find the required volume flow rate.

24. A ventilation duct supplies fresh filtered air to a clean room where semiconductor devices are manufactured. The cross section of the filter medium is 1.2 m × 1.6 m. If the volume flow rate of air to the clean room is 3 m^3/s, find the average velocity of the air as it passes through the filter. If ρ = 1.194 kg/m^3 for the air, find the mass flow rate.

25. A converging rectangular duct carries nitrogen (ρ = 1.155 kg/m^3) at a mass flow rate of 4 kg/s. The small section of the duct measures 30 cm × 40 cm, and the large section measures 50 cm × 60 cm. Find the volume flow rate and the average velocities in each section.

26. A nozzle is a device that accelerates the flow of a fluid. A circular nozzle that converges from an inside diameter of 10 cm to 6 cm carries a gas at a volume flow rate of 0.25 m^3/s. Find the change in average velocity of the gas.

27. A diffuser is a device that decelerates the flow of air in order to recover a pressure loss. For the diffuser shown in Figure P27, find the mass flow rate and the average velocity of the air at the exit of the diffuser. For air, let ρ = 1.194 kg/m^3.

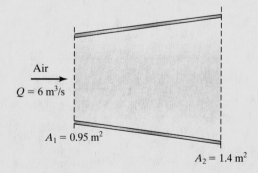

Figure P27.

28.   A pipe branch is illustrated in schematic form in Figure P28. Find the mass flow rate $\dot{m}_4$. Does the fluid in branch 4 enter or leave the junction?

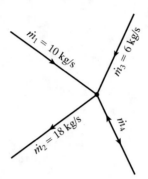

Figure P28.

29.   The average velocity of the water in a 0.75-in diameter pipe connected to a shower head is 12 ft/s. The shower drain, which is partially clogged with hair, allows 0.03 slug/s to flow into the drain. If the bottom of the shower measures 2.5 ft square and 6 inch deep, how much time is required for the shower to overflow?

30.   A duct carrying conditioned air from a refrigeration unit splits into two separate ducts that supply cool air to different parts of a building. The supply duct has a 1.8 m × 2.2 m inside cross section, and the two duct branches have inside cross sections of 0.9 m × 1.2 m and 0.65 m × 0.8 m. The average velocity of the air in the supply duct is 7 m/s, and the average velocity of the air in the smaller duct branch is 18 m/s. Find the volume flow rates, and mass flow rates, in each branch. For air, use $\rho = 1.20 \ \text{kg/m}^3$.

31.   The mixing chamber shown in Figure P31 facilitates the blending of three liquids. Find the volume flow rate and mass flow rate of the mixture at the exit of the chamber.

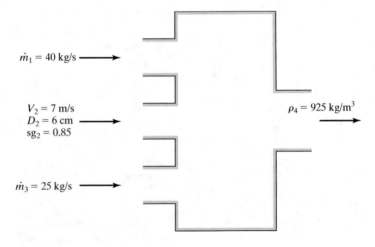

Figure P31.

16

Introduction to Technical Communications

1   INTRODUCTION

Some people think the term *technical communications* is a contradiction in terms. Technical information, they say, is just numbers. They may snicker that engineers are not always natural after-dinner speakers. Why spend your time on the presentation side of things when some engineers are more comfortable grinding out the numbers?

People with these attitudes are sadly misinformed. Engineering often results in complex answers that need to be communicated simply and effectively. The truth is that *engineering work has no impact unless the message is delivered successfully*.

Technical presentations also must "tell a story." The conclusions of the story, of course, must be supported by data and solid reasoning. In evaluating your own technical writing or technical presentations, it is always important to ask yourself, Has the audience understood my story?

The purpose of this chapter is to introduce you to the importance of technical communications (Sections 2 and 3) and present ground rules common to all technical communication (Sections 4 through 9). In Section 4, the important questions you should answer before you start writing your report or technical talk will be discussed. Some techniques for organizing the presentation material will be presented in Section 5. In Sections 6, 7, and 8, you will learn in detail the ways that data are presented, including the design and construction of tables and figures. Section 9 discusses creativity in technical presentations.

You will notice some new terminology in this chapter. The recipients of the presentation will be referred to simply as the "audience," since the recipients could be either *readers* of your technical document or *listeners* of your technical talk. The word "presentation" will include both written documents and technical talks.

OBJECTIVES

After reading this chapter, you will be able to:

- explain why technical communication skills are important to engineers;
- list common misconceptions about technical communication;
- discuss how the presentation goals, the target audience, and the constraints shape technical communication;
- devise an outline for a technical presentation;
- use tables and figures to communicate technical information effectively.

2   ROLE OF TECHNICAL COMMUNICATION IN ENGINEERING

2.1   Technical Communication as a Professional Skill

Your interest in engineering may have been fueled by the important role of engineers in society and the challenges that engineers face every day. Take a moment to make a mental list of what engineers do.

PONDER THIS

Key idea: Technical presentations must tell a story; always ask yourself whether the audience understood your story.

What activities do engineers perform?

Your list may include activities such as designing, modeling, testing, building, and optimizing. While most engineers do at least one of these activities *some* of the time, all engineers communicate *all* the time. In a real sense, engineering is not engineering until you, the engineer, successfully communicate the results to someone else. Technical communication is not effective unless the audience understands the message you wish to deliver.

2.2   Technical Communication and Employment

Key idea: Strong technical presentation skills aid in obtaining a job and in advancing a career.

If you remain unconvinced of the importance of technical communication, consider a more practical reason to improve your communication skills. Engineering faculty frequently receive telephone calls requesting information about students (or former students) applying for jobs. Nearly every potential employer asks two questions: Can the person *write* effectively? Can he or she *speak* well? Potential employers ask these questions because they know that engineers spend a great deal of their time communicating. The result of a survey of graduates from the University at Buffalo's School of Engineering and Applied Sciences showed that respondents spent an average of *64% of their working hours* on written communication, oral presentations, and other oral discussions. To compete for employment opportunities, engineers must develop strong technical communication skills. Technical excellence is necessary (but not sufficient) to secure a good job in today's employment market.

Technical communication skills affect not only your ability to get a job, but also your ability to progress in your profession. In a survey cited by Paradis and Zimmerman (1997), over half of the research and development engineers and scientists polled (and 71% of the managers) knew of cases where technical communication skills had a serious impact on a person's career. Respondents to the University at Buffalo survey indicated that good technical communication skills can make the difference between receiving a raise and not receiving a raise. Good technical communication skills are prerequisites for success in your career.

3   MISCONCEPTIONS ABOUT TECHNICAL COMMUNICATIONS

Few areas of the engineering profession are more poorly understood or more underappreciated than technical communication. Common misconceptions are discussed in the next several sections.

3.1   Misconception #1: Technical Communication Is Inherently Boring

Key idea: Technical communication is a creative process.

Some people feel that engineers excel in dry facts and even drier numbers. How can an engineer possibly communicate creatively? The truth is that designing effective communication strategies is one of the most creative activities in engineering. Technical communication does not mean linking dull facts to form a sleep-inducing document or boring oral presentation. Today, engineers have many tools at their disposal for communicating ideas: everything from sketches on the back of a napkin to 3-D visualization techniques to Internet-based teleconferencing. Effectively communicating technical work is a challenging part of the optimization process that lies at the heart of engineering. Creativity in technical communication is discussed in more detail in Section 9.

Technical talks are *not* inherently boring.

3.2   Misconception #2: Engineering Communication Is Passive

Key idea: Technical communication is usually meant to be persuasive.

Many people think of technical communication as flat and one-sided. In this view, technical speakers and writers lay out a smorgasbord of facts that the audience records passively (as in a poorly designed lecture). In truth, much technical communication is both interactive and *persuasive*. Engineers often try to convince others of their point of view. Facts and figures rarely speak for themselves. They require thoughtful presentation to convince people of their worth.

3.3   Misconception #3: Technical Communication Is Best Left to Nonengineering Specialists

Key idea: Engineers can benefit from communication specialists, but the engineer must take responsibility for making sure the correct message is delivered.

In your career, you will benefit from working with many other professionals. Engineers often work collaboratively with communication specialists, such as technical writers and graphic designers. However, *you as the engineer are always responsible for making sure that the technical information is communicated clearly and concisely to the intended audience*. Remember, all your work (whether in a homework assignment or the design of a multimillion-dollar facility) is for naught if the intended audience does not understand your message. Taking control of the message is as important as taking control of the design calculations.

3.4   Misconception #4: Good Technical Communicators Are Born, Not Made

Key idea: All engineers can improve their technical communication skills.

It is true that not all of us will mesmerize* our audiences each time we stand before them or each time we put pen to paper. However, each of us can improve our speaking and writing skills *every time* we set out to communicate with our peers and others. Specific steps for honing your technical communication skills will be presented in Sections 4 through 9. Whatever level of comfort you have now with public speaking and technical writing, *know that you can improve your communication skills throughout this semester, throughout your university days, and throughout your career.*

---

*The word "mesmerize" comes from the Austrian-born physician Friedrich Anton Mesmer (1734–1815), who popularized the idea that doctors could induce a hypnotic state by manipulating a force he called "animal magnetism."

4   CRITICAL FIRST STEPS

Before you write a single word of a technical presentation, three elements must be identified clearly: the goals of the presentation, the target audience, and the constraints on the presentation. Each of these elements will be discussed in more detail in this section.

4.1   Presentation Goals

Key idea: Before preparing a technical presentation, write down the goals of the presentation.

One of the most important activities in the design of any technical talk or document is the identification of the *presentation goals*. It is absolutely critical to know what you are trying to accomplish in a presentation. The presentation will fail unless its goals are identified. Why? First, you cannot decide what information should be presented (or how to present it) unless you have described the objectives thoughtfully. Second, you need to know the goals to evaluate whether or not you have communicated the ideas successfully. In fact, *every* engineering project requires objectives so that the success of the project can be determined at its conclusion.

You should write out the presentation goals. For example, you might write, "The goal of the lab write-up is to tell the professor about the experimental methods employed, the results obtained, and the answers to the three discussion questions." This goal allows you to decide what should go in the lab write-up and how the material should be prioritized. Also, you now have a tool to judge whether your write-up was successful. You could compare the completed lab report with the goal to see if you met the goal. Remember, *a goal not written down is just a dream*.

4.2   Target Audience

target audience: the intended recipients of the information to be presented

The presentation goal should identify the **target audience**. The target audience consists of the intended recipients of the information you are presenting.

PONDER THIS

> **What is the target audience of this text?**

Although professors order the text and professionals may read it, the target audience of this text is freshman engineering students.

As with presentation goals, identification of the target audience is critical to the success of your presentation. In your career, you will give oral and written presentations to many audiences, including colleagues (i.e., fellow engineers), managers, elected officials, students, and the general public. You must keep the background and technical sophistication of the target audience in mind when developing your presentation material. For example, you would not use the same approaches to communicate a bridge design to a city council as you would to communicate the same ideas to a professional engineering society.

Key idea: Identify the target audience (and their technical sophistication, interests, and backgrounds) before preparing a technical presentation.

The interests and backgrounds of the audience are as important as their technical sophistication. Each audience member will interpret the presentation through his or her own point of view. To engage the audience fully, you must know the backgrounds of its members. As an example, consider the choices available to an engineer presenting an idea for a new computer design. For an audience of managers and corporate executives, she may wish to emphasize the low cost and high profit margin of the new personal computer. For fellow engineers, she would likely focus on the technical specifications and performance data. Subtle changes often can make the presentation match the interests and background of the audience more closely.

4.3   Constraints

Identification of *constraints* on the presentation also is important. Engineering, like life, is a constrained optimization problem. Similarly, technical presentations almost always are

Know your audience

Key idea: Before preparing a technical presentation, quantify the constraints on the presentation (i.e., length limits, your time, and other resource limitations).

constrained. Common constraints are *presentation length* (page limits for written documents or time limits on oral presentations) and *resource limitations* (e.g., your time or money for photographs or specialized graphics). It is very important to heed the presentation length constraints. In oral presentations, going well over or under the allotted time limit is rude and unprofessional. With technical documents, many engineering proposals (and term papers) have gone unread because they exceeded the imposed page limit.

The resources required for technical presentations cannot be ignored. As a student, you know you must allocate time for *writing* a term paper as well as time for reading about the term paper topic. Similarly, practicing engineers learn to budget time for report preparation. Other resources required to produce a high-quality technical document (or oral presentation) include money for personnel, graphics creation, printing, reproduction, and distribution.

Common constraints on technical communication: time and money

5   ORGANIZATION

Once you have identified the goals, target audience, and constraints, you can begin to write the presentation. Technical documents and talks can be made or broken on their degree of organization. In a well-organized presentation, the audience always knows where in the presentation they are and where they are going. There are two keys to creating an effectively organized presentation: *structuring the material* and *showing your structure* to the audience.

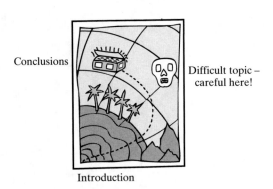

Organization is the map that guides your audience through the presentation.

5.1   Outlines

outline: a list of the major headings and subheadings in the presentation, showing the order of the main ideas and showing the secondary topics supporting the main ideas

The primary tool used to structure a presentation is the **outline**. An outline is a structured (or hierarchical) list showing the skeleton of the presentation. An example is shown in Example 1.

The purpose of the outline is to divide the presentation into manageable pieces. An outline shows three elements of the presentation:

- The main ideas (listed in the outline as major headings)
- The order of the main ideas
- The secondary topics (subheadings) that support and flesh out the main ideas

The main ideas, of course, depend on the goal of the presentation and the audience.

EXAMPLE 1 OUTLINE

Write an outline for a technical presentation on computer-aided manufacturing (CAM) in the production of aircraft.

SOLUTION

An example outline, with the parts of the outline labeled, is as follows:

Computer-Aided Manufacturing (CAM) in Aircraft Production

    I.   Introduction [major heading]

    II.   Background

         A.   History [subheading]

         B.   Contemporary examples

         C.   Current problems

> III. Use of CAM in Aircraft Production
>
> > A. CAM principles
> > B. Applications
> > > 1. potential barriers [subheading]
> > > 2. examples
> > C. Future trends
>
> IV. Conclusions

Key idea: To organize a presentation, structure the material using an outline and show the structure to your audience.

The outline is a wonderful tool for organizing a presentation. It shows at a glance the relationships between parts of the document or talk. The outline helps you to see if the presentation is balanced; that is, whether the level of detail in a certain part of the presentation corresponds to the importance of that part in achieving your goals. The outline also helps determine the needs for more data or more presentation tools (i.e., more tables and figures). An outline can be changed easily as the presentation evolves. In fact, as the outline is annotated (that is, as more levels of subheadings are added), the document or oral presentation will nearly write itself.

signposting: indicators used to show the audience where they are in the presentation

5.2 Signposting

Organizing a presentation is only half the battle. You also must *let the audience know* that you are well organized. Showing the audience that you are organized is called **signposting**. An example of signposting is the headings used in this text. The consistency of the headings tells you where you are in the text:

Chapter title: 32 point Futura font, with the initial letters capitalized

Example: # Introduction to...

Section titles: 11-point Copperplate30ab font, all caps

Example: **5   ORGANIZATION**

Subsection titles: 11-point Futura Book font, initial letters capitalized

Example: **5.2   Signposting**

6   USING TABLES AND FIGURES TO PRESENT DATA

Nearly every technical presentation you develop will contain data. The number of ways of presenting quantitative information is limited only by your imagination. However, some data presentation tools are more appropriate in a given situation than others.

6.1 Use of Tables and Figures

The two main ways to present numbers are *tables* and *figures*. Tables are used when the *actual values are important*. For example, a table would be an excellent way to show the estimated construction, operation, and maintenance costs for three polymer extruder designs. In this case, the exact costs are important and the audience wants to see the numbers.

Key idea: Use tables when actual values are important; use figures to show trends in the data.

On the other hand, figures are used to *show trends in the data*: that is, to show the relationships between variables. For example, suppose you collect data on the movement of an artificial limb in response to stimuli of varying voltage. A figure would be an appropriate way to show the trend in the dependent variable (here, the limb movement) as a function of the independent variable (here, the applied voltage).

6.2   Common Characteristics of Tables and Figures

Key idea: Tables and figures should have a number (by which they are referred to in the text) and a short, descriptive title.

While tables and figures are very different, they share several features. First, every table and figure in a technical document must have a number. Many numbering schemes are possible (e.g., "Table 1" or "Figure 4.2" or "Table II" or "Figure C"), but table and figure numbers are essential in technical writing. Why number your tables and figures? A number allows the figure or table to be *referred to* from the text. For example, in the text, you may write

> In Figure 2.3, the average wait time at the stoplight is plotted against the daily pedestrian traffic.

> Remember, *do not include a table or figure in a technical document that is not referred to by number in the text.*

Second, every table and figure in a technical document must have a title. Titles are needed to give the audience a short description of the content of the table or figure. Titles should be concise and descriptive. They need not be complete sentences. Examples of table and figure titles are listed in Table 1. The numbers and titles appear together either at the top or bottom of the table or figure. Commonly (but not universally), table titles are placed at the *top* of tables and figure titles are placed at the *bottom* of figures. (Note that Table 1 has a number and title located together at the top of the table. Also, Table 1 was referred to in the text, so you knew when to look at it.)*

Key idea: Tables and figures must be interpreted in the text.

Third, tables and figures must be *interpreted*. This means that you should discuss the table or figure in the text. To continue the example at the beginning of Section 6.2, you may write

> In Figure 2.3, the average wait time at the stoplight is plotted against the daily pedestrian traffic. Note that the average wait time increases from baseline only when the pedestrian traffic exceeds 150 people per day.

Many inexperienced technical writers make the mistake of simply throwing the data at the audience rather than *presenting* the data. They write

> The data from the first study are shown in Figure 2.3. A second study was conducted in May 2005.

You included the table or figure for a reason. To satisfy that reason (and help you achieve your presentation goals), you need to guide the audience through the interpretation of the data in your tables and figures.

Key idea: Include units in the row or column headings of tables and the axes of figures.

Fourth, units must be listed for all data in tables and figures. In tables, units usually accompany the column or row headings. In figures, the axes must be labeled with units shown. You may want to take a moment and look through this text for examples of tables and figures with units in the headings or axis labels.

TABLE 1   Examples of Poor and Improved Table and Figure Titles

Poor Title	Problems with Poor Title	Improved Title
Table 2: Experimental Data	too vague: what data will the table contain?	Table 2: Ergonomic Data for Three Automobile Seat Designs
Figure 4.2: Problems with Acid Rain	insufficient detail: figure titles usually list the dependent and independent variables	Figure 4.2: Effects of pH on the Survivorship of Brown Trout in Lakes Receiving Acid Rain
Figure A.32: Current vs Voltage	insufficient detail: lists *only* the dependent and independent variables without putting the information in context	Figure A.32: Current–Voltage Curves for Four Electrode Configurations

*The astute reader will notice that some pictures in this text have no title and are not referred to in the text. An example is the cartoon labeled "Know your audience" in Section 4. The use of such pictures for illustrative purposes is common in textbooks and reflects the fact that the target audience of the text is students.

7   TABLES

Key idea: In tables, list the independent variables in the leftmost columns.

As stated previously, tables are used to present data when the actual values are important. Tables should be limited to the minimum number of columns needed to show the relevant data. In general, independent variables are listed in the first or leftmost columns, with dependent variables listed in the columns to the right.

With today's software, it is easy to create tables with myriad types of lines, shadings, colors, and font styles. However, these devices should be used sparingly and consistently. Each table has a goal; "bells and whistles" should be used only to make your point clearer.

An example table is given in Table 2.

PONDER THIS

Critique Table 2.

Table 2 is well constructed. Note that it is numbered and has a descriptive title. The independent variable (reinforcing bar type) is listed first. Units are given for all data (i.e., for every column). Lines are used minimally and mainly serve to separate the table from the surrounding text.

To demonstrate the importance of the order of the columns, examine Table 3. Table 3 contains the same data as Table 2, but the column order has been changed. Note how difficult it is to interpret Table 3. Even though the most important information probably is the weight, placing a dependent variable first does not communicate the information very effectively.

Table 4 demonstrates the potential for distractions in table design. The use of many fonts, lines, and types of shading adds little to the message and can be distracting.

TABLE 2   Characteristics of Standard Steel Reinforcing Bars

[*Caution:* Table may contain errors! See text for discussion.]

Type	Diameter (in)	Weight (lb/ft)
#2	0.250	0.167
#3	0.375	0.376
#4	0.500	0.668
#5	0.625	1.043
#6	0.750	1.502

TABLE 3   Characteristics of Standard Steel Reinforcing Bars

[*Caution:* Table may contain errors! See text for discussion.]

Weight (lb/ft)	Type	Diameter (in)
0.167	#2	0.250
0.376	#3	0.375
0.668	#4	0.500
1.043	#5	0.625
1.502	#6	0.750

TABLE 4 Characteristics of Standard Steel Reinforcing Bars

[*Caution*: Table may contain errors! See text for discussion.]

Type	Diameter (in.)	Weight (lb/ft)
#2	0.250	0.167
#3	0.375	0.376
#4	0.500	0.668
#5	0.625	1.043
#6	0.750	1.502

8   FIGURES

Key idea: Use scatter (*x–y*) plots when the independent variable is continuous.

scatter (x–y) plot: a type of plot using symbols or lines that is employed when the independent variable is continuous

Key idea: In general, use symbols for data and lines for calculated values (i.e., model output).

Recall that figures are used when the relationships between variables are important. There are three common types of figures used in technical presentations: scatter (or *x–y*) plots, bar charts, and pie charts.

8.1   Scatter Plots

The **scatter plot** (or **x–y plot**) is the most common type of graph in technical work. It is used when the *independent variable is continuous*; that is, when the independent variable could take any value. Examples of continuous variables are time, flow, and voltage. In the scatter plot, the independent variable is plotted on the *x*-axis (also called the *abscissa*) and the dependent variable is plotted on the *y*-axis (also called the *ordinate*). In general, symbols are used for data and lines are used for calculated values (i.e., for model fits or model predictions). An example of a scatter plot is shown in Figure 1.

PONDER THIS

Critique Figure 1.

In Figure 1, the independent variable (vapor pressure) is continuous. Thus, a scatter plot is appropriate. Note the important elements: figure title (here, at the bottom of the figure), axis titles with units, tick marks (small lines) near axis labels, and symbols that represent data. If more than one dependent variable were plotted, a legend would

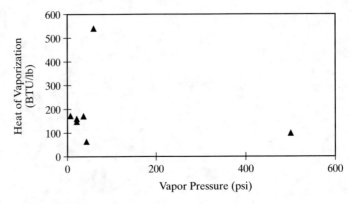

Figure 1. Heat of Vaporization of Some Common Refrigerants [*Caution*: Figure may contain errors! See text for discussion.]

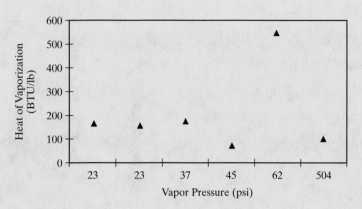

Figure 2.   Heat of Vaporization of Some Common Refrigerants [*Caution*: Figure may contain errors! See text for discussion.]

Key idea: Use the line chart type carefully in technical presentations (or, better yet, avoid it completely).

be necessary. Note that *a legend is not necessary if only one dependent variable is plotted*. (Legends are discussed with bar charts in Section 8.2.)

One final note on scatter plots. Most common graphing programs (including Microsoft Word, Microsoft Excel, Corel WordPerfect, and Corel QuattroPro) have a figure type (also called a *chart type*) called "line." With the line chart type, the *x* data points are spaced evenly, *regardless of their values*. The data in Figure 1 are replotted as a line chart in Figure 2. Notice that the relationship between heat of vaporization and vapor pressure appears to be distorted in the line chart. There are almost no cases where the line type is the *best* way to present technical data. It is recommended that *you avoid the line chart type completely*.

8.2   Bar Charts

bar chart: a type of plot using bars that is employed when the independent variable is not continuous

Key idea: Use bar charts when the independent variable is not continuous.

legend: a listing of the property represented by each symbol, bar, or line

Key idea: In figures, select the axis ranges to encompass all the data without distorting the relative values.

Bar charts are used when the independent variable is discrete (i.e., not continuous). Discontinuous independent variables are common in engineering. For example, you may wish to show how the properties of magnets vary with material type or how energy efficiency varies with industry category. The type of material or category of industry is a discrete variable and the use of a bar chart is appropriate.

An example of a bar chart[*] is given in Figure 3. Note the descriptive title, inclusion of units, and tick marks on the *y*-axis. Tick marks generally are not used on the *x*-axis in bar charts with vertical bars, since the tick marks would interfere with the bars. Note also in Figure 3 that two *y*-axes are used. Multiple *y*-axes are useful when the independent variables have different units or vastly different scales.

In Figure 3, two variables are plotted; therefore, a legend is required. A *legend* tells the audience the meaning of each symbol, bar, or line. In this case, the legend tells you that the white bar represents the resistivity and the black bar represents tensile strength.

In both scatter and bar charts, you must select the ranges of the axes carefully. Clearly, the ranges must be selected to encompass all data. In addition, it is generally a good idea to start the *y*-axis at zero.[†] Why? Starting at zero gives the audience a better view of the relative values of your data. In Figure 3, for example, it is obvious that the tensile strength of silver is about twice that of gold. If the data are replotted using smaller ranges for the *y*-axes, a skewed view of the relative resistivities and tensile strengths is created (see Figure 4). For example, the tensile strength of silver appears to be about five times that of gold in this figure.

---

[*]The common name for the plot in Figure 3 is a bar chart. Some software packages call it a *column chart* if the bars are vertical and a *bar chart* if the bars are horizontal.
[†]Do not, of course, start the *y*-axis at zero if you have negative *y* values. Also, avoid starting the *y*-axis at zero if the *y* values cluster around a large value.

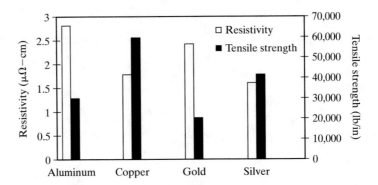

Figure 3.   Physical Properties of Conductors

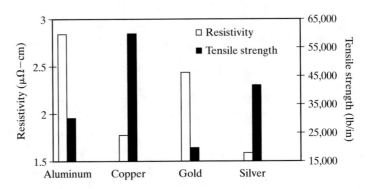

Figure 4.   Physical Properties of Conductors [*Caution*: Figure may contain errors! See text for discussion.]

Key idea: Do not accept the default table or figure produced by the software without questioning whether it meets your objectives.

pie chart: a type of plot using pie slices that is employed to show the relative contributions of several factors to a whole

Key idea: Use pie charts to show relative contributions.

This lesson can be extrapolated. In general, *do not let the software pick the look of your tables and figures.* Always look critically at the default table or figure produced by the software package. Use your judgment: edit tables and figures to best meet your presentation goals.

8.3   Pie Charts

Pie charts are used to show the relative contributions of several factors to a whole. In most cases, pie charts are used to show percentages. Thus, pie charts have no independent variable. Although pie charts are not used very frequently in engineering, they can show the relative importance of discrete factors very effectively.

An example of a 3-D pie chart is shown in Figure 5. The slices of the pie may be defined with a legend or labels.

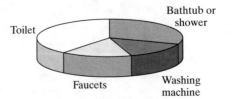

Figure 5.   Water Use in the Home

An example of how the design of a figure may influence engineering decision making is shown in the *Focus on Figures: Of Plots and Space Shuttles*.

FOCUS ON FIGURES: OF PLOTS AND SPACE SHUTTLES

The explosion of the Space Shuttle *Challenger* on the cold morning of January 28, 1986, rocked the world. Subsequent investigation into the disaster pointed to the likely cause: hot gases from fuel combustion bypassed two seals, leading to the destruction of the booster segment and the loss of the lives of all seven astronauts. The booster segments were sealed with O-rings made out of a rubber-like material called Viton®. The two O-rings (primary and secondary) protected the segments from the combustion gases. The primary O-ring was closest to the fuel.

The *Challenger* disaster is often discussed as an example of engineering ethics. Although some facts are in dispute, it is clear that some of the engineers involved vigorously argued that the launch should be aborted. Why? The temperature at launch was forecasted to be much lower than previously experienced. Like typical rubber, the flexibility of Viton (and thus its ability to seal against the enormous pressures at launch) is dependent on temperature.

It has been argued (Tufte, 1993) that the available data, if plotted in the most meaningful way, would have provided overwhelming evidence for aborting the launch. According to this argument, the engineers were remiss in not presenting the data in the most powerful way. In other words, technical communication problems may have contributed to the launch and loss of *Challenger*. This point of view has been strongly challenged by the engineers involved (Robison et al., 2002). The arguments and counterarguments are complex and cannot be summarized in this short section. The interested reader is urged to read the cited papers. The purpose here is to show how data presentation can lead and mislead the engineer.

To appreciate the importance of how the data were plotted, it is necessary to understand what data were available at the time. There are several indicators of O-ring damage. One indicator is soot marks made by blackened grease as it blows through the primary O-ring. Soot is a very bad sign, indicating that the primary O-ring has been breached and the shuttle health depends only on the remaining secondary O-ring. The size of the soot marks (for shuttle launches with measurable

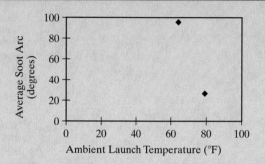

Figure 6. Influence of Temperature on Soot Including Only Data Where Soot Was Observed

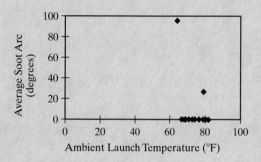

Figure 7. Influence of Temperature on Soot Including All Available Data

soot) are shown as a function of ambient temperature at launch in Figure 6. Based on these data, would you recommend launching at the launch temperature of 26°F on January 28, 1986?

Based on the data plotted in Figure 6, you *might* conclude that a launch at 26°F is inadvisable. Although there *appears* to be a trend that soot area increases with decreasing temperature, two data points are hardly enough to justify a quantitative relationship. The picture becomes even cloudier when all available data are included (Figure 7). Note that no soot was observed at many launch temperatures between the values shown in Figure 6. Does the trend appear weaker now?

Results of the testing of isolated rockets revealed no soot at O-ring temperatures between 47 and 50°F (see Figure 8). How would the rocket test data influence your decision to launch?

History proved that the advice not to launch was justified. It is impossible to know with certainty whether a plot such as Figure 7 or Figure 8 would have enhanced the argument of the engineers. Rather than a clear-cut lesson in technical communications, we are left with a tragedy.

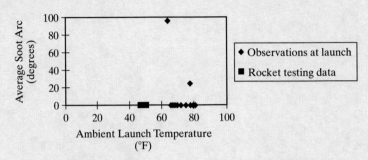

Figure 8. Influence of Temperature on Soot Including All Available Data and Rocket Testing Results

9   CREATIVITY IN TECHNICAL PRESENTATIONS

This chapter has emphasized the need for structure in technical presentations and has introduced numerous rules. However, please do not forget that technical communication is a creative process. Much of the creativity in technical presentations is focused on two areas: conciseness and thinking visually.

9.1   Creative Conciseness

When in doubt, favor conciseness over verbosity in technical presentations. Simply filling the page or presentation time with words is always obvious and insulting to the audience. In addition, calculations, data, or analysis that are necessary, but secondary to the main points being made, can be very distracting. In a written document, they may be best placed in an appendix.

Finding the right degree of conciseness is not easy. Technical presentations, like homemade bread, are hard to digest if they are too dense. To use another food analogy: wine can be very pleasant. It can be distilled into a complex brandy. Overdistill and you end up with ethanol: harsh and undrinkable. Often a dense presentation can be made more palatable by building in repetition and explanatory text.

The idea of conciseness also applies to figures. Consider the three plots of the same data in Figure 9. The top panel is a typical figure produced by the built-in plotting software of a word processing program.

PONDER THIS   **What unnecessary elements do you see in the top panel of Figure 9?**

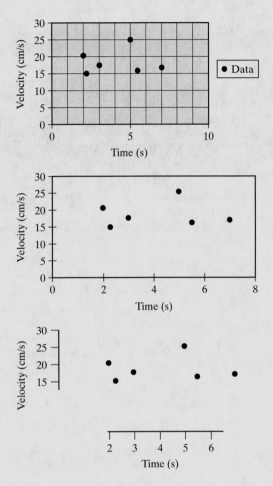

Figure 9. Example of Conciseness in Figures [*Caution*: Figure may contain errors! See text for discussion.]

The extraneous graphical elements in the top panel of Figure 9 include background color, grid lines, and legend. (No legend is needed, since there is only one set of symbols.) A clearer presentation (middle panel of Figure 9) is produced by eliminating the extraneous elements. In the bottom panel of Figure 9, nearly all extraneous lines have been removed. For most engineers, the bottom panel is on the verge of being too abstract: perhaps too much information has been removed. Figure 9 shows that some redundancy is needed to best communicate the information.

9.2   Thinking Visually

Another important creative element in technical presentations is the ability to *think visually*. The layout of the page or the slides can help make your points or distract the audience from your goal.

For more details (and fascinating examples), peruse the books by Edward Tufte listed in the references (Tufte, 1983, 1990). These are truly amazing and beautiful books that will greatly influence your thinking about the design of figures and tables.

10   SUMMARY

Technical communication is important in turning engineering ideas into reality. In addition, good technical communication skills are essential for obtaining an engineering job and advancing in the engineering profession.

Engineers must take responsibility for communicating their ideas and their work to a large and varied audience. As an engineer, you should think about technical communications as a creative and persuasive engineering tool. You must take control of the message, ask yourself if your message is understood, and seek to improve your communication skills at every opportunity.

Several general aspects of technical presentations (i.e., technical writing and technical speaking) were discussed in this chapter. Before putting pen to paper, you should take several steps. First, always identify the goals of the presentation, the target audience, and the constraints of the presentation. Second, organize the material to be presented. This can be done by using an outline to structure the information. Be sure to show your structure to the audience. Third, use the proper technique to present data. Tables are used when the actual values are important, while figures are used to show trends in the data. Every table and every figure in a technical document must have a number and a descriptive title. In addition, every table and figure must be referred to from the text of a written document, and its main points must be summarized.

Be sure to use the most appropriate type of figure: scatter (x–y) plots when the independent variable is continuous, bar charts when the independent variable is not continuous, pie charts to show relative proportions, and line charts almost never. Look critically at the default table or figure produced by software and ask how it could be modified to best meet *your* presentation goals.

SUMMARY OF KEY IDEAS

- Technical presentations must tell a story; always ask yourself whether the audience understood your story.
- Strong technical presentation skills aid in obtaining a job and in advancing a career.
- Technical communication is a creative process.
- Technical communication is usually meant to be persuasive.
- Engineers can benefit from communication specialists, but the engineer must take responsibility for making sure the correct message is delivered.
- All engineers can improve their technical communication skills.
- Before preparing a technical presentation, write down the goals of the presentation.
- Identify the target audience (and their technical sophistication, interests, and backgrounds) before preparing a technical presentation.
- Before preparing a technical presentation, quantify the constraints on the presentation (i.e., length limits, your time, and other resource limitations).
- To organize a presentation, structure the material using an outline and show the structure to your audience.
- Use tables when actual values are important; use figures to show trends in the data.
- Tables and figures should have a number (by which they are referred to in the text) and a short, descriptive title.

- Tables and figures must be interpreted in the text.
- Include units in the row or column headings of tables and the axes of figures.
- In tables, list the independent variables in the leftmost columns.
- Use scatter (x–y) plots when the independent variable is continuous.
- In general, use symbols for data and lines for calculated values (i.e., model output).
- Use the line chart type carefully in technical presentations (or, better yet, avoid it completely).
- Use bar charts when the independent variable is not continuous.
- In figures, select the axis ranges to encompass all the data without distorting the relative values.
- Do not accept the default table or figure produced by the software without questioning whether it meets your objectives.
- Use pie charts to show relative contributions.

Problems

1. Identify the goals, target audience, and constraints for the following types of communication:
   a. Two roommates discussing how to divide the telephone bill
   b. A review article on the avian flu virus in a newsmagazine
   c. A NASA news briefing on the evidence of water on Mars

2. Write an outline for a research paper on career opportunities in the engineering field of your choice.

3. Discuss whether you would use a figure or a table to present the following data. If you choose a figure, state which type of figure you would use.
   a. The chemical composition (in percent by weight) of a concrete formulation
   b. Operation and maintenance costs of three pavement types
   c. Effect of fiber-optic cable length on the transmission of photons
   d. Percentage of zebra mussels killed under a specified treatment regime

4. Figure titles often are missing or incomplete in the popular press. Find two data figures in a newspaper or newsmagazine. Critique the figure titles and then write your own.

5. Find two data tables in a newspaper or newsmagazine. Critique and write your own table titles. Edit the table, if necessary, following the principles discussed in this chapter.

6. Some people refer to line charts as "bar charts with symbols." Explain this definition of line charts.

7. Write Newton's Second Law of Motion in a concise form for a technical audience and in a more expansive form for a general audience.

8. Pick a figure in this text, critique it, and improve upon its design. State why your design is an improvement.

9. Interview a practicing engineer and write a paragraph about the importance of technical communication in his or her professional life.

10. Explain the differences and similarities between technical communication and written or oral presentations you did in high school in nontechnical courses.

17

Written Technical Communications

1 INTRODUCTION

In this chapter, written technical communications will be discussed in much detail. Organization is the key to good technical communication. Thus, most of the chapter (Sections 2 and 3) is devoted to the organization of written documents. Grammar and spelling issues are reviewed in Section 4. Section 5 provides details on the types of engineering documents you will write, from formal reports to casual email.

2 OVERALL ORGANIZATION OF TECHNICAL DOCUMENTS

2.1 Introduction

The key to good written and oral presentations is organization. Technical documents must be organized on several levels. In this section, the general organization of technical documents will be discussed. Organization at the paragraph, sentence, and word levels is the subject of Section 3.

2.2 General Organization Schemes

Outlines should be used to develop organized presentations. What headings and subheadings should be employed? Clearly, the details of the outline will depend on the goal of the presentation and nature of the technical work. Although every technical report is different, several elements are common to many technical presentations. Important elements found in many technical presentations are given in Table 1. The common elements are as follows:

OBJECTIVES

After reading this chapter, you will be able to:

- list the elements of technical documents;
- organize a technical document;
- identify common grammatical and spelling errors in technical documents;
- proofread technical documents;
- write an effective technical document.

Key idea: Organize technical documents from the largest to smallest scale: outline level, paragraph level, sentence level, and word level.

Key idea: Common elements of technical documents include the abstract (or executive summary), introduction/ background/literature review, methods, results, discussion, conclusions/ recommendations, and references.

Key idea: The abstract should contain a summary of each element of the report.

- Abstract
- Introduction/Background/Literature Review
- Methods/Modeling
- Results
- Discussion
- Conclusions/Recommendations
- References

Each of the common elements will be illustrated with a report on a laboratory exercise conducted to test the conservation of momentum.

2.3   Abstract

Technical documents typically begin with an *abstract*. The purpose of the abstract is to provide a brief summary of the remainder of the document. The abstract should include the important points from each element in the document. An extended abstract (often written for nontechnical audiences) is sometimes called an *executive summary*.

A properly written abstract should be a miniature version of the entire technical document. The word *abstract* comes from the Latin *abstractus*, meaning drawn off. In a true sense, think of the abstract as being *drawn off of the whole document*. Thus, an abstract should include the following sections:

- An introduction (with enough background material to show the importance of the work),
- A statement on the methods or models employed,
- A short summary of the results and their meaning, and
- Conclusions and recommendations.

For the lab report on the conservation of momentum, the abstract might read as follows:

Abstract

The purpose of this lab was to test the law of conservation of momentum. Experiments were conducted with disks designed to remain together after collision. The masses and velocities of the disks were measured before and after collision. On average, the total momentum of the system after the collision was 101% of the total momentum before the collision. The calculated momentums were interpreted to be consistent with the conservation of momentum law.

TABLE 1   Elements in a General Technical Document

Section Title	Purpose
Abstract or Executive Summary	Summarizes the entire report, including all other elements
Introduction or Background or Literature Review	Brings the reader to the topic of the report; may give project history and/or a review of the appropriate technical literature
Methods or Modeling	Describes study approach, methods used, and model development (if any)
Results	Presents the results, including "raw" data with trends indicated but little interpretation of the data
Discussion	Interprets of the results
Conclusions and Recommendations	Summarizes main points and gives suggestions for further work, often in a list format
References	Lists references cited (may be in an appendix)

Note that the abstract contains all the elements of the full report: introduction (first sentence), methods (second and third sentences), results (fourth sentence), and conclusion (last sentence).

2.4   Introduction

Key idea: The introduction should take the reader from the report title to an understanding of why the report was written.

The next element is the *introduction*. In writing the introduction section, assume that the reader knows only the information in the title of the report. After reading the introduction, the reader should have a good idea of the *motivation* for the report (i.e., why the report was written).

In some cases, the introduction section may be fairly long. It may include a discussion of the project history, a review of pertinent technical literature, and a presentation of the goals and objectives of the work. On other occasions, the introduction is short and the other material is placed in separate sections (i.e., a background or a literature review section or a goals/objectives section).

The introduction section takes the reader from the title to an appreciation of why the document was written.

For the lab report on the conservation of momentum, the introduction might read as follows:

Introduction

Science and engineering are founded on a number of conservation laws. One example is the conservation of momentum. Momentum is the product of the mass of an object and its velocity. The law of conservation of momentum states that the momentum of a closed system remains unchanged.

The conservation laws are impossible to prove experimentally because of error. However, the data collected in a well-planned experiment should be consistent with the conservation laws. In this lab, a comparison was made between the momentum calculations from laboratory data and the law of conservation of momentum.

2.5   Methods

Key idea: In the methods section, justify the study approach, present data collection techniques, and discuss data analysis methods.

The introduction is usually followed by a section on the *methods* employed in the study. The methods section should describe three elements of the work. First, the methods section should justify the *study approach*. In most engineering studies, there are many ways to achieve the study goals.

PONDER THIS

How many ways can you think of to "test" the law of conservation of momentum?

For example, you could explore the conservation of momentum law under controlled conditions with billiard balls or model cars or hockey pucks. You also could collect data in the real world. For example, a visit to a county fair would allow you to make measurements using bumper cars or the demolition derby. Even in this simple example, there are many ways to test the hypothesis of interest. As an engineer, you *choose* to follow a certain approach. It is important to justify your choice.

Second, the methods section should discuss the techniques involved in data collection. For experimental work, this means describing the measurement methods. For modeling studies, this means presenting the models developed specifically for your study.

Third, the methods section should discuss the approaches used to analyze the data. For example, suppose you measured temperature using a thermistor. A thermistor is a resistor that has a resistance related to temperature in a known fashion. In a study using a thermistor, it may be necessary in the methods section to describe how the temperature was calculated from electrical measurements.

The three parts of the methods section can be summarized as follows:

- *Why* did you do the work? (study approach)
- *How* did you do the work? (experimental procedure)
- *What* did you do with the work? (data analysis)

Often, the information about experimental set-up can be communicated most effectively by drawings or photographs. It should be noted that in some technical fields, information on methods is placed in an appendix rather than in the body of a report.

Elements of a methods section

For the lab report on the conservation of momentum, the methods section might read as follows:

Methods

Data collection was performed in a laboratory setting to enhance reproducibility. Tests were conducted on an air table to minimize friction.

Six experiments were conducted. For each experiment, the masses of two plastic disks were recorded. The disks were 5 cm in diameter and 0.5 cm thick. The rims of the disks were covered with a strip of Velcro tape to allow the disks to stick together upon impact. The disks were positioned about 2 m apart. One disk was propelled by hand towards the other disk. Disk velocities were measured immediately before and after collision.

Masses were determined with a Model 501 balance. To measure disk velocities, a digital video camera (VideoCon Model 75) capable of recording images at 30 frames per second was positioned above the initially stationary disk. The sides of the air table were marked in 0.1 cm increments. Images were examined frame by frame, with the instantaneous velocity calculated as (distance traveled between frames) divided by (time between frames). The velocities of the disks were averaged over one second prior to and after collision.

The average momentum was calculated as $p = mv$, where m represents mass and v denotes velocity.

In this example, the study approach is presented and justified in the first paragraph. The second paragraph gives the overall experimental procedure, with the measurement details in the third paragraph. The fourth paragraph outlines the data analysis approach.

2.6   Results and Discussion

Key idea: In the results section, present the results and note the general trends.

Key idea: Interpret data in the discussion section.

The results section comes next. In this section of the typical engineering report, the results are *presented* but not *interpreted*. The general trends shown by the data in tables and figures should be highlighted as the data are presented.

In the results section, there is generally little interpretation of the data. Data interpretation comes in the *discussion* section. Here, elements of the results section are combined and interpreted to reach the main conclusions of the engineering study. Often, data are compared with predictions from models in the discussion section. In a design report, alternative designs may be compared and a final alternative selected in this section.

In a results section:

The measured force values are shown against mass in Figure 1. The measured force (in newtons) increased nearly linearly with the increase in mass (in kg).

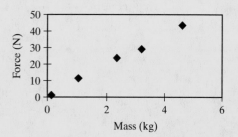

Figure 1: Dependency of Measured Force Values on Mass

In a discussion section:

Measured forces are compared with model predictions in Figure 2. The experimental results were consistent with the model, $F = ma$.

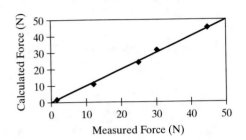

Figure 2: Comparison of Measured Forces and Model Results
(Line is calculated force = measured force)

The division between the results and discussion sections is not always clear cut. In fact, the results and discussion sections usually are combined in short reports. To illustrate the difference between the results and discussion sections, consider a large report on the effects of fatigue on the performance of assembly line workers. In the results section, the data on fatigue measures and performance measures might be reported. General trends (for example, that time to completion of critical tasks decreased as the level of fatigue increased) may be noted. More detailed interpretation of the data would be placed in the discussion section, where, for example, the predictions of a performance model might be compared with the data collected in the study.

For the conservation of momentum lab report, the results and discussion sections probably would be combined because the scope of the report is small. Example results and discussion sections are separated here for illustrative purposes.

Results

Measured masses and mean velocities from the six experiments are shown in Table 1. Note that the measured masses of the single disk (before collision) are similar, as expected. In addition, the measured masses of the coupled disks (after collision) are nearly double the masses of the single disk. By inspection of the data in Table 1, it appears that the velocity decreased by nearly a factor of two as the mass increased by about a factor of two.

TABLE 1   Measured Mass and Mean Velocity Data

	Before Collision		After Collision	
Experiment	Mass (g)	Mean Velocity (cm/s)	Mass (g)	Mean Velocity (cm/s)
1	2.5	99	5.0	51
2	2.5	102	5.1	48
3	2.4	96	4.9	48
4	2.5	93	5.0	45
5	2.6	102	5.1	51
6	2.5	105	5.1	54

Discussion

The calculated momentum values before and after collision are listed in Table 2. Note that the calculated momentum values before and after collision are nearly equal. As shown in the fourth column of Table 2, the momentum after collision averaged 101% of the momentum before the collision.

TABLE 2   Calculated Momentum Values (p) Before and After Collision

Expt.	p **Before Collision** (g-cm/s)	p **After Collision** (g-cm/s)	(p **After)/(p Before)** (%)
1	250	260	104
2	260	240	92
3	230	240	104
4	230	230	100
5	270	260	96
6	260	280	108
mean			101

The approach used in this lab was to compare two momentum values. Therefore, it is important to estimate the uncertainty in the mass and velocity measurements. The precision of the mass measurements can be estimated by the precision of the balance (given by the manufacturer as ±0.01 g). The instantaneous velocity was calculated as (distance traveled between frames) divided by (1/30 second per frame). The distance traveled was rounded to the nearest 0.1 cm, since the scale of the side of the table was marked in 0.1-cm increments. A difference of 0.1 cm over 1/30 s represents $(0.1 \text{ cm})/(1/30 \text{ s}) = 3$ cm/s. The uncertainty in velocity (3 cm/s) represents about 1.2% of the average velocity of 250 cm/s. Thus, the difference of 1% between momentum values before and after collision is not unreasonable. Given the uncertainty, the data collected are consistent with conservation of momentum during the collision of two disks.

2.7   Conclusions and Recommendations

Key idea: Conclusions and recommendations are often in list form and should be written very carefully.

The last main section of a typical engineering report is the *conclusions and recommendations* section. The conclusions and recommendations must be among the most carefully worded sections of an engineering report, since many readers may turn here first. Conclusions and recommendations often appear in a list format. The conclusions should stem directly from the discussion. In other words, no *new* information should be presented in the conclusions.

The recommendations section is a critical part of an engineering report. Why? Recall that engineers often select intelligently from among alternatives. The preferred alternative often is highlighted in the recommendations section.

An example of a conclusions section is given next.

Conclusions

An experimental study was conducted to explore the conservation of momentum law as applied to a collision of two discs on an air table. The momentum after the collision averaged 101% of the momentum before the collision. The experimental results were consistent with the conservation of momentum.

2.8   References

Key idea: Although many reference formats are acceptable, the references must be complete and consistent.

The last section of a technical report (often found in an appendix) is a list of references. There are many acceptable formats for listing references in technical material. The guiding rules are that the references should be *complete* (so that the reader can find the referenced material easily) and *consistent* (i.e., use the same format for all books or journals cited). Following are some examples of reference formats:

For books:

Author's last name, author's initials (for second authors, initials followed by name), book title in bold, publisher's name, publisher's location, publication date.

Example: Keller, H. **The Story of My Life**. Doubleday, Page & Co., New York, NY, 1903.

For journal articles:

Author's last name, author's initials (for second authors, initials followed by name), article title, journal name in bold italic, volume number, issue number in parentheses, page range, date.

Example: Dallard, P., A. J. Fitzpatrick, and A. Flint. The London Millennium Footbridge. **Structural Engineer**, **79**(22), 17–35, 2001.

For Web pages:

Author's last name, author's initials (for second authors, initials followed by name), article title, URL, date visited in parentheses.

Example: Anon., Standard Contract Documents, http://www.nspe.org/ejcdc/home.asp (visited March 21, 2005).

bibliography: a list of useful sources of information, including sources not cited in the text (as contrasted with the references, in which only cited material is listed)

Be careful about the differences between a list of references and a **bibliography**. A reference list consists only of the material cited in the text. A bibliography lists all useful sources of information, even if they are not specifically cited in the text. For examples, please see the References appendix of this text.

2.9　Signposting in Technical Writing

As discussed in Section 2.2, a good technical presentation is well organized and the organization is clear to the audience. The idea of showing the audience where you are in a technical presentation is called *signposting*. A common mistake in technical writing is to give the reader page after page of text with no guide to the content of the text.

Key idea: Use section headings or numbering schemes as signposts in technical documents.

In technical documents, signposting is usually accomplished in one of two ways. First, you may use *section headings* to show the readers where they are in the document. The divisions described in Section 2.1 (e.g., Introduction, Methods, Results, and so on) may be good section headings. Be sure to use a consistent theme to show the hierarchy of the headings. For example, major headings might be left aligned, while subheadings are indented. Or major headings might be all in capital letters, while subheadings are in initial caps.

Second, you can signpost with a *numbering scheme*. Numbers are an excellent way to show the hierarchy of headings. For example, a major section may be given a number (e.g., "3. Assessment of Alternatives"), with subheadings listed as sections under the number (e.g., "3.1 Soldered Joints Alternative"). Hierarchy can be shown by the numbering scheme (4, 4.1, 4.1.1, or I, I.A, I.A.1, or others), indentation, or use of boldface fonts.

Regardless of the system used, signposting *must be applied consistently*. If you use a bold font with initial caps with second-level subheadings, then use a bold font with initial caps with *all* second-level subheadings. Your readers will rely on your signals. Do not confuse the reader with inconsistent signposting.

3　ORGANIZING PARTS OF TECHNICAL DOCUMENTS

3.1　Paragraph Organization

Beyond organizing the overall presentation, each paragraph also should be structured. Each paragraph should tell a complete story and be structured by sentence. The paragraph should begin with a **topic sentence**. The topic sentence states the purpose of the paragraph. Each following sentence should *support the topic sentence*. Paragraphs should end with a *concluding sentence*, which summarizes the main points of the paragraph. Thus, each sentence in the paragraph has a specific purpose.

topic sentence: the first sentence in a paragraph in which the purpose of the paragraph is stated

PONDER THIS

Reread the previous paragraph and evaluate whether it is structured correctly.

3.2   Sentence Organization

Key idea: Each sentence should express a single idea.

A sentence is a grammatical structure containing a subject and a verb. Sentences should express a *single idea*. There are two common problems with sentences in technical documents: overly long sentences (with more than one idea) and too short sentences (lacking a subject or verb). Avoid using conjunctions (e.g., *and, but, or, nor, for, so,* or *yet*) to combine disparate ideas into one sentence. Consider the following sentence:

> Design parameters were calculated by standard procedures and all results were rounded to three significant figures.

This sentence contains two ideas. It should be split into two sentences at the word *and*:

> Design parameters were calculated by standard procedures. All results were rounded to three significant figures.

sentence fragment: an incomplete sentence (usually lacking a subject or verb)

Sentences can be *too short* if they do not include both a subject and a verb. Incomplete sentences are called **sentence fragments**. A common sentence fragment in technical writing creeps in when stating trends. For example,

> The higher the temperature, the shorter the annealing time.

PONDER THIS

Why is the sentence fragment "The higher the temperature, the shorter the annealing time" *not* **a sentence?**

This fragment has no verb and thus is not a sentence. Try to avoid such constructions in your technical writing. Say instead: "Annealing time decreased as the temperature was increased."

3.3   Word Choice

Key idea: Choose words to make your writing concise, simple, and specific.

The lowest level of organization is the choice of words. In choosing words to form sentences, try to be as *concise*, *simple*, and *specific* as possible.

Concise writing means that you should use the minimum number of words to express the thought clearly. To write concisely, avoid long prepositional phrases. Examples of common wordy phrases and suggested substitutions are listed in Table 2.

TABLE 2   Examples of Long Prepositional Phrases to Be Avoided
(adapted from Smith and Vesiland, 1996)

Wordy Prepositional Phrase	Possible Substitute
due to the fact that . . .	because . . .
in order to . . .	to . . .
in terms of . . .	reword sentence and delete phrase[a]
in the event that . . .	if . . .
in the process of . . .	delete, or use "while" or "during"
it just so happens that . . .	because . . .
on the order of [b] . . .	about . . .

[a] *Example*: The sentence "In terms of energy use, Alternative 3 was lowest" could be rewritten as "Alternative 3 had the lowest energy use."

[b] This phrase sometimes is used to indicate an order of magnitude (i.e., a power of 10), as in the following sentence: "On the order of 10,000 bolts were employed in the construction project."

For example, instead of writing

In order to find the optimum temperature, we conducted experiments.

it is preferable to write

To find the optimum temperature, we conducted experiments.

Although the general public sometimes feels that technical writing is impenetrable, written technical communication should be *simple*. In other words, use simple words to express your ideas as clearly as possible. Avoid sentences such as

System failure mode was encountered on three sundry occasions.

Instead, write more clearly:

The system failed three times.

Key idea: Avoid making up new words or new uses of words in conventional technical writing.

A common and annoying device used to make writing sound more technical is the use of nouns as verbs. One way this is accomplished is by adding the suffix *-ize* to almost any noun (e.g., initialize, prioritize, customize, and the like). Writers are converting nouns into verbs with increasing frequency. For example, a nationwide company offering photocopying services used to advertise itself as "The new way to office." (What does "to office" mean?) In your writing, avoid making up new verbs from nouns.

The heart of technical writing is its *specificity*. Make your writing specific by avoiding general adjectives such as *many, several, much,* and *a few*. Quantify your statements when you can:

Engine temperatures were 5°C above normal.

not

Engine temperatures were several degrees above normal.

4   GRAMMAR AND SPELLING

Important ideas about spelling and grammar will be reviewed in this section. The purpose of this discussion is not to provide you with a comprehensive list of the rules of grammar, but rather to identify common trouble spots in technical writing.

There are no excuses for errors in grammar or spelling in technical writing. The most important rules are reviewed here. Problem words will be discussed at the end of this section. For more details, please examine any of the excellent books listed in the bibliography at the end of the text.

You should be aware that there is some disagreement on several grammatical rules. It is important to differentiate firm rules from one writer's opinion. It is frustrating to learn and use one approach from a mentor, only to have it totally dismantled by another mentor. When in doubt about the feedback you have received, always ask questions.

4.1   Subject–verb match

Key idea: Make sure that the subject and verb agree in number (i.e., they must be both singular or both plural).

The subject and verb must match in number. In other words, use plural forms of verbs with plural nouns and singular forms of verbs with singular nouns. For example, you should write

The contacts of the integrated circuit were corroded.

not

The contacts of the integrated circuit was corroded.

The subject of the sentence is plural ("contacts") and thus a plural verb ("were") is required.

In most cases, the "subject–verb match" rule is simple. However, some sticky situations arise. For example, is the noun "data" plural or singular? In most technical literature, the word *data* is considered to be a plural noun. (Formally, it is the plural of the noun *datum*.) A growing number of technical writers consider *data* to be singular when referring to a specified set of data. The safe bet is to treat *data* as a plural noun:

The data fall within two standard deviations of the mean.

not

The data falls within two standard deviations of the mean.

If you wish to use a singular noun, use *data set*:

The data set was larger last year.

4.2   Voice

In grammar, *voice* refers to the person (people) or things doing the action. There are two general voices: active and passive. In the active voice, the subject is identified. In the passive voice, the person performing the action is not identified (either directly or by category).

There is some difference of opinion about which voice is best for technical writing. In general, the active voice is preferred. Why? In engineering, you usually want to know who did the action. You should write

Field technicians backfilled the soil.

not

The soil was backfilled.

The passive voice is appropriate when the identity of the person doing the action is obvious or unimportant. Thus, you will find the passive voice used in many engineering reports where the subject already has been identified. For example, the passive voice was used in the conservation of momentum example in Section 3. Regardless of the voice used, be consistent and use the same voice throughout.

Although the active voice is preferred, you should always avoid the use of the first person in technical writing. For example, write

XYZ Engineering personnel developed an ergonomic design.

or

We developed an ergonomic design.

not

I developed an ergonomic design.

4.3   Tense

Tense refers to when the action occurred. In technical writing, use the present tense unless describing work done in the past. Thus, write

Values were calculated by a nonlinear optimization algorithm.

This is in the past tense, since the calculation took place in the past. On the other hand, you might write

The results indicate the importance of the new quality assurance procedures.

Use the present tense here, since the results and their interpretation exist now.

4.4   Pronouns

Pronouns are substitutes for nouns. Examples of pronouns include *he*, *she*, *it*, *they*, and *them*. An all-too-common problem with pronouns in technical (and nontechnical) writing is *gender bias*. In the older technical literature, scientists and engineers were identified as males. It used to be common to write

An engineer must trust his abilities. [*incorrect*]

This construction is *not* proper, as it implies that all engineers are men.

One approach to remedying this situation is the use of the pronouns *they* or *their* in place of *he* and *his*. This leads to the statement

An engineer must trust their abilities. [*incorrect*]

Unfortunately, the solution is grammatically incorrect.

> **What is wrong with the statement, "An engineer must trust their abilities"?**

In this case, the subject ("an engineer") is singular and the pronoun ("their") is plural. A much better solution to gender-specific pronouns is to rework the sentence completely so that the subject and pronouns match in number:

Engineers must trust their abilities.

Another common problem is the proper use of the pronouns *who*, *that*, and *which*. When in doubt, use *who* for human subjects and *that* or *which* for nonhuman subjects. The pronoun *that* is used in reference to a specific noun, while *which* adds information about a noun and usually is used in clauses set off by commas. Thus,

Key idea: Use *who* as a pronoun for human subjects, *that* for specific nonhuman subjects, and *which* for nonhuman subjects in clauses set off by commas.

The engineer *who* was on site had the contract documents.

The human subject takes the pronoun *who*. On the other hand,

The bolt *that* ruptured was installed improperly.

Here, use *that* in referring to a specific bolt. (We are discussing a particular bolt: the bolt that ruptured.) Finally,

The submitted proposal, *which* was missing page three, was thrown in the garbage can.

In this case, use *which* to add information in a separate clause. Often, you can avoid *who*, *that*, and *which* problems by incorporating the information as an adjective. For the examples just presented, you could write

The on-site engineer had the contract documents.

The ruptured bolt was installed improperly.

The submitted proposal was missing page three. It was thrown in the garbage can.

4.5   Adjectives and Adverbs

Adjectives modify nouns and adverbs modify verbs. Avoid using long lists of adjectives, sometimes called **adjective chains**. In adjective chains, it is often difficult to identify the noun. Consider the sentence:

adjective chain: a long list of modifiers to a noun (to be avoided)

High-grade precut stainless steel beams were specified.

The beam characteristics are clearer if the sentence is rewritten:

Precut beams made of high-grade stainless steel were specified.

Adjective and adverb *placement* also can be problematic. You should avoid placing an adverb between the word *to* and the verb. This construction is called a **split infinitive**. For example, you should write

split infinitive: insertion of a word between *to* and the verb (to be avoided)

The gear ratio was designed to drive the system efficiently.

not

The gear ratio was designed to efficiently drive the system.

Key idea: With adjectives and adverbs, avoid adjective chains and make sure the adverb or adjective modifies only the verb or noun you intend to modify.

Having railed against them, it should be noted that split infinitives are a tricky construction. The rule against split infinitives appears to stem from Latin, where splitting an infinitive is impossible. Place an adverb between *to* and the verb only to emphasize the adverb or to produce a sentence that sounds better. For example, there is a split infinitive in the phrase

To boldly go where no one has gone before ...

However, it sounds better (at least to many people) than

To go boldly where no one has gone before ...

Adjectives should be located next to the nouns they modify. Consider the following two sentences:

They only constructed three prototypes.

They constructed only three prototypes.

In the first sentence, *only* modifies *constructed*: they only *constructed* the prototypes, they did not construct and test the prototypes. In the second sentence, *only* modifies *three* (which, in turn, modifies *prototypes*): they constructed only *three* prototypes, rather than four prototypes. Make sure that the adverb (or adjective) modifies only the verb (or noun) you intend to modify.

4.6   Capitalization and Punctuation

Many neophyte technical writers find it necessary to use nonstandard capitalization and abbreviations. Please do not give in to this temptation. Few words in technical writing are capitalized. As suggested by Smith and Vesiland (1996), you usually capitalize the names of organizations, firms, cities, counties, districts, agencies, and states. In general, do not capitalize general references to these entities. Thus, you can write

The City of Rochester contracted for engineering services.

Here, capitalize "city" because it is specific to Rochester, New York, but

The city council met for three hours.

or

The federal government will meet the deadline.

Key idea: Avoid nonstandard capitalization and abbreviations.

Do not capitalize "city" and "federal" because they are general adjectives here. In addition, the titles of engineering reports are capitalized, and official titles of people are capitalized when they precede the names of the people (but not when they follow the name).

Standard abbreviations for scientific and engineering units and parameters should be used. If in doubt, define an abbreviation *the first time it is used*. There is no need to capitalize the words as an abbreviation is defined. Thus, write

The standard operating procedure (SOP) was followed.

not

The Standard Operating Procedure (SOP) was followed.

and not

The SOP was followed.

The last construction is improper if using the abbreviation for the first time, but desirable if the abbreviation *SOP* already has been defined in the document.

Common nontechnical abbreviations include the following:

e.g. (*exempli gratia* = for example)

i.e. (*id est* = that is)

etc. (*et cetera* = and so forth), and

et al. (*et alia* = and others)

(*Note*: The last term is **not** abbreviated et. al or et. al.) These common abbreviations sometimes are italicized (e.g., *e.g.*) to indicate their non-English origins.

Commas should be used to define clauses and separate items in a list. Usually, a comma is used even before the last item in a list. For example,

Materials included wood, steel, and concrete.

If the items in a list are long (or the items include commas or conjunctions), use semicolons to separate them:

Materials included wood, natural materials, and fiber; steel and concrete; and thermoplastic resins.

4.7   Spelling

Key idea: Never assume a document is free of errors because it passes the spell checker.

There is no room for spelling errors in technical documents. One misspelled word could destroy an otherwise strong document. The fundamental rule of spelling is *Never, never, never trust your spell checker*. Spell-checking software is a good first start, but you must learn to proofread your writing very carefully. Spell checkers miss misspellings that result in another word (e.g., house/horse, dear/deer). A proofreading example is given in Section 4.10.

4.8   Citation

plagiarism: using someone else's words or ideas without proper credit

You are professionally and morally obligated to give credit when you use ideas from other people. Taking someone else's words or ideas without credit is called ***plagiarism***. Plagiarism is defined in the University at Buffalo's University Standards and Administrative Regulations as

copying or receiving material from a source or sources and submitting this material as one's own without acknowledging the particular debts to the source (quotations, paraphrases, basic ideas), or otherwise representing the work of another as one's own.

Key idea: Make sure you give credit (by use of a citation) when presenting someone else's words or ideas.

Students who plagiarize are subject to disciplinary action. Engineers who plagiarize can lose their professional licenses.

Plagiarism is not just copying *words* from someone else. Plagiarism also means taking another person's *ideas* without giving them due credit. Always read your work carefully to make sure that you have not inadvertently included someone else's ideas "without acknowledging the particular debts to the source."

Credit is shown by *citing the work from which the material was taken*. There are many citation styles. One style (employed in this text) is to list the author's name and publication date in parentheses following the material cited, as in "Smith (2002)." Numbers, usually written as superscripts (e.g., Smith[2]), may be used with a numbered reference list.

paraphrase: to rewrite an idea in your own words

In nearly all cases, you ***paraphrase*** the material (i.e., rewrite it in your own words). On rare occasions (when the original words are required), it may be necessary to quote the words exactly. Quotation should be done sparingly and the citation always must be given. Indicate a direct quotation by the use of quotation marks or by doubly indenting the material. Examples of paraphrasing and quotation are shown in Example 1.

EXAMPLE 1 PARAPHRASING AND QUOTATION

Use the following material, from Paradis and Zimmerman (1997), in a paragraph, and cite it properly:

"Long sentences, often amounting to more than 30 words, are usually too complicated. Determine the main actions of the sentence. Then sort these into two or more shorter sentences."

SOLUTION

Here are several citation options:

1. Paraphrase with citation (preferred approach):

    Long sentences should be broken up into smaller sections according to their main actions (Paradis and Zimmerman, 1997).

2. Quotation using quotation marks with citation:

    Overly long sentences can be problematic. According to Paradis and Zimmerman (1997): "Long sentences, often amounting to more than 30 words, are usually too complicated. Determine the main actions of the sentence. Then sort these into two or more shorter sentences."

3. Quotation using indentation with citation:

    Overly long sentences are confusing to the reader. Several approaches have been developed to identify and eliminate run-on sentences. For example,

    > Long sentences, often amounting to more than 30 words, are usually too complicated. Determine the main actions of the sentence. Then sort these into two or more shorter sentences. (Paradis and Zimmerman, 1997).

The following approach is plagiarism because the work is paraphrased but no citation is given [*Warning*: **This material is not cited properly!**]

Long sentences—some can be up to 30 words long—should be subdivided. To do this, find its main actions and create a shorter sentence for each main action.

4.9   Other Problem Areas

In addition to the rules discussed previously, several other words and phrases cause problems in technical writing. Most of the words and phrases listed below were found in Strunk and White (1979) or Smith and Vesiland (1996):

affect/effect: These two words cause many difficulties in technical writing, but the rule regarding their use is simple. The word *affect* is almost always a *verb*. The word *effect* is almost always a *noun*. Thus, write "The effects of temperature were noted" (*effects* is a noun) and "Temperature affected the results" ("affected" is the verb).*

among/between: Use *between* when two people or things are involved and *among* when more than two or more people or things are involved. For example, write "The voltage was split between two capacitors," but "The work was divided among four engineers."

comprise: *Comprise* means *to consist of*: "The frame comprises four steel rods" (i.e., the frame *consists of* four steel rods) and "Four steel rods make up the frame" (*not* "Four steel rods comprise the frame").

Key idea: Avoid double negatives in formal writing.

double negatives: Avoid the **use** of two or more negatives (*not* or words starting with *un*) in the same sentence. Rewrite by canceling out pairs of negatives: "The project was like our previous work" (*not* "The project was not unlike our previous work.")

farther/further: *Farther* refers to distance, while *further* refers to time or quantity. Thus, "The ultrahigh-mileage vehicle went farther on a tank of gas," while "Further negotiations are necessary to seal the contract."

---

*While *affect* is usually a verb, it is used in psychology as a noun (for example, the Jones affect). The word *effect* almost always is a noun, but it is used *very rarely* as a verb, as in "Temperature effected a change in elasticity." (This means temperature *brought about* a change in elasticity.)

fewer/less: *Fewer* is used in reference to the *number* of things, while *less* refers to the *quantity* (or amount) of an object. For example, "Our model has fewer adjustable parameters" (i.e., fewer number of parameters), and "The high-efficiency engine used less gasoline" (i.e., a lesser amount of gasoline).

irregardless: *Irregardless* is an example of a double negative. The prefix *ir-* and the suffix *-less* both negate *regard*. Please write *regardless* anytime you are tempted to write *irregardless*.

its/it's: Here is a nagging exception to the rule that you add an apostrophe to indicate the possessive form. The word "its" is the possessive form: "Its color was red." The word *it's* is a contraction of *it is*: "It's hot today." In general, *avoid contractions in formal writing*.

Key idea: Avoid contractions in formal writing.

personification: Personification (also called anthropomorphism) is the assignment of human characteristics to nonhuman objects, as in "The day smiled on me." Personification should be avoided in technical writing. Some people dislike the assignment of any active verb to any inanimate objects. In this view, some say you should avoid statements such as "The data show . . ." or "The experiments demonstrate . . . ." Although there is a difference of opinion on this matter, it is best to avoid egregious examples of personification in your technical writing (such as "The data really grabbed me by the throat," which is too informal as well).

precede/proceed: *Precede* means *to come before*, while *proceed* means *to continue or move forward*. Thus, "The air-conditioning study preceded the heating study" (meaning that the air-conditioning study was conducted first) and "The work proceeded without interruption" (meaning that the work continued without interruption).

presently: *Presently* means both *soon* and *currently*. Strunk and White (1979) suggest that *presently* be used only in the sense of *soon*.

4.10   Proofreading

Key idea: Always proofread your work.

The secret to good proofreading is practice. You can check your proofreading skills by asking others to read your work and give you feedback. An example of proofreading is given in Example 3.

EXAMPLE 3: PROOF-READING

Read the following paragraph and list the errors you encounter. Allow 60 seconds for this exercise. Rewrite the paragraph to eliminate the errors. [*Warning:* **The following text may contain errors!**]

Abstract

Project personnel conducted a laboratory study to definitively determine the engineeering feasability of polychlorinated biphenyl (PCB) removal by granular activated carbon. The study used an expanded bed granular activated carbon reactor in the upflow mode. PCB concentrations in the column effluent was measured by standard techniques. Study data is consistent with surface diffusion as the rate-limiting step, although much scatter in the data is observed. Columns were sacrificed at the conclusion of the study and carbon analysis revealed PCB saturation is the first 50% of the bed. Future studies will be conducted on the affect of the recycle rate on column performance.

SOLUTION

A list of errors (with the corresponding section numbers in parentheses) is given in Table 3.

TABLE 3 Errors in Proofreading Example

Sentence	Error(s)
First sentence	"to definitively determine" is a split infinitive (4.5), "engineeering" (engineering) and "feasability" (feasibility) are misspelled (4.7)
Second sentence	" . . . expanded bed granular activated carbon reactor . . . " contains an adjective chain (4.5)
Third sentence	" . . . concentrations . . . was . . . " is a subject/verb mismatch (4.1). The use of the passive voice (4.2) is discouraged, unless it is clear who analyzed the samples from other parts of the report.
Fourth sentence	" . . . data is . . . " is a subject/verb mismatch (4.1). *Note*: The sentence " . . . much scatter in the data is . . . " is fine, since the subject, "scatter," is singular.
Fifth sentence	This sentence is a long sentence (3.2). Also, the sentence should read, " . . . saturation *in* the first . . . " (rather than " . . . saturation *is* the first . . . ").
Sixth sentence	Use of passive voice is inconsistent with the active voice used elsewhere in the paragraph (4.2). Also, "affect" should be "effect" (4.9).

Here is an improved version of the abstract:

Abstract

Project personnel conducted a laboratory study to determine definitively the engineering feasibility of polychlorinated biphenyl (PCB) removal by granular activated carbon (GAC). The study used an expanded bed GAC reactor in the upflow mode. A contract laboratory measured PCB concentrations in the column effluent by standard techniques. Study data are consistent with surface diffusion as the rate-limiting step, although much scatter in the data is observed. Columns were sacrificed at the conclusion of the study. Carbon analysis revealed PCB saturation in the first 50% of the bed. We plan to conduct future studies on the effect of the recycle rate on column performance.

5 TYPES OF ENGINEERING DOCUMENTS

5.1 Introduction

Thus far in this chapter, you have been exposed to the organization of engineering reports. Reports are used to present the results of a study. A report may transmit the results of the entire project (called a *final* or *full report*), transmit the results of a portion of the project (called a *progress report*), or transmit a small piece of a report in a short form (often called a *letter report*).

In addition to reports, engineers write several other kinds of documents. Common document types include letters, memorandums, and email.

5.2 Reports

Key idea: Reports should include a cover page and a transmittal letter.

The general outline of an engineering report was discussed in Section 2. Two other elements of a report deserve mention. First, every report should have a cover page. A cover page includes the names of the authors (and their professional titles), the names of the recipients (and their professional titles), the report or project title, a project identifier, and the date. Many formats are possible, as long as this information is included. Locate the required information for a cover page in the example cover page in Figure 1.

Second, most reports have a *transmittal letter* (also called a *cover letter*). The transmittal letter is a short letter that accompanies the report. The format of letters is presented in Section 5.3.

> **Pumping Options for Stormwater Management
> in Rivertown, Ohio**
>
> Draft Final Report for
> Rivertown DPW Project #2005-5-1214
>
>
> Submitted to:
>
>
> Mary J. Bremer, PE
> Director of Public Works
> Rivertown Public Works Department
> 1120 Bank Road
> Rivertown, Ohio
>
>
> Submitted by:
>
>
> John H. Seal, PE
> Senior Associate Engineer
> AZA Engineering
> 12 Cunningham Parkway, Suite 114
> Warsaw, Ohio
>
>
> February 7, 2007

Figure 1.   An Example of a Cover Page

Key idea: Letters should have a heading (including the date, recipient's name, and title), closing (including your name, title, and signature), and structured paragraphs (the first paragraph should summarize previous correspondence and state the purpose of the letter, the next paragraphs should present supporting information, and the last paragraph should summarize the main point and state the required actions or follow-up communication).

memorandum: a short note used to document engineering work

Key idea: Memos should have a heading (including to whom the memo is written, who wrote the memo, the memo topic, the date, and the word *Memorandum*), and the same structured paragraphs as a letter.

5.3   Letters

Engineers use letters to document the transmission of ideas to the client or other agency. Letters must have structure. The heading of a letter includes the date and recipient's name and title. The first paragraph of a letter should summarize previous correspondence and state the purpose of the letter. In the next paragraph or paragraphs, supporting information should be presented. The last paragraph of the letter should summarize the main points and state the required actions or follow-up communication. In the closing information of a letter, include your name, title, and signature. An example letter is shown in Figure 2. Note the heading information; introductory, supporting, and concluding paragraphs; and closing information.

5.4   Memorandums

A **memorandum** (plural: memorandums or memoranda) is a short note. Similar to letters, memorandums are used for short documentation of engineering work. In fact, the word *memorandum* is a shortened form of the phrase *memorandum est*—Latin for "it is to be remembered." Memorandums are frequently used for messages inside an organization (called *internal memorandums*).

Memorandums (or memos) are structured similarly to letters (see Section 5.3), but without the heading and closing information of a letter. Heading information in a memo tells you to whom the memo is written, who wrote the memo, the memo topic, the date, and the word *Memorandum*.

AZA *Engineers*
Warsaw • Milton • Cleveland

March 10, 2006

Mary J. Bremer, PE
Director of Public Works
Rivertown Public Works Department
1120 Bank Road
Rivertown, Ohio

Dear Ms. Bremer,

As per our telephone conservation of March 9th, I am writing to summarize your comments on the draft stormwater report. Our responses to your comments also are included in this letter.

My notes indicate that your staff had three main comments on the draft report. First, the name of the Bilmore Pump Station was misspelled on page 6-2. Second, the flow calculations for the West Branch were based on 1980-2000 rainfall data, while all other system design calculations were based on 1970-2000 rainfall data. Third, your staff requested that the cradle design for Option 4 use a smaller factor of safety than the 2.5 safety factor in the report (p. 7-7).

We will correct the spelling error on page 6-2 and update the design calculations for the West Branch with rainfall data from 1970-2004. However, we feel best engineering practice requires the safety factor of 2.5 in the pump cradle design. Based on conversations with the pump manufacturer, lower safety factors will increase the chance of catastrophic failure. Therefore, we wish to retain the 2.5 safety factor in the design of Option 4.

To summarize, we plan to resubmit the report before March 31, 2006 with the spelling error corrected and with the design calculations for the West Branch updated to use rainfall data from 1970-2000. We will retain the safety factor of 2.5 in the pump cradle in Option 4.

Thank you for your thoughtful comments. I will call you next week to confirm the changes. We look forward to delivering you the final report on this project.

        Sincerely,

J H Seal

John H. Seal, PE
Senior Associate Engineer

Figure 2. Example of a Technical Letter

MEMORANDUM

To: Yvonne Ringland
From: J.H. Seal, PE
Re: Comments on Rivertown stormwater report
Date: March 9, 2006

I spoke with Mary Bremer at the Rivertown DPW today about the draft stormwater report. She requested that we use the same rainfall data for the West Branch design calculations as we did for the rest of the report. We used 1970-2000 rainfall data for the majority of the report.

Please redo the West Branch design with 1970-2000 rainfall data. The final report is due by March 31st. Please have the revisions to me by March 25th so we can get the changes to the word processing staff.

If you have questions about the requested changes, please call me at extension 36.

Figure 3.   Example of a Memorandum

Memo paragraphs are similar to those of letters: previous correspondence and memo purpose should be summarized in the first paragraph, supporting information in the following paragraphs, and main points summarized in the last paragraph. An example of a memo is given in Figure 3. Note the heading information and purpose of each of the three paragraphs. A copy of this memo likely would be placed in the project file to document the internal communication of the consulting firm.

5.5   Email

Key idea: When writing business email, avoid contractions and emoticons, proofread carefully, double-check the recipient list, and do not include anything in an email that you would not include in other business documents.

Nearly every college student in the 21st century has used email, usually for informal conversation. Email also can be used in formal business correspondence, sometimes in place of a letter or memo.

Although email is less formal than other forms of written communication, it is easy to let an overly familiar style creep into your formal email correspondence. You use different words in speaking to clients and colleagues than you use to speak to friends at a party. Similarly, use more formal language in business email. Following are some rules for business email correspondence:

- Avoid email contractions (e.g., *RU* for *are you* and *°s°* for *smile*).
- Avoid *emoticons*—text characters used to express emotions (such as :-) for a smiley face).
- Proofread carefully before you hit "send." Look for language that may be offensive or inappropriate.
- Double-check the names on the "to" list before you send the email. "Replying to all" with the results of your recent medical check-up (when you intended to forward the results to your roommate) is a serious breach of business protocol.

- Emails are as much a part of the technical and legal record as are other documents. Do not include anything in an email that you would not include in other business documents.

An example of a business email message is shown in Figure 4.

Email is not the only kind of electronic written document in engineering today. For a look at the future of written technical communication, see the *Focus on Writing: Whither Paper Reports?*

To: Roger Yee (rty@azaengineers.com)
From: John H. Seal (jhs@azaengineers.com)
Subject: Pump cradle design for Rivertown Project
Cc: Cynthia Cronin (cronin@rgoldpumps.com)
Bcc:
Attached: Draft Rivertown report.doc

Roger -

Rivertown has questioned our use of a 2.5 safety factor for the cradle design in Option 4 of the stormwater project. Attached is the draft report.

Are we sure about this safety factor? If so, please help me to justify it. I am copying Cindy Cronin at Rheingold Pumps on this message. We are specifying Rheingold Pumps and Cindy might be able to help.

Please get back to me by the end of the day on this, Roger.

Thanks,

John H. Seal
Senior Associate Engineer
AZA Engineering

Figure 4.   Example of a Business Email

FOCUS ON WRITING: WHITHER PAPER REPORTS?

BACKGROUND

Probably since the first pyramid was built, engineers have been summarizing their work by writing reports. This chapter was devoted to helping you write better reports and other engineering documents. There are many cases in which the results of engineering work are better communicated by electronic documents. Many clients now are requesting electronic or on-line reports.

ELECTRONIC MANUALS

As an example of electronic reporting, many industries are replacing entire bookshelves of operation and maintenance (O&M) manuals with *on-line manuals*. The on-line O&M manuals typically are written in HTML, XML, or other programming languages used in Web page development. In addition, manuals and other electronic engineering documents commonly are written in Adobe's proprietary *portable document format* as PDF files.

Electronic manuals have a number of advantages over traditional documentation. First, they reduce the need for operations and maintenance training. Perez et al. (2001) estimated that the effectiveness of O&M training at a drinking-water treatment plant was increased four- to sixfold using on-line materials as compared with paper manuals. More effective training results in fewer errors and cost savings.

Second, electronic manuals are much easier to keep current. Engineers struggle to maintain current sets of plans about engineered systems. Facilities personnel need to know the actual conditions of the structure (as-built conditions), not the system as originally designed (design conditions). Electronic manuals allow engineers to update material very quickly and accurately. The underlying database of equipment and other system attributes can be updated centrally, allowing users to access up-to-date information from any location.

Third, electronic manuals are easier to access. Facility personnel sometimes dread the thought of flipping through literally thousands of pages of manuals in three-ring binders to find the information they need. Electronic manuals are written with *hyperlinks* (as on Web pages). This allows the user to find related information quickly. In fact, electronic manuals look like Web pages. As with the Web itself, e-manuals can be very graphically oriented, with liberal use of drawings, photographs, and videos. In addition, electronic manuals can be linked to manufacturer's Web pages. If, say, you need a new gasket for a pump, you can click on the manufacturer's link and find the part easily.

Fourth, electronic manuals are portable. Many electronic manuals are mounted on company intranets, allowing for secure access by facility personnel from any location. In other cases, the manuals are burned onto CD-ROMs. One CD-ROM can replace up to 1,540 pounds of paper manuals (Perez et al., 2001).

WILL YOU EVER SEE A PAPERLESS OFFICE?

For the foreseeable future, engineers probably will continue to produce reports on paper. The "paperless office" continues to be frustratingly just out of reach. However, the engineer's life is becoming increasingly "webcentric" (i.e., centered on the World Wide Web). As an engineer of the future (and as a person brought up to think of the Internet as an important resource), you should think creatively about how information needs in engineering can be addressed by electronic sources. Always ask whether electronic documents will add value to the information (by allowing linkage to other data sources or by providing real-time data or by using multimedia formats).

Perhaps in your lifetime, paper reports will become as quaint as slide rules and manual typewriters. Regardless of the delivery medium, engineering reports will still be based on the principles outlined in this text: organization, signposting, and clarity.

6   SUMMARY

The key to good written technical documents is *organization*. The typical structure of an engineering report includes several aspects: the abstract (or executive summary), introduction/background/literature review, methods, results, discussion, conclusions/recommendations, and references.

Technical documents also must be organized at the paragraph, sentence, and word levels. Choose words to make your writing concise, simple, and specific. In your technical writing, be aware of the rules of grammar and spelling. Strive to use the active voice and avoid gender-specific language. Always proofread your work before allowing it to leave your hands.

In addition to reports, engineers produce letters, memos, and emails almost daily in their working lives. Letters have a heading, a closing, and structured paragraphs. The first paragraph summarizes previous correspondence and states the purpose of the letter. The next paragraphs present supporting information. The last paragraph summarizes the main points and states the required actions or follow-up communication. Memos have the same paragraph structure, with a different heading and no closing. Business emails are part of the business record and should be created and sent in a professional manner.

SUMMARY OF KEY IDEAS

- Organize technical documents from the largest to smallest scale: outline level, paragraph level, sentence level, and word level.
- Common elements of technical documents include the abstract (or executive summary), introduction/background/literature review, methods, results, discussion, conclusions/recommendations, and references.
- The abstract should contain a summary of each element of the report.
- The introduction should take the reader from the report title to an understanding of why the report was written.
- In the methods section, justify the study approach, present data collection techniques, and discuss data analysis methods.
- In the results section, present the results and note the general trends.
- Interpret data in the discussion section.
- Conclusions and recommendations are often in list form and should be written very carefully.
- Although many reference formats are acceptable, the references must be complete and consistent.
- Use section headings or numbering schemes as signposts in technical documents.
- Each sentence should express a single idea.
- Choose words to make your writing concise, simple, and specific.
- Avoid making up new words or new uses of words in conventional technical writing.
- Make sure that the subject and verb agree in number (i.e., they must be both singular or both plural).
- Use a consistent voice, with preference for the active voice.
- Generally use the present tense, unless describing work done in the past.
- Avoid the use of gender-specific pronouns.
- Use *who* as a pronoun for human subjects, *that* for specific nonhuman subjects, and *which* for nonhuman subjects in clauses set off by commas.
- With adjectives and adverbs, avoid adjective chains and make sure the adverb or adjective modifies only the verb or noun you intend to modify.
- Avoid nonstandard capitalization and abbreviations.
- Never assume a document is free of errors because it passes the spell checker.
- Make sure you give credit (by use of a citation) when presenting someone else's words or ideas.
- Avoid double negatives in formal writing.
- Avoid contractions in formal writing.
- Always proofread your work.

- Reports should include a cover page and a transmittal letter.
- Letters should have a heading (including the date, recipient's name, and title), closing (including your name, title, and signature), and structured paragraphs (the first paragraph should summarize previous correspondence and state the purpose of the letter, the next paragraphs should present supporting information, and the last paragraph should summarize the main points and state the required actions or follow-up communication).
- Memos should have a heading (including to whom the memo is written, who wrote the memo, the memo topic, the date, and the word *Memorandum*) and the same structured paragraphs as a letter.
- When writing business email, avoid contractions and emoticons, proofread carefully, double-check the recipient list, and do not include anything in an email that you would not include in other business documents.

Problems

1. Pick two textbooks other than this one. What kinds of signposting are used in the texts? Describe the scheme used to show hierarchy in the signposting.

2. What are the characteristics of a good sentence?

3. What are the three aspects of good word choice in technical writing? Find good and poor examples of word choice in a newspaper or technical journal.

4. List whether the following nouns should take a singular or plural verb form: engineer, axes, phenomena, axis, datum, criterion, thermodynamics, phenomenon, Microsoft, and criteria. You may need to use a dictionary.

5. Find five examples of the use of passive voice in this text. Rewrite them in the active voice.

6. Repair the following paragraph, if necessary. [**Warning: The following material may contain errors!**]

   Plans and specifications who lack careful preparation may be faulty. The engineer must use all his skill to find and correct the problems. The engineer that refines her own design is more likely to find their own errors.

7. For each of the following, identify the problem or problems in the use of adjectives or adverbs, if any, and correct the errors. [**Warning: The following material may contain errors!**]

   a. "The mass-produced germanium junction transistor was a major advance."
   b. "The project manager attempted to slowly accelerate the production rate."
   c. "The contract only required plant construction, not the operation of the plant."
   d. "Alternating current power transmission first occurred at Niagara Falls in 1895."

8. Select any paragraph in this text. Paraphrase the idea without a direct quotation, and include a citation and a reference. Repeat with a paragraph from a technical journal of interest to you.

9. Write a letter to your professor asking for permission to take a make-up exam.

10. Write a memo to a classmate to organize a study session for one of your courses.

18

Oral Technical Communications

1 INTRODUCTION

Few activities intimidate new engineers more than public speaking. Technical oral presentations need not be painful. They can be tamed by focusing on three kinds of activities:

- What to do *before* the talk,
- What to do *during* the talk, and
- What to do *after* the talk.

Many people think that the *delivery* is the key to technical talks. While the delivery is important, the truth is that oral presentations are made or broken by the work put in *before* the talk is delivered. A good technical talk is well organized, with instructive visual aids. It is delivered with the help of useful but nonintrusive memory aids. The talk will be rehearsed, but not overly practiced. These critical activities—organization, visual aids design, memory aids design, and practice—take place well before the oral presentation is made to the audience. The details of talk organization and preparation will be presented in Sections 2 through 4.

What is your gut reaction to the thought of standing up before a handful or dozens or hundreds of people and delivering technical material? If your palms are sweating already, then Section 5 may help. In Section 5, your plan of action immediately before the talk (including how to deal with nervousness) will be reviewed. You will learn what to say and how to say it.

Finally, improvement in your technical speaking skills is made only by what you do after the talk. Section 6 will provide hints on obtaining feedback and implementing good speaking habits.

OBJECTIVES

After reading this chapter, you will be able to:

- organize a technical oral presentation;
- design visual aids;
- design memory aids;
- deliver an effective technical oral presentation.

2   BEFORE THE TALK: ORGANIZATION

Key idea: Technical presentations can be improved by considering the activities before the talk, during the talk, and after the talk.

Key idea: Identify the presentation goals, target audience, and constraints on the presentation (especially time constraints).

visual aids: media used to accompany oral presentations (e.g., slides and overhead transparencies)

title slide: visual aid containing the presentation title and information about the authors

Recall that before writing a single word of the oral presentation, you must identify the goals of the presentation, the target audience, and the constraints on the presentation. The main constraint on oral presentations is the time allotted for the talk. In your career, almost every oral presentation you give will have time constraints. One key to good oral presentations is to respect your audience's time and use their time wisely.

Only after identifying goals, audience, and constraints can an outline be written. With an outline in place, the individual **visual aids** can be designed. Technical talks usually begin with a **title slide**.* The title slide contains the title of the talk and the names and affiliations of the authors. The title slide is the oral presentation equivalent of the cover page. Any example title slide is shown in Figure 1.

In many technical presentations, the second slide is an outline or overview of the talk. While an outline slide is optional, it serves as a good road map for the remainder of the talk. Audiences may feel more comfortable if they know where the presentation is going. The outline slide is the first opportunity for signposting in an oral technical presentation. An example outline slide is shown in Figure 2.

Biochemical Engineering of Artifical Skin

A.D. Leising, PhD
Chief Chemical Engineer
DermaTech, Inc.

Presented at the VentureCap Expo, Sept. 8, 2005

Figure 1.   An Example of a Title Slide

 Outline

- Background
  - History of artificial skin
  - Barriers to commercialization
- Approach
- Results
  - Synthesis of smart plastics
  - Results of animal trials
  - Commercialization potential
- Conclusions

Figure 2.   An Example of an Outline Slide

---

*To simplify the language here, visual aids in general will be called "slides." Information of the types of visual aids may be found in Section 3.2.

Key idea: Use an outline to organize the talk and an outline slide to show your organization.

The remaining sections of a technical talk vary with the goals and target audience. A generic structure that includes an introduction/background, methods, results, discussion, conclusions, and recommendations is a good place to start. Technical talks rarely include an abstract, formal literature review, or list of references.

3   BEFORE THE TALK: DESIGNING VISUAL AIDS

Key idea: The number of visual aids should be about $3/4$ times the number of minutes allotted to the presentation.

Once the outline has been established, you can start to design the visual aids. A major difference between written and oral presentations is the reliance on visual aids in oral communication. You must select the number, type, and content of visual aids.

3.1   Number of Visual Aids

The number of visual aids depends most strongly on the length of the presentation. *To estimate the maximum number of visual aids, multiply the number of minutes in the presentation by 0.75.* For example, a 30-minute talk should have no more than 21 to 23 slides.

The natural tendency is to prepare too many visual aids. After all, if the number of slides is $3/4$ of the number of minutes, then the average time per slide is $4/3$ minutes = 80 seconds. Many first-time speakers reason that several of the slides in the presentation (e.g., the title and outline slides) will take much less than 80 seconds to present. They conclude that they can have *many more* slides than the number calculated from $3/4$ (number of minutes). *This logic almost always leads to very rushed and incoherent presentations.* Until you become very experienced in oral technical presentations, use the "$3/4$ times the number of minutes" value as a firm guide.

3.2   Types of Visual Aids

Several types of visual aids are available, including slides, overhead transparencies, poster boards and flip charts, blackboards and whiteboards, and computer displays and projectors. Physical models and material to be passed around the audience also are used as visual aids.

Key idea: In selecting the type of visual aid, consider image quality, eye contact, and production cost and time. Then use only one type of visual aid in a talk.

In selecting a type of visual aid, three factors are important: image clarity, maintenance of eye contact, and production cost and time. The advantages and disadvantages of several types of visual aids are summarized in Table 1. In many professional presentations, image clarity may be paramount. It may be worth the money to produce the highest quality images available.

Eye contact is important for two reasons. First, it allows you to get feedback from the audience. Are they bored? Engaged? Having trouble hearing you? Second, eye contact allows the audience to be drawn into your words. Try listening to a movie or television program with your eyes shut. The magic is reduced when the eye contact is lost. Still not convinced? The next time you speak before a group of people, notice how much time the audience spends looking at your *eyes* rather than the screen.

Visual aids also can be expensive and time-consuming to produce. Always estimate the cost and time required to produce any visual aid before committing to a type of visual aid. If the turnaround time for producing visual aids is long, you may have to adjust your schedule to meet the presentation deadline.

Regardless of the type of visual aid selected, it is important to use only one type of visual aid. Switching back and forth between two types can be distracting to the audience, especially if the room lights are turned on and off repeatedly. For the vast majority of technical talks, stick to one type of visual aid. Each type of visual aid will be discussed in more detail.

Slides

Color photographic slides provide the sharpest images. Slides come with a major disadvantage: they require the room to be darkened. In a dark room, you risk losing eye contact with the audience. Slides also can be expensive and time-consuming to produce.

Overhead Transparencies

Overhead transparencies, also called *overheads*, provide a good trade-off between image clarity and eye contact. The images may be poorer than slides (although color laser printers are capable of producing very high quality overheads on special transparency film).

In presenting overheads, the room lights generally are on, but dimmed. Thus, eye contact is still possible. Unless you have an assistant, overheads require you to stand

TABLE 1 Types of Visual Aids and Their Characteristics

Type	Image Quality	Eye Contact	Cost and Time	Other
Slides	Very high	Moderate (room dark)	Moderate	Image very sharp
Overhead transparencies	High	Good	Small	Good compromise
Poster boards and flip charts	Very high	Excellent	Moderate to large	Good for smaller audiences
Whiteboards and blackboards	Low	Excellent	Very small	For informal work
Computers	Can be very high	Moderate (room dark)	Small	Watch compatibility problems

near the projector. Avoid blocking the audience's view of the projection screen with your body.

Poster Boards and Flip Charts

Poster boards and flip charts are large-format visual aids, displayed on an easel. They are used frequently by consulting engineers because they allow the lights to be on; thus, they maximize eye contact with the audience and increase audience participation. Poster boards and flip charts are not appropriate for large audiences.

Blackboards and Whiteboards

Blackboards and whiteboards are appropriate for informal technical presentations. Their use allows the audience to write notes at the same pace as the speaker/writer. They are a good choice when note taking is important or when audience participation is critical.

Computers

Computer-based presentations quickly are becoming the most common delivery mode for technical presentations. Computer-based presentations have a number of advantages over other media:

- They can be changed at the last moment.
- They can include Internet-based materials, videos, and animations.
- They avoid the expense and lead time required to make photographic slides.

Computer-based presentations have several disadvantages as well. Compatibility problems often arise between notebook computers and projection devices. It is important to make sure that your notebook computer interfaces properly with the intended projector. The ability to change computer-based presentations at the last minute may tempt you to throw together the talk at the last minute. As always, do not let the technology control the message.

Computer-based presentations offer their own challenges regarding the content of the slides. Information on content specific to computer-based presentations is presented in Section 3.5.

3.3   Content of Visual Aids: Word Slides

There are two types of visual aid content: word slides and data slides. Word slides typically contain only words, symbols, and/or equations. Data slides communicate data and may include tables or figures.

Key idea: Word slides should contain as few words as possible.

Word slides should contain as few words as possible to communicate the required information. *It is undesirable to fill a word slide with text*: the audience will read the words rather than look at you.* *You* want to take control of the material and present it to the audience yourself.

Sometimes, symbols or equations can be used in place of words. The choice of equations or words depends on the audience. For a technical audience, a word slide about Newton's Second Law of Motion might contain the equation $F = ma$. For a less technical audience, the gist of the Second Law may be more clearly made with words:

---

*You can prove this point to yourself with a simple experiment. Gather a group of 20 or so people. Prepare two overheads: one with a wordy message and one with an abbreviated form (e.g., "The rain in Spain falls mainly in the plains" and "Spain: Rains in plains"). Show the first overhead and present the message word for word. Show the second overhead and use the same word-for-word speech as the first overhead. You will notice that the audience's eyes are on the screen when you show the first overhead. Their eyes are more likely to be on you when you show the second overhead.

"Force is proportional to both acceleration and mass." For a nontechnical audience, perhaps a cartoon would best illustrate the point.

For a technical audience:
    Newton's Second Law

$$F = ma.$$

For a less technical audience:
    Newton's Second Law

        Force is proportional to both acceleration and mass.

For a nontechnical audience:

Newton's Second Law

The force doubles when the mass doubles.

Word slides should take into account the shape of the visual aid. For example, overhead transparencies and computer-based presentation slides have a length-to-width ratio of $11{:}8.5 \approx 1.3{:}1$. Photographic slides usually have a ratio of about 0.7:1. It is pleasing to the eye to have the word shape match the visual aid shape.

Matching the word shape to the visual aid shape also means that the font size can be as large as possible. It is important in word slides to use a large font size. Typically, slides and overheads should have font sizes from about 28 to 44 point. Use consistent font sizes (i.e., major headings all in one size and minor headings all in another size). Presentation software (such as Microsoft PowerPoint or Corel Presentations) can help in maintaining a consistent presentation format. Two word slide examples may be found in Figures 3 and 4.

History of Chemical Engineering (ChE) Education

- 1888: First ChE B.S. degree
- 1901: "Handbook of Chemical Engineering" (G.E. Davis)
- 1908: AIChE formed
- 1915: "Unit operations" (intro. by A.D. Little)
- 1925: First accredited degrees

Figure 3.   Word Slide Example 1 (dates from http://www.cems.umn.edu/~aiche_ug/history/h_toc.html)

A Short History of Education in Chemical Engineering

- 1888: First chemical engineering B.S. degree offered
- 1901: G.E. Davis published "Handbook of Chemical Engineering"
- 1908: American Institute of Chemical Engineering (AIChE) formed
- 1915: The concept of "unit operations" was first introduced by A.D. Little
- 1925: First accredited degrees offered

Figure 4.   Word Slide Example 2

PONDER THIS

Critique the examples in Figures 3 and 4. Which would be more appropriate for an oral presentation? How could both examples be improved?

Note the use of abbreviations in Figure 3. Abbreviations allow for a larger font size to be used. Small words (*the* and *of*) are eliminated to avoid having the audience read the text rather than listen to the words. In both examples, the slide needs to be *presented*. Figure 3 would make a better slide in an oral presentation. Figure 4 might be better in a written document, where no additional words are used to explain the text.

3.4   Content of Visual Aids: Data Slides

Key idea: Create tables specific to the point you wish to make.

Data slides can be tables or figures. In oral presentations, it is critical that *tables contain only the data required*. Speakers sometimes photocopy large tables onto overhead transparencies and present the tabular material as follows: "I know you can't read all the numbers in this table, but note that the gear ratio of 20-to-1 was optimal." If you wish to speak about a gear ratio of 20:1, design a data or word slide specific to that point.

Properties of Air

Temp. (°C)	Density (kg/m³)	Viscosity (N·s/m²)	Speed of Sound (m/s)
−40	1.514	1.57	306.2
−20	1.395	1.63	319.1
0	1.292	1.71	331.4
20	1.204	1.82	343.3
40	1.127	1.87	349.1
60	1.060	1.97	365.7

"I know you can't read all the tiny numbers, but the speed of sound in air is less than 350 m/s in the temperature range of 0 to 20°C."

"As you can see, the speed of sound in air is less than 350 m/s in the temperature range of 0 to 20°C."

Properties of Air

Temperature (°C)	Speed of Sound (m/s)
0	331.4
20	343.3

Make tables specific to the points you wish to emphasize.

3.5   Special Notes about Computer-Based Presentations

Today's software allows you to prepare amazing computer-based presentations, with vibrant colors, inspiring animations, and hundreds of fonts. While all those embellishments are possible, you must ask yourself if they are right for your presentation and your audience.

PONDER THIS

How can you decide if animations and other embellishments are appropriate?

Key idea: With computer-based presentations, watch the colors, number of fonts, and animations.

Use the same criteria that you applied to all other aspects of your presentation: Do the embellishments help you to deliver your message to the target audience?

You should keep a few thoughts in mind as you design computer-based presentations. First, *go easy on the color combinations*. Start with the prepackaged color combinations in the presentation software. Stick with two to four colors, using them consistently for signposting. If you have poor color vision or are unsure of your artistic skills, then you may wish to have a friend review your work prior to presentation.

Second, *use a small number of font families*. You can use font size and font weight (bold, italic, etc.) to create a style, but using many font families is distracting. For example, some textbooks are written with only two font families (Times New Roman and Arial), but over a dozen combinations of font size and weight. If you use nonstandard fonts, then you can run into font availability problems if you use a different computer for the presentation than you used to create the talk.

Third, *be very careful about animations* (e.g., flying text and swirling slide transitions). Some people find animations very annoying. Use them sparingly unless you know your audience well.

4   BEFORE THE TALK: PREPARING TO PRESENT

4.1   Practicing Oral Presentations

Several tricks can make your practice time more valuable. First, practice your talk for the first time *before* the visual aids are finalized. In this way, you can identify and edit

Key idea: Practice before the visual aids are finalized.

any slides that do not make your points as cleanly as you want. Last-minute changes in visual aids can be expensive and stressful (although computer-based presentations are making last-minute changes easier).

Second, record the duration of *each section* of your talk during the first few practice rounds. This approach allows you to judge the *balance* of the talk. The meat of the talk (e.g., the results and discussion if you are presenting project results) should occupy at least half the time. Timing the talk also helps you to know where cuts or additions should take place if the first run-throughs show that the talk is too long or too short.

Key idea: When practicing, time each section as you practice alone and in front of others.

Third, practice the talk both by yourself and in front of others. When practicing by yourself, always *speak aloud* so you can rehearse any troublesome phrases or transitions. In addition, try to practice in front of others to get feedback about the talk before the main presentation (see also Section 6).

How often should you practice the talk before the big day? This is a matter of personal preference. Some people require many practice runs before they feel comfortable with the material, while others become stale after just a few practice sessions. *Experiment with different degrees of practicing to determine what level of preparation suits your personality.*

memory aids: notes used to help remember the main points in the talk

4.2   Memory Aids

Memory aids are the notes or devices that help ensure a smooth talk. Memory aids should be designed to help you remember the main points in the talk. Always practice the talk with the same memory aids you intend to use in the final presentation. Common memory aids include

- An outline of the talk
- Note cards containing a list of the key points for each slide
- Speaker's notes in presentation software

An outline lets you see quickly where you are in the presentation. Note cards are useful for making sure that you cover the important points before you go to the next slide. Most computer-based presentation software allows you to put your speaker notes near a miniature version of the slide so you can remind yourself to make the main points you wish.

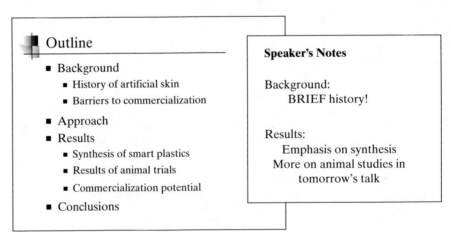

Speaker's notes in a computer-based presentation

It pays to take a few seconds to glance at your notes or outline before you change slides. Although a few seconds may feel like an eternity when you are in front of an audience, the slight pause will help you gain confidence that you are not forgetting anything important. Audiences generally appreciate the small respites as well.

Key idea: Avoid memorizing or reading oral presentations.

A final note about memory aids. Do not read the talk or memorize it completely. We all write differently than we talk. A read speech usually sounds "written." A memorized talk almost always sounds mechanical and forced. Read or memorized talks have another pitfall. If you lose your place or become flustered when reading or reciting by memory, general meltdown often occurs. If you use streamlined notes, it is much easier to get back on track.

5   DURING THE TALK

5.1   Pre-Talk Activities

Key idea: Learn about the facilities and coordinate introductions well before the talk.

Before walking to the podium or to the front of the conference room to give your talk, it is important to know what to expect. Examine the podium or speaking area well before the talk begins. Before you begin speaking, you want to know the answers to several questions:

- Is there a pointer?
- Is the projection equipment in working order?
- Who is responsible for changing computer or slide-projector slides? Are personnel available to help with your overhead transparencies?
- What type of microphone is in use?
- Is there a podium light to allow you to read your notes when the room lights go off? (Memory aids are useless if the room is in complete darkness, a fact you do not want to learn during your first technical presentation!)

It is also helpful to find and introduce yourself to the person who will introduce you. He or she may require some background information from you and may be able to help answer questions about the availability of pointers and the like. You should ask whether he or she will signal you when the allotted time has nearly expired.

5.2   Group Presentations

Key idea: Practice transitions between speakers in group presentations.

Group presentations raise their own set of challenges. It is critical to practice the transitions between the speakers. In general, it is better not to have too many speakers in a short period of time. Make sure the responsibilities of each speaker are understood, including whether one speaker will introduce the next speaker.

5.3   Nervousness

The main concern of most neophyte speakers is the control of nervousness. Being nervous means you care about the presentation. This is a positive attribute, as long as you can control the outward signs of nervousness.

Key idea: Do not worry about *being* nervous; learn to control or avoid the *signs* of nervousness.

The key to dealing with "the jitters" is to determine how nervousness affects you. If being nervous makes you speak more quickly, then focus on slowing your pace. If nervousness makes your hands shake, then avoid holding anything (such as notes or a pointer) during the talk. *It is natural to be a little apprehensive, but desirable to minimize the manifestations of nervousness.*

Remember also that for many talks you will give, the audience *wants* you to succeed. You are giving the talk for a reason. It is likely that the members of the audience desire the information you will share with them. Engineers face truly hostile audiences only rarely in their career.

5.4   What to Say

Technical presentations consist of two elements: presentation of word or data slides and making transitions between slides. When presenting word slides, it is often useful to paraphrase the material rather than reading it to the audience (see also Section 3.3). Again, you are trying to control the message. With lists, gesture to each item as you present it to remind the audience where you are in the slide.

Keep a mental checklist of the items to be covered during the presentation of figures. You should

1. Tell the audience what the figure represents.
2. Identify the axes (with units).
3. Communicate the meaning of each plot (i.e., state the legend information).
4. Enumerate the main points to be made.

Figure 5 contains a sample figure and text showing how the figure would be presented orally. Look at the text in Figure 5 carefully and note the elements presented: a description of what the figure is showing ("removal of dye over time using the new technology"), identification of the axes with units ("time in minutes" and "dye concentration in milligrams per liter"), the meaning of each plot ("solid squares are the experimental data and the line is the first-order model fit"), and enumeration of the main points ("two points to notice in this figure. First, the technology . . . ").

Recall that it is necessary to remind the audience of your organization. This is crucial in oral presentations. If audience members feel lost, they will tune out completely. There is an old doctrine in public speaking called the **Tell 'em Rule**. According to the Tell 'em Rule, you present information three times in a talk: you tell 'em what

Key idea: Paraphrase information in word slides and point to each item in a list.

Key idea: When presenting figures, tell what the figure is showing, identify the axes, communicate the meaning of each plot, and enumerate the main points to be made.

Tell 'em Rule: the idea that you present information three times in a talk: you tell 'em what you will tell them, then tell 'em the information, and finally tell 'em what you just told them

Sample Presentation Text:
Shown here is the removal of dye over time using the new technology. The x-axis is time in minutes and the y-axis is the dye concentration in milligrams per liter. The solid squares are the experimental data and the line is the first-order model fit. There are two points to notice in this figure. First, the technology could reduce the dye concentration to below two milligrams per liter in 20 minutes. Second, the exponential model fits the data reasonably well.

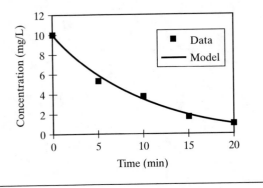

Figure 5. Example of the Presentation of Data in a Figure

you will tell them, then tell 'em the information, and finally tell 'em what you just told them. Following this rule allows for smooth transitions (also called *segues*) between parts of the talk. For example, you may say,

> I wish to give you a little background information on rotary engines. Rotary engines were used first in the automotive industry in .... [text omitted for clarity]. Now that I've told you about the history of rotary engines, let's turn to the modern versions of this unique engine type.

Notice the three presentations of the information ("I wish to give you . . . ," "Rotary engines were used first . . . ," and "Now that I've told you about . . . "). Also note the transition to the modern versions of the rotary engine (" . . . let's turn to the . . . ").

Key idea: Use signposting liberally in technical oral presentations.

The process of telling the audience where you are during transitions between major portions of a talk is called *signposting*. The word *signposting* comes from the analogy with road signs: well-spaced markers tell the audience where you are in the talk. Most technical speakers do not signpost enough. Audiences are much more comfortable when they know they are in synch with the speaker. To assist in signposting, it is helpful to present an outline of the presentation near the beginning of the talk. By referring to the outline, you can keep the audience with you through the talk. Intermediate outlines can be placed in the middle of the talk for complicated sections. For example, you may wish to have an outline of the results to guide the audience through the results section.

5.5   How to Say It

The audience responds to two features of a speaker: the speaker's voice and body. The voice should vary in pitch and intensity: a monotone voice leads to a sleeping audience. Speak through each sentence to avoid swallowing words at the end of the sentence. Be aware of the *speed* and *volume* of your voice. It is useful to have a colleague in the audience signal you (discreetly, of course) if you are speaking too quickly or too softly. The volume of your speech depends on the room and amplification.

Key idea: Speak loudly and slowly. Use meaningful hand gestures and move your body without pacing.

Your body movements should be purposeful and strong. The main problem for most speakers concerns what to do with the hands. Use them to your advantage! Hand gestures are a great way to emphasize important points. For the most important messages, make your gestures higher. Avoid holding pens, pencils, or other mental crutches, and **never** leave your hands in your pockets.

Your legs can work for you as well. Avoid standing stock-still. Walk toward the audience and engage its members at critical points in the talk. While mechanical pacing should be avoided, small steps can make a speaker seem more human to the audience.

In spite of your best preparation, things sometimes go wrong in oral presentations. A few true stories are shared in the *Focus on Talks: Horror Stories*.

6   AFTER THE TALK

Key idea: Seek feedback and incorporate changes into your speaking style.

After a talk, seek out feedback from colleagues in the audience. Listen to their constructive criticism and think about modifications to your speaking style that will make communication more effective. Do not be afraid to identify weaknesses in your speaking style and practice ways to overcome them.

Finally, be an attentive listener. Listen critically to other speakers (such as colleagues, professional speakers, actors, and your professors) and note what you like and dislike about their speaking styles. Ask yourself why you like or dislike their speaking style. Why do good speakers engage you personally? Are they friendly, open, and confident? Incorporate the good aspects and avoid the bad in your next presentation.

FOCUS ON TALKS: HORROR STORIES

INTRODUCTION

Even after reading this chapter, you may still approach your first professional oral presentation with some trepidation. In this section, a few true stories of oral presentations gone awry are shared. Do not panic when you read these stories. They are offered in the spirit of comic relief and to show you that bad things sometimes happen to good presenters. (*Note*: Stories labeled "Lytle" come from the "Stress of Selling" articles compiled by Chris Lytle on the Monster.com Web site. Stories labeled "Hoff" come from Ron Hoff's (1992) very readable book on oral presentations. All other stories come from my experiences or the experiences of my colleagues.)

FROM THE "DRESS FOR SUCCESS" DEPARTMENT

Numerous speakers have walked back to their seat after an oral presentation, only to discover in horror that their pants or skirt zipper was in the down position. Perhaps "check your zipper" is as important as "check your slides." During a graduate course, I noticed my students giggling every time I turned to face them after writing on the blackboard. When I asked them what was going on, they gleefully informed me that I had a sticker of a lamb on my derrière (courtesy of my then-two-year-old daughter). I keep the sticker on my class notebook to this day to remind me to check my attire.

FROM THE "LOCATION, LOCATION, LOCATION" DEPARTMENT

A colleague of mine relates the tale of a presentation he gave for a job interview. He used a long wooden pointer to emphasize his points. But being a good speaker, he kept good eye contact with the audience. Part way through the talk, he realized that he was pointing *behind* the screen with the pointer.

Podiums also can be a source of frustration. Lytle collected the story of a presenter who stood on a stool behind the podium during a speech to 1,500 people. Shortly after the presentation started, the heel of her pump broke. She fell off the stool and crashed onto the concrete floor. Her sympathetic audience gave her the courage to complete the presentation.

Hoff reports that the Queen of England stepped up to a podium during a visit to the United States, only to find that the podium was higher than her head.

FROM THE "NEVER LET THEM SEE YOU SWEAT" DEPARTMENT

Obviously nervous presenters make the audience a little uncomfortable, so never draw attention to your nervousness. I witnessed a student presentation at a state conference where the speaker was using a laser pointer. The pointer danced all over the screen as the speaker's hand shook. Rather than letting it pass, he said, "Well, look at that—I must be really nervous!"

Hoff reports a company treasurer starting a speech with "I'm so nervous this morning. I hope you can't see how badly my knees are shaking." Guess where the audience's eyes were glued for the remainder of the speech. Of course, you should avoid bringing attention to overconfidence as well. Al Gore probably regrets the sighs picked up by microphones during the first presidential debate of 2000.

FROM THE "EQUIPMENT MALFUNCTION" DEPARTMENT

A colleague of mine gave a technical talk in another country, where a more powerful slide projector bulb was in use. She stared in shock as her first slide literally melted before her eyes. Needless to say, she completed the talk without slides.

Lytle reports a presenter panicking when the overhead projector did not turn on. Reaching down to plug in the power cord resulted in a loud ripping noise as the seam of his pants gave out.

FROM THE "WATCH YOUR LANGUAGE" DEPARTMENT

Word choice is important in oral presentations. Lytle relates a story from a salesman giving a presentation before a defense contractor with a product representative (rep). The product rep had a way of choosing the worst possible words to express himself. Quoting from the Web site: "Discussing the ease with which you can use the product, the other rep stated, 'You don't have to be a rocket scientist to use this.' Twenty rocket scientists [in the audience] sat back in their chairs and crossed their arms. After 20 minutes of weasel words to get their interest back ... [the rep said], 'We just have to get your propeller heads to talk to our propeller heads to work it out.' With that, their propeller heads stood up and walked out." Phrases like *propeller head* or *gear head*—both derogatory terms for technical staff—are inappropriate in formal speech.

Written words on slides can bite you, too. A consulting engineer reports that she made up slides with the client's names based on a telephone call she made to the client. Unfortunately, several of the names were misspelled, leading to embarrassment and, not surprisingly, an unsuccessful bid for the project.

The moral of these stories? Be prepared, be relaxed, and go with the flow. While you never may face the discomfort of the speakers in these stories, remember that audiences often are pulling for you. If something unusual happens, finish with grace and hope for the best.

7   SUMMARY

Most of the work in an oral presentation occurs before the talk is presented. Before the talk, take the time to organize the material, construct the visual aids (which should number no more than $3/4$ times the number of minutes), and practice. Learn about the facilities in the room before you walk to the podium.

During the talk, do not worry about being nervous, but learn to control or avoid the signs of nervousness. Take your time in presenting data slides (especially figures). During transitions from one part of the talk to another, be sure to "tell 'em" three times: preview the material, present the material, and summarize the material. Modulate the speed and volume of your voice and use your hands effectively.

After the talk, seek feedback to become a better speaker. Remember, the best way to become an effective technical speaker is to take every opportunity to give technical talks.

SUMMARY OF KEY IDEAS

- Technical presentations can be improved by considering the activities before the talk, during the talk, and after the talk.
- Identify the presentation goals, target audience, and constraints on the presentation (especially time constraints).
- Use an outline to organize the talk and an outline slide to show your organization.
- The number of visual aids should be about $3/4$ times the number of minutes allotted to the presentation.
- In selecting the type of visual aid, consider image quality, eye contact, and production cost and time. Then use only one type of visual aid in a talk.
- Word slides should contain as few words as possible.
- Create tables specific to the point you wish to make.

- With computer-based presentations, watch the colors, number of fonts, and animations.
- Practice before the visual aids are finalized.
- When practicing, time each section as you practice alone and in front of others.
- Avoid memorizing or reading oral presentations.
- Learn about the facilities and coordinate introductions well before the talk.
- Practice transitions between speakers in group presentations.
- Do not worry about *being* nervous; learn to control or avoid the *signs* of nervousness.
- Paraphrase information in word slides and point to each item in a list.
- When presenting figures, tell what the figure is showing, identify the axes, communicate the meaning of each plot, and enumerate the main points to be made.
- Use signposting liberally in technical oral presentations.
- Speak loudly and slowly. Use meaningful hand gestures and move your body without pacing.
- Seek feedback and incorporate changes into your speaking style.

Problems

1. Pick an engineering topic of interest to you and identify a target audience. How will the target audience influence the visual aids you select and the material you present in your talk?

2. Write an outline for a 15-minute talk on the topic and target audience selected in Problem 1.

3. How would your outline change if you were asked to prepare a five-minute talk? A two-minute talk?

4. How many visual aids will you need for the talk?

5. Prepare visual aids for the talk using the principles presented in this chapter.

6. Practice the 15-minute talk. Prepare a table showing the percentage of time in the talk devoted to each of the major sections of the presentations. Refine the talk to better use the time allotted and summarize your refinements.

7. Before presenting the talk, what questions do you anticipate from the audience?

8. Present the talk to a group of people pretending to be your target audience. Did you predict (in Problem 7) the questions that were asked? What feedback did you receive from the audience?

9. Rewrite your talk using double the number of visual aids that you prepared in Problem 7. Present the revised talk to a group of people pretending to be your target audience. What feedback did you get about the number of visual aids?

10. Attend lectures delivered by three different public speakers. For each speaker, list and explain two aspects of his or her speaking style that appeal to you the most and two aspects that appeal to you the least.

19

Introduction to the Engineering Profession and Professional Registration

1 INTRODUCTION

In this part of the text, you will explore engineering as a profession. To do so, you must consider two questions. First, what does *profession* mean? If you are getting paid, is that enough to qualify a job as a profession? This area will be explored in Section 2.

Second, does engineering qualify as a profession? To answer this question, the characteristics that make engineering unique and important in today's society will be discussed.

2 PROFESSIONAL ISSUES

2.1 What Is a Profession?

A profession is more than just a job requiring specialized knowledge and intensive study.

Common elements include (Martin and Schinzinger, 1989)

- Compensation
- Professional practices that result in public good
- Need for formal education
- Requirement for judgment, discretion, and skill in performing your job
- Requirement to be admitted to the profession
- Self-policed conduct

Do these concepts make sense? You can apply them against known professions, such as medicine and law. Both medicine and law require all these elements. The fact that doctors and lawyers satisfy the first four criteria is obvious: they are paid, they do good, they are trained formally, and their jobs require judgment, discretion, and skill.

OBJECTIVES

After reading this chapter, you will be able to:

- explain why engineering is a profession;
- explain the benefits of becoming a licensed professional engineer;
- list the steps in the registration process.

What other elements come to mind when you think of the word *profession*?

Key idea: Common elements of a profession include compensation; performing a public good; a need for formal education; a requirement for judgment, discretion, and skill; a requirement to be admitted to the profession; and self-policing.

Key idea: Engineers must exercise professional judgment in the practice of their profession.

The fifth criterion also is satisfied, since both jobs require admission to the profession (passing medical board examinations or the bar examination). The admission to both professions is regulated by each state. In other words, doctors are licensed and lawyers are admitted to the bar by the state in which they practice. Finally, practicing professionals sit on the boards regulating professional conduct (for example, medical and legal ethics panels). Thus, the last criterion is satisfied.

2.2   Engineering as a Profession

For engineering to be a profession, it must satisfy the elements listed in Section 2.1. That engineers are compensated is obvious. Further, it is sincerely hoped that you are convinced by now that engineering practice results in public good. What about formal education? You are at the beginning of your formal education now.

What about the requirements for judgment and discretion, admission to the profession, and self-policing? In fact, these elements are at the heart of engineering as a profession.

2.3   Judgment and Discretion in Engineering

Engineering is all about generating alternative solutions to a problem and choosing from among alternatives. Thus, judgment is a critical part of engineering decision-making. Professional judgment is at the core of "thinking like an engineer."

What about discretion in engineering?

PONDER THIS

Why should engineers be thoughtful and discreet?

Key idea: Discretion in engineering is important because (1) engineering affects public safety and health, and (2) public trust in engineers must be preserved, since engineering work is not easy to understand.

There are two reasons why discretion and thoughtfulness are imperative for engineers. First, engineering has a significant impact on public safety and health. A poorly designed automobile or bridge or electric transmission line could result in terrible suffering and loss of human life. Any profession that affects *every* citizen *every* day (as is the case with engineering) should be held to the highest standards of ethical behavior.

Second, most engineering work is difficult for the average person to comprehend. As a result, the public must trust the word of engineers. If an engineer declares that the probability of the collapse of a high-rise building is extremely small, then the public is reassured. Reassurance comes *without* an understanding of the details of the materials employed or the construction techniques or even elementary statics. To *preserve the public trust*, engineers must be held accountable to a very strict professional code.

2.4   Admission to the Profession

Engineering also satisfies the criteria that you must be formally accepted into the profession. To use the title "engineer" to make money, you must be *admitted* to the profession. This process is called *registration*. The steps required for professional registration are discussed in more detail in Section 4.

2.5   Self-Policing

Engineers police themselves. Self-policing is accomplished by having engineers sit on state review boards that oversee licensing and the removal of licenses.

For professionals to police themselves, the profession needs a list of guidelines. Engineering has such guidelines, called *professional ethics*.

Thus, engineering fulfills all the requirements normally associated with being a profession. This analysis does not capture the awesome potential you have for influencing society or the serious responsibilities you will carry with pride as an engineer. As a source of inspiration, read the *Focus on Professionalism: Standing on the Shoulders of Giants*.

FOCUS ON PROFESSIONALISM: STANDING ON THE SHOULDERS OF GIANTS

The formal analysis of whether engineering is a profession misses the most important point: *you* are joining this profession, this band of brothers and sisters devoted to changing the world in a positive way. You will reap the satisfaction of helping others and you will make part of your being the obligations of excellence.

You are not alone. The contributions you will make build on the advances made by engineers before you. As Isaac Newton (1642–1727) said, "If I have seen further, it is by standing on the shoulders of giants." By standing on such a tall perch, you should feel that your potential to help others is unlimited.

In your everyday world of studying and working, it is easy to lose sight of the traditions of engineering, of the pride and obligations implicit in the profession. Presented here are two statements of engineering pride and obligations. The first statement, the "Obligation of an Engineer," is recited as part of the ceremony of joining the American association called the Order of the Engineer. The "Obligation of an Engineer" was written as an engineering version of the Hippocratic Oath taken by physicians. The Order of the Engineer was formed in 1970.

Obligation of an Engineer

(from the Order of the Engineer)

I am an Engineer, in my profession I take deep pride. To it I owe solemn obligations.

Since the Stone Age, human progress has been spurred by the engineering genius. Engineers have made usable Nature's vast resources of material and energy for Humanity's benefit. Engineers have vitalized and turned to practical use the principles of science and the means of technology. Were it not for this heritage of accumulated experience, my efforts would be feeble.

As an Engineer, I pledge to practice integrity and fair dealing, tolerance and respect, and to uphold devotion to the standards and the dignity of my profession, conscious always that my skill carries with it the obligation to serve humanity by making the best use of Earth's precious wealth.

As an Engineer I shall participate in none but honest enterprises. When needed, my skill and knowledge shall be given without reservation for the public good. In the performance of duty and in fidelity to my profession, I shall give the utmost.

The American ceremony was based on the Canadian "Ritual of the Calling of an Engineer," which dates back to 1926. The Canadian engineer's oath, called "The Obligation," was written (in three weeks!) by Nobel Laureate Rudyard Kipling.

The Obligation

(from the Iron Ring Ceremony in the Canadian Ritual of the Calling of an Engineer)

I (your name), in the presence of these my betters and my equals in my Calling, bind myself upon my Honour and Cold Iron, that, to the best of my knowledge and power, I will not henceforward suffer or pass, or be privy to the passing of, Bad Workmanship or Faulty Material in aught that concerns my works before mankind as an engineer, or in my dealings with my own Soul before my Maker.

My Time I will not refuse; my Thought I will not grudge; my Care I will not deny towards the honour, use, stability and perfection of any works to which I may be called to set my hand.

My Fair Wages for that work I will openly take. My Reputation in my Calling I will honourably guard; but I will in no way go about to compass or wrest judgement or gratification from any one with whom I may deal. And further, I will early and warily strive my uttermost against professional jealousy and the belittling of my working-colleagues in any field of their labour.

For my assured failures and derelictions I ask pardon beforehand of my betters and my equals in my Calling here assembled, praying that in the hour of my temptations, weakness and weariness, the memory of this my Obligation and of the company before whom it was entered into, may return to me to aid, comfort, and restrain.

Upon Honour and Cold Iron, God helping me, these things I purpose to abide.

When times are tough—when you have two tests on Tuesday and two homework assignments due tomorrow and you wonder why you ever wanted to be an engineer—reread the "Obligation of an Engineer" and "The Obligation." Remind yourself of your potential and your obligations to help.

3   PROFESSIONAL ENGINEERS

registration: the act of being admitted to the engineering profession

professional engineer (PE): a licensed (registered) engineer

Key idea: People become licensed to show their competence and commitment, to perform duties unavailable by law to unlicensed personnel, and to gain personal benefits.

3.1   Introduction

Engineering is a profession in part because engineers are admitted to practice. Every state regulates the practice of all professions. Examples include medicine (e.g., physicians, dentists, optometrists, and nurses), law, and engineering. In engineering, admission to the profession is called *registration* (or licensing). A registered engineer is called a *professional engineer* or PE. In this chapter, the registration process will be described.

3.2   Why Become a Professional Engineer?

The registration process (described in Section 4) is long, typically requiring at least seven years. Why go to the trouble of becoming licensed? The most important reason to become licensed is that it demonstrates your extra commitment to the profession. In addition, it is a badge of honor that shows your increased level of competence in the field.

Another reason to become licensed is that a PE may conduct professional activities that unlicensed personnel are forbidden to do. For example, only a licensed engineer may prepare, approve, and submit engineering plans and drawings to a public authority. Only a licensed engineer may approve engineering work for public and private clients. Consulting engineers in positions of authority over work performed in their office must, by law, be licensed. In general, you cannot use the term *engineer* in your title unless you are licensed. State engineering boards are successfully using the courts to impose civil penalties on individuals using the term *engineer* without an engineering license. As a example, penalties have been imposed on people without a PE doing business as *software engineers*.

In addition, PEs reap personal benefits from registration. Surveys have shown that professional engineers can expect salaries 15% to 25% higher than unlicensed colleagues. Some jobs are available only to professional engineers. This is particularly true in some government positions, where obtaining a PE license often is required for promotion. PEs also may find themselves more desirable to another firm in the event of downsizing. For advice about registration from professional engineers, see the *Focus on Registration: PE or Not PE?*

In spite of these arguments, not all engineers become licensed. Registration is more common in some disciplines than others. In particular, engineers working primarily in private practice (e.g., civil and environmental engineers) are more likely to become licensed than engineers working primarily in industry.

4   THE REGISTRATION PROCESS

4.1   Overview

Key idea: The steps in the registration process are as follows: obtain a baccalaureate degree from an accredited engineering department, pass the Fundamentals of Engineering Exam, acquire the requisite experience, and pass the Principles and Practice Exam.

Engineer-in-Training: a prelicensure certificate given to individuals completing the first steps in the registration process

The registration procedure for engineers is a four-step process. First, would-be engineers must obtain a baccalaureate degree from an accredited engineering department. Second, after earning the degree (or in the final stages of the program), potential engineers must take and pass a written test called the Fundamentals of Engineering Examination (or FE Exam). At this point, individuals can earn a prelicensure certificate. This level of licensing generally is called the *Engineer-in-Training* (or EIT). Third, EITs must acquire experience under the supervision of a licensed engineer. Finally, the would-be engineer must take and pass the Principles and Practice Examination in a specific engineering discipline. At this point (after the requisite licensing fees are paid), a person may be called an engineer and have the title *professional engineer*. You indicate the title by the initials *PE* after your name. Each of these steps will be discussed in more detail.

4.2   The Accredited Degree

The registration process starts at a college or university.* In accordance with the idea that professions require extensive training, potential engineers must obtain an undergraduate degree through an accredited engineering program.

What does *accredited* mean? To ensure the high technical level of the profession, engineering programs must request accreditation through the Accreditation Board for Engineering and Technology (ABET). Engineering programs must be reaccredited periodically, typically every six years. ABET's Engineering Accreditation Commission conducts site visits of each department seeking accreditation.

In 2005, there were over 1,600 accredited engineering programs in the United States. For a list of accredited programs, see the ABET Web site (www.abet.org).

The accreditation process is the beginning of the self-policing feature of the engineering profession. To be eligible for professional registration later, it is important for you to seek a degree from an accredited engineering program. Accreditation is awarded to each program, not the college or university in general.

4.3   Fundamentals of Engineering Examination

Fundamentals of Engineering (FE) Exam: an eight-hour exam covering general science, general engineering, and discipline-specific engineering topics

The *Fundamentals of Engineering Examination* (FE Exam) generally is taken in the last semester of the undergraduate program. The FE Exam† is administered by the National Council of Examiners for Engineering and Surveying (NCEES). The FE Exam consists of two parts. The morning portion deals with general science and engineering concepts and is common to all disciplines. The morning portion consists of 120 one-point questions to be answered in four hours. Topics include (with the percentage of questions in parentheses)

- Chemistry (9%)
- Computers (6%)

---

*In most states, the requirement for a baccalaureate degree can be satisfied by many years of experience. However, the most common pathway for professional registration includes an undergraduate degree from an accredited engineering program.
†You may hear the FE Exam referred to by its previous name: the EIT Exam.

- Dynamics (7%)
- Electrical circuits (10%)
- Engineering economics (4%)
- Ethics (4%)
- Fluid mechanics (7%)
- Materials science/structure of matter (7%)
- Mathematics (20%)
- Mechanics of materials (7%)
- Statics (10%)
- Thermodynamics (9%)

The afternoon session is discipline-specific. It consists of 60 two-point questions to be answered in four hours. Afternoon sessions are offered in chemical, civil, electrical, environmental, industrial, and mechanical engineering. A general engineering section also is available.

Following successful completion of the FE Exam, the potential engineer is eligible for certification as an Engineer-in-Training (or EIT; in some states, it is also called an Intern Engineer or Engineer Intern). The EIT receives a registration number from the state.

4.4   Experience

Key idea: For registration purposes, your work experience must be under the direction of a PE.

For an EIT to become a PE, you first must acquire engineering experience. Most states require four years of experience under the supervision of a PE. This distinction is important. If a newly minted EIT takes his or her first job at a firm that has no PEs on staff, it would be difficult to acquire experience under the direction of a PE. Thus, the first job after becoming an EIT is very important for future licensure. A portion of the time spent obtaining a graduate degree in engineering typically may be applied towards the experience requirement.

4.5   Principles and Practice Examination

Principles and Practice (PP) Exam: an eight-hour exam of a specific engineering discipline

After acquiring the necessary experience, potential engineers can apply to take the **Principles and Practice Examination** (PP Exam).° Like the afternoon session of the FE Exam, the PP Exam is discipline-specific. Exams are offered in 17 areas. Not all areas are offered in every state.

The PP Exam is eight hours long and may be all essay questions, all multiple-choice, or a mixture of essay and multiple-choice questions. The exam, administered by NCEES, is the same nationwide, but each state sets its own passing grade.

5   AFTER REGISTRATION

To maintain registration, an engineer must follow the ethical guidelines of his or her field and maintain competence in the field. Some states require PEs to engage in continuing education activities. Even without such requirements, maintaining state-of-the-art knowledge of the field is mandated by the ethical codes. In addition, fees must be paid periodically to the state to maintain the license.

reciprocity: the recognition of a license in one state by another state

There is general agreement between the states on the licensing process. Most states recognize licenses obtained in another state (a process known as **reciprocity**). Thus, it is often possible for a engineer licensed in one state to gain licensure in another state relatively easily.

°The PP Exam is sometimes referred to by its previous name: the PE Exam.

FOCUS ON REGISTRATION: PE OR NOT PE?

In this section, advice will be presented from registered professional engineers. The professional engineers offer sound comments on why to become licensed and suggestions for the licensing process. The quotations are from interviews published on one of the Web sites run by the National Council of Examiners for Engineering and Surveying (www.engineeringlicense.com).

Kathy Caldwell, PE; civil engineer

President, JEA Construction Engineering Services

. . . (T)ake the FE exam just as soon as you possibly can before you leave the college environment. It's very difficult to go back and take the fundamentals exam once you have been practicing in your major area of practice. A lot of fundamentals slip away from you and it becomes much more difficult to go back and relearn the fundamentals later.

Jim Parrish, PE; electrical engineer

General Manager, Duke Energy, Energy Delivery Services International

Achieving a PE also means that I have more career choices and can benefit from higher financial rewards that are commensurate with industry-recognized professional status. In my [unit of Duke Energy], engineers without a PE license can be promoted to only certain levels of engineering-related management jobs.

Brett Pielstick, PE; civil engineer

Vice President, PTG Construction Services

I think people know that as an engineer with a PE I will provide an honest day's work, an honest answer, and that they can trust in what we're going to do for them.

Deborah Grubbe, PE; chemical engineer

Corporate Director of Safety and Health, The DuPont Company

Ethics is an important aspect of professional licensure. Obtaining a PE (license) registration not only targets technical competence, but also requires a clear understanding of both ethics and professionalism. Ethics is essential to one's personal reputation, and once compromised, can almost never be reclaimed. Personal credibility becomes even more important when working outside the United States.

6   SUMMARY

In all aspects of the word, engineering qualifies as a profession. First, engineers are compensated for their work. Second, the general public benefits significantly from engineering practice. Third, engineers require a formal education prior to practicing their craft. Fourth, engineering practice requires judgment, discretion, and skill. Fifth, to legally use the title *engineer*, a person must be admitted to the engineering profession. The process of admission to the profession in engineering is called registration. Sixth, the professional conduct of engineers is self-policed through strong written codes of professional ethics.

Professional registration as a professional engineer (PE) is a demonstration of competence and commitment to the engineering profession. Registration also allows engineers to perform duties unavailable by law to unlicensed personnel and to gain personal benefits. Registration is a four-step process: obtain a baccalaureate degree from an accredited engineering department, pass the FE Exam, acquire the requisite experience (generally four years under the supervision of a PE), and pass the PP Exam. To maintain registration, PEs must follow the ethical guidelines of their field and maintain professional competence in the field.

SUMMARY OF KEY IDEAS

- Common elements of a profession include compensation; performing a public good; a need for formal education; a requirement for judgment, discretion, and skill; a requirement to be admitted to the profession; and self-policing.
- Engineers must exercise professional judgment in the practice of their profession.
- Discretion in engineering is important because (1) engineering affects public safety and health, and (2) public trust in engineers must be preserved, since engineering work is not easy to understand.
- People become licensed to show their competence and commitment, to perform duties unavailable by law to unlicensed personnel, and to gain personal benefits.
- The steps in the registration process are as follows: obtain a baccalaureate degree from an accredited engineering department, pass the Fundamentals of Engineering Exam, acquire the requisite experience, and pass the Principles and Practice Exam.
- For registration purposes, your work experience must be under the direction of a PE.

Problems

1. Write a short essay to justify why engineering is a profession.

2. List the steps in the professional registration process. Make a timeline to show when you plan to complete each step.

3. From the ABET Web site, make a list of accredited engineering programs in your discipline of interest in your state.

4. Can a person without a PE license use the title "Web design engineer" in a business? Why or why not?

5. Using data from an interview with a practicing engineer or from the Internet, determine the impact of earning a PE on salary in your area.

6. Find and report the distribution of questions on the disciple-specific portion of the Fundamentals of Engineering Examination for an engineering discipline of interest to you.

7. Find and report the distribution of questions on the disciple-specific portion of the Principles and Practice Examination for an engineering discipline of interest to you.

8. Some states have continuing education requirements for professional engineers. Report on the continuing education requirements, if any, for professional engineers in your state.

9.   Some states do not offer reciprocity without further examination. Research and report on any additional examination for obtaining a PE license in civil engineering by reciprocity in California.

10.   Using the Web site of your state licensing office, find a case of an engineer who lost his or her license (for reasons other than nonpayment of fees). What did the engineer do to lose it?

20

Engineering Ethics

1 INTRODUCTION

Engineering is a profession. This means in part that engineers must practice their profession in accordance with high ethical standards. In this chapter, you will explore *why* engineers must act ethically and examine the basic codes of engineering ethics. Examples will be used to illustrate the ethical conflicts that occur on the job.

Ethics can be studied on many levels. Please understand that the discussions in this chapter are on a very practical level. The philosophy of ethics (sometimes called *formal ethics*) is a beautiful and interesting field of study. This is not a chapter on formal ethics. Rather, the purpose of this chapter is to provide you with guidance on how to live your life as an engineer.°

2 PROFESSIONAL ISSUES

Ethics refers to a system of moral principles. All professions have standards of ethics to which their members are bound. In fact, a code of ethics allowing practitioners to "police themselves" is really a prerequisite for a profession.

Ethical issues in the medical, legal, and political arenas appear almost daily in the newspaper. Engineers also must follow ethical standards.

OBJECTIVES

After reading this chapter, you will be able to:

- explain why engineers should be ethical;
- list the canons in the NSPE Code of Ethics;
- identify the correct ethical choices in engineering applications.

°A student of moral philosophy might say that this chapter is about *normative ethics* (i.e., the principles that guide how we should live our lives), rather than *metaethics* (i.e., the study of what is good).

Why should engineering follow ethical standards?

ethics: a system of moral principles

Recall that engineering ethics is important because (1) engineering affects public safety and health, and (2) public trust in engineers must be preserved, since engineering work is not easy to understand.

3 CODES OF ETHICS

3.1 Introduction

Many engineering societies have their own codes of ethical behavior. Engineering societies having codes of ethics (and other ethics documents) are listed in Table 1. The differences between the codes are fairly minor. Most of the ethical standards are modeled after the code of ethics of the National Society of Professional Engineers (NSPE). To understand the concepts underlying the various ethics doctrines, the NSPE Code of Ethics will be examined in more detail.

3.2 NSPE Code of Ethics

NSPE Fundamental Canons of Ethics: the six basic principles outlining the professional responsibilities of engineers

Board of Ethical Review: an NSPE committee that offers commentary on ethics cases

Key idea: Engineers shall hold paramount the safety, health, and welfare of the public.

NSPE has established six principles called the **Fundamental Canons of Ethics**. The principles refer to the responsibilities of engineers when conducting their work and when approving documents. When a PE approves a document, he or she is *personally certifying* that the work meets professional standards. An NSPE committee called the **Board of Ethical Review** (BER) offers commentary on ethics cases to show engineers how the fundamental canons have been interpreted in the past. Each of the fundamental canons will be presented with examples on their interpretation. (*Note*: The entire NSPE Code of Ethics is given at the end of the chapter. More examples of the interpretation of the fundamental canons can be found in the Rules of Practice and Professional Obligations sections of the NSPE Code of Ethics.)

Canon 1: Engineers shall hold paramount the safety, health, and welfare of the public. This is the most important of the fundamental canons. It states that nothing—not profit, not inconvenience, not personal gain—comes before the safety, health, and welfare of the public. Remember, safety, health, and welfare are paramount. If you face a contradiction in your work life between canons, Canon 1 prevails.

Canon 1 has three important interpretations. First, the canon has been interpreted to mean that individual engineers must notify their employer, client, or the proper authorities when life or property is endangered. Notification must occur *even if the client requests that data or any other engineering work be held back*. For example, if you discover a potentially dangerous situation in the course of your professional work, you **must** report it even if the paying client *demands* that you squelch the information.

TABLE 1 Engineering Societies with Codes of Ethics

Organization	Last Revision	Other Ethics Documents
American Consulting Engineers Council (ACEC)	1980	none
American Institute of Chemical Engineers (AIChE)	1989	none
American Society of Civil Engineers (ASCE)	1993	ASCE's Guidelines on Practice
American Society of Mechanical Engineers (ASME)	1991	ASME Criteria for Interpretation of the Canons
Institute of Electrical and Electronics Engineers (IEEE)	1990	Employment Guidelines

Safety outweighs all other considerations.

A second implication of the first canon is that engineers must approve only documents that conform to applicable standards. Approving plans that you know are not in compliance with standards is an ethical violation and grounds for loss of your engineering license.

A third implication of the first canon is that engineers have a responsibility to report any violations of the code of ethics. Reporting known violations is a form of *whistle-blowing*. Professionals who come public with mistakes made by themselves, their firm, or their colleagues risk being fired or ostracized. However, because of the overriding importance of the safety, health, and welfare of the public, engineers have a moral duty to report ethical violations committed by themselves or others.

Canon 2: Engineers shall perform services only in the areas of their competence. At present, engineers usually are licensed in a particular discipline. This canon makes it clear that engineers must stay in their areas of expertise. Thus, a chemical engineer cannot approve structural engineering plans.

One ramification of this canon is that you must approve only documents prepared under your supervision. For example, a mechanical engineer cannot approve heating, ventilation, and air conditioning (HVAC) plans drawn up by people being supervised by another engineer. As a practical matter, the second canon means that each technical portion (e.g., electrical, mechanical, and structural portions) of a set of plans usually must be approved individually.

Canon 3: Engineers shall issue public statements only in an objective and truthful manner. As stated in Section 2, the engineering profession thrives because of the public trust. This canon states that you must be honest in your dealings with the public. For example, you must acknowledge if you are being paid to issue a public statement about an engineering issue. Suppose you are being paid by a developer to lay out a new neighborhood. If you speak before a city council meeting in favor of the development, then you must identify yourself as an engineer paid by the developer.

Canon 4: Engineers shall act for each employer or client as faithful agents or trustees. The practice of engineering depends on the trust between the engineer and the public. Engineering also is dependent on the trust between the engineer and the client. This canon says in part that the client has the right to expect that the engineer will use his or her best engineering judgment in solving the client's problems.

This canon also is interpreted to mean that engineers must disclose to the client all known or *potential* conflicts of interest. Identification of potential conflicts of interest can be difficult. Clearly, the engineer cannot represent two clients who may come into conflict. For example, you could not represent both a potentially polluting industry and

Key idea: Engineers shall perform services only in the areas of their competence.

Key idea: Engineers shall issue public statements only in an objective and truthful manner.

Key idea: Engineers shall act for each employer or client as faithful agents or trustees.

the town owning the wastewater treatment facility or both a developer and a city where the developer does work.

Key idea: Engineers shall avoid deceptive acts.

Canon 5: Engineers shall avoid deceptive acts. This canon has implications in the procurement of work. For example, it is a violation of the code of ethics to falsify your qualifications. In addition, it is considered unethical to offer or give a contribution to influence a public authority's decision about who should be awarded a contract.

The difference between ethical and unethical behavior can be very small. Clearly, it is improper to offer a bribe to the head of a housing authority to get a contract. What about taking the town engineer out to lunch right before a contract is awarded? What about giving the daughter of the mayor extra playing time on the soccer team you coach?

Key idea: Engineers shall conduct themselves honorably, responsibly, ethically, and lawfully so as to enhance the honor, reputation, and usefulness of the profession.

Canon 6: Engineers shall conduct themselves honorably, responsibly, ethically, and lawfully so as to enhance the honor, reputation, and usefulness of the profession. This canon greatly affects the lives of engineers. It means that engineers must advise their clients if the engineers believe a project will *not* be successful. In addition, engineers are prohibited by this canon from accepting free material from suppliers or contractors in return for specifying their products or services.

Language similar to that in the sixth canon is used by the Accreditation Board for Engineering and Technology (ABET) in the fundamental principles section of their code of ethics. (One responsibility of ABET is to certify undergraduate engineering programs.) The ABET fundamental principles state that engineers can "uphold and advance the integrity, honor, and dignity of the engineering profession by"

I. Using their knowledge and skill for the enhancement of human welfare;

II. Being honest and impartial, and serving with fidelity the public, their employers, and clients;

III. Striving to increase the competence and prestige of the engineering profession; and

IV. Supporting the professional and technical societies of their disciplines (Wright, 1994).

Although the NSPE canons remain silent on the issue, both the ABET and ASCE codes of ethics include ethical obligations for professional development. In other words, engineers are ethically obligated to continue their technical training and education throughout their career. Thus, even though some states do not require continuing education for relicensing as a professional engineer, continued technical training is part of your ethical obligation as an engineer.

4   EXAMPLES OF ENGINEERING ETHICS

Engineering ethics can become very complex. Sometimes, one ethical canon contradicts another. Two examples will be presented to illustrate the applications of the fundamental canons. These examples are taken from case studies developed by NSPE's Board of Ethical Review. Take a moment to consider your responses before reading the comments that follow the discussion questions. For examples of ethics that crop up in business practice, see the *Focus on Ethics: Workplace Ethics*.

4.1   Not Reporting Violations

Case: A civil engineer is hired to assess the structural integrity of a 60-year-old apartment building. The structure of the building is determined to be sound. However, during the inspection, mechanical and electrical problems are noted. The problems are severe enough that they may lead to safety concerns. The engineer tells the client of the problems, but does not include them in the report. The client reminds the engineer of his obligations regarding client confidentiality and then moves to sell the building quickly without repairs. The engineer decides not to report the violations to the authorities.

Discussion: This example represents a conflict between the responsibility to protect public safety (Canon 1) and client confidentiality (Canon 4). Does Canon 2 (not working outside your area of expertise) play in this case?

PONDER THIS

Which factor is more important? Could the engineer have avoided the conflict by including the problems in his original report?

Board of Ethical Review comments: The Board concluded that the engineer had an ethical obligation to report the problems to the authorities because of the paramount importance of public safety (Canon 1). The engineer was correct not to include the problems in his report, since the problems were outside of the engineer's area of expertise (Canon 2).

4.2   Whistle-Blowing

Case: The city engineer/director of public works for a medium-sized city is the only licensed professional engineer in a position of responsibility within the city government. The city has several large food processing plants that discharge large amounts of waste into the sewage system during canning season. The engineer is responsible for the wastewater treatment plant. She reports to her supervisor about the inadequate capacity of the treatment plant to handle potential overflow during the rainy season and offers several possible solutions. The engineer also privately notifies other city officials about the plant problem, but her supervisor removes the responsibility for the wastewater treatment plant from her. She also is placed on probation and warned not to discuss the matter further or she will be fired.

Discussion: This example explores what engineers must do to meet their ethical obligations.

PONDER THIS

Has the engineer discharged her ethical responsibilities by notifying city officials of the potential problem?

Board of Ethical Review comments: The Board concluded that removal of responsibility for the treatment plant did not terminate the engineer's ethical obligations, even when threatened with loss of employment. Again, public health and safety are of highest importance (Canon 1). The Board thought that the engineer should have reported the potential problem to higher authorities in the state or federal government.

5   SUMMARY

Engineers are professionals and must meet high ethical standards. Engineering ethics is required for two reasons. First, engineering directly influences public safety, health, and welfare. Second, engineering work is not easy to understand, so the trust between the public and engineers must not be diminished by unethical behavior.

Several codes of engineering ethics exist. Most are similar to the six NSPE Fundamental Canons of Ethics. The six canons require that engineers shall (1) hold paramount

Engineering ethics often is taught with the high-stakes ethics cases discussed in Problems 4 through 6. While interesting and instructive, the large cases do not provide you as a new engineer with tools you can use to address everyday ethics questions.

In this section, you will be presented with a series of ethics questions and possible solutions. You may wish to discuss the questions in a group, so that you can exchange ideas. One of the lessons is that ethics questions often do not have one correct answer. Responses to ethical dilemmas in the workplace can be ranked from better to worse. (Of course, some responses are just plain wrong.)

The questions below are from an ethics game called *Gray Matters*. The game was devised by George Sammet, Jr., to teach business ethics to the employees of Martin Marietta (now Lockheed Martin). Sammet was Vice President of International Ethics and Business Conduct for Lockheed Martin and now works for Grainer and Associates in Ottawa. The questions presented here were selected for their relevance to the engineering workplace and interest to entry-level engineers.

For each question below, a Web site is given to allow you to select from potential responses. The questions are quoted from the onlineethics.org Web site.

Enjoy the game and your discussion of the answers.

GrayMatters Case #8
Appropriating Office Supplies for Personal Use

"Two of your subordinates routinely provide their children with school supplies from the office. How do you handle this situation?"

Web site: http://onlineethics.org/corp/graymatters/case8.html

---

GrayMatters Case #64
Instructed to Distort the Truth?

"You are on a proposal-writing team. In the orientation briefing, the head of the team gives the following guidance: 'We really have to win this one. I want you to be really optimistic in what you write.' How do you interpret her advice?"

Web site: http://onlineethics.org/corp/graymatters/case64.html

---

GrayMatters Case #87
Supplier Offers You a Discount

"You are in Production Control. Planning on adding a porch onto your house, you visit a lumberyard to get ideas and a price. During the discussion, the sales manager says, 'Oh, you work for XYZ Company. They buy a lot from us, so I'm going to give you a special discount.' What do you do?"

Web site: http://onlineethics.org/corp/graymatters/case87.html

---

GrayMatters Case #24
HIV Positive Employee

"A female employee tells you, her manager, that a fellow employee is HIV positive. What do you do?"

Web site: http://onlineethics.org/corp/graymatters/case24.html

---

GrayMatters Case #72
He Calls All the Women "Sweetie"

"When a male supervisor talks to any female employee, he always addresses her as 'Sweetie.' You have overheard him use this term several times. As the supervisor's manager, should you do anything?"

Web site: http://onlineethics.org/corp/graymatters/case72.html

---

How did you do in your group? The maximum and minimum possible scores for the five scenarios above are +50 and −55, respectively.

the safety, health, and welfare of the public; (2) perform services only in the areas of their competence; (3) issue public statements only in an objective and truthful manner; (4) act for each employer or client as faithful agents; (5) avoid deceptive acts; and (6) conduct themselves honorably, responsibly, ethically, and lawfully to enhance the honor, reputation, and usefulness of the profession.

SUMMARY OF KEY IDEAS

- Engineers shall hold paramount the safety, health, and welfare of the public.
- Engineers shall perform services only in the areas of their competence.
- Engineers shall issue public statements only in an objective and truthful manner.
- Engineers shall act for each employer or client as faithful agents or trustees.
- Engineers shall avoid deceptive acts.
- Engineers shall conduct themselves honorably, responsibly, ethically, and lawfully so as to enhance the honor, reputation, and usefulness of the profession.

Problems

1. What are the six canons in the NSPE Code of Ethics?

2. Is there a hierarchy among the canons in the NSPE Code of Ethics?

3. Review the Professional Obligations section of the NSPE Code of Ethics at the end of the chapter. Discuss the ethical implications of engineering consulting firms making campaign contributions.

4. Discuss the ethical behavior of engineers in the Space Shuttle *Challenger* disaster. For background information, see the World Wide Web Ethics Center for Engineering and Science, hosted by Case Western Reserve University at http://www.onlineethics.org. This site contains a fine discussion of engineering ethics, including detailed examples of whistle-blowing in engineering.

5. Discuss the ethical behavior of engineers in the walkway collapse at the Kansas City Hyatt Regency Hotel. For background information, see Pfrang and Marshall (1982).

6. Discuss the ethical behavior of engineers with regard to the structural problems in New York City's Citicorp Towers. For background information, see the World Wide Web Ethics Center for Engineering and Science, hosted by Case Western Reserve University at http://www.onlineethics.org.

7. Pick a field of engineering and discuss how an ethical violation would adversely affect public health, safety, or welfare.

Problems 8 through 10 are taken from actual ethics cases that came before NSPE's Board of Ethical Review. For each scenario, discuss the applicable parts of the NSPE Code of Ethics and decide whether the behavior was ethical.

8. Due to potential dangers during construction, an engineer recommends to a client before a project begins that a full-time person should be hired for on-site monitoring of the project. The client rejects the request for on-site monitoring, stating that

the monitor would increase project costs to an unreasonable level. The engineer starts work on the project anyway. Was it ethical for the engineer to begin the project knowing that the client would not agree to hire an on-site monitor?

9.   A company was advised by a state agency to get permission to discharge waste into a river. The company hires a consulting engineer to help them respond to the state's request. The engineer finds that the waste will degrade the quality of the river below established standards and that treating the waste will be expensive. The engineer tells the company of these findings orally, before the final report is written. The company then pays the engineer, terminates the engineering service agreement, and tells the engineer not to write a report. The engineer hears later that the company reported to the state agency that the waste discharge will not degrade the quality of the river. Does the engineer have an ethical obligation to report the findings to the state agency?

10.   A state agency hires an engineer to conduct a feasibility study on a proposed highway spur. The spur will go through an area near where the engineer owns property. The engineer tells the state agency of the potential conflict of interest, but the agency does not object to the engineer working on the project. The engineer completes the study and the highway spur is built. Did the engineer act ethically by performing the study, even though the engineer's property may be affected?

NSPE CODE OF ETHICS FOR ENGINEERS
Preamble

Engineering is an important and learned profession. As members of this profession, engineers are expected to exhibit the highest standards of honesty and integrity. Engineering has a direct and vital impact on the quality of life for all people. Accordingly, the services provided by engineers require honesty, impartiality, fairness, and equity, and must be dedicated to the protection of the public health, safety, and welfare. Engineers must perform under a standard of professional behavior that requires adherence to the highest principles of ethical conduct.

I. Fundamental Canons

Engineers, in the fulfillment of their professional duties, shall:

1. Hold paramount the safety, health and welfare of the public.

2. Perform services only in areas of their competence.

3. Issue public statements only in an objective and truthful manner.

4. Act for each employer or client as faithful agents or trustees.

5. Avoid deceptive acts.

6. Conduct themselves honorably, responsibly, ethically, and lawfully so as to enhance the honor, reputation, and usefulness of the profession.

II. Rules of Practice

1. Engineers shall hold paramount the safety, health and welfare of the public.

   a. If engineers' judgment is overruled under circumstances that endanger life or property, they shall notify their employer or client and such other authority as may be appropriate.

   b. Engineers shall approve only those engineering documents that are in conformity with applicable standards.

c. Engineers shall not reveal facts, data, or information without the prior consent of the client or employer except as authorized or required by law or this Code.

d. Engineers shall not permit the use of their name or associate in business ventures with any person or firm that they believe are engaged in fraudulent or dishonest enterprise.

e. Engineers shall not aid or abet the unlawful practice of engineering by a person or firm.

f. Engineers having knowledge of any alleged violation of this Code shall report thereon to appropriate professional bodies and, when relevant, also to public authorities, and cooperate with the proper authorities in furnishing such information or assistance as may be required.

2. Engineers shall perform services only in the areas of their competence.

a. Engineers shall undertake assignments only when qualified by education or experience in the specific technical fields involved.

b. Engineers shall not affix their signatures to any plans or documents dealing with subject matter in which they lack competence, nor to any plan or document not prepared under their direction and control.

c. Engineers may accept assignments and assume responsibility for coordination of an entire project and sign and seal the engineering documents for the entire project, provided that each technical segment is signed and sealed only by the qualified engineers who prepared the segment.

3. Engineers shall issue public statements only in an objective and truthful manner.

a. Engineers shall be objective and truthful in professional reports, statements, or testimony. They shall include all relevant and pertinent information in such reports, statements, or testimony, which should bear the date indicating when it was current.

b. Engineers may express publicly technical opinions that are founded upon knowledge of the facts and competence in the subject matter.

c. Engineers shall issue no statements, criticisms, or arguments on technical matters that are inspired or paid for by interested parties, unless they have prefaced their comments by explicitly identifying the interested parties on whose behalf they are speaking, and by revealing the existence of any interest the engineers may have in the matters.

4. Engineers shall act for each employer or client as faithful agents or trustees.

a. Engineers shall disclose all known or potential conflicts of interest that could influence or appear to influence their judgment or the quality of their services.

b. Engineers shall not accept compensation, financial or otherwise, from more than one party for services on the same project, or for services pertaining to the same project, unless the circumstances are fully disclosed and agreed to by all interested parties.

c. Engineers shall not solicit or accept financial or other valuable consideration, directly or indirectly, from outside agents in connection with the work for which they are responsible.

d. Engineers in public service as members, advisors, or employees of a governmental or quasi-governmental body or department shall not participate in decisions with respect to services solicited or provided by them or their organizations in private or public engineering practice.

e. Engineers shall not solicit or accept a contract from a governmental body on which a principal or officer of their organization serves as a member.

5. Engineers shall avoid deceptive acts.

a. Engineers shall not falsify their qualifications or permit misrepresentation of their or their associates' qualifications. They shall not misrepresent or exaggerate their responsibility in or for the subject matter of prior assignments. Brochures or other presentations incident to the solicitation of employment shall not misrepresent pertinent facts concerning employers, employees, associates, joint venturers, or past accomplishments.

b. Engineers shall not offer, give, solicit or receive, either directly or indirectly, any contribution to influence the award of a contract by public authority, or which may be reasonably construed by the public as having the effect of intent to influencing the awarding of a contract. They shall not offer any gift or other valuable consideration in order to secure work. They shall not pay a commission, percentage, or brokerage fee in order to secure work, except to a bona fide employee or bona fide established commercial or marketing agencies retained by them.

III. Professional Obligations

1. Engineers shall be guided in all their relations by the highest standards of honesty and integrity.

a. Engineers shall acknowledge their errors and shall not distort or alter the facts.

b. Engineers shall advise their clients or employers when they believe a project will not be successful.

c. Engineers shall not accept outside employment to the detriment of their regular work or interest. Before accepting any outside engineering employment they will notify their employers.

d. Engineers shall not attempt to attract an engineer from another employer by false or misleading pretenses.

e. Engineers shall not promote their own interest at the expense of the dignity and integrity of the profession.

2. Engineers shall at all times strive to serve the public interest.

a. Engineers shall seek opportunities to participate in civic affairs; career guidance for youths; and work for the advancement of the safety, health, and well-being of their community.

b. Engineers shall not complete, sign, or seal plans and/or specifications that are not in conformity with applicable engineering standards. If the client or employer insists on such unprofessional conduct, they shall notify the proper authorities and withdraw from further service on the project.

   c. Engineers shall endeavor to extend public knowledge and appreciation of engineering and its achievements.

3. Engineers shall avoid all conduct or practice that deceives the public.

   a. Engineers shall avoid the use of statements containing a material misrepresentation of fact or omitting a material fact.

   b. Consistent with the foregoing, engineers may advertise for recruitment of personnel.

   c. Consistent with the foregoing, engineers may prepare articles for the lay or technical press, but such articles shall not imply credit to the author for work performed by others.

4. Engineers shall not disclose, without consent, confidential information concerning the business affairs or technical processes of any present or former client or employer, or public body on which they serve.

   a. Engineers shall not, without the consent of all interested parties, promote or arrange for new employment or practice in connection with a specific project for which the engineer has gained particular and specialized knowledge.

   b. Engineers shall not, without the consent of all interested parties, participate in or represent an adversary interest in connection with a specific project or proceeding in which the engineer has gained particular specialized knowledge on behalf of a former client or employer.

5. Engineers shall not be influenced in their professional duties by conflicting interests.

   a. Engineers shall not accept financial or other considerations, including free engineering designs, from material or equipment suppliers for specifying their product.

   b. Engineers shall not accept commissions or allowances, directly or indirectly, from contractors or other parties dealing with clients or employers of the engineer in connection with work for which the engineer is responsible.

6. Engineers shall not attempt to obtain employment or advancement or professional engagements by untruthfully criticizing other engineers, or by other improper or questionable methods.

   a. Engineers shall not request, propose, or accept a commission on a contingent basis under circumstances in which their judgment may be compromised.

   b. Engineers in salaried positions shall accept part-time engineering work only to the extent consistent with policies of the employer and in accordance with ethical considerations.

   c. Engineers shall not, without consent, use equipment, supplies, laboratory, or office facilities of an employer to carry on outside private practice.

7. Engineers shall not attempt to injure, maliciously or falsely, directly or indirectly, the professional reputation, prospects, practice, or employment of other engineers. Engineers who believe others are guilty of unethical or illegal practice shall present such information to the proper authority for action.

    a. Engineers in private practice shall not review the work of another engineer for the same client, except with the knowledge of such engineer, or unless the connection of such engineer with the work has been terminated.

    b. Engineers in governmental, industrial, or educational employ are entitled to review and evaluate the work of other engineers when so required by their employment duties.

    c. Engineers in sales or industrial employ are entitled to make engineering comparisons of represented products with products of other suppliers.

8. Engineers shall accept personal responsibility for their professional activities, provided, however, that engineers may seek indemnification for services arising out of their practice for other than gross negligence, where the engineer's interests cannot otherwise be protected.

    a. Engineers shall conform with state registration laws in the practice of engineering.

    b. Engineers shall not use association with a nonengineer, a corporation, or partnership as a "cloak" for unethical acts.

9. Engineers shall give credit for engineering work to those to whom credit is due, and will recognize the proprietary interests of others.

    a. Engineers shall, whenever possible, name the person or persons who may be individually responsible for designs, inventions, writings, or other accomplishments.

    b. Engineers using designs supplied by a client recognize that the designs remain the property of the client and may not be duplicated by the engineer for others without express permission.

    c. Engineers, before undertaking work for others in connection with which the engineer may make improvements, plans, designs, inventions, or other records that may justify copyrights or patents, should enter into a positive agreement regarding ownership.

    d. Engineers' designs, data, records, and notes referring exclusively to an employer's work are the employer's property. The employer should indemnify the engineer for use of the information for any purpose other than the original purpose.

    e. Engineers shall continue their professional development throughout their careers and should keep current in their specialty fields by engaging in professional practice, participating in continuing education courses, reading in the technical literature, and attending professional meetings and seminars.

    —As revised January 2003

Appendix: Review of Physical Relationships

1   INTRODUCTION

The purpose of this appendix is to review the physical relationships referred to in the body of this text. This appendix is not a replacement for a class on statics or dynamics or circuits. It is intended to supplement and extend the material in the text. In addition, examples of the physical relationships discussed in the text will be summarized in this appendix.

2   DEFINITIONS

2.1   Kinematic Parameters

A number of physical parameters were referred to in this text, often without formal definitions. The definitions of some kinematic measures are given in Table 1.

2.2   Fundamental Forces*

Definitions of terms related to forces are given in Table 2. Force can be defined from kinematics as the change in momentum with respect to time:

$$F = d(mv)/dt$$

At constant mass, this becomes Newton's Second Law of Motion:

$$F = ma$$

If the main source of acceleration is Earth's gravitational field, then $a = g$ and $F = mg$.

Although Newton's Second Law of Motion is extremely valuable for engineers, it hides where forces come from. We know of only four sources of forces (called the *fundamental forces*): gravity, electromagnetic, strong, and weak forces. The strong force holds the nucleus of an atom together and does not play a role in traditional engineering (but may influence nanoengineering). Similarly, the weak force is responsible for radioactive decay and does not play a role in the professional lives of most engineers.

---

*The discussion of fundamental forces and other forces was influenced in part by Holtzapple and Reece (2000).

TABLE 1   Definitions of Kinematic Parameters

Parameter	Definition	Text Example
Velocity (v)	v = distance/time	controllability settling velocity
	instantaneous $v = dx/dt$	trebuchet
Momentum (p)	$p = mv$	See Table 5
Acceleration (a)	instantaneous $a = dv/dt = d^2x/dt^2$	trebuchet

x = distance (m) m = mass (kg)
t = time (s) p = momentum (kg-m)
v = velocity (m/s) a = acceleration (m/s^2)

TABLE 2   Types of Forces

Parameter	Definition	Text Example
Newton's Second Law	$F = ma$	novel propulsion system
		waterbed
		parachuting
		moving van ramp
		forces on a car
		in technical communications
		bridge lateral acceleration
		projectiles
Gravitational	$F = G\dfrac{m_1 m_2}{r^2}$ (for Earth, $F = mg$)	
Electrostatic	$F = \dfrac{1}{4\pi\varepsilon_0}\dfrac{q_1 q_2}{r^2}$	
Magnetic	$F = \dfrac{3\mu_0}{2\pi}\dfrac{\mu_1 \mu_2}{r^4}$	
Friction	$F = \mu$(perpendicular force)	moving van ramp
		forces on a car
Drag	$F = \frac{1}{2}C_d\rho v^2 A$	parachuting
		forces on a car
		moving belt
Spring	$F = kx$ (Hooke's Law)	Hooke's Law statement
		bungee jumping
	$F/A = E\delta/L$	compression of bed legs

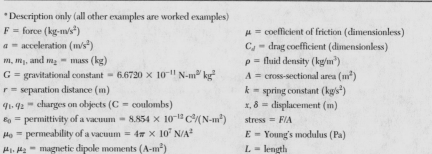

° Description only (all other examples are worked examples)

F = force (kg-m/s^2)

a = acceleration (m/s^2)

$m, m_1,$ and m_2 = mass (kg)

G = gravitational constant = 6.6720×10^{-11} N-m^2/kg^2

r = separation distance (m)

q_1, q_2 = charges on objects (C = coulombs)

ε_0 = permittivity of a vacuum = 8.854×10^{-12} C^2/(N-m^2)

μ_0 = permeability of a vacuum = $4\pi \times 10^7$ N/A^2

μ_1, μ_2 = magnetic dipole moments (A-m^2)

μ = coefficient of friction (dimensionless)

C_d = drag coefficient (dimensionless)

ρ = fluid density (kg/m^3)

A = cross-sectional area (m^2)

k = spring constant (kg/s^2)

x, δ = displacement (m)

stress = F/A

E = Young's modulus (Pa)

L = length

The main fundamental force used in this text is the force from gravity.[°] Gravitational force is responsible for Newton's Second Law of Motion. The gravitational force is proportional to the product of the masses of two objects and inversely proportional to their separation distance squared:

$$\text{gravitational force} = G\frac{m_1 m_2}{r^2}$$

where G = gravitational constant (6.6720×10^{-11} N-m^2/kg^2); m_1 and m_2 = masses of the objects; and r = separation distance. Most engineers deal with objects near the surface of the Earth, where m_2 = mass of the Earth = 5.98×10^{24} kg and r = radius of the Earth = 6.37×10^6 m. Thus,

$$Gm_2/r^2 = (6.6720 \times 10^{-11} \text{ N-m}^2/\text{kg}^2)(5.98 \times 10^{24} \text{ kg})/(6.37 \times 10^6 \text{ m})^2$$
$$= 9.8 \text{ m/s}^2$$
$$= g = \text{Earth's gravitational acceleration}$$

Thus, for objects near the surface of the Earth,

$$\text{gravitational force} = Gm_1 m_2/r^2 = mg$$

2.3   Other Forces

Three other forces of interest to engineers are the friction, drag, and spring forces. Your common experience is that you must exert a force to start an object in motion and to keep the object in motion at constant velocity. This suggests you are overcoming another, "unknown," force, the *friction force*. The friction force is proportional to the perpendicular force. The proportionality constant is called the *coefficient of friction*.[†]

Friction also occurs if you push an object through a fluid. The friction force in opposition to the direction of movement is called the *drag force*. In some engineering applications, the drag force is calculated using a dimensionless parameter called the *drag coefficient* (C_d):

$$\text{drag force} = \tfrac{1}{2}C_d \rho v^2 A$$

where ρ = fluid density and A = cross-sectional area of the object.

Finally, engineers often deal with devices and materials that experience the following behavior: the force exerted by the material is proportional to the displacement (i.e., proportional to the distance moved or stretched). A force that is proportional to the displacement is called a *spring force*. An example, not surprisingly, is a spring. The force exerted by a spring is usually given by Hooke's Law:

$$\text{spring force} = kx$$

where k is the spring constant and x is the displacement. Another example is the stress–strain constitutive relationship:

$$\text{stress} = E(\text{strain})$$

where stress = force per unit area, E = Young's modulus, and strain = displacement per unit length.

2.4   Energy, Work, and Power

The concepts of energy and work are interrelated. Energy is the ability to do work. Work is the transfer of energy by a force acting over a distance. How are we to break this circle of definitions?

[°]The electromagnetic force is usually modeled as electrostatic and magnetic forces. For completion, the electrostatic and magnetic forces are listed in Table 2.

[†]The proportionality constant is called the *coefficient of static friction* if the object is not moving (but on the threshold of movement) and is called the *coefficient of kinetic friction* if the object is moving. The value of the coefficient of static friction typically is greater than the value of the coefficient of kinetic friction.

TABLE 3 Energy and Power Examples

Parameter	Text Example (section in parentheses)
Energy	champagne cork (6.6.3)
	rocket (6.3.2°, 6.3.3)
	bungee jumping (6.6.2)
	kinetic energy (8.4.6°)
	trebuchet projectile (24.3.1)
Power	electrical power loss (5.4.3, 6.5.4, 22.3.1)
	automobile power losses (7.6)
	hydraulic power loss (22.3.1)
	friction power loss (22.3.1)

° Description only (all other examples are worked examples)

Perhaps it is better to start with the definition of work as

$$\text{work} = \text{force} \times \text{distance}$$

With this definition, it is clear that work should have units of N-m, where 1 N-m = 1 joule = 1 J. Work is the transfer of energy, so energy also must have units of joules.

Energy often is divided into three types: internal, kinetic, and potential energy. Internal energy is the energy inside the system. Kinetic energy is the energy associated with motion. Potential energy is the energy that comes from the position of an object in a potential field. An example of a potential field is a gravitational field. Common expressions for kinetic energy and the potential energy in the Earth's gravitational field are

$$\text{kinetic energy} = \tfrac{1}{2}mv^2$$

$$\text{potential energy} = mgh$$

Power is the work produced per unit time. The units of power are J/s, where 1 J/s = 1 watt = 1 W. Power loss in electrical systems is given by

$$\text{power loss} = VI$$

Combining power loss with Ohm's Law ($V = IR$, see Section 5) yields

$$\text{power loss} = (IR)I = I^2R$$

Examples where energy and power are used in this text are shown in Table 3.

3 DECOMPOSITION BY VECTORS

3.1 Position Vectors

We typically describe the relationship between two objects in space by a vector. In other words, the difference in position has both magnitude and direction. To get from Point A to Point B below, you would move five units in a direction of about 53.1° from the horizontal. Another way to move from Point A to Point B is to move horizontally three units to the right, then move vertically for four units (see Fig. 1). In this approach, you have decomposed the position into an x component (+3 units, if positive x is to the right) and a y component (+4 units, if positive y is up).

3.2 Other Vectors

If position is a vector, then the other parameters derived from position also are vectors. From Tables 1 and 2, it follows that velocity, acceleration, momentum, and force also are vector quantities. Velocity and force were decomposed into x and y components several times in this text, as indicated in Table 4.

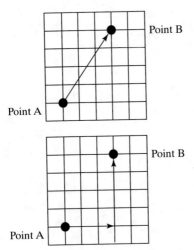

Point B

Point A

Point B

Point A

Figure 1. Position Vectors

TABLE 4 Decomposition of Velocity and Force

Parameter	Text Example
Velocity	champagne cork
Force	moving van ramp
	automobile
	trebuchet projectile

4   CONSERVATION LAWS

Examples of the laws of the conservation of mass, momentum, angular momentum, energy, and charge are listed in Table 5.

TABLE 5 Examples of Conservation Laws

Conservation Law	Text Example
Mass	moles as combining proportions
	disinfection device (number balance)
	parts inventory
	chemical doses
	flow in = flow out
Momentum	ink flow in inkjet printer
	baseball
	crash dummy's head
	example laboratory report
Angular momentum	Kepler's Second Law
Energy	global warming
	refrigeration system
	airplane wing lift
	Kirchhoff's Voltage Law
	rocket escape velocity
	bungee jumping
	kinetic energy
	trebuchet
Charge	pH of acid rain
	Kirchhoff's Current Law
	ionization smoke detector
	current in subcircuits

* Description only (all other examples are worked examples)

5   GRADIENT-DRIVEN PROCESSES

A number of processes of interest to engineers are driven by gradients. In other words, flux of some property is proportional to the difference in the value of a parameter across space. (Flux is the change in the property over time.) The proportionality constant is a kind of conductivity, while the inverse of the proportionality constant is a kind of resistance:

$$\text{flux} = (\text{conductivity})(\text{gradient}) = (1/\text{resistance})(\text{gradient})$$

As an example, consider the flux of electrons (also called the *current density* $= I/A$, where I = current and A = area). Why do electrons flow? Electrons flow because of a difference in potential (voltage). Formally,

$$I/A = \sigma(\Delta V/\Delta x)$$

where V is the voltage, σ is the electric conductivity, and Δ represents a difference in a property. We often use the symbol V to represent the voltage difference, so

$$I = A\sigma V$$

As discussed, the term $A\sigma$ represents the inverse of the *resistance* to the flow of electrons. Thus,

$$I = (1/R)V$$

or

$$V = IR$$

where R = resistance. This is Ohm's Law.

Examples of gradient-driven processes in the text are given in Table 6. Only one-dimensional spatial gradients are shown in Table 6. Another common gradient-driven process of interest to engineers is Fourier's Law of Heat Conduction:

$$\text{heat flux} = k(\Delta T/\Delta x)$$

where k = thermal conductivity and $\Delta T/\Delta x$ is the temperature gradient.

TABLE 6   Gradient-Driven Processes

Name	Equation	Text Example
Fick's Law	diffusive flux $= -DA(\Delta C/\Delta x)$	dissolution
Newton's Law of Viscosity	shear stress $= \mu(\Delta v/\Delta x)$	viscosity units
Ohm's Law	$I/A = \sigma(\Delta V/\Delta x)$ or $V = IR$	electrical power loss
		definition
		resistances in series

° Description only (all other examples are worked examples)

D = diffusion coefficient (m^2/s) v = velocity (m/s)
A = cross-sectional area (m^2) V = voltage (V = volts)
C = mass concentration (kg/m^3) I = current (A = amperes)
x = distance (m) R = resistance (Ω = ohms)
μ = viscosity (kg/m-s) σ = electric conductivity ($1/\Omega$-m or S/m, S = siemens = $1/\Omega$)

Appendix

Mathematical Formulas

1   ALGEBRA

1.1   Quadratic equation

The quadratic equation

$$ax^2 + bx + c = 0 \quad (a \neq 0)$$

has the solution

$$x = \frac{-b \pm \sqrt{b^2 - 4ac}}{2a}$$

The two roots of the quadratic equation are either (a) both real or (b) complex conjugates.

1.2   Laws of exponents

$$x^m x^n = x^{m+n}$$
$$(x^m)^n = x^{mn}$$
$$(xy)^n = x^n y^n$$
$$(x/y)^n = x^n/y^n \qquad (y \neq 0)$$
$$(x^m/x^n) = x^{m-n} \qquad (x \neq 0)$$
$$x^m/x^n = 1 \qquad \text{if } m = n$$
$$x^0 = 1$$
$$x^{-n} = 1/x^n \qquad (x \neq 0)$$

1.3   Logarithms

In the relations that follow, the parameter a is called the *base*. These relations hold when $a > 0$ and $a \neq 1$. Typically, $a = 10$ (the common logarithm), or $a = e$ (the natural logarithm). The common logarithm is usually written as $\log (x)$, and the natural logarithm is usually written as $\ln(x)$:

$$v = \log_a u \qquad\qquad \text{if } a^v = u$$
$$x = \log_a a^x$$
$$\log_a(xy) = \log_a x + \log_a y$$

$$\log_a(x/y) = \log_a x - \log_a y$$
$$\log_a 1 = 0$$
$$\log_a(x^c) = c \log_a x$$
$$\log_a a = 1$$

1.4   Exponential Function

The same relations that apply to the laws of exponents apply to the exponential function $\exp(x) = e^x$:

$$e^m e^n = e^{m+n}$$
$$(e^m)^n = e^{mn}$$
$$(e^m/e^n) = e^{m-n}$$
$$e^m/e^n = 1 \qquad \text{if } m = n$$
$$e^0 = 1$$
$$e^{-n} = 1/e^n$$

The exponential function $\exp(x)$ and the natural logarithm $\ln(x)$ are inverse functions. Thus,

$$\ln(\exp(x)) = x$$
$$\exp(\ln(x)) = x$$

2   GEOMETRY

2.1   Areas

Rectangle $A = ab$

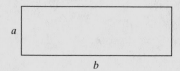

Parallelogram $A = bh$

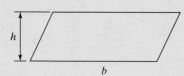

Trapezoid $A = \frac{1}{2} h(a + b)$

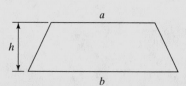

Triangle $A = \frac{1}{2} bh$

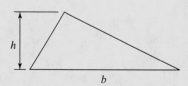

Circle	$A = \pi R^2 = \frac{1}{4}\pi D^2$	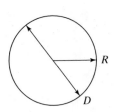

Circular sector	$A = \frac{1}{2}R^2\theta$ (θ in radians)	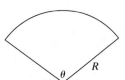

Circular segment	$A = \frac{1}{2}R^2(\theta - \sin\theta)$ (θ in radians)	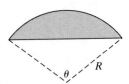

Regular polygon	$A = nr^2\tan(180°/n)$ $\quad = \frac{1}{2}nR^2\sin(360°/n)$ n = number of sides	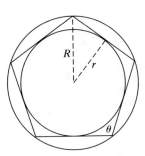

A.2.2 Solids

A = Surface area
V = Volume

Parallelpiped	$A = 2(ab + ac + bc)$ $V = abc$	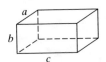

Cylinder	$A = 2\pi RL = \pi DL$ (ends excluded) $A = 2\pi R(L + R)$ (total) $V = \pi R^2 L$	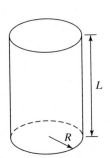

Sphere $\qquad$ $A = 4\pi R^2 = \pi D^2$

$$V = \frac{4\pi R^3}{3} = \frac{\pi D^3}{6}$$

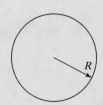

Cone $\qquad$ $A = \pi R(R^2 + h^2)^{1/2}$ (base excluded)

$A = \pi R[R + (R^2 + h^2)^{1/2}]$ (total)

$$V = \frac{\pi R^2 h}{3}$$

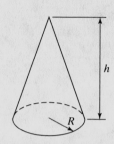

Torus $\qquad$ $A = 4\pi^2 Rr$

$V = 2\pi^2 Rr^2$

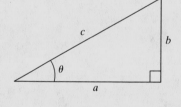

3   TRIGONOMETRY

3.1   Trigonometric Functions

$$\sin\theta = \frac{\text{opposite side}}{\text{hypotenuse}} = \frac{b}{c}$$

$$\cos\theta = \frac{\text{adjacent side}}{\text{hypotenuse}} = \frac{a}{c}$$

$$\tan\theta = \frac{\sin\theta}{\cos\theta} = \frac{\text{opposite side}}{\text{adjacent side}} = \frac{b}{a}$$

$$\cot\theta = \frac{1}{\tan\theta} = \frac{a}{b}$$

$$\sec\theta = \frac{1}{\cos\theta} = \frac{c}{a}$$

$$\csc\theta = \frac{1}{\sin\theta} = \frac{c}{b}$$

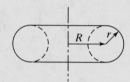

3.2   Identities and Relationships

$$\sin(-\theta) = -\sin(\theta)$$

$$\cos(-\theta) = \cos(\theta)$$

$$\tan(-\theta) = -\tan(\theta)$$

$$\sin^2\theta + \cos^2\theta = 1$$

$$1 + \tan^2\theta = \sec^2\theta$$

$$1 + \cot^2 \theta = \csc^2 \theta$$

$$\sin \theta = \cos(90° - \theta) = \sin(180° - \theta)$$

$$\cos \theta = \sin(90° - \theta) = -\cos(180° - \theta)$$

$$\tan \theta = \cot(90° - \theta) = -\tan(180° - \theta)$$

$$\sin(\theta \pm \alpha) = \sin \theta \cos \alpha \pm \cos \theta \sin \alpha$$

$$\cos(\theta \pm \alpha) = \cos \theta \cos \alpha \mp \sin \theta \sin \alpha$$

$$\tan(\theta \pm \alpha) = \frac{\tan \theta \pm \tan \alpha}{1 \mp \tan \theta \tan \alpha}$$

$$\sin 2\theta = 2 \sin \theta \cos \theta$$

$$\cos 2\theta = \cos^2 \theta - \sin^2 \theta = 2 \cos^2 \theta - 1 = 1 - 2 \sin^2 \theta$$

$$\tan 2\theta = \frac{2 \tan \theta}{1 - \tan^2 \theta}$$

$$\sin(\theta/2) = \pm\sqrt{\frac{1 - \cos \theta}{2}}$$

$$\cos(\theta/2) = \pm\sqrt{\frac{1 + \cos \theta}{2}}$$

$$\tan(\theta/2) = \frac{\sin \theta}{1 + \cos \theta} = \frac{1 - \cos \theta}{\sin \theta}$$

3.3 Laws of Sines and Cosines

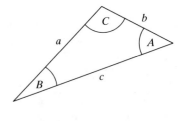

Law of sines
$$\frac{\sin A}{a} = \frac{\sin B}{b} = \frac{\sin C}{c}$$

Law of cosines
$$a^2 = b^2 + c^2 - 2bc \cos A$$
$$b^2 = a^2 + c^2 - 2ac \cos B$$
$$c^2 = a^2 + b^2 - 2ab \cos C$$

4   CALCULUS

In the following formulas, u and v represent functions of x, while a and n represent constants:

4.1   Derivatives

$$\frac{d(a)}{dx} = 0$$

$$\frac{d(x)}{dx} = 1$$

$$\frac{d(au)}{dx} = a\frac{du}{dx}$$

$$\frac{d(uv)}{dx} = u\frac{dv}{dx} + v\frac{du}{dx}$$

$$\frac{d(u^n)}{dx} = nu^{n-1}\frac{du}{dx}$$

$$\frac{d(\ln u)}{dx} = \frac{1}{u}\frac{du}{dx}$$

$$\frac{d(e^u)}{dx} = e^u\frac{du}{dx}$$

$$\frac{d(\sin u)}{dx} = \frac{du}{dx}(\cos u)$$

$$\frac{d(\cos u)}{dx} = -\frac{du}{dx}(\sin u)$$

4.2   Integrals

$$\int a\,dx = ax$$

$$\int a\,f(x)\,dx = a\int f(x)\,dx$$

$$\int x^n\,dx = \frac{x^{n+1}}{n+1} \quad (n \neq -1)$$

$$\int e^x\,dx = e^x$$

$$\int e^{ax}\,dx = \frac{e^{ax}}{a}$$

$$\int \ln(x)\,dx = x\ln(x) - x$$

Appendix

Unit Conversions

Acceleration	1 m/s^2	$= 3.2808 \text{ ft/s}^2$
		$= 39.370 \text{ in/s}^2$
		$= 4.252 \times 10^7 \text{ ft/h}^2$
		$= 8053 \text{ mi/h}^2$
Area	1 m^2	$= 10^4 \text{ cm}^2 = 10^6 \text{ mm}^2$
		$= 10.7636 \text{ ft}^2$
		$= 1550 \text{ in}^2$
	1 acre	$= 43{,}560 \, ft^2$
Density	1 kg/m^3	$= 1000 \text{ g/m}^3 = 0.001 \text{ g/cm}^3$
		$= 0.06243 \text{ lb}_m/\text{ft}^3$
		$= 3.6127 \times 10^{-5} \text{ lb}_m/\text{in}^3$
		$= 0.001940 \text{ slug/ft}^3$
Energy, work, heat	1055.06 J	$= 1 \text{ Btu}$
	1.35582 J	$= 1 \text{ ft} \cdot \text{b}_f$
	4.1868 J	$= 1 \text{ cal}$
	252 cal	$= 1 \text{ Btu}$
	1 kWh	$= 3412 \text{ Btu} = 3600 \text{ kJ}$
Force	1 N	$= 10^5 \text{ dyne}$
		$= 0.22481 \text{ lb}_f$
	1 lb_f	$= 32.174 \text{ lb}_m \cdot \text{ft/s}^2$
Heat transfer, power	1 W	$= 1 \text{ J/s}$
		$= 3.6 \text{ kJ/h}$
		$= 3.4121 \text{ Btu/h}$
	745.7 W	$= 1 \text{ hp}$
		$= 550 \text{ lb}_f \cdot \text{ft/s}$
		$= 2544.4 \text{ Btu/h}$
	1.3558 W	$= 1 \text{ lb}_f \cdot \text{ft/s}$

Length	1 m	$= 100$ cm $= 1000$ mm
		$= 3.2808$ ft
		$= 39.370$ in
		$= 3.0936$ yd
	2.54 cm	$= 1$ in
	1 ft	$= 12$ in
	5280 ft	$= 1$ mi
	1 km	$= 0.6214$ mi $= 0.5400$ nautical mi
Mass	1 kg	$= 1000$ g
		$= 2.20462$ lb$_m$
		$= 0.06852$ slug
	1 slug	$= 32.174$ lb$_m$
	1 short ton	$= 2000$ lb$_m$
	1 long ton	$= 2240$ lb$_m$
Mass flow rate	1 kg/s	$= 2.20462$ lb$_m$/s
		$= 7937$ lb$_m$/h
		$= 0.06852$ slug/s
		$= 246.68$ slug/h
Pressure	1 kN/m^2	$= 1$ kPa
		$= 20.8855$ lb$_f$/ft^2
		$= 0.14504$ lb$_f$/in^2 $= 0.14504$ psi
		$= 0.2953$ in Hg
		$= 4.0146$ in H$_2$O
	101.325 kPa	$= 1$ atm
		$= 14.6959$ lb$_f$/in^2 $= 14.6959$ psi
		$= 760$ mm Hg at 0°C
	1 bar	$= 10^5$ Pa
Specific heat	1 kJ/kg$\cdot$°C	$= 1$ kJ/kg$\cdot$K $= 1$ J/g$\cdot$°C
		$= 0.2388$ Btu/lb$_m\cdot$°F
		$= 0.2388$ Btu/lb$_m\cdot$°R
Stress, modulus	1 kN/m^2	$= 1$ kPa
		$= 0.14504$ lb$_f$/in^2 $= 0.14504$ psi
	1 MN/m^2	$= 1$ MPa
		$= 1000$ kPa
		$= 145.04$ lb$_f$/in^2 $= 145.04$ psi
	1 GN/m^2	$= 1$ GPa
		$= 1000$ MPa
		$= 1.4504 \times 10^5$ lb$_f$/in^2
		$= 1.4504 \times 10^5$ psi
		$= 145$ ksi
Temperature	T(K)	$= T(°C) + 273.15$
		$= T(°R)/1.8$
		$= [T(°F) + 459.67]/1.8$
	T(°F)	$= 1.8\,T(°C) + 32$

Temperature difference	$\Delta T(K)$	$= \Delta T(°C)$
		$= \Delta T(°F)/1.8$
		$= \Delta T(°R)/1.8$
Velocity	1 m/s	$= 3.2808$ ft/s
		$= 11,811$ ft/h
		$= 2.2369$ mi/h
		$= 3.6000$ km/h
		$= 0.5400$ knot
Viscosity (dynamic)	1 kg/m $\cdot$ s	$= 1$ Pa $\cdot$ s $= 10$ poise
		$= 0.6720$ lb_m/ft $\cdot$ s
		$= 2419$ lb_m/ft $\cdot$ h
Viscosity (kinematic)	1 m^2/s	$= 10,000$ stoke
		$= 10.7639$ ft^2/s
		$= 38,750$ ft^2/h
Volume	1 m^3	$= 1000$ L
		$= 35.3134$ ft^3
		$= 61,022$ in^3
		$= 264.17$ gal

Appendix:
Greek Alphabet in Engineering, Science, and Mathematics

Letter	Symbols	Common Use in Engineering, Science, and Mathematics
alpha	A, α	α: generalized angle, thermal diffusivity
beta	B, β	β: coefficient of bulk expansion
gamma	Γ, γ	γ: specific gravity or specific weight
delta	Δ, δ	Δ: change, δ: small change
epsilon	E, ε	ε: dielectric constant
zeta	Z, ζ	
eta	H, η	η: Stefan–Boltzmann coefficient
theta	Θ, θ	θ: generalized angle or dimensionless time
iota	I, ι	
kappa	K, κ	
lambda	Λ, λ	λ: wavelength
mu	M, μ	μ: prefix meaning 10^{-6} or viscosity or population mean
nu	N, ν	ν: frequency
xi	Ξ, ξ	ξ: permeability
omicron	O, o	
pi	Π, π	Π: product of a series of numbers
		π: circumference of circle/diameter of circle $= 3.14159\ldots$
rho	P, ρ	ρ: density or resistivity
sigma	Σ, σ	Σ: sum of a series of numbers
		σ: population standard deviation or surface tension or conductivity
tau	T, τ	τ: shear stress
upsilon	Y, υ	
phi	Φ, ϕ	Φ: potential
chi	X, χ	
psi	Ψ, ψ	
omega	Ω, ω	Ω: ohm (unit of electric resistance)
		ω: radial frequency or angular velocity

Appendix:
References and Bibliographies

1   REFERENCES

Adams, S. *The Dilbert Principle*. HarperCollins Publ., Inc., New York, NY, 1996.

BLS (Bureau of Labor Statistics, U.S. Department of Labor). *Occupational Outlook Handbook, 2002–03 edition, Engineers*. On the Internet at http://www.bls.gov/oco/ocos027.htm (visited February 20, 2004).

Conan Doyle, A. A Scandal in Bohemia. In *Adventures of Sherlock Holmes*. Harper & Brothers, London, 1892.

Dallard, P., A.J. Fitzpatrick, and A. Flint. The London Millennium Footbridge. *Structural Engineer*, 79(22), 17–35, 2001.

Davis, M. Thinking Like an Engineer: The Place of a Code of Ethics in the Practice of a Profession. *Phil. Public Affairs*, 20(2), Spring, 1991.

DeFazio, K., D. Wittman, and C.G. Drury. Effective Vehicle Width in Self-Paced Tracking. *Appl. Ergonomics*, 23(6), 382–386, 1992.

Drury, C.G. Movements with Lateral Constraint. *Ergonomics*, 14(2), 293–305, 1971.

Drury, C.G., M.A. Montazer, and M.H. Karwan. Self-Paced Path Control as an Optimization Task. *IEEE Trans.*, SMC-17.3, 455–464, 1987.

Drury, C.G. Human Factors Good Practices in Borescope Inspection. *Proceedings of the Fifth Joint NASA/FAA/DoD Conference on Aging Aircraft*, September 10–13, 2001.

Foran, J. (undated) The Day They Turned the Falls On: The Invention of the Universal Electrical Power System. On the Internet at http://ublib.buffalo.edu/libraries/projects/cases/niagara.htm (visited May 28, 2003).

Fraser, D.M. Introducing Students to Basic ChE Concepts: Four Simple Experiments. *Chem. Eng. Ed.*, 33(3), 190–195, 1999.

Griggs, F.E. Amos Eaton Was Right! *J. Prof. Issues in Eng. Educ. Practice*, 123(1), 30–34, 1997.

Harte, J. *Consider a Spherical Cow: A Course in Environmental Problem Solving*. University Science Books, Herndon, VA, 1988.

Harte, J. *Consider a Cylindrical Cow: More Adventures in Environmental Problem Solving*. University Science Books, Herndon, VA, 2001.

Henderson, J.M., L.E. Bellman, and B.J. Furman. A Case for Teaching Engineering with Cases. *J. Eng. Educ.*, January 1983.

Herreid, C.F. What Is a Case? *J. College Science Teaching*, 27(2), 92–94, 1997.

Hoff, R. *I Can See You Naked*. Andrews and McMeel, Kansas City, MO, 1992.

Holtzapple, M.T., and W.D. Reece. *Foundations of Engineering*. McGraw-Hill, Boston, MA, 2000.

Hyman, B. *Fundamentals of Engineering Design*. 2d ed., Prentice Hall, Upper Saddle River, NJ, 2003.

Karlin, S. "The purpose of models is not to fit the data but to sharpen the questions." *Eleventh R.A. Fisher Memorial Lecture at the Royal Society of London, April 20, 1983* (Furman University Mathematical Quotations Server). On the Internet at http://math.furman.edu/%7Emwoodard/ascquotk.html (visited May 28, 2003).

Mackay, A.L. *Dictionary of Scientific Quotations*. A. Hilger, Bristol, UK, 1991.

Martin, M.W., and R. Schinzinger. *Ethics in Engineering*, 2d ed., McGraw-Hill, New York, NY, 1989.

Merriam-Webster OnLine: *Word for the Wise*. On the Internet at http://www.m-w.com/cgi-bin/wftw.pl (visited May 28, 2003).

Moore, T.C. *Ultralight Hybrid Vehicles: Principles and Design*. Presented at the 13th International Electric Vehicle Symposium (EVS-13), Osaka, Japan, October 14, 1996.

NSF (National Science Foundation, Division of Science Resources Statistics). *Characteristics of Recent Science and Engineering Graduates: 2001*, NSF 04-302, Project Officer John Tsapogas, Arlington, VA, 2003.

Paradis, J.G., and M.L. Zimmerman. *The MIT Guide to Science and Engineering Communication*. The MIT Press, Cambridge, MA, 1997.

Perez, A.L., C.D.A. Earle, and S. Ramcharansingh. Development of an On-Line O&M Manual. *Florida Water Resources J.*, 27–28, May, 2001.

Petroski, H. *To Engineer Is Human: The Role of Failure in Successful Design*. Vintage Books, New York, NY, 1992.

Pfrang, E.O., and R. Marshall. Collapse of the Kansas City Hyatt Regency Walkways. *Civil Engineering*, 65–68, 1982.

Revelle, C.S., E.E. Whitlatch, and J.R. Wright. *Civil and Environmental Systems Engineering*. 2d ed., Prentice Hall, Upper Saddle River, NJ, 2003.

Rosenbaum, A. *Measuring Output Prices for Engineering Services in the United States*. Presented at the 17th Voorburg Group Meeting, Nantes, France, September 23–27, 2002.

Saarinen, E. "Always design a thing by considering it in its next larger context—a chair in a room, a room in a house, a house in an environment, an environment in a city plan." In Simpson, J.B. *Simpson's Contemporary Quotations*. Houghton Mifflin Company, Boston, MA, 1988.

Schumacher, E.F. *Small Is Beautiful: Economics as if People Mattered*. Harper and Row, New York, NY, 1973.

Sibly, P., and A. Walker. Structural Accidents and Their Causes. *Proc. Inst. Civil Engineers*, 62(Part 1), 191–208, May, 1977.

Smith, J.G., and P.A. Vesiland. *Report Writing for Environmental Engineers and Scientists*. Lakeshore Press, Woodsville, NH, 1996.

Steiber, J., and B. Surampudi. *Design and Implementation of a Reconfigurable Virtual Electric Vehicle Simulator, 03-9196*. Southwest Research Institute, IR&D Research Summary 03-9196 for 07/01/00-09/30/00. On the Internet at http://www.swri.edu/3pubs/IRD2000/03-9196.htm (visited May 28, 2003).

Strunk, Jr., W., and E.B. White. *The Elements of Style*, 3d ed. Allyn and Bacon, Needham Heights, MA, 1979.

Tufte, E.R., *The Visual Display of Quantitative Information*. Graphics Press, Cheshire, CT, 1983.

Tufte, E.R. *Envisioning Information*. Graphics Press, Cheshire, CT, 1990.

Wright, P.H. *Introduction to Engineering*, 2d ed. John Wiley and Sons, New York, NY, 1994.

2   ANNOTATED BIBLIOGRAPHY: TECHNICAL COMMUNICATIONS

There are a number of excellent books on technical communications. A few good sources of information are listed next. This list is by no means exhaustive.

Alley, M., L. Crowley, J. Donnell, and C. Moore (eds.). *Writing Guidelines for Engineering and Science Students*.

> This excellent on-line guide is available on the Internet at http://filebox.vt.edu/eng/mech/writing/index.html (visited June 6, 2003).

Dodd, J.S. *The ACS Style Guide*. American Chemical Society, Washington, DC, 1986.

> Although the emphasis is on technical writing in chemistry, this official guide of the American Chemical Society is a good general reference on technical writing.

McMurrey, D.A. *Online Technical Writing: Online Textbook—Contexts*.

> This is a fine guide to technical writing. It can be found on the Internet at http://www.io.com/~hcexres/tcm1603/acchtml/acctoc.html (visited May 28, 2003).

Paradis, J.G., and M.L. Zimmerman. (See "References" for the full citation.)

> This is a good reference with many examples of technical writing.

Sageev, P. *Helping Researchers Write ... So Managers Can Understand*. Batelle Press, 1968.

> The emphasis here is on technical writing in the corporate setting.

Strunk and White. (See "References" for the full citation.)

> This is a classic reference and very inexpensive. It should be on your reference shelf, along with a good dictionary.

White and Vesiland. (See "References" for the full citation.)

> White and Vesiland cover most aspects of technical writing, with many examples from environmental engineering.

3   BIBLIOGRAPHIES FOR *FOCUS ONS*

The Real McCoy?

Gibbs, C.R. *Black Inventors: From Africa to America*. Three Dimensional Press, Silver Spring, MD, 1995.

James, P.P. *The Real McCoy: African-American Invention and Innovation, 1619–1930*. Smithsonian Institution, Washington, DC, 1989.

For a more complete description of the operation of the McCoy lubricator, see http://www.usi.edu/science/engineering/MISC/emccoy/mccoyop1.htm (visited May 28, 2003).

A Square Peg in a Round Hole

Lovell, J., and J. Kluger. *Apollo 13* (previously published as *Lost Moon*). Houghton Mifflin Co., Boston, MA, 1994.

NASA (National Aeronautics and Space Administration). *Apollo 13 Mission Report*, September, 1970. Available on the Internet at http://www.hq.nasa.gov/office/pao/History/alsj/a13/a13mr.html (visited May 28, 2003).

The Multimillion Dollar Units Mistake

Mars Climate Orbital Mishap Investigation Board. *Phase I Report,* November 10, 1999.

Of Plots and Space Shuttles

Robison, W., R. Boisjoly, D. Hoeker, and S. Young. Representation and Misrepresentation: Tufte and the Morton Thiokol Engineers on the Challenger. *Science Eng. Ethics*, 8(1), 59–81, 2002.

Tufte, E.R. *Visual Explanations: Images and Quantities, Evidence and Narrative*. Graphics Press, Cheshire, CT, 1993.

Index